THIRD EDITION

THE
VERTEBRATE
BODY

ILLUSTRATED

ALFRED SHERWOOD ROMER
Alexander Agassiz Professor of Zoology,
Museum of Comparative Zoology,
Harvard University.

W. B. SAUNDERS COMPANY
Philadelphia · **London**

W. B. Saunders Company: West Washington Square
Philadelphia, Pa. 19105

12 Dyott Street
London, W.C.1

Reprinted December, 1962, October, 1963, June, 1964 and May, 1966

The Vertebrate Body

PREFACE TO THE THIRD EDITION

The present edition follows closely the pattern of earlier ones, with one exception. Although the endocrine organs do not form a natural anatomical system, neither do they have (in general) any close relationship to the organ systems from which they have been derived—and, to a considerable degree, they do form a functional system. In this edition I have, therefore, gathered together the data on them in a concluding chapter. I have rewritten large segments of a number of chapters—notably Chapters 4 and 5—and have made countless minor changes throughout to add newly discovered facts and new interpretations, to improve clarity and to correct inaccuracies. I have added approximately a score of new illustrations and in numerous cases have either substituted new figures for old or modified those already used. In several areas I have been permitted an increased use of color, which will, I hope, make for readier interpretation of figures in such matters as nerve components, blood vessels, etc.

I have received friendly criticisms from a number of users of the book, including among others Drs. P. Sears Crowell, Jr., Stuart O. Landry, Jr., Roland Walker, and Warren F. Walker, Jr.; and, as far as possible, I have followed their welcome suggestions. I am grateful to Dr. George Wald for advice regarding Chapter 4, to Dr. Sydney Smith for aiding in revision of Chapter 5, and to Dr. Stanley Cobb for suggestions about improving Chapter 15. Miss Nelda Wright has, as in the earlier editions, aided greatly in the preparation of the text and illustrations. And, while I did not call upon them for aid in the present instance, the book owes much to the earlier advice and criticisms of Drs. Tilly Edinger and Ernest E. Williams.

ALFRED SHERWOOD ROMER

APOLOGIA

I have attempted to give an introductory account of the vertebrate body, of the varied forms which this versatile and plastic structural type has assumed during its long evolutionary development, and of the functional story associated with this morphologic history. A number of admirable texts cover much of the area included here. This book was written for the reason that none, even if excellent in many ways, fully satisfied me in all regards as to the fashion in which the material should be treated. Desirable are:

1. *Fairly adequate illustration.* Even though a student may cover considerable ground in the laboratory, he cannot see all types and structures of interest, and may fail to see the forest for the few trees visible to him.

2. *A truly comparative treatment.* Overemphasis of human structure is not desirable, even for the premedical student. Such a course should be, for him, essentially a "cultural" background, to give him better understanding of the peculiarities and seemingly irrational construction of the human body.

3. *Proper paleontologic background.* The known facts of vertebrate history should be utilized to give, not only adequate treatment of the skeletal and other systems to whose evolution paleontology contributes, but also a modern phylogenetic point of view.

4. *A developmental viewpoint.* Embryologic history is crucial in the establishment of homology, a leitmotiv of comparative anatomy. Further, the time element should be kept in mind in the consideration of any vertebrate body, for an "adult" is merely one stage in a long developmental series.

5. *Inclusion of histologic data.* The wielder of the scalpel is liable to forget the basic materials of which gross structures are composed. Such an organ as a stomach is merely a flabby, rather revolting and uninteresting object unless we consider the varied internal epithelia and minute glands which furnish much of its excuse for existence.

6. *Consideration of function.* The almost complete separation of form and function prevalent in instruction today is both unnatural and unfortunate. It is doubtful if there is such a thing as a nonfunctioning structure, although mention of function is often taboo in morphologic works. Nor do functions take place *in vacuo* or without purpose in benefiting the structures which compose the organism, despite the contrary feeling that some physiologic treatises imply. Even if attention be held to comparative anatomy in a narrow sense, the study of ho-

v

mology immediately raises the question of the changes of function associated with the changes, often remarkable, undergone by homologous structures.

A critical reader may look askance at the considerable length of the section on the skeleton and suggest that I have been partial to a system of which I am especially fond. I am forced to admit that such a criticism is partly true. But I may plead, in extenuation, that I have been no more partial than many another author; that I have included in that chapter various topics, such as the dermal skeleton and the general history of fins and limbs, that might well have been treated elsewhere; and that more detailed discussion of the skeleton is merited because of the fact that our extensive knowledge of it and our possession of a fine paleontologic record gives us, as for no other system, a really adequate evolutionary story.

I have attempted to give a comparative study of the muscular system, rather than the few vague generalities with which the musculature is often (with a shudder) dismissed. I am, however, rather doubtful as to the success of this undertaking.

The attempt to give a treatment of this sort to the story of the vertebrate body has led me into many fields of which I know little. I hope that my friends will deal gently with me and with this book.

Miss Nelda Wright has helped greatly and constantly throughout the preparation of this book. Original drawings are the work of Miss Jeannette Sullivan. I am very grateful to Dr. W. K. Gregory for permission to use a number of valuable figures by the late Bashford Dean, originally published in the latter's "Fishes Living and Fossil." It is my regret that relatively few of the illustrations are original and the reader acquainted with the subject will recognize all too many figures which are all too familiar to him.

I am most especially indebted to Dr. Tilly Edinger for aid in the preparation of the manuscript. She has critically read—and re-read—the entire manuscript to my great profit, and helped in many other ways; many sections are as much her work as mine. Dr. George Wald gave valuable criticism of Chapter 4; Dr. Leigh Hoadley read critically the section on embryology. Dr. Vincent Hall of the University of Illinois has given numerous useful suggestions. Mr. Russell Olsen furnished valuable aid with regard to the derivation of scientific terms.

While a formal dedication for a book of the limited scope and elementary level of the present work is neither proper nor customary, I may venture to render homage to the two men, now *professores emeriti* at Columbia University, who many years ago instilled in me an interest, which has never flagged, in the story of the vertebrates: Dr. William King Gregory, under whom I studied as a graduate student, and Dr. J. H. McGregor, whom I served as a teaching assistant in vertebrate zoology.

ALFRED S. ROMER

CONTENTS

1

INTRODUCTION

This work is designed to give, in brief form, a history of the vertebrate body. Basic will be a comparative study of vertebrate structures: the domain of comparative anatomy. This is in itself an interesting and not unprofitable discipline. Of broader import, however, is the fact that the structural modifications witnessed are concerned with functional changes undergone by the vertebrates—changes correlated with the varied environments and modes of life found in the course of their long and eventful history. The evolutionary story of the vertebrates is better known than that of any other animal group, and vertebrate history affords excellent illustrations of many general biologic principles. Knowledge of vertebrate structure is of practical value to workers in many fields of animal biology. To the future medical student such a study gives a broader understanding of the nature of the one specific animal type on which his later studies will be concentrated.

For the most part (Chap. 6–17) the present volume is devoted to a consideration, *seriatim,* of the various organs and organ systems. In the present chapter is given a "bird's eye" view of vertebrate structure, together with certain introductory matters. Other early chapters discuss general or preliminary topics, including the evolutionary history of the vertebrates and their kin (Chap. 2 and 3); cells and tissues as the basic structural elements (Chap. 4); and embryonic development (Chap. 5).

THE VERTEBRATE BODY PLAN

Bilateral Symmetry. A primary feature of the vertebrate structural pattern is the fact that members of this group are bilaterally symmetric, with one side of the body essentially a mirror image of the other. Vertebrates share this type of organization with a number of invertebrate groups, notably the annelid worms and the great arthropod phylum, which includes crustaceans, arachnids, insects, and so forth. In strong contrast is the radial symmetry of coelenterates and echinoderms, in which the body parts radiate out from a central axis like the spokes of a wheel. The degree of activity of animals appears to be correlated with the type of symmetry which is present. The radiate echinoderms and coelenterates are in general sluggish types, slow-moving or fixed to the bottom or, if free-floating, mainly drifters with the current rather than active swimmers. Vertebrates, arthropods, and marine annelids are, on the other hand, generally active animals. Activity would seem to have been one of the keys to the success of the vertebrates and is in a sense as diagnostic as any anatomic feature.

Regional Differentiation.   In any bilaterally symmetric animal we find some type of longitudinal division into successive body regions—in the annelid worms, for example, a rather monotonous repetition of essentially similar segments, or in insects a pattern in which such segments are consolidated into head, thorax, and abdomen. Vertebrates, too, have well-defined body regions, although these regions are not directly comparable to those of invertebrate groups.

There is in vertebrates a highly specialized *head,* or cephalic region; in this region are assembled the principal sense organs, the major nerve centers which form the brain, and the mouth and associated structures. Here, as in all bilaterally symmetric animals (even a worm), there is a strong tendency toward *cephalization*—a concentration of structures and functions at the anterior end of the body.

In all higher, land-dwelling vertebrate groups a *neck* is present behind the head; this is little more than a connecting piece, allowing movement of the head on the trunk. The presence of a neck region is not, however, a primitive vertebrate feature. In lower, water-breathing vertebrates this section of the body is the stout *gill region,* containing the breathing apparatus. The appearance of a distinct neck occurs only with the shift to lung breathing and the reduction of the gills.

The main body of the animal, the *trunk,* is the next following region; this terminates in the neighborhood of the anus or cloaca. Within the stout trunk are the body cavities containing major body organs, the viscera. In mammals the trunk is divisible into *thorax* and *abdomen,* the former containing the heart and lungs within a rib basket, the latter enclosing most of the digestive tract; there is, however, no clear subdivision here in lower vertebrates.

In most bilateral invertebrates the digestive tube continues almost the entire length of the body. Among the vertebrates, however, we find, in contrast, that the digestive tract and other viscera stop well short of the end of the body; beyond the trunk there typically extends a well-developed *tail* or *caudal region,* with flesh and skeleton, but without viscera. The tail is, of course, the main propulsive organ in primitive water-dwelling vertebrates. In land animals it tends to diminish in importance, but is often long and stout at the base and well developed in many amphibians and reptiles. In mammals it is generally persistent, but is merely a slender appendage. In birds it is shortened and functionally replaced by the tail feathers, arising from its stump; in some forms—frogs, apes, and man—it is, exceptionally, lost completely as an external structure.

Gills.   The presence, in embryo if not in adult, of internal gills developed in a paired series of clefts or pouches leading outward from an anterior part of the gut—the pharynx—is one of the most distinctive features (perhaps the most distinctive feature) of the vertebrates and their close kin. In higher vertebrates the gills are functionally replaced by lungs, but gill pouches are nevertheless prominent in the embryo. In lower water-dwelling vertebrates gills are the primary breathing organs. Among small invertebrates, many with soft membranous surfaces can get enough oxygen through such membranes to supply their wants. But in forms with a hard or shelly surface, and especially in large forms, where the surface area is of course small compared with the bulk of the body, gill structures of some sort are a necessity. Typical invertebrate gills, as seen in crustaceans or molluscs, are feathery projections from the body surface. The vertebrate gill, however, is an internal development, connected with the digestive tube. Water enters the "throat," or pharynx (usually through the mouth), and passes outward through slits or pouches; on the surface of these passages are gill membranes, at which an exchange of oxygen from the water for carbon dioxide in the blood takes place. Quite in contrast is the gill function in certain lowly relatives of the vertebrates. There, as we shall see, the gills and gill slits are of primary importance in food collection—a fact tending to explain the unusual vertebrate condition of an association of the breathing organs with the digestive tube.

Notochord. In the embryo of every vertebrate there is found, extending from head to tail the length of the back, a long, flexible, rodlike structure—the notochord. In most vertebrates the notochord is much reduced or absent in the adult, where it is replaced by the vertebral column, or backbone. But it is still prominent in some of the lower vertebrates, and is the main support of the trunk in certain simply-built vertebrate relatives (such as Amphioxus) in which no vertebral column ever forms. So significant is this primitive supporting structure that the vertebrates and their kin are termed the phylum Chordata, a name referring to the presence of a notochord.

Nervous System. Longitudinal nerve cords are developed in various bilaterally symmetric invertebrate groups. These, however, are frequently paired and may be lateral or ventral in position. Only in the chordates do we find developed a single cord, dorsally situated and running along the back above the notochord or the vertebrae. Invertebrate nerve cords are solid masses of nerve fibers (and supporting cells) running between equally solid clusters of nerve cells, termed ganglia. The chordate nerve cord is, in contrast, a hollow, nonganglionated structure, with a central, fluid-filled cavity. In various invertebrates the process of cephalization has tended to a concentration of nerve centers in a brainlike structure. Independently, we believe, the vertebrates have evolved a hollow *brain*, with characteristic subdivisions, at the anterior end of the hollow nerve cord—the *spinal cord*. Not exactly matched in any invertebrate group is a series of characteristic *sense organs* developed in the head region of vertebrates—paired eyes and, primitively, a third, median eye; nasal structures, usually paired; paired ears with equilibrium as their primary function.

Digestive System. All metazoans (with degenerate exceptions) have some sort of digestive cavity with a means of entrance to and exit from it. In many of the more primitive metazoans there is but a single opening, serving as both mouth and anus. In vertebrates, as in other more progressive metazoans, there are separate

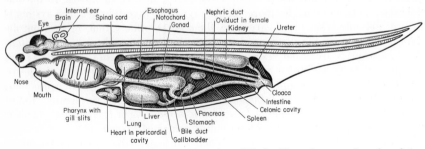

Fig. 1. Diagrammatic longitudinal section through an "idealized" vertebrate, to show the relative position of the major organs.

anterior and posterior openings. The mouth is situated near the front end of the body, typically somewhat to the underside. In arthropods and annelids the digestive tube reaches to the posterior end of the body. In vertebrates, however, this is not the case; the anus is situated at the end of the trunk, leaving, as we have seen, a caudal region in which the digestive tube is absent.

In most vertebrates the digestive tube is divided into a series of characteristic regions serving varied functions—*mouth, pharynx, esophagus, stomach,* and *intestine* (the last variously subdivided). In lower vertebrates the esophagus may be almost nonexistent, and in some groups the stomach even may be absent. In mammals and certain other vertebrates the digestive tract terminates externally at the *anus.* In most groups, however, there is a terminal gut segment, the *cloaca,* into which urinary and genital ducts also lead.

A *liver* which performs to some extent a secretory function, but is in the main a seat of food storage and conversion, is present in vertebrates as a large, single ventral outgrowth of the digestive tube. Somewhat similar but variable structures are present in many invertebrates.

Kidneys.   Among invertebrates some type of kidney-like organs for the disposal of nitrogenous waste and the maintenance of a proper composition of the internal fluids of the body are often present, typically as rows of small tubular structures termed *nephridia.* Of chordates below the vertebrate level, Amphioxus has nephridia of a special type. In true vertebrates however, the *kidney tubules* serving such a function are of a markedly different type and are characteristically gathered into compact paired kidneys, dorsal in position. *Kidney ducts,* of variable nature, lead to the cloacal region or to the exterior, and a *urinary bladder* may develop along their course.

Reproductive Organs.   Male and female sexes are almost invariably distinct in the vertebrates, as they are in many invertebrate groups. The tissues containing the germ cells—the *gonads*—develop into either *testis* or *ovary.* In all except the lowest vertebrates a duct system leads the eggs or sperm to or toward the surface (frequently by way of the cloaca); and in the female, special duct regions may be present for shell deposition or for development of the young.

Circulatory System.   In vertebrates, as in many invertebrates, there is a well developed organ system containing a body fluid, the blood, with tubular vessels and a pump, the *heart,* to bring about its circulation. The heart in vertebrates is a unit structure, ventrally and rather anteriorly situated. In certain invertebrates the circulation is of an "open" type: the blood is pumped from the heart to the tissues in closed vessels, but is then released and makes its return to the heart by oozing through the tissues without being enclosed in vessels. In the vertebrates, as in some of the more highly organized invertebrates, the system is closed; not only is the blood carried by the *arteries* to the various organs, but the return to the heart, after passing through the tissues in small tubes, the *capillaries,* is also made in closed vessels, the *veins.* In most vertebrates *lymph vessels* are present as an additional means of returning fluid from the cells to the heart. Many invertebrates contain in their blood streams pigmented metallic compounds in solution which aid in the transportation of oxygen. Among vertebrates, almost exclusively, the iron compound *hemoglobin* is the oxygen carrier; and, further, this chemical is not free in the blood, but is contained in *blood cells.*

In annelids the circulation of the blood is in general forward along the dorsal side of the body, backward ventrally in its return to the tissues. The reverse is true of the vertebrates. The blood from the heart passes forward and upward (primitively via the gills) and back dorsally to reach the organs of trunk and tail, and a major return forward—from the digestive tract—is ventral to the gut (although dorsal veins are important).

Celom. In certain invertebrates the internal organs are embedded in the body tissues. In others, however, there develop body cavities—celomic cavities—filled with a watery fluid, in which most of the major organs are found. This latter condition is present among vertebrates. A major body cavity—the *abdominal cavity*—occupies much of the trunk and contains most of the digestive tract; various other organs (reproductive, urinary) project into it. Anteriorly there is a discrete *pericardial cavity* enclosing the heart, and in mammals the lungs are contained in separate *pleural cavities.*

Muscles. Musculature in the vertebrates is of two types, *striated* and *smooth* (or nonstriated), the two differing sharply in minute structure and in distribution in the body. The former, roughly, includes all the voluntary musculature of the head, trunk, limbs, and tail, and the muscles of the gill region; the smooth musculature, more diffuse, is mainly found in the lining of the digestive tract. The musculature of the heart is in various respects intermediate in microscopic structure. The striated musculature of the trunk develops, unlike most other organ systems, as a series of segmental units.

Skeleton. Hard skeletal materials are present in all vertebrates, and in all except certain degenerate or (doubtfully) primitive groups consist in part, at least, of bone. Superficial skeletal parts, the *dermal skeleton*, correspond functionally to the "armor" of certain invertebrates, and are typically bony; internal skeletal structures, the *endoskeleton*, are formed as *cartilage* in the embryo, but are frequently replaced by bone in the adult. Cartilage-like materials are found in invertebrates. *Bone*, however, is a unique vertebrate tissue. It differs in texture and minute structure from the typical chitinous or calcareous skeletal materials of invertebrates, and, in the fact that the salts deposited in this tissue are mainly calcium phosphate, it differs from most (but not all) invertebrate skeletal structures—in which carbonate is the common calcium compound.

Appendages. Two pairs of limbs, *pectoral* and *pelvic*, are found in most vertebrates in the form of fins or legs and become increasingly prominent in higher members of the group. They are, however, little developed or are absent in the lowest of vertebrates, living and extinct, and hence are not absolutely characteristic. Their structure (in contrast to arthropod limbs) includes internal skeletal elements, with muscles for their movement arrayed above and below.

Segmentation. The great invertebrate phyla of Arthropoda and Annelida are notable for the presence of *metamerism:* a serial repetition of body parts in a long series of body segments. In annelids this segmentation is readily apparent; in arthropods the metameric structure may be more or less obscured in the adult, but is clearly seen in embryos or larvae.

Vertebrates, too, are segmented. but the segmentation is limited and has obviously developed independently from that of invertebrate groups, in which all structures, from skin inward to the gut, exhibit segmentation. Among the vertebrates neither skin nor gut is segmented; the metameric arrangement is primarily that of the trunk muscles. In relation, however, to the attachments of these muscles and their nerve supply, much of the skeleton and nervous system has taken on a segmental character.

The Body in Section (Fig. 2). We have noted some of the more important body features, with particular regard in many cases to their anteroposterior position in the body. We may now briefly consider the general organization of the body as seen in cross section.

Structurally, the most simple region of the body is that of the tail, strongly developed in most vertebrate groups. The section of a tail (Fig. 2, *A, C*) is typically a tall oval, the surface skin-covered. Somewhat above the center is seen the notochord, or the central region of the vertebrae which typically replace it in the adult, and, above this, a cross section of the nerve tube; the two structures are invariably closely associated topographically. The body cavity and associated viscera are absent in this region; representing them (in a sense) are caudal blood vessels lying below the notochord. Almost all the remainder of the tail is occupied by musculature, usually powerful. This musculature is arrayed in right and left halves, with a median dividing septum above and below.

A typical section through the trunk is more complicated, even when, as in Figure 2, *B*, this is represented in its most generalized condition. One may consider the trunk as essentially a double tubular system, roughly comparable in structure to the casing and inner tube of an automobile tire. The outer tube in itself contains all the major elements seen in the section of the tail—notochord and nerve cord, and musculature descending on either side beneath an outer covering of skin. Internally, it is as if we had taken the little area below the notochord in the tail, where only the blood vessels were present, and expanded this to enormous proportions as the celomic cavity of the abdomen. With the development of this cavity the outer "tube" of the trunk now has an inner as well as an outer surface. The surface lining the body cavity is the *peritoneum*, and that part of this lining which forms the inner surface of the outer tube is the *parietal peritoneum*. The part of the outer tube between celomic cavity and the surface of the body is the body wall.

The "inner tube" is primarily the tube of the digestive tract. The outer lining, facing the celomic cavity, is peritoneum—*visceral peritoneum*. The inner lining is the epithelium lining the digestive tract. Between the two, analogous to the musculature in the body wall, are present smooth muscle and connective tissues. In the embryo the gut is connected with the "outer tube" both dorsally and ven-

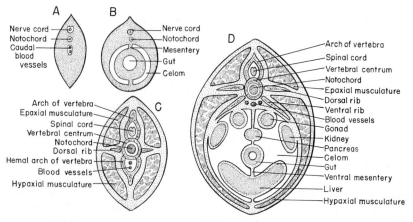

Fig. 2. Cross sections through the body of a vertebrate. *A, B,* Much simplified sections through tail and trunk, to show the essential structure of the trunk as a double tube; in the tail the "inner tube" of the gut is absent. *C, D,* More detailed diagrammatic sections of the tail and trunk to show the typical position of main structures.

trally by *mesenteries*—thin sheets of tissue bounded on either side by peritoneum. The dorsal mesentery—that above the gut—always persists, but the ventral portion frequently disappears for most of its length.

Although we shall treat of the arrangement of the organs in the celom in more detail in a later chapter, we may here go somewhat further in considering the position of the body viscera. (It must be noted that the relative size of the body cavity is never so great as represented in this and other diagrams; the viscera actually fill most of the available space.) In Figure 2, *D*, we have indicated the fact that the digestive tube is not a simple tubular structure, but has various outgrowths—most characteristically the liver ventrally and the pancreas dorsally. These are (in theory and in the embryo, at any rate) median structures, and are developed within the ventral and dorsal mesenteries. Further, we may have other organs projecting into the body cavity, but arising from tissues external to it. The kidneys in many groups project into the abdominal cavity at either upper lateral margin, and the reproductive organs—ovaries or testes—typically project into the cavity more medially along its upper border.

DIRECTIONS AND PLANES

Although the vertebrate body is essentially a bilaterally symmetric structure, there are many exceptions to this general statement. Organs which primitively lay in the midline may be displaced: the heart may be off center; the abdominal part of the gut—stomach and intestine—is usually twisted and the intestine may be convoluted in a complicated asymmetric fashion. Again, in paired structures those of the two sides may differ markedly; for example, in birds but one of the two ovaries (the left) is functional in the adult. A still greater asymmetry is seen in the flounders, where the whole shape of the body is affected by the substitution of the two sides for the normal top and bottom of the animal.

Either in theory or in practice the body of an animal may be sectioned in various ways at various angles. If the body is considered as sliced crossways, as one would cut a sausage, the plane of section is considered *transverse*. If the line of cleavage is vertical and lengthwise, from snout to tail, the plane is a *sagittal* one. Sometimes this latter term is restricted to a cut actually down the midline—the mediosagittal plane—and similar sections to one side or the other are termed parasagittal; but frequently such cuts are considered parts of a series of sagittal sections in a broad sense. The third major plane of cleavage, in the remaining direction, is that of slices cut the length of the body, but horizontally, each going through the width of the body. Such a plane is termed a *frontal* one—that is, one parallel to the "forehead" of the animal.

Direction within the body is of importance in the description of structural relationships and the naming of the various organs. Terms in this category, fixing a position or pointing out a direction, may be considered.

The head and tail ends of the body are, in most vertebrates, the direction toward which and from which movement of the animal normally takes place. *Anterior* and *posterior* are the common terms of position in this regard; *cranial* and *caudal* are less used, but are essentially synonymous. Upper and lower surfaces —back and belly aspects—are reasonably named *dorsal* and *ventral*. Position in the transverse plane is of course given with reference to the midline; *medial* refers to a position toward the midline; *lateral*, a more removed position.

A fourth pair of terms of less positive meaning but of considerable use are *proximal* and *distal*. The former refers in general to the part of a structure closer to the center of the body or some important point of reference; the latter, to a part farther removed. These terms are clearly available to limb and tail structures. Within the head and trunk their use is less clear, but we may, for example, speak of proximal and distal parts of a nerve with obvious reference to the spinal cord or brain as a center, proximal and distal regions of arteries with reference to the heart as the assumed center, and so on.

For these adjectives of position there are, of course, corresponding adverbs ending in *ly*, and others (rather awkward) to denote motion in a given direction, ending in *ad*, as *posteriorly, caudad.*

The major directional terms, anterior, posterior, dorsal, and ventral, apply with perfect clarity to almost all known vertebrates. But in man we have an exception, an aberrant form which stands erect—and hence might have different directional terms applied to him.

It is unfortunate that in the terminology most generally used in medical anatomy this is the case (Fig. 3). The head and "tail" ends of the body are, in the erect human position, above and below rather than fore and aft, and are termed *superior* and *inferior,* rather than anterior and posterior. ("Cranial" and "caudal" could, of course, have been used instead, but medical people seem to like these alternatives no better than comparative anatomists.) More confusing, however, is the fact that anterior and posterior have generally been used in man —quite needlessly—to replace dorsal and ventral, so that the back side of the human body has been generally termed *posterior* and the belly surface *anterior.* Thus this pair of terms may have contradictory meanings in special human anatomy and in more normal usage, causing needless confusion. For example, each spinal nerve has two roots (cf. Fig. 364, p. 503). In a dissecting room the two roots in a human cadaver have been generally termed posterior and anterior. But if a neurologist working with (say) rats tries to use the same nomenclature, he is in an obviously absurd position; one root is no more "anterior" or "posterior" than the other. In both rat and man, however, designation of the nerve roots as dorsal and ventral is reasonable and logical. Long established customs, no matter how illogical, are hard to break down; but in a recently adapted revision of human anatomic nomenclature the use of dorsal and ventral has been agreed to in such cases.

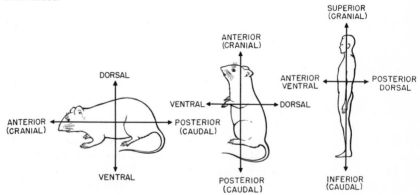

Fig. 3.   Diagram to show the contrast in positional terms between normal vertebrates and man.

THE HOMOLOGY CONCEPT

Even in the early days of zoologic research it was recognized that within each major animal group there was a common basic pattern in the anatomic plan of the body. The same organs could be identified in many or all members of a group, although frequently much modified in size, form, or even function in correlation with changing habits or modes of existence. With the acceptance by biologists of the principle of evolution in the 60's and 70's of the last century, real significance was given to the concept of *homology:* the thesis that specific organs of living members of an animal group have descended, albeit with modification, slight or marked, from basically identical organs present in their common ancestor. For many decades the tracing out of homologies was a leading motif in zoologic research.

Many of the results of such studies were novel and exciting. It was found, for example, that the three little auditory ossicles of our own middle ear (p. 491) were in earlier days part of the jaw apparatus of our piscine ancestors, and appear still earlier to have been part of the supports of the gills of ancestral vertebrates. The muscles with which we smile or frown are derived from those which once helped our fish forebears to pump water through their gills.

Homologous organs are those which are identical—the same—in the series of forms studied. But what do we mean by "the same"? One tends, unthinkingly, to believe that the same actual mass of material, the very same limb or lung or bone, has been handed down, generation by generation, like an heirloom. This is quite absurd, but such a concept has obviously influenced, unconsciously, the minds of many workers. In reality, of course, every organ is re-created anew in every generation, and any identity between homologues is based upon the identity or similarity of the developmental processes which produce them.

The development of the science of genetics has given us a firm base for the interpretation of these processes. They are controlled by hereditary units, the *genes.* These tiny structures are present to the number of some thousands, at least, in every animal cell. The development of the individual is directed by the genes transmitted to the fertilized egg by the parents. Each gene may affect the development of a number of structures or parts of a body; conversely, every organ is influenced in its development by a considerable number of genes. If the genes remain unchanged from generation to generation, the organ produced will remain unchanged (apart from transient environmental effects upon an individual), and the homology is absolute.

Changes, however, do occur in genes, as *mutations;* these mutations produce changes in the structures to which the genes give rise. If the mutations produce effects of small magnitude and occur in only a few of the genes concerned, the organ will be little modified, and its homology with the parent type will remain obvious. If, however, the mutations are numerous and marked in their effects, the organ may be radically modified and its pedigree much less clear. In a sense, a study of organ homology is merely a study of phenomena produced by genes. If the genetic constitution of all animal types were well known, the determination of homology between structures might well rest upon the degree of identity of the genes concerned in their production. But this is not a matter of practical import, for there are few animals whose genetic constitution is adequately known, and it is improbable that our range of knowledge will ever be broadened to the necessary degree.

What are the best criteria for the establishment of homology? Function is no sure guide, for organs which are clearly homologous in two animals may be put to quite different uses. Observation shows that the shape, size, or color of a structure gives little positive evidence of identity. Similarity in general anatomic position and relations to adjacent organs is a more useful clue to identification. Best of all is similarity in developmental history. Embryologic processes in vertebrates tend to be conservative, and organs which are quite different in the adult condition may reveal their homology through similarity in early embryonic stages.

Homology is generally applied to structural identity. Some have proposed that the concept be broadened to include functional identity. This suggestion has not, however, met with general acceptance. The term *analogy* is in some regards a parallel, on the functional side, to homology; analogous organs are those which have similar functions. It is, however, somewhat restricted, for as generally used it implies that the organs concerned are not homologous. A lung and a fish gill, for example, are analogous, for both are used for respiration, but the two are quite different structures.

ADAPTATION AND EVOLUTION

The varied modifications which vertebrate structures have undergone and the varied functions which they have assumed have, of course, come about as the result of evolution. One cannot make a comparative study of the vertebrates without formulating some general concept of the nature of evolutionary processes. Most structural and functional changes in the vertebrate body are quite clearly adaptive modifications to a variety of environments and modes of life. How have these adaptations been brought about? Proper discussion would require a volume in itself; we can here merely indicate the general nature of the problems concerned, and current majority opinion as to their interpretation.

We sometimes speak, thoughtlessly, of adaptation changes, as if the animal "willed" them or as if its needs or desires in themselves brought new structures or structural changes into being. It would be advantageous, one might say, for a fish to be able to walk on land, and so some fishes made themselves legs; it would be "nice" if the cow's early ancestors developed teeth better able to cope with grain and grass, and so the teeth promptly deepened.

Obviously, such ideas are absurd. They are, however, not far removed from certain theories of evolution which have had, and still have, a certain vogue. These assume that evolution is an unnatural phenomenon; that changes have been brought about by some "inner urge" within the organism, or are the result of the "design" of some supernatural force. Since such theories are nonscientific, they cannot be scientifically disproved; but we are at liberty to look for more reasonable explanations of evolution, based on known facts. If someone tells me that the operation of my automobile engine is controlled by an invisible demon dwelling therein, I cannot prove him wrong. But nothing is gained by adding this hypothetic demon, and I would prefer an attempt to explain the engine's working in terms of known mechanical principles, the nature of electric currents, and the explosive structure of hydrocarbon molecules.

A more plausible attempt at interpretation of structural evolutionary changes was that first advocated over a century ago by Lamarck—a belief in the inheritance of acquired characters through the effect of use and disuse. If the giraffe's ancestors stretched their necks after foliage on high branches, the effects of stretching, this theory assumes, would be transmitted to their offspring, generation after generation, and an elongate neck gradually developed in the hereditary pattern. If the snake's lizard ancestors ceased to use their legs in locomotion, the cumulative result of disuse would be the eventual loss of the limbs. This attractive theory seems simple, reasonable, and natural. But its present standing is poor indeed. We may summarize by saying that no one, despite repeated efforts, has been able to furnish any valid proof of any instance of the inheritance of an acquired characteristic. Structures useful to an animal may and often do increase in size or complexity in the course of time, and useless or little-used structures may diminish. But there is not the slightest evidence that the use or disuse of parts by an individual has any effect whatever upon the build of its offspring.

The science of genetics has in recent decades demonstrated that evolutionary changes are due to mutations. These may produce effects of some magnitude, but most cause only minor modifications: a mutation in a fruit fly may, for example, have no greater visible result than the splitting of a single bristle. We do not fully understand the various ways in which mutations are caused, although we are currently beginning to gain an idea of the chemical structure of the materials involved, and of chemical and physical influences (such as radiation) which play important roles in bringing them about. As for evolutionary theories, however, two things stand out clearly: (1) There is no evidence of "design" or "direction" in mutations. They appear to be quite random, rather than tending in any one direction. Some may well be advantageous; most, however, are obviously harmful, and many are lethal. (2) There is no evidence that mutations have any relation whatever to use or disuse of body organs; characters acquired by the individual have no specific influence on the nature of mutations of the genes in its sex cells—mutations whose effect is transmitted to the offspring.

The process of mutation thus seems to be merely one of blind, random change. But vertebrate evolution certainly appears to have resulted in changes both useful and adaptive. How can such results have come out of the mutation process?

Part, at least, of the answer was given by Darwin nearly a century ago. He was, of course, quite ignorant of the data now available from genetics, but reasonably assumed that there existed some hereditary mechanisms of the sort with which we are now familiar. Given a supply of random mutations, *natural selection* will act powerfully to eliminate unfit types and preserve the better-fitted forms in which one or a group of useful mutations have occurred in the germ plasm. Even the slowest breeders among animals produce more individuals than can survive. Many are destined to die before becoming adults and reproducing—an act which is nature's standard of success. Which individuals are eliminated is partly a matter of chance. But both observation and experiment indicate that even small mutations in an adaptive direction have a distinct survival value and may become dominant in a species in a short time. This natural selection of such a random series of mutations as have adaptive value would appear to be a major mechanism of evolutionary change.

Evolution, however, is a much more complicated process than a mere adaptive selection of features developed in a given individual. We may note, for example, the fact that in general genes are carried in duplicate in the cells of every animal (one gene coming from each parent); if the members of a gene pair differ in their potentialities, one tends to dominate over the other in the structures or functions which it controls. It is obvious that selection can have no influence over the "weaker" of such a pair of genes—technically termed recessive—unless by chance both members of the pair of genes concerned are of the same recessive nature. A little consideration makes it clear that as a result of this situation it is practically impossible to eliminate completely a recessive mutant, even if highly deleterious, from an animal stock in which it is once established. It is reasonable to believe that with numerous variables of this sort present in a stock, circumstances might arise (particularly in changed environments) in which certain "suppressed" variants or combinations of them might eventually prove highly advantageous if they should come to light in an individual and result in evolutionary change in the population as a whole.

SURFACE-VOLUME RELATIONS

It is frequently seen that in any group of animals large and small forms differ notably in the relative size of various organs or parts. The reason for many of these proportionate differences lies in a geometric principle so obvious that it is generally overlooked, namely, the fact that *as the size of an animal* (or any other object) *changes, surfaces increase* (or decrease) *proportionately to the square of linear dimensions, while volumes change proportionately to the cube of linear dimensions.*

This principle is of wide application, for surface-volume relationships are to be found in a variety of structural and functional features of vertebrates. We cite obvious examples: (1) The strength of a leg (like any supporting column) is proportional to its cross section, which varies as the square of linear dimensions, whereas the weight which it supports is proportionate to the cube of linear dimensions. In consequence an elephant cannot have gazelle-like legs. (2) The amount of food which an active animal needs is roughly proportionate to its volume;* the amount of foodstuffs which its intestine can absorb depends upon the area of the intestinal lining. In consequence, large animals have a disproportionately elongated intestine or one with a complicated structure, resulting in a greater internal surface area for digestion.

NOMENCLATURE

The student of vertebrate morphology is confronted with a bewildering array of unfamiliar names of anatomic structures. This is unfortunate but inescapable. Vertebrate structures are numerous; for many there are no every-day terms. Even where such names are available, they are often vague and not exactly defined in common usage. Further, it is desirable to have some international system of terms understood in the same sense by scientists of every country.

When anatomy was first studied, all "learned" works were, as a matter of course, written entirely in Latin. In consequence, Latin names where already in existence were applied to anatomic structures, and if no term existed, one was manufactured from Greek or Latin roots and cast in Latin form. Some notes regarding the formation of anatomic terms are given in Appendix II. Today Latin

---

* Emphasis on *active;* basal metabolism in a resting condition is quite another thing.

has ceased to be an international language as far as the general text of scientific books is concerned. Latin anatomic terms, however, are still in vogue. We cannot do without them, although we often use them in a somewhat "anglicized" form—speaking, for example, of the "deltoid muscle" of the shoulder rather than the "musculus deltoideus," or of the "parietal bone" rather than the "os parietalis."

Latin is, of course, an inflected language, and its nouns and adjectives have a variety of endings to express not merely singular and plural numbers, but also a variety of cases and a rather arbitrary system of genders. Until recent decades some knowledge of Latin grammar was part of the equipment of every college student, and the manipulation of Latin terminology presented no difficulty. Today this is not the case; rather unfortunately, for a biologist should at least know enough to avoid such gaucheries as speaking of "humeruses" instead of humeri, "femurs" instead of femora. Fortunately the number of noun and adjective endings ordinarily used in anatomic terms is limited, and these can be readily learned.

It is accepted procedure in anatomic nomenclature that where a structure is present in mammals—particularly in man—the name there used be applied to the same structure in other forms. Thus, for example, man and many mammals have a clavicle, or collar bone, and the equivalent element in the shoulder structure should be called by the same name in reptiles, amphibians, or fishes, even though its appearance is radically different. Sometimes, however, too hasty an identification may be made and a name wrongly applied. Teleost fishes have a bone similar in position to the clavicle, and that name was customarily given to it; we now know, however, that the teleosts have lost the true clavicle; the bone present there is a different one (the cleithrum, p. 187). If homologies are in doubt, it is better to use a different name for the structure in question. For example, there is a muscle in the thigh of reptiles which may be homologous with the sartorius muscle of mammals; but since there is some doubt of the homology, it is customary to give the reptilian muscle a different name—the ambiens muscle (p. 271). If a structure encountered in a lower group has no mammalian equivalent, a new name must, of course, be coined.

Although anatomic terminology has been in general a rather stable and uniform system, there arose, quite naturally, a number of differences in terminology between different schools of work and in different countries. Motivated by the laudable desire to achieve uniformity, the German anatomic association, in convention at Basel some decades ago, brought forward a comprehensive scheme of terms which they hoped would receive universal adoption in human anatomy. This terminology, usually referred to as the "BNA," was adopted by medical schools and has been widely used in medical work. Quite a number of the terms in this code were, unfortunately, ineptly chosen, and we noted earlier the conflicts in terms of body position. At an international congress of anatomists in Paris in 1955 a modified code was drawn up, improving the situation to a considerable degree, and the revisions embodied in the new "PNA" are now gradually supplanting the older terms in medical school practice.

2

THE
VERTEBRATE
PEDIGREE

Although the present work primarily concerns the vertebrates alone, we must recognize that there exist various animal types lacking a backbone, but closely allied to the vertebrates. Study of these more lowly forms contributes to our understanding of vertebrate structure and history. Further, although (as will be seen) we have little certain knowledge of the early ancestry of the vertebrates, the subject of their pedigree deserves consideration. In this chapter we will first describe, as lower chordates, certain small marine animals definitely allied in some fashion to the vertebrates, then discuss possible relationships of the vertebrates to various invertebrate phyla, and, finally, attempt to plot out a reasonable vertebrate pedigree.

The vertebrates do not in themselves constitute a major division of the animal kingdom. They are considered merely one subdivision—although by far the largest subdivision—of the *phylum Chordata,* the other members of which are to be considered briefly here. The *"lower chordates"* lack the backbone and many other advanced structures of their vertebrate relatives. They do, however, exhibit, to a variable degree, basic features characteristic of the vertebrates and not found elsewhere in the animal kingdom. These features indicate that they are truly related to vertebrates and hence properly included in a common group with them. The term Chordata itself implies that a notochord (or chorda), or some structure thought to be equivalent to a notochord, is generally present. Again, a dorsal nerve cord is a common feature. Most characteristic of all is the fact that gill slits are almost universally present in chordates.

Amphioxus. By many workers the phylum Chordata is subdivided into four subphyla—in roughly ascending order, Hemichordata, Urochordata, Cephalochordata, and Vertebrata. Here we reverse the order and begin our discussion of the lower chordates with the *Cephalochordata,* in which the similarities to the vertebrates are most obvious. The subphylum includes only a few closely related forms, all commonly termed Amphioxus (Figs. 4, 5). They are translucent animals, fishlike in appearance and proportions, found in shallow marine waters in

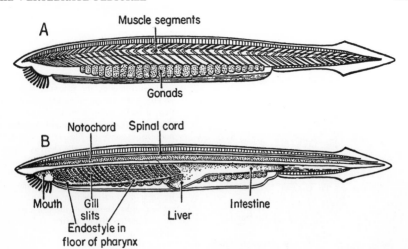

Fig. 4. Amphioxus, a primitive chordate. *A*, As seen through the transparent skin; *B*, a sagittal section. (After Gregory.)

various regions of the world, and sometimes locally abundant. As the shape suggests, they can swim readily, but because of poor development of fins, rather ineffectively; for the most part they spend their time with the body buried in the sands of the bottom, with merely the anterior end projecting.

Despite the piscine appearance, it is obvious that we are dealing with forms far more primitive than any fish. There are no paired fins or limbs of any sort. Cartilage-like materials stiffen the gills, dorsal fin, and mouth parts, but no part of the normal vertebrate skeleton of vertebrae, ribs, or skull is to be found. The main skeletal structure (apart from connective tissues) is a highly developed notochord, which persists through life and (in contrast to the vertebrates) extends clear to the tip of the "nose"—a feature to which the group owes its name. The notochord prevents telescoping during vigorous swimming and serves as a convenient central "peg" on which to hang the body organs. There are nerves serially arranged along a typical, dorsal, hollow nerve cord; but although the cord is somewhat larger anteriorly, there is no true brain, and there are only dubious traces of sense organs which might correspond to nose or eye. Much as in fishes the major musculature consists of a segmental series of muscle blocks arranged in V's down either side of the body; alternating waves of contraction of these muscles bring about the swimming movements.

For the most part the digestive tract is of a very simple nature. There is a mouth cavity (*buccal cavity*) surrounded by a circle of stiffened projecting cirri. The pharynx is greatly elongated, extending about half the total length of the body. Back of the pharynx, the gut is a straightforward tube with little sign of division into successive chambers, although chemical treatment of food appears to predominate in the anterior part of its length, absorption at the back. There is a large pouchlike outgrowth which is generally compared to a liver although the homology is dubious. As in vertebrates, the tube ends at the anus, far short of the end of the body, which thus terminates in a true tail.

The pharynx is highly specialized for food collecting. Amphioxus lives on particles gathered from the sea water; these are taken in through the mouth by

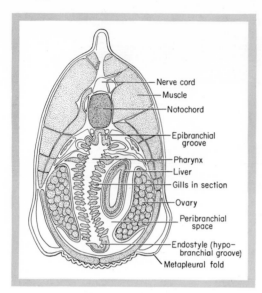

Nerve cord
Muscle
Notochord
Epibranchial groove
Pharynx
Liver
Gills in section
Ovary
Peribranchial space
Endostyle (hypo- branchial groove)
Metapleural fold

Fig. 5. Cross section of Amphioxus through the pharynx. The peribranchial space surrounding the pharynx, liver, and so on, is, despite its seeming internal position, actually external to the body and is somewhat analogous to the gill chamber of bony fishes, and the like. It is formed by the downgrowth around the pharynx of great folds meeting one another ventrally, and it connects with the exterior through a posteriorly placed opening. Since the gills lie in a diagonal position such a vertical section as that shown cuts through a number of successive bars. (After Delage and Hérouard.)

ciliary action and strained out from the water as it passes out of the body through the gill slits. These slits are very numerous, far more so than in any vertebrate, for there may be as many as fifty or more pairs of them, and each gill is essentially a double structure, developing in much the horseshoe-shaped fashion seen in acorn worms (Fig. 9). A peculiar hood grows downward and encloses the whole gill system, serving as a protection to these delicate organs when Amphioxus is buried in the sand, and forms a pocket, the *atrium,* opening to the surface only by a pore at the back of the pharynx. But while the gill slits, by their major development, emphasize the animal's relationships to the vertebrates, they differ from the typical vertebrate gill apparatus in both purpose and mode of operation. It appears that much of the "breathing" of Amphioxus is done through the skin—which, in contrast to that of vertebrates, is quite thin—and that here, as we shall see in other lower chordates, the gills are primarily feeding devices. Further, water currents through the gills in vertebrates are effected by muscular pumping; in Amphioxus ciliary action alone is responsible, and cilia are highly developed in the pharynx. A prominent feature is the development of a longitudinal midventral (hypobranchial) groove termed the *endostyle,* running the length of the pharynx; in this a sticky mucus is abundantly secreted. Ciliary currents carry streamers of this material up the pharynx walls, past the gill slits; catching up trapped food particles on the way, the mucus collects in a dorsal (epibranchial) groove. From this point cilia carry back the mucus and the enclosed food particles in a continuous slimy band to the intestine; the animal feeds itself by a conveyor-belt system.

The major blood vessels of Amphioxus are laid out clearly on the vertebrate pattern (Fig. 305), with the blood coursing forward ventrally and back dorsally after passing upward through the gill region. There are, however, no blood cells, red or white, or blood pigments and, further, there is no heart; movement of the blood is accomplished by wave contraction of some of the principal vessels, together with the contraction of numerous tiny heartlike bulbs situated along the course of the arteries below the gill region. The gonads differ from those of vertebrates—indeed, from those of all other chordates—in being numerous and seg- mentally arranged. Still more divergent from the vertebrate plan is the nature of the excretory organs. The vertebrate kidney is of a unique type, composed of dis- tinctive water-filtering units which will be described in detail later. In Amphioxus, on the other hand, the structures are of a very different sort; they are, as in inverte- brates generally, segmentally arranged nephridia, which in Amphioxus resemble to a degree those characteristic of many annelid worms.

Where does Amphioxus stand in relation to the vertebrates? A few theorists, for whose ideas as to vertebrate evolution the existence of Amphioxus is incon- venient, deny that it is related. But the features in which Amphioxus resembles the backboned animal are so numerous and so basic that this position is unten- able. Strongly in contrast is the suggestion that Amphioxus is a degenerate verte- brate. As we shall see, the young of lampreys, quite unlike the adults, live a life as sedentary filter-feeders and are comparable to Amphioxus in many ways. Is Amphioxus a lamprey which has, so to speak, never grown up and hence re- tained, as an adult, the simplicity of structure of the larva? It is probable, as we shall see presently, that the phenomenon known as *neoteny*, in which a larva lin- gers long in a youthful state before finally changing into an adult, and the more extreme condition of *paedogenesis* in which it becomes sexually mature without ever reaching the adult condition, are factors to be kept in mind in studies of evolutionary lines. But Amphioxus shows many features which are not merely more primitive but different from those expected in the young of a lamprey an- cestor—too many to make this suggestion of relationship by degeneration plausi- ble. As a working hypothesis we shall here, like a majority of students of the subject, interpret Amphioxus as a somewhat specialized survivor of a type of ani- mal ancestral to the vertebrates. As will be seen later, it is important to realize that Amphioxus is not only more primitive structurally than any vertebrate, but has a mode of life essentially different from and more primitive than that of ver- tebrates. In general vertebrates actively and aggressively seek large food objects, eat by muscular movements of jaws or analogous structures and typically use their gills—operated by means of well-developed muscles—exclusively for breath- ing purposes. It is often tacitly assumed that the vertebrate ancestor was likewise a vigorous, active swimming form. But Amphioxus, although able to swim, is es- sentially sedentary and, as we have noted, is in contrast a filter-feeder, using cilia rather than muscles in food gathering and utilizing the gills for feeding rather than breathing.

Tunicates (Figs. 6–8). In seeking further lowly relatives of the verte- brates we may be well advised to look for other filter-feeders which, even if more simple in structure than Amphioxus, show at least some of the basic chordate characters, such as gill slits, notochord or nerve cord. Such a group is that of the *Urochordata*, the *tunicates* or *sea squirts* and their relatives. These are rather com- mon small marine organisms. They are essentially inactive; the adult does not seek its food, but is a highly developed filter-feeder, accepting such particles as it can attract by ciliary action. Many tunicates are found floating freely in the water, singly or in groups, often as tiny barrel-shaped structures; others are at- tached to the bottom, either as branching colonies or as individuals (Fig. 8, *C-E*). Simplest are the solitary tunicates (Fig. 6, *B*). As an adult, such an animal is an almost formless lump attached to a rock or other underwater object and covered with a leathery-looking "tunic." The only structural features seen externally are an opening at the top, into which water passes, and another, lateral, opening,

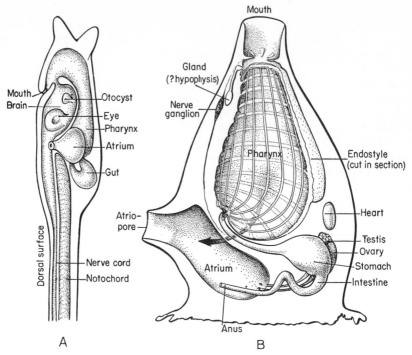

Fig. 6. A solitary tunicate. *A*, Diagram of the structures seen in the free-swimming larva (head end above, and only a short section of tail figured). The otocyst is a simple ear structure. *B*, The sessile adult, formed by elaboration of the structures at the anterior end of the larval body. The original dorsal side lies at the left: The large pharynx is attached to the body wall above and below (left and right in the figure); the atrium (corresponding to the peribranchial space of Amphioxus) bounds it on either side. Water passing through the latticework gills of the pharynx enters the atrium and, as indicated by the arrow, streams out through the atriopore. (After Delage and Hérouard.)

through which the water current flows outward. The creature shows no external resemblances to the vertebrates, and internally much of the structure is equally unfamiliar to a student of that group. There is no notochord. Nor is there a nerve cord; instead, there is a simple nerve ganglion with a few nerves splaying out from it.

Much of the interior of the animal is occupied by a barrel-shaped structure which serves as the food-gathering device. The water current, entering it through ciliary action, is strained through slits in the sides of the barrel into a surrounding chamber, the *atrium*, which leads to the lateral excurrent opening. On closer examination it becomes obvious that the barrel is an exaggerated set of internal gills, constituting the pharyngeal region of the animal; there is even an endostyle comparable to that noted in Amphioxus. Behind the enormous pharynx, the digestive tube narrows to form esophagus, stomach, and intestine—all of modest size.

We have here, in the pharyngeal gill apparatus, a high degree of development of one of the primary characters to be sought in a relative of the vertebrates. For other chordate characters, however, we must turn to the developmental history. In many tunicates propagation takes place in the main by a process of budding. But in some there is a distinct larval form (Figs. 6, *A*, 7), which

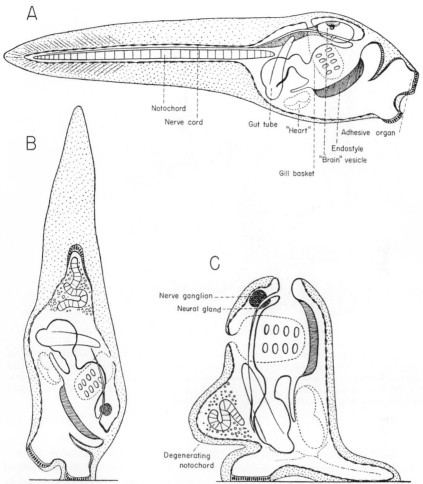

Fig. 7. Metamorphosis of a solitary tunicate. *A*, The free-swimming larva (cf. Fig. 6, *A*). *B*, The larva has attached itself to the bottom, and tail degeneration is under way. *C*, Except for remains of the notochord, the "somatic" structures have disappeared, and the build is close to that of the degenerate adult. (After Dawydoff.)

has rather the appearance of an amphibian tadpole (in one small group of tunicates the larval form persists in the sexually mature state). The "head" of the larva corresponds to the entire body of the adult. The tail is a swimming organ, useful in transporting the young tunicate about in its search for a home. Once the animal attaches and "settles down" to its sedentary adult existence, the tail dwindles and is absorbed into the body. In this tail, however, are to be found major proofs of vertebrate relationship of the tunicates. There is in the larval tail (as the group name implies) a well-developed notochord and, above this, a typical hollow dorsal nerve cord. These tail structures are, however, less advanced than those of Amphioxus, for there is here no segmentation of the swimming muscles or of the nerves supplying them. Anteriorly, there are in the larva a rudimentary brain and sense organs. At metamorphosis, the notochord and the larval nerve cord (unnecessary in the sessile adult) disappear.

Fig. 8. Tunicates and hemichordates. *A,* An individual of the pterobranch genus Rhabdopleura projecting from its enclosing tube. *B,* A part of a colony of the same. *C,* A colonial sessile tunicate; each polygonal area is a separate individual of the colony. *D,* External view of a solitary tunicate (cf. Fig. 6, *B*). *E,* A free-floating tunicate, or salp. *F,* An acorn worm (Balanoglossus). *a,* Anus; *c,* collar region; *l,* lophophore; *m,* mouth; *p,* pore or opening from celom; *pd,* stalk (peduncle) by which individual is attached to remainder of colony; *pr,* proboscis or anterior projection of body; *s,* siphon which carries off water and body products. (Mainly after Delage and Hérouard.)

The tunicates, thus, are definitely chordates and definitely related to the vertebrates. How do they fit into the evolutionary story? Those who believe that the vertebrate ancestors were from the earliest times actively swimming animals would regard the tunicates as a degenerate side branch of the vertebrate ancestral line and consider that the common ancestor of vertebrates and tunicates was as an adult a free-swimming form, somewhat like the larval tunicate. From this, it is suggested, the vertebrates "ascended" by an improved continuation of an active mode of life, whereas the tunicates tended to become degenerate and lost most progressive structural features except for the food-straining gill barrel; became, in fact, fit subjects for evolutionary sermons on the results of slothful living. There is, however, another interpretation which one may consider; namely, that the chordate ancestor of the vertebrates was, rather, a sessile food strainer somewhat like an adult tunicate; that the tail first appeared as an adaptation in the larva, rendering easier the search for a suitable place in which the animal could "settle down"; and that the development of higher forms came about by the retention of the tail and the free-swimming habit in adult life with the elimination of a sessile adult stage.

Acorn Worms. The third group of forms definitely related to the vertebrates is that of the *Hemichordata.* Here the key chordate characters are little developed, and many writers would erect the hemichordates into a phylum separate from the Chordata, although related to them.

The best known hemichordates are the *acorn worms*, such as Balanoglossus (Figs. 8, 9), termed as a group the *Enteropneusta* and found not uncommonly in tidal flats. The long, slender body suggests that the acorn worms are active animals, as one might hope for in vertebrate ancestors. This is not the case; they are essentially sedentary mud burrowers and are filter-feeders comparable in their general mode of life to the tunicates. The general body shape is wormlike, but there the resemblance ends, for their structure is not at all comparable to that of ordinary annelid worms. Even externally the acorn worms are distinctive. The body terminates anteriorly in a tough yet flexible and muscular "snout" or proboscis, of variable length, which serves as a burrowing organ. Behind the proboscis there is a distinct thickened section of the body, the "collar" region; the name acorn worm is due to the fact that in some forms the proboscis and collar have the appearance of an acorn in its cup.

In most regards the acorn worm shows no especial resemblance to the vertebrates or other chordates. For a short distance—in the collar region—there is a dorsal nerve cord which is more or less hollow. But over the rest of the body the nerve cells and fibers are rather diffusely distributed in the skin, although there is some development of solid dorsal and ventral strands of nerve tissue. There is no proper notochord, although a stout pouch of tissue at the base of the proboscis has been compared (rather dubiously) to an imperfectly developed structure of that sort.

But—as in tunicates—we find that a vertebrate type of gill system is present in characteristic and highly developed fashion. The gills are not so pronounced as they are in tunicates, but there is, behind the collar, an extended pharynx (partitioned off from the food passage to the stomach), from which on either side open out gill slits quite comparable—even in details of structure and development—to those of Amphioxus. Vertebrates are surely not descended from acorn worms as such, but these forms may reasonably be interpreted as a group not distantly removed from our early chordate ancestors—essentially sedentary food-

Fig. 9. Longitudinal section through the head of an acorn worm. (After Dawydoff.)

strainers in which, however, some degree of potential motility is present in the adult.

The acorn worms show, in the gill slits at least, definite proof of vertebrate relationships. But in a second type of hemichordates, the *Pterobranchia* (Fig. 8, *A*, *B*), hardly a trace of vertebrate structure is to be found, and were it not clear that they are affiliated with the enteropneusts, one would hardly suspect that they belonged to this general stock. The pterobranchs are tiny, rare marine animals of which only a few genera are known. They form little plantlike colonies, whose individuals project like small flowers at the ends of a branching series of tubes. The short body is doubled back on itself, so that the anus opens anteriorly back of the head. Proofs of relationship to the acorn worms lie in the fact that there is a snoutlike anterior projection beyond the mouth, corresponding to the enteropneust proboscis, and back of this a short collar region. But other resemblances to acorn worms—to say nothing of more highly developed chordates—are almost lacking. There is little development of a nervous system, no trace of a hollow nerve cord, and not the slightest suggestion of a notochord. And the feeding mechanisms are of a very different type. True, these plantlike animals feed, as do more typical lower chordates, on food particles drawn in by ciliary action. But the gill mechanism, which is so important in the filter-feeding of acorn worms, tunicates and Amphioxus, is almost absent. One of the two pterobranchs has a single pair of small gill openings, the other none at all. Instead, there project from the collar region large tentacle-like structures, termed *lophophores;* these are supplied with bands of cilia which collect food particles and bring them to the mouth.

So unchordatelike are these small creatures that one is tempted to suggest that they are degenerate, perhaps relatively modern in development. But it has recently been suggested that they are a very ancient group indeed. Paleontologists have long been familiar with a variety of small tubelike structures termed *graptolites* which were abundant in the seas far before the appearance of the oldest vertebrates. It is claimed that these tubes are similar to those which shield the modern pterobranchs.

With the pterobranchs we conclude the series of lowly chordates.* What do they teach us as to vertebrate origins? The answer is far from clear. As we have said, one, at first thought, would hopefully expect the ancestral line to lead through active little forms, paralleling, at least, such invertebrate groups as the various worm phyla and the progressive arthropods such as crustaceans and insects. But consideration of the lower chordates tends to dim such expectations. For the most part we see sluggish and sedentary habits, and instead of forms actively searching for food, passive filter-feeders. But before attempting to reach a conclusion let us survey the various invertebrate phyla in search of possible chordate relatives.

Invertebrate Phylogeny. In recent decades students of invertebrate zoology have tended to agree on a fairly uniform scheme of phylogeny of the major groups of animals without backbones (Fig. 10). The coelenterates (or Cnidaria, as some authorities term the group) including such forms as jellyfishes, sea anemones, and corals may lie close to the basal stock of metazoans—all animals, that is, above the level of protozoans and sponges. The coelenterates have

---

* Possibly allied to chordates also are some tiny, deep sea forms termed the Pogonophora; but they are poorly known, and obviously degenerate, and we may leave them, without loss, in oblivion.

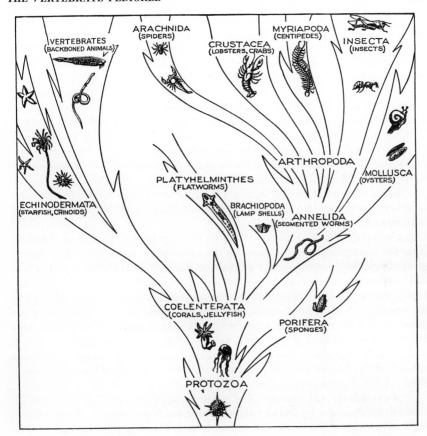

Fig. 10. A simplified family tree of the animal kingdom, to show the probable relationships of the vertebrates. (After Romer, Man and the Vertebrates, University of Chicago Press.)

a simple, two-layered structure, with little between the "skin"—the ectoderm—and the lining, termed the endoderm, of the inner gut cavity. Above the coelenterate level most animals have a third intermediate body layer, the mesoderm, from which muscular, circulatory, and other systems are formed; the mesoderm becomes—in bulk, at any rate—the most important of the three tissues. Further, many invertebrates develop a celom within the mesodermal tissues.

Two contrasting methods of embryonic formation of this third body layer are to be seen. In one type especially characteristic of echinoderms—starfishes, sea urchins, sea lilies and the like—the mesoderm arises in the form of pouches growing outward from the gut walls; these pouches remain in the adult as closed body cavities. In a second type the mesoderm arises as solid masses of cells budded off from an area near the posterior end of the body, and the body cavities, when formed, arise by cleavage within the masses of mesodermal cells. To this second type belong the annelid worms and the molluscs. The great group of jointed-legged animals, the arthropods, appear to belong to this second group as well, although their developmental pattern is much modified; and certain other forms, such as the flat worms, appear to be offshoots from the base of this major stock. We thus have the concept that, above the coelenterate level, the invertebrates form two great branches, in Y-fashion, with the echinoderms at the end of one branch and the great host of familiar advanced invertebrates clustered on the other. A few of the less familiar sessile marine forms, such as the lamp shells (brachiopods) and moss animalcules (bryozoans), do not fit well on either main branch but are perhaps somewhat closer to the echinoderms.

The two stocks contrast not only in the type of formation of the middle body layer, but also in the larval development. Both echinoderms on the one hand and water-dwelling annelids and molluscs on the other grow from the egg into tiny larvae of simple structure, with bands and tufts of cilia arranged in characteristic patterns on the surface of the body. The echinoderm larva has an arrangement of the ciliated bands and other features which differ markedly from those of the larvae of annelid worms and molluscs.

From what point on this family tree of the invertebrates does the chordate (and vertebrate) branch arise? Theories on this subject have been numerous, but have given few positive results.

One solution to the problem might be to suggest a direct origin of chordates from the most primitive metazoans on the coelenterate level. Here there are no great difficulties to overcome, for animals on this level of evolution have few specialized features which must be lost before starting on the path toward the vertebrates. But in reality, advocacy of coelenterate descent would seem to be begging the question. A number of basic advances not made by the coelenterates are found in almost all other invertebrate phyla—development of a middle body layer, presence of both mouth and anus in the digestive tract, and so forth. It seems highly improbable that the vertebrates acquired these progressive features entirely independently of other groups. Search seems warranted for possible relatives—if not direct ancestors—on a higher level.

Annelids as Ancestors. The annelid worms offer a possible point of departure; the theory of vertebrate origin from annelids was warmly advocated during later decades of the nineteenth century. The lowly angleworm is none too prepossessing as an ancestor; but there are numerous marine annelids of a more progressive and attractive nature. Annelids have a typical bilateral symmetry, as do vertebrates, and, in correlation with this, some are, like typical vertebrates, active animals in contrast with the sessile types common in many invertebrate phyla. Then too, they are segmented forms, as the vertebrates are to at least some extent. As in vertebrates, the central nervous system is composed of a brainlike mass at the anterior end of the body and a longitudinal nerve cord.

So far, so good. But beyond this point the comparison breaks down. Even the segmentation is not a perfect argument; for the annelid is segmented in every respect, from skin to gut lining, whereas the segmentation of a vertebrate is primarily confined to part of the middle body layer. The annelid has, it is true, a longitudinal nerve cord. But it is solid, not hollow, and it is ventral rather than dorsal in position. This last point is especially troublesome to advocates of this theory. They have "resolved" the difficulties by assuming that a vertebrate is a worm upside down (Fig. 11). This is hard to swallow (even a worm may have some idea of which way is up) and involves further perplexities. The worm mouth is on the under side of the head, and so is that of a vertebrate. A reversal of surfaces implies that the old mouth of the worm has closed and been replaced, historically, by a new one. Attempts have been made to find traces of the theoretic old mouth opening in vertebrate embryos—it should pass upward and forward through the brain to the top of the head!—but without convincing results.

Fig. 11. Diagram to illustrate the supposed transformation of an annelid worm into a vertebrate. In normal position this represents the annelid with a "brain" (s) at the front end and a nerve cord (x) running along the underside of the body. The mouth (m) is on the underside of the animal, the anus (a) at the end of the tail; the blood stream (indicated by arrows) flows forward on the upper side of the body, back on the underside. Turn the book upside down

and now we have the vertebrate, with nerve cord and blood streams reversed. But it is necessary to build a new mouth (ps) and anus (pd) and close the old one; the worm really had no notochord (nt): and the supposed change is not as simple as it seems. (From Wilder, History of the Human Body, by permission of Henry Holt & Co., publishers.)

Even if this difficulty in orientation be solved, there are more ahead. There is no trace in an annelid of a notochord or of internal gills. This may be discounted, perhaps, by the fact that (as we have seen) these structures are little developed in some of the simplest chordates. But a crucial difference is that the type of mesoderm formation is in contrast, for in chordates the pouch type of mesoderm formation is the basic pattern. There is, thus, almost no positive reason to believe in a descent of vertebrates from annelids; and there are so many difficulties in the way that there is today little reason to take stock in an annelid theory.

Arachnids as Ancestors. The arthropods, including crustaceans, myriapods, arachnids, and insects, are, it is agreed, descended from annelids or from worm ancestors closely related to them. The arthropods include the most progressive and successful of all invertebrate animals, and it is not unnatural that they have received considerable attention as possible vertebrate ancestors. Among the arthropods it is the arachnids that have been selected as the most likely candidates for vertebrate kinship. Spiders are the commonest of arachnids; but the scorpions are more generalized types. Still more primitive are aquatic arachnids, including the horseshoe crab (Limulus) and relatives of high geological antiquity; one ancient extinct group, the eurypterids, has been thought by some to be close to the ancestry of the vertebrates.

In arachnids, as in annelids, there is a ventral nerve cord. This gives us the same problem that was encountered in the worms: the upper and lower surfaces must, it seems, be reversed, a new mouth exchanged for an old one, and so on. Again as in annelids we find conspicuous differences from vertebrates in segmentation; still again, there is no trace in arachnids of notochord or internal gills. An added difficulty with arachnids as ancestors of the vertebrates is the presence of numerous, complex jointed legs of arthropod character. It is impossible that these were transformed into fish fins, and the arthropod legs must be done away with before the development of vertebrate appendages can begin. The old eurypterids were covered with chitinous armor, which in some cases had a superficial resemblance to the bony armor of certain archaic fishes, such as those shown in Figure 18. But even this resemblance is meaningless; for the resemblance is a top-to-top one, whereas, because of the reversal of surfaces, it should be the bottom of the arachnid which resembles the upper side of the vertebrate. To sum up, to make a backboned animal out of an arachnid, the supposed ancestor must have lost almost every characteristic feature he once possessed and reduced himself practically to an amorphous jelly before resurrecting himself as a vertebrate.

An amusing variant of the arachnid theory removes a whole series of difficulties caused by the necessity of turning the arachnid over to make a vertebrate. Under this theory there has been no reversal of surfaces. It is pointed out that the arthropod digestive tube has expansions and subdivisions which rather resemble the cavities of the brain and spinal cord of vertebrates. This particular theory assumes that the original ventral nerve cord of arachnids migrated upward to surround the original digestive tube, which actually became the cavities of the nervous system; and that meanwhile a brand new digestive tract developed by a closing over of the furrows present ventrally between the jointed legs. Technically, this theory solves the difficulties encountered in turning the animal over; but it appears to offer fresh problems as difficult as those solved. There is no adequate explanation for this change from one digestive system to another; and the intermediate stages are, to say the least, difficult to imagine.

Echinoderm Affinities. Unlikely as it seems at first sight, the best clues to chordate relationships are to be found in a study of the echinoderms—the starfish, sea urchins, and the like. Several lines of work suggest that, despite the obvious and strong contrasts, the two phyla are nevertheless related. In most vertebrates mesoderm formation is a complex process, but in Amphioxus we find mesoderm forming from gut pouches just as it does in echinoderms. Another item of interest is the fact that in certain of the hemichordates there is a ciliated larva (Fig. 12) of the same type as that of echinoderms—so similar, in fact, that until the life history was known, the hemichordate larvae were thought to be those of starfish!

Even biochemistry helps to establish the case. The proteins of blood serum vary greatly from form to form, and it appears in general that the more closely related two animals are, the more similar are these proteins. Tests of the sera of acorn worms and other lower chordates show their definite relationships to those of echinoderms, but not to other invertebrates. Again, muscle chemistry tends to link the two groups. In all animals with musculature, phosphorus compounds are present which speed up the energy release for muscle activity. In vertebrates a material combined with the phosphate is creatine (cf. Chap. 9); in most nonvertebrate groups another compound, argenine, is present instead. But some echinoderms have creatine as well as argenine, and argenine is present in some tuni-

Fig. 12. Diagrammatic side views of the larvae of (*A*) an acorn worm, (*B*) a starfish, and (*C*) a sea cucumber, all much enlarged. The black lines represent ciliated bands. The digestive tract (stippled) appears through the translucent body. Views are from the left side; the larvae are bilaterally symmetric. (After Delage and Hérouard.)

cates and present (as well as creatine) in some hemichordates—facts which tend further to link the two groups.

   Chordate Phylogeny.   What do these resemblances mean? Surely the vertebrates and their chordate relatives are not derived from echinoderms, with their specialized organs and skeletal plates, and their pronounced radial symmetry. Such a form as a starfish or a sea urchin is obviously far off any line leading to a vertebrate. But one important point may be kept in mind. Most echinoderms are free-living and capable of locomotion to some degree; but the fossil record clearly proves that the ancestral echinoderms were sessile forms and one group of living echinoderms, the crinoids or sea lilies, are fixed in habitus. Attached by a stalk to the sea bottom, they spread out above their compact bodies a series of feathery arms; ranged the length of these arms are bands of cilia which filter out from the water the food particles upon which the sea lily subsists and carry them down to the mouth.

   Here lies, one may believe, the clue to the whole story. This mode of life is precisely that of the little pterobranchs which, we have seen, are unquestionably related to vertebrate ancestry despite their simple structure and the absence in them of almost every diagnostic character of vertebrates and even of chordates in general.

   Despite the contrasts between primitive echinoderms and pterobranchs, the two can be derived readily from an ancient common ancestor and, except for the little proboscis and a collar development which tend to tie them to the acorn worms, the pterobranchs are certainly close to the pattern expected in this ancestor.

   It seems clear that we must abandon preconceived ideas that the ancestral chordate was an active, bilaterally-shaped swimmer, and accept the evidence indicating that this ancestor was a sessile bottom dweller, subsisting on food particles gathered and brought to the mouth by outstretched lophophore arms. On this basis a reasonable theory of chordate evolution can be erected (Fig. 13). Little animals of this character, collecting food by lophophore arms, are not uncommon today, notable being brachiopods or lamp shells (so called because the body and lophophore are protected by a paired shell) and the tiny bryozoans—the "moss animalcules." These forms are suspected of at least distant relationships to echinoderms and chordates, and the chordate ancestor was rather surely one of a series of such lophophore-bearers. From it, with elaboration of varied specialized organs, may have arisen the echinoderms, and from it, with little change except a thickening of a collar region and a small proboscis, may have come the pterobranchs.

   A first major development of true chordate characters was a shift in the method of obtaining food particles, the substitution of gill-filtering for lophophores. Even in one of the pterobranchs a single pair of gill slits has developed, apparently aiding in the flow of food materials into the digestive tract. With the increase and elaboration of the gill-filtering system, lophophores were abandoned. The acorn worms, still essentially sessile although not stalked, appear to represent a side branch at this stage of evolution.

   Further elaboration of the gill-straining device led eventually, in one higher branch, to the typical tunicates, in which the whole animal seems to be little more than an elaborate food-filter. But as this stage was approached, there entered, it would seem, a new adaptation which was to radically alter the whole picture of higher chordate evolution.

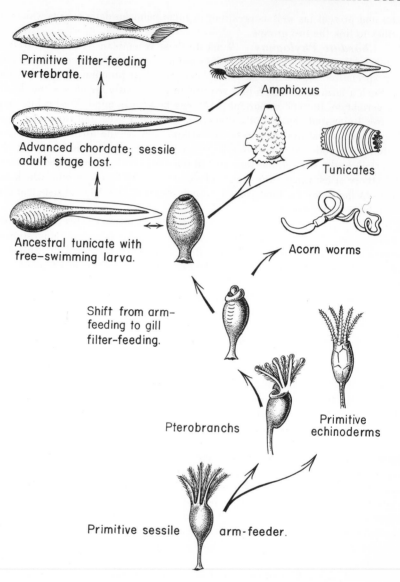

Primitive filter-feeding
vertebrate.

Amphioxus

Advanced chordate; sessile
adult stage lost.

Tunicates

Ancestral tunicate with
free-swimming larva.

Acorn worms

Shift from arm-
feeding to gill
filter-feeding.

Pterobranchs

Primitive
echinoderms

Primitive sessile   arm-feeder.

Fig. 13. A diagrammatic family tree suggesting the possible mode of evolution of vertebrates. The echinoderms may have arisen from forms not too dissimilar to the little pterobranchs; the acorn worms, from pterobranch descendants which had evolved a gill-feeding system but were little more advanced in other regards. Tunicates represent a stage in which, in the adult, the gill apparatus has become highly evolved, but the important point is the development in some tunicates of a free-swimming larva with advanced features of notochord and nerve cord and free-swimming habits. In further progress to Amphioxus and the vertebrates the old sessile adult stage has been abandoned, and it is the larval type that has initiated the advance. (From Romer, The Vertebrate Story, University of Chicago Press.)

The embryo or larva of a sessile organism must find a proper place on the sea bottom on which to settle down for adult life. How to reach and select it? Some acorn worms, we have noted, have a ciliated larva; but such a larva's powers of locomotion are limited. Much better is the tadpole-like larva which may have developed before the tunicate level was reached. Here a muscular tail is present; a notochord stiffens the structure; a nerve cord and nerves are evolved to supervise locomotion; sense organs are developed which guide the movements of this new swimming structure toward a proper place for fixation and adult existence.

Once this new larval structure was evolved, a radical change of direction in chordate evolution opened out. A new active type of life became possible. Conservative forms remain as tunicates. But for others, paedogenesis appears to have entered the picture. The animal ceased to "settle down." The larval locomotor structures were retained throughout life, even though filter-feeding long continued to be the means of sustenance; the pharyngeal filtering apparatus could be transported from place to place as favorable opportunities presented themselves. Amphioxus, although a bit off the direct ascending line, represents a more advanced stage, in which filter-feeding persists but the ancestral fixed adult condition has been abandoned. But for the most part, chordates did not stop at this level. A major burst of evolutionary activity resulted from the development of these new locomotor potentialities and led on to the major story of vertebrate evolution.

"Visceral" and "Somatic." In later chapters we will frequently encounter the terms "visceral" and "somatic"—visceral and somatic skeletal structures, visceral and somatic muscles, visceral and somatic nerves. The "visceral" structures have mainly to do with the gut and its appendages (particularly the pharynx); the "somatic" structures are those of the "outer" tube of the body. One might assume that the two terms had a mere topographic meaning and nothing more. But it is highly probable that there is a long phylogenetic history behind visceral-somatic distinctions (Fig. 14).

Fig. 14. Diagrams to show the contrast between "visceral" and "somatic" components of the chordate body. *A*, A theoretical type of chordate essentially similar to the tunicate larva, but with the somatic component retained in the adult; below, a true vertebrate. The area of the visceral component is outlined in black. In *A* the somatic animal lies posterior to the visceral animal (representing the ancestral chordate), except that sense organs and anterior part of the nerve cord extend forward dorsally. In *B*, the visceral and somatic components overlap to a considerable degree and integration of the two is advancing.

Such a lower chordate as a solitary tunicate consists of little else than a pharynx and appended gut tube, plus such necessary additions as the gonads and a very simple nervous system. Except that it is, of course, sheathed externally by skin or tunic, the whole animal represents essentially the visceral component of the vertebrate. The somatic component is the new, added series of locomotor devices—swimming muscles, notochord and, for their direction, a more highly evolved nervous system and sense organs. At first these somatic structures were for the most part appended posteriorly to the visceral animal. As vertebrate evolution progressed, the two became more broadly overlapping and coordinated with one another. But even today, as seen in development and in adult structure, the original distinctions tend to persist. In many ways one can regard a vertebrate as two distinct animals, visceral and somatic. The two are welded into a single structure, but some traces of the distinctions between them still persist; the "weld" is an imperfect one.

3

WHO'S WHO
AMONG THE
VERTEBRATES

The study of organs and organ systems and their varied forms and functions—the main concern of the present work—gives us but a one-sided account of the vertebrates. What one should know is not merely the discrete parts, but the total animal; its life and its place in nature. Our present study no more gives us a rounded picture of the vertebrates than the dissection of a cadaver and a course in physiology would give us a complete knowledge of mankind. It is to be hoped that the student will read some work on the "natural history" of vertebrates and thus gain an idea of the living animals whose bodies are verbally dissected in this volume. We shall here give merely a brief survey of the membership of the vertebrate groups in order to place the forms discussed within a phylogenetic framework.

THE GEOLOGIC RECORD

The fossil record and the extinct animals included in it require attention in this regard. In comparative anatomy one compares the organs of *existing* members of different groups as if one had descended from the other; as if mammals had descended from the existing reptiles, and these from existing amphibians and fishes. Obviously, however, this is not the case. A turtle is a reptile, but it is not a mammal ancestor; it has had just as much time to diverge from the common primitive reptilian stock as has the mammal. A frog is an amphibian; but it is definitely not the sort of amphibian from which more progressive land vertebrates were derived. Only through paleontology, the study of fossils, can we hope to discover the true nature of the common ancestors from which the varied living vertebrates arose.

In discussing fossils, some notion of the geologic time scale is necessary (cf. Table 1). The earth's history of several billion years is divided by geologists into

Table 1.   Geologic Periods Subsequent to the Time When Fossils First Became Abundant

(The Carboniferous is generally subdivided into two periods, Mississippian [earlier] and Pennsylvanian [later]. The time estimates are based on the rate of disintegration of radioactive materials found in a number of deposits.)

ERA (AND DURATION)	PERIOD	ESTIMATED TIME SINCE BEGINNING OF EACH PERIOD (IN MILLIONS OF YEARS)	EPOCH	LIFE
Cenozoic (age of mammals; about 70 million years)	Quaternary	1	Recent	Modern species and subspecies; dominance of man.
			Pleistocene	Modern species of mammals or their forerunners; decimation of large mammals; widespread glaciation.
	Tertiary	70	Pliocene	Appearance of many modern genera of mammals.
			Miocene	Rise of modern subfamilies of mammals; spread of grassy plains; evolution of grazing mammals.
			Oligocene	Rise of modern families of mammals.
			Eocene	Rise of modern orders and suborders of mammals.
			Paleocene	Dominance of archaic mammals.
Mesozoic (age of reptiles; lasted about 155 million years)	Cretaceous	135		Dominance of angiosperm plants commences; extinction of large reptiles and ammonites by end of period.
	Jurassic	180		Reptiles dominant on land, sea, and in air; first birds; archaic mammals.
	Triassic	225		First dinosaurs, turtles, ichthyosaurs, plesiosaurs; cycads and conifers dominant.
Paleozoic (lasted about 375 million years)	Permian	270		Radiation of reptiles, which displace amphibians as dominant group; widespread glaciation.
	Carboniferous	350		Fern and seed fern coal forests; sharks and crinoids abundant; radiation of amphibians; first reptiles.
	Devonian	400		Age of fishes (mostly fresh water); first trees, forests and amphibians.
	Silurian	440		Invasion of the land by plants and arthropods; archaic fishes.
	Ordovician	500		Appearance of vertebrates (ostracoderms); brachiopods and cephalopods dominant.
	Cambrian	600		Appearance of all major invertebrate phyla and many classes; dominance of trilobites and brachiopods; diversified algae.

a few major time units termed *eras;* these are subdivided into a number of *periods.* For the earlier eras there is little adequate knowledge of life of any sort; the fossil record is almost entirely confined to the last three eras, spanning somewhat over half a billion years of earth history.

The first of these three, the *Paleozoic Era* or Age of Ancient Life, covered about 370 million years, and is divided into half a dozen periods. The fossil record remaining from the seas of the oldest period (Cambrian) contains abundant representatives of almost every major animal group, except the vertebrates. The first faint traces of backboned animals have been found in the rocks of the following Ordovician period, and a modest number of archaic fishes have been found in the Silurian period that followed. The paucity of early vertebrate fossils may be the result of the group's having evolved in fresh waters; the sediments of the older Paleozoic periods are mainly marine. In the Devonian period fishes were abundant in fresh-water deposits—so abundant that this period is sometimes termed the Age of Fishes—and many had invaded the seas as well. The continental sediments of the Devonian indicate to the geologist that much of the land was subject to marked seasonal droughts, as are certain tropical regions today; times of abundant rainfall alternated with seasons when streams ran dry and pools were stagnant. These conditions appear to have had a major influence on the history of fishes and in the development of terrestrial life.

At the very end of the Devonian appeared the first land vertebrates, the amphibians, and primitive members of that group are common in the swamp deposits that characterize the Carboniferous period, the age during which the earth's major coal seams were formed. Before the end of that period the first reptiles had evolved, and early reptile orders were common land animals in the Permian period, with which the Paleozoic Era closed.

The *Mesozoic Era,* the "Middle Age" of the story of life, is frequently termed the Age of Reptiles, for members of that class dominated the land life of that era, and many types of reptiles now extinct flourished in the seas and in the air as well. The highest of vertebrate groups, further, had their beginnings in the Mesozoic; the oldest mammals appeared at about the boundary between Triassic and Jurassic periods and the oldest known birds appeared toward the end of the Jurassic, but both groups remained inconspicuous till the end of the era.

The *Cenozoic Era* is the Age of Modern Life or Age of Mammals. At the end of the Mesozoic the reptile hordes became greatly reduced, leaving that class of vertebrates in its modern impoverished phase. Modern bird types appeared early in the Cenozoic, and, most conspicuously, the mammals rapidly evolved into the varied progressive groups which dominate the land today.

VERTEBRATE CLASSIFICATION

The backboned animals constitute the subphylum Vertebrata of the phylum Chordata. The next step in classification is a division of the varied vertebrates into a series of classes. The distinguishing features of certain of these classes are obvious to anyone who has the slightest familiarity with nature. The *class Mammalia* includes the mammals, the familiar warm-blooded, hair-clothed animals among which man himself is to be included; the birds, *class Aves,* are readily distinguished by the presence of feathers and wings and by their possesion, equally with mammals, of a high, controlled body temperature. The *class Reptilia,* lacking the progressive features of the birds and mammals, represents a lower level of land life, with lizards, snakes, turtles, and crocodiles as living representatives. A fourth group is that of the *class Amphibia*, including frogs, toads, and salamanders—four-legged animals, but reminiscent of fishes in many respects.

One commonly lumps the remaining lower vertebrates as "fish," and these forms (or most of them) are sometimes included in a single vertebrate class—the attitude being that, after all, they seem to be built on a common plan, as water dwellers with gills and locomotion performed by fins rather than limbs. But this is a rather personal, human viewpoint. An intellectual and indignant codfish could point out that this is no more sensible than putting all land animals in a single class, since, from his point of view, frogs and men, as four-limbed lung-breathers, are much alike. Actually, when we look at the situation objectively, a codfish and a lamprey, at two extremes of the fishy world, are as different structurally as amphibian and mammal. The fishes are perhaps best arranged in four classes of lower vertebrates: *class Agnatha* for jawless vertebrates, such as the living lampreys and fossil relatives; *class Placodermi* for primitive jawed fishes of the Paleozoic, now extinct; *class Chondrichthyes*, cartilaginous fishes, sharks, and their relatives; *class Osteichthyes*, the higher bony fishes which today constitute most of the piscine world.

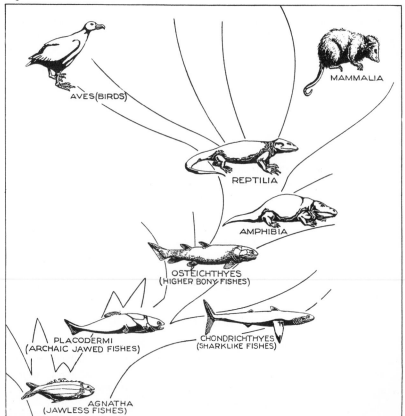

Fig. 15. A simplified family tree of the classes of vertebrates. (From Romer, The Vertebrate Story, University of Chicago Press.)

If we wish to group these eight classes, we may for convenience consider the four higher land groups as constituting a *superclass Tetrapoda,* or four-footed animals, the fishes as making up a *superclass Pisces:*

Superclass Pisces. . . . . .Class Agnatha
Class Placodermi
Class Chondrichthyes
Class Osteichthyes
Superclass Tetrapoda. . . . . .Class Amphibia
Class Reptilia
Class Aves
Class Mammalia

This is but one of several alternative methods of grouping the vertebrate classes. Some, placing emphasis on the development of jaws, would contrast with the Agnatha all the remaining vertebrates as *Gnathostomata,* "jaw-mouthed" forms. Still another grouping is to consider the three highest classes as forming a group termed *Amniota,* the remaining five constituting the *Anamniota.* This is based upon the fact that the lower types generally have a rather simple mode of reproduction, with eggs laid in the water and young developing there, whereas reptiles evolved a shelled egg, laid on land, within which a complex sort of development (described in a later chapter) takes place. Some reptiles and nearly all mammals bear their young alive, but have retained the same general pattern of embryonic development, and the name Amniota is derived from the amnion, one of the membranes surrounding the growing embryo in mammals and birds as well as reptiles.

A synoptic classification of vertebrates is given at the end of the book. In its simplest form the phylogeny of the vertebrate classes (Fig. 15) may be diagrammed thus:

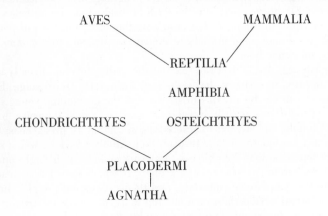

JAWLESS VERTEBRATES

Living *lampreys* and *hagfishes,* together termed *cyclostomes* (Figs. 16, 17), are representatives of a lowly group, the *class Agnatha*—jawless vertebrates. Best known is the marine lamprey (Petromyzon). This fish is eel-like in appearance, but much more primitive in its structure than true eels (which are highly developed bony fishes). The lamprey is soft-bodied and scaleless and, though having a

Fig. 16.   Three types of cyclostomes. *A,* The slime hag, Bdellostoma; *B,* the hagfish, Myxine; *C,* the lamprey, Petromyzon. (From Dean.)

feeble skeleton of cartilage, lacks bones entirely. There are no traces of paired fins, and, most especially, jaws are totally lacking. The adult lamprey is predaceous, nevertheless; the rounded mouth cup forms an adhesive disc by which it attaches to the higher types of fishes upon which it preys, and a rasping tongue-like structure within the mouth is a fairly effective substitute for the absent jaws. There is but a single nostril, opening high on top of the head, and having a hypophysial pouch (cf. p. 463) combined with it. The gill passages are not slits, as in typical fishes, but spherical pouches, connected by narrower tubes with gut and body surface. In various less obvious structural characters, noted in later chapters, the lampreys likewise show a series of features in which they differ from typical fishes—features which appear to be in part primitive, in part aberrant.

The excessively slimy hagfishes are, like Petromyzon, marine in habit, but differ in a number of ways. The rasping tongue is present, but the mouth is surrounded by short tentacles instead of a sucker. The hags are scavengers rather than active predators, burrowing into the flesh of dead or moribund fishes. The nostril is at the tip of the snout rather than atop the head, and the gill pouches in some hagfishes do not open directly to the surface but join to a common external opening on either side.

The hagfish eggs are laid in the sea and the young develop directly there; the marine lamprey, in contrast, has a distinct fresh-water larval stage. Every spring, lampreys run up the streams to spawn, and the developing young spend several years of their lives as little larvae (ammocoetes) which lie nearly buried in the mud of brooks and streams. These larvae are not at all predaceous; there is no tongue rasp, no mouth sucker. Instead, they are filter-feeders, which strain food particles much as does Amphioxus. A stream of water is brought into the mouth by ciliary action, passes through a pharynx which even has a structure comparable to the Amphioxus endostyle, and thence flows out the gill slits. At the end of the larval period there is a sudden marked change in structure—a *metamorphosis*—and the young lamprey, with adult features fully developed, descends to the sea. It is possible, however, for lampreys as adults to remain in fresh waters—the sea lamprey has successfully invaded the American Great Lakes —and certain small fresh-water species of lampreys never take up a predaceous life, but reproduce and die shortly after metamorphosis in their native streams.

It is generally agreed that the absence of jaws, and, probably, of fins, is a primitive feature of cyclostomes. Other characters, however, are more dubiously

Fig. 17. Longitudinal section of a slime hag, Bdellostoma. *A*, Anus; *AO*, ventral aorta; *AP*, abdominal pore; *AT*, atrium of heart; *B*, brain; *BR*, gill pouch; *C*, duct from nasal pit to throat; *D*, horny, toothlike structures; *DA*, dorsal aorta; *DR*, dorsal fin rays; *I*, intestine; *IBO*, internal gill openings; *IV*, septum between muscle plates; *L*, liver; *M*, muscle segments; *MO*, mouth; *N*, nostril sac; *NA*, sheath of spinal cord; *NC*, notochord; *NT*, neural tube (spinal cord); *OE*, pharynx; *S*, sheath of notochord; *T*, extrusible "tongue"; *UG*, urogenital organs; *V*, ventricle of heart; *VC*, posterior cardinal vein. (From Dean.)

primitive. There is considerable reason to regard the absence of a bony skeleton as a degenerate feature; the predaceous or scavenging habits can hardly have been present in ancestral vertebrates (mutual cannibalism is not, to say the least, advantageous), and the tongue rasp is a cyclostome specialty. Cyclostomes represent a primitive level of vertebrate development; they are not, however, in themselves ancestral vertebrates.

When we look into the fossil record, we find that the oldest and most primitive of fossil vertebrates, found in Ordovician and Silurian deposits, mainly fresh water, and surviving into the Devonian, were small fishlike creatures known as *ostracoderms* (Figs. 18, 19). Superficially there is little resemblance to the cyclostomes, but study shows that ostracoderms were jawless ancient representatives of the class Agnatha. In a majority of ostracoderms there was, as in cyclostomes, but a single nostril, and that high atop the head. Many ostracoderms (like cyclostomes) lacked paired appendages, although in some there were paired spines or peculiar flaps projecting from the body behind the head.

The ostracoderms were, in the absence of jaws or other biting or rasping structures, nonpredaceous. We find that in most of them there was a greatly expanded "head" region, most of which was occupied by large gill chambers (Fig. 232, p. 326). It seems obvious that these oldest vertebrates, like their chordate ancestors and like the larval lampreys of today, made their living by straining food materials through their gill system. Many of them, although capable of locomotion with a fishy tail, were much flattened and must have been relatively sluggish animals.

A major contrast with the modern cyclostomes lies in the skeleton. All ostracoderms were covered by a good bony armor, and in certain of them there was developed an internal bony skeleton as well. It was formerly assumed that the primitive vertebrates were (like the living cyclostomes and sharks) boneless forms, with a skeleton of cartilage only. This may have been true of the still older ancestral chordates and immature ostracoderms. But the prevalence of bone in the oldest known fossil vertebrates, and evidence of reduction instead of increase in ossification in the later history of many fish groups, suggest that ancestral vertebrates were armored as adults, and that absence of bone in the lower living vertebrates is a degenerate rather than a primitive characteristic. As to the reasons

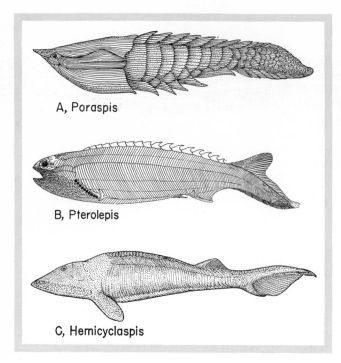

A, Poraspis

B, Pterolepis

C, Hemicyclaspis

Fig. 18. Fossil ostracoderms. *A,* Poraspis, representative of a group (Heterostraci) in which the nostrils were presumably paired and ventral in position. The gills opened by a common slit behind the main armor plates on either side. *B,* Pterolepis, member of a group (Anaspida) of relatively active swimmers. The tail is tipped downward, the reverse of the shark condition. The gill openings are rounded circles on the flank; small spines are present at the point where paired pectoral and pelvic fins develop in higher fishes. The nostril opening lay dorsally between the eyes. *C,* Hemicyclaspis, a member of the Cephalaspis group (order Osteostraci). The head and gill region are enclosed above in a solid, bony shield. The nostril opening is, again, placed dorsally between the orbits. The gills opened ventrally beneath the broad "head" (cf. Figs. 19 *B,* 232, p. 326). Flipper-like structures are seen in the position of pectoral paired fins. (*A* and *C* after Heintz; *B* after Kiaer.)

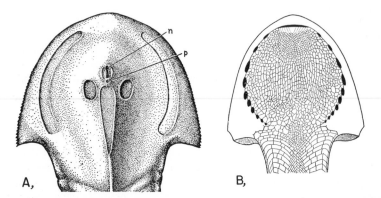

A,   B,

Fig. 19. *A,* Dorsal and *B,* ventral views of the head region of a fossil ostracoderm of the Cephalaspis type (cf. Fig. 15, *C*). Dorsally are seen openings for the paired eyes, median eye (*p*), and a median slit (*n*) for nostril and hypophyseal sac. Ventrally, the throat was covered by a mosaic of small plates, covering an expanded set of gill pouches (Fig. 232). Round openings on either side are for the gill orifices; the mouth is a small anterior slit. (After Stensiö.)

for this early development of bone, we are none too certain. One suggestion lies in the fact that we find in association with the oldest vertebrates, in the stream deposits in which they are found, remains of eurypterids—ancient water scorpions and less familiar crustaceans termed ceratiocarids. Both of these arthropod types were voracious and, on the average, considerably larger than the little ostracoderms amidst which they lived. It may be that in their earliest phases the vertebrates were the underdogs in the world of fresh-water life; bony armor may have been a defense against these invertebrate enemies. Later, as vertebrates became larger, speedier, and themselves predaceous, the eurypterids vanished from the fossil record and the ceratiocarids shrank to insignificance.

PLACODERMS

The ostracoderms were at the peak of their development during the Silurian. At the end of that period there appeared somewhat more advanced fish types which were exceedingly prominent in the following Devonian period, but became extinct before the close of the Paleozoic. These were mostly grotesque forms, quite unlike any fishes living today. It is far from certain that they form a truly natural group, but they are currently considered to form a special class of vertebrates, the *Placodermi,* the name referring to the fact that most were, like ostracoderms, covered to a variable degree by armor plating.

All had jaws. This represents a major advance over the ostracoderms, one which opened up new avenues of life to fishes and enabled them to become more active and wider-ranging animals. The term *gnathostome*—"jaw-mouthed"—is often applied to placoderms and all higher vertebrates in contrast with the Agnatha. The jaws of placoderms, however, are frequently of peculiar types and are seemingly primitive or aberrant in build—nature was still "experimenting" with these new structures. Paired fins, too, were developing, in connection with the new freedom which fishes were acquiring, but these structures also were variable and often oddly designed (from a modern point of view). The early placoderms were essentially fresh-water dwellers, like the ostracoderms before them; but during the Devonian, many of them had invaded the seas.

Of placoderms, the most "normal" in appearance were the *acanthodians* (Fig. 20, *A*), usually termed "spiny sharks." The general body proportions were sharklike, but the acanthodians were most unsharklike in other respects—particularly the fact that they were fully clad in well-developed bony scales comparable to those found in some of the higher bony fishes. The fins mainly consisted of spines—sometimes of large size—with, apparently, but a small web of skin behind them. More common in much of the Devonian were the *arthrodires*—jointed-necked fishes (Fig. 20, *B*). In these the head and gill region was covered by a great bony shield, and a ring of armor sheathed much of the body, the two sets of armor connected by a pair of movable joints (hence the name). Peculiar bony plates served the function of jaws and teeth. The posterior part of the body was quite naked in typical arthrodires. In some forms there have been found true paired fins, but in the most primitive arthrodires all we find is a pair of enormous, hollow, fixed spines projecting outward from the shoulder region—some sort of holdfast or balancing structures. Related to the arthrodires were the *antiarchs* of the Devonian (Fig. 20, *C*)—grotesque little animals which had two sets of armor like the arthrodires, but small heads, tiny nibbling jaw plates and, for limbs, a

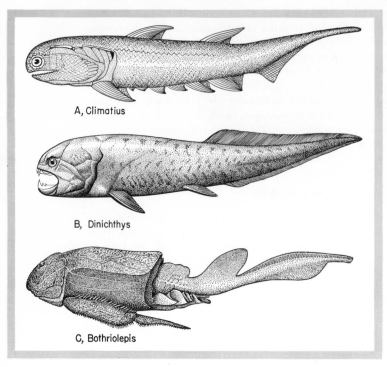

A, Climatius

B, Dinichthys

C, Bothriolepis

Fig. 20. Fossil Devonian placoderms. *A,* An acanthodian (spiny "shark"), with large fin spines and accessory fins between pectoral and pelvic pairs. *B,* Giant arthrodire with "head" and thoracic armor plating and a naked body. *C,* An antiarch with peculiar bony "flippers" in the place of pectoral fins. (*A,* data from Watson; *B* after Heintz; *C* after Patten.)

pair of jointed "flippers" projecting from the body like bony wings. Still other (but poorly known) placoderms had reduced armor and more normal fin development and rather suggest a transition from armored ancestors to shark types.

Most of the placoderms were obviously far off the main lines of vertebrate evolution, and few, if any, of the known types may possibly be regarded as actual ancestors of later vertebrates. As a group, however, they appear to represent nature's first essay in the development of jawed vertebrates. Most of these "experimental models" were not, in the long run, successful; others—poorly known or still unknown—gave rise to the two classes of more advanced fishes.

SHARKLIKE FISHES

The modern sharks are the typical representatives of a major surviving group of jaw-bearing marine fishes—the *Chondrichthyes*. This name, "cartilaginous fishes," refers to the fact that bone is unknown in any member of the group. It seems probable that the absence of bone in sharks is due to a process of reduction; the toothlike denticles present in the shark skin and the spines sometimes present on the fins appear to be the last remnants of the armor which once sheathed their placoderm forebears.

The *sharks* are almost purely predaceous in habits and with few exceptions are purely marine. Except for skeletal degeneration, the sharks appear to be in general "proper" fishes of a fairly primitive type. Absent are the peculiarities of the cyclostomes and the curious structural "experiments" seen in grotesque arthrodires. The nostrils are double, and placed beneath the tip of the snout; there are

Fig. 21. Diagrammatic dissection of a female shark. *A*, Anal fin; *B*, basal elements of fin; *BR*, basal and radial elements, upper and lower lobes of caudal fin; *C*, caudal fin; *C'*, centrum; *CA*, conus arteriosus; *CC*, cartilaginous cranium; *CL*, cloaca; *D*, dorsal fins; *D'*, dermal rays of fin; *GS*, gill slits; *HM*, hyomandibular; *I*, intestine with spiral valve; *K*, kidney; *L*, liver; *LL*, lateral line; *M*, mandible; *N*, *N'* anterior and posterior openings to nasal pouch; *NC*, notochord; *NM*, "nictitating membrane" of eye; *OV*, ovary; *OVD*, oviduct; *PF*, pectoral fin; *PQ*, upper jaw cartilage; *R*, radials of fin; *S*, stomach; *SP*, spiracle; *UD*, urinary duct; *VF*, pelvic (ventral) fin. (From Dean.)

well-formed jaws, although, in the absence of bone, there is no formed skull and
the upper jaws are independent of the braincase. The gills border slitlike passages, typically five in number, which open separately to the surface, and there is
generally a small accessory anterior opening (the spiracle). There are well-developed paired fins, and a powerful tail fin, with the tip of the body curving into its
upper lobe. A feature of sharks and their relatives which is probably not primitive is the fact that they produce large eggs containing considerable yolk. These
eggs are, in many members of the group, encased in a horny shell before they
are laid. To effect this, they must be fertilized before leaving the mother's body,
and the male sharks have developed "claspers" projecting from the pelvic fins to
aid in introduction of the sperm. Internal fertilization allows the possibility of
development of the young within the body of the mother. In various sharks and
rays the fertilized eggs are retained in the mother's reproductive tract, and develop there, so that the young are born alive. (Many reptiles and nearly all mammals have similarly developed this procedure.) Sharks first appear in the latter
part of the Devonian, and Cladoselache (Fig. 22, *A*) of that period is a form

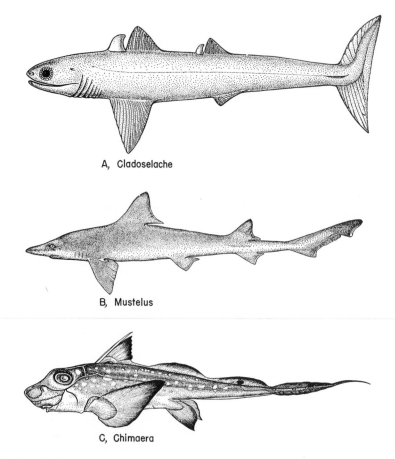

A, Cladoselache

B, Mustelus

C, Chimaera

Fig. 22. Cartilaginous jawed fishes. *A*, Primitive Devonian shark; *B*, a modern shark type; *C*, a chimaera. (*A* after Dean and Harris; *B* after Garman; *C* after Dean.)

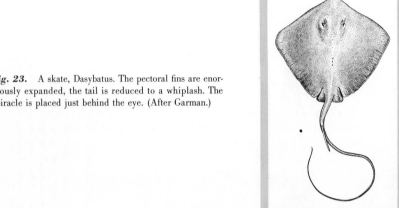

Fig. 23. A skate, Dasybatus. The pectoral fins are enormously expanded, the tail is reduced to a whiplash. The spiracle is placed just behind the eye. (After Garman.)

which may be roughly ancestral to many, if not all, of the later cartilaginous fishes. There was a variety of shark forms in the seas of the late Paleozoic, and toward the end of the Mesozoic we find shark types similar to those in modern oceans (Figs. 21; 22, *B*). In the Mesozoic, too, there appears the first of the *skates* and *rays* (Fig. 23), forms derived from sharks; they have taken to a mollusc-eating diet and a bottom-dwelling mode of life with which is correlated the flattened body shape of these unattractive fishes. In typical rays the tail and pelvic fins are much reduced, but the pectoral fins greatly expanded and, stretching forward above the gill openings, may meet in front of the head; locomotion is accomplished by undulatory movements of these broad appendages. Since in a resting position the mouth may be buried in the mud or sand of the sea bottom, the spiracle (small or even absent in sharks) is here a large opening behind the eyes through which water enters the pharynx.

A distinct group of cartilaginous fishes is that of the *chimaeras* or rat-fish— the Holocephali (Figs. 22, *C*; 24, p. 44), which are relatively rare oceanic forms. These are, like the skates, mainly mollusc-eaters; but the body is not greatly depressed, and their peculiarities include, among other features, the development of large tooth plates, and of upper jaws which (in contrast to those of sharks) are solidly fused to the braincase. A flap of skin covers the gill region (much as does a series of bony plates in both placoderms and higher bony fishes). It is presumed that the chimaeras were derived from the early sharks; the fossil record, however, is imperfect.

BONY FISHES

The class *Osteichthyes* includes the vast majority of fishes. As the name implies, they are forms in which a bony skeleton has been retained, and improved upon. A characteristic pattern is to be found, with variations, in most members of the group, in the bones of the skull, jaws, gill coverings, and in a set of bony scales covering the body. It was once believed that these fishes were descendants

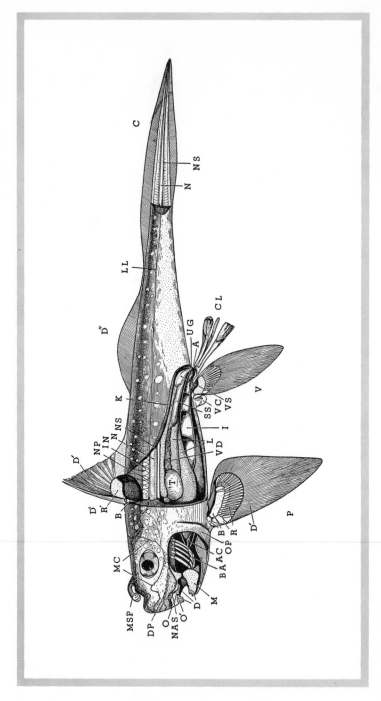

Fig. 24. Diagrammatic dissection of a male chimaeroid. *A*, Anus; *AC*, conus arteriosus; *B*, basal element of fin; *BA*, branchial arches; *C*, caudal fin; *CL*, clasper; *D*, dental plates; *D'*, dorsal fins; *D''*, dorsal rays of fin; *D''*, dorsal fins; *DP*, small dermal plates of lateral line canal; *I*, intestine with spiral valve; *IN*, interneural cartilages of vertebral column; *K*, kidney; *L*, liver; *LL*, lateral line groove; *M*, lower jaw cartilage; *MC*, lateral line canals (mucous canals) of head; *MSP*, frontal spine peculiar to male; *N*, notochord; *NAS*, nasal pouch; *NP*, neural arch; *NS*, sheath of notochord; *O*, *O'*, grooves leading to and from nasal cavity, covered by fold of skin; *OP*, operculum; *P*, pectoral fin; *R*, radial cartilages of fin; *R'*, fused radials of anterior dorsal fin; *SS*, sperm sac; *T*, testis; *UG*, urogenital opening; *V*, pelvic (or ventral) fin; *VC*, anterior accessory clasper; *VD*, epididymis; *VS*, sperm vesicle. (From Dean.)

of sharklike forms and that bone was in them a new acquisition. It now, however, appears more probable that the bony skeleton here is simply a retention and perfection of that which was present in ostracoderms and placoderms.

The first Osteichthyes are found in rock of early Devonian age; the class is, thus, much older than the sharks. By the middle of the Devonian, bony fishes were already the dominant forms in fresh waters; and they were present in great variety and abundance in later Paleozoic periods. In the Mesozoic they invaded the seas as well, and marine waters became the headquarters of the class. Lungs appear to have been present in all primitive bony fishes, although today such structures usually have been lost or converted into a hydrostatic organ, the swim bladder. Lungs were presumably an aid to survival under conditions of seasonal drought; such conditions may have been present in the fresh waters in which the ancestral Osteichthyes lived. Later, with climatic changes and particularly with the movement of most surviving bony-fish types into the sea, the lung lost its importance.

The phylogeny of the bony fishes is complicated, but must be reviewed in order to keep in mind the position on the family tree of many interesting and anatomically important types (Fig. 25). At the very beginning of their known history the Osteichthyes had already subdivided into two major groups, termed the subclasses Sarcopterygii and Actinopterygii.

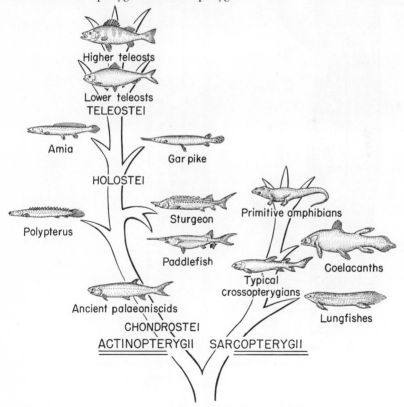

Fig. 25. A simplified family tree of the bony fishes, to show their relations to one another and to the amphibians.

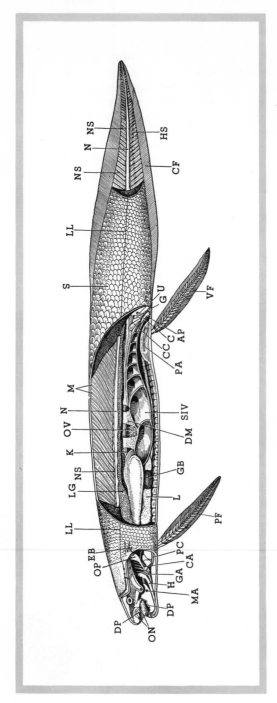

Fig. 26. Diagrammatic dissection of a lungfish. *AP*, Abdominal pore; *C*, cloaca; *CA*, conus arteriosus; *CC*, rectal gland; *CF*, caudal fin; *DM*, dorsal mesentery; *DP*, tooth plates; *EB*, external gills; *GA*, gill arches; *G*, genital duct; *GB*, gallbladder; *H*, ceratohyal; *HS*, hemal spines; *K*, kidney; *L*, liver; *LG*, lung; *LL*, lateral line; *M*, muscle segments; *MA*, lower jaw; *N*, notochord; *NS*, neural spine; *ON*, external and internal openings of nostril; *OP*, operculum; *OV*, ovary; *PA*, pelvic girdle; *PC*, pericardium; *PF*, pectoral fin; *S*, scales; *SIV*, spiral valves of intestine; *U*, urinary duct; *VF*, pelvic (ventral) fin. (From Dean.)

Sarcopterygii. From the viewpoint of the descent of land animals the Sarcopterygii are the most important of the two, for they contain the order Crossopterygii, from which land vertebrates appear to have descended, and the order Dipnoi, the lungfishes, which are surviving cousins of our piscine ancestors. Some of the sarcopterygians have, in contrast to the other subclass, internal nostrils, as do all land vertebrates. (Because of the presence of such structures these fishes have sometimes been called the Choanichthyes.) In stronger contrast with the actinopterygians is the fact that there are fleshy-lobed paired fins (a feature to which the group name refers) and, as a technical character, scales which in early forms were of a structure quite distinct from those of the actinopterygians (the cosmoid scale, cf. p. 156).

CROSSOPTERYGIANS. In the Devonian the commonest of bony fishes were crossopterygians (Fig. 27, *A*), aggressive, predaceous fishes which show important structural features of a sort to be expected in the ancestors of the amphibians. In the Carboniferous, however, they became relatively rare, and typical crossopterygians were extinct by the close of the Paleozoic.

Meantime, however, a peculiar side branch of the crossopterygians had developed, termed the coelacanths (Fig. 27, *B*). These were forms with stub snouts, feeble jaws and teeth, which migrated into the Mesozoic seas. The last fossil coelacanths are found in Cretaceous rocks, and it was long taught that our crossopterygian relatives had been extinct since the days of the dinosaurs. In 1939, however, to the surprise of science, a strange fish caught off the coast of South Africa proved to be a coelacanth! This single specimen was, unfortunately, incompletely preserved; recently, however, other, better specimens have been obtained from deep waters off the Comoro Islands in the Indian Ocean, and their structure is being studied intensively by French scientists. Knowledge of the structure of this fish is highly important, since we have here the closest living fish relative of the tetrapods. But it must be kept in mind that the coelacanths have changed markedly in habitat during their long history. It is hence probable that many of their structures may have become specialized in correlation with changed habits rather than retaining truly ancestral conditions.

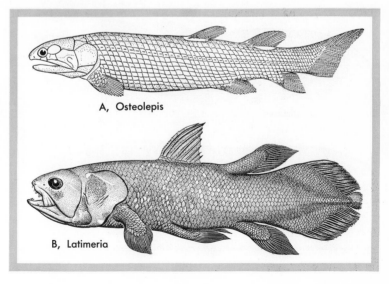

Fig. 27. Crossopterygians. *A*, Typical Devonian form; *B*, the only living coelacanth. (*A* after Traquair; *B* after Millot.)

A, Osteolepis

B, Latimeria

LUNGFISHES.   The Dipnoi, or lungfishes (Figs. 26, 28), are represented today by three genera, living, one each, in tropical regions of Australia, Africa, and
South America. In many anatomic features and in their mode of development the
lungfishes closely resemble the amphibians, and they were once thought by many
to be actual amphibian ancestors. But it is now more reasonable to believe that
these features were present as well in their relatives, the ancestral crossopterygians, and that the lungfishes are to be regarded as "uncles" rather than the actual progenitors of land vertebrates. The skull structure of lungfishes, living and
fossil, is of a peculiar type obviously unlike that of a proper amphibian ancestor,
and ossification is much reduced in the skeleton as a whole. In connection with a
diet of invertebrates and plant materials, there are present in all lungfishes specialized fan-shaped toothplates. It is of interest that the lungfishes have survived
only in regions where we find today conditions of seasonal drought similar to
those which we believe to have been present in the Devonian. The Australian
form can survive in stagnant water by air breathing; the other two are able to
withstand even the complete drying up of the water by digging a burrow in the
mud in which they "hole up" until the wet season of the year comes round. So
dependent is the African lungfish on air, that it will "drown" if kept under water.

Actinopterygii.   As types ancestral to higher vertebrates, the Sarcopterygii are of major interest; but as successful fishes, the Actinopterygii, or ray-
finned fishes, are vastly more important. From Carboniferous times on, these have
been the dominant fishes. In contrast with many sarcopterygians, internal nostrils
are absent; the scales were primitively of quite another type; and except in a few
primitive forms there is never a fleshy lobe to the fins. Instead, as the name implies, the paired fins are webs of skin supported by horny rays.

The actinopterygians have long been divided into three groups—here considered as superorders—which are, in ascending order: the Chondrostei, Holostei,
and Teleostei. The names are not particularly appropriate from the point of view
of our present knowledge of the evolution of ray-finned fishes, but may be retained for convenience.

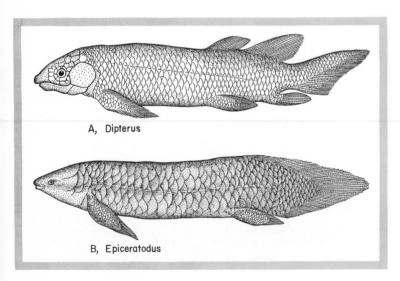

A, Dipterus

B, Epiceratodus

Fig. 28.   Lungfishes. *A*,
The oldest Devonian fossil
type; *B*, Epiceratodus of
Australia. The median fins
have changed greatly dur-
ing the history of the group.
(*A* after Traquair; *B* after
Dean.)

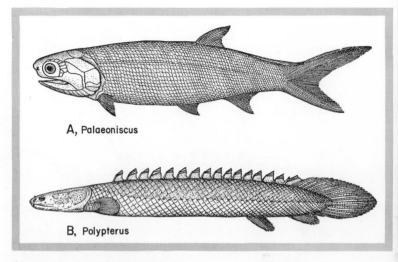

Fig. 29. Primitive ray-finned fishes. *A*, An early Paleozoic type; *B*, a living representative of the ancient palaeoniscoids, with modified fin structure. (*A* after Traquair; *B* after Dean.)

A, Palaeoniscus

B, Polypterus

CHONDROSTEI. In the Paleozoic the ray-finned fishes were represented by abundant genera of Chondrostei known as *palaeoniscoids* (Fig. 29, *A*). These were generally fishes of small size, with rather uptilted sharklike tails (the hetero-cercal type, cf. Fig. 121 *A*, p. 183) and with scales covered by a shiny material known as ganoine (cf. p. 157). (The term "ganoid" is sometimes applied to fishes of this group, but is to be avoided, for it is usually applied indiscriminately and variably to any old fish with shiny scales.) In the earliest days of bony fish history, primitive ray-finned forms were outnumbered by crossopterygians and lungfishes, but by the Carboniferous they were far more numerous than their early rivals and swarmed in the ancient lakes and streams in immense numbers and variety. In the Triassic they were still abundant, but mainly represented by advanced types transitional to the Holostei; the palaeoniscoids then rapidly declined and became extinct before the end of the Mesozoic.

This primitive ray-finned group still survives in the form of three aberrant types. Two, the *sturgeons* and *paddlefishes* (both represented in North America), are rather degenerate (Fig. 30). They have lost the ganoid scale covering of their ancestors. Scales may still be present on the tail, but the paddlefish has otherwise only a naked skin, the sturgeon a partial armor of rows of plain bony plates. The internal skeleton, highly ossified in their ancestors, is nearly as degenerate as that of the sharks, for it is mainly cartilaginous; little bone remains. Degenerate, too, is their method of feeding. In both sturgeons and paddlefishes the jaws are feeble. In advance of the jaws is a sensitive rostrum which explores for food ahead of them; sturgeons and paddlefishes are bottom-dwelling scavengers or food-strain-ers. Only in their persistently sharklike tail fin is there much evidence of the trade-marks of the older palaeoniscoids.

The third type of chondrostean survivor is *Polypterus* (Fig. 29, *B*), the *bichir* of Central Africa, which lives in much the same environment as the lungfish of that continent.* In its fins Polypterus is much modified from the ancestral type.

---

* Calamoichthys is a closely related form, but with a more elongate eel-like shape, from the same region. I have made no reference to this genus in later sections, but comments on Polypterus usually apply to Calamoichthys as well.

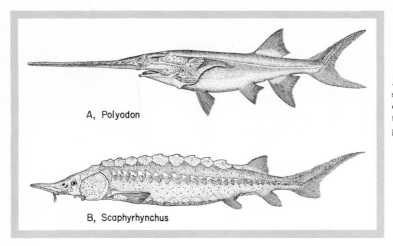

A, Polyodon

B, Scaphyrhynchus

Fig. 30. Chondro-steans. *A*, The paddlefish or "spoon-billed cat" of the Mississippi; *B*, a stur-geon. (After Goode.)

Its tail fin has become essentially symmetric; its dorsal fin is split up into a series of small sail-like structures (to which its scientific name refers), and its paired fins, unlike those of any proper actinopterygian, have a fleshy lobe. Again unique among actinopterygians is the fact that Polypterus has typical lungs, whereas other ray-finned fishes have in their place a structure termed the swim bladder (cf. p. 328), which almost never has breathing functions and is, instead, a hydro-static organ.

Because of the presence of lungs and the fleshy paired fins, Polypterus was long considered to be a crossopterygian. But closer study shows this to be incor-rect. Lungs were probably present in all primitive bony fishes, and the survival of Polypterus in peculiar drought conditions appears to be due (as with the lung-fish) to their retention. Although the fins are fleshy, they differ markedly in pat-tern from those of crossopterygians. The anatomy of the animal is as a whole in agreement with that of actinopterygians rather than that of the sarcopterygians, and the scales are of the true ganoid type, contrasting strongly with those of the sarcopterygians. Polypterus is surely a somewhat modified descendant of the an-cient palaeoniscoids.

HOLOSTEI.   Succeeding the chondrosteans as dominant fishes in the middle Mesozoic were the *holosteans*. In them the old, long, upturned sharklike tail had become shortened, the jaws tended to have a shorter gape, and the scales, in many cases, tended to lose their shiny ganoid covering. Another trend, too, was apparent at this time: the ray-finned fishes were invading the seas. The major center of actinopterygian evolution from the Jurassic period onward was the ocean. The oceanic holosteans, however, are extinct (the group became rare in the Cretaceous) and the only two survivors are North American fresh-water forms. The *gar pikes*, Lepidosteus (Fig. 31, *A*), are fast swimming fishes fairly represen-tative of the ancestral holosteans in many ways, but specialized in their elongated jaws associated with predaceous habits. A more advanced type is *Amia* (Fig. 31, *B*), a lake and river fish of the Midwest and South, popularly termed the "dog-fish," "mudfish" or bowfin. In these holosteans the internal skeleton is not at all degenerate, but in Amia the scales have lost their ganoine covering, and the tail is much like that of the teleosts.

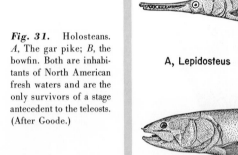

Fig. 31. Holosteans. *A*, The gar pike; *B*, the bowfin. Both are inhabitants of North American fresh waters and are the only survivors of a stage antecedent to the teleosts. (After Goode.)

A, Lepidosteus

B, Amia

TELEOSTEI. The teleosts, as the name suggests, form the end group of the ray-finned fishes, and are the fishes dominant in the world today. They appear to have originated from the holosteans in the Mesozoic oceans, and before the close of the Cretaceous had replaced the older group as the most flourishing of fish types. In teleosts the originally sharklike tail has been reduced, and the tail fin has a superficially symmetric appearance. The paired fins are small; the pectorals, are usually well up the sides of the body, and may function as effective brakes; the pelvic fins frequently are found well forward. The scales have lost all trace of the original shiny ganoid covering, and are generally thin, flexible, bony structures.

In the oceans where they originated the teleosts constitute (despite the presence of sharks and skates) the vast majority of all piscine inhabitants. They have invaded every possible marine habitat from the strand line to the abyssal depths. They have reinvaded fresh waters as well, where they constitute almost the entire fish population. Teleosts are unquestionably the most numerous of all vertebrates. It is estimated that there are about 20,000 different species, and the number of individuals of one species alone—the common herring—is probably on the order of a billion billion! The prosperity of the teleosts may be due in part to an efficient body organization, but is at least partially due to extraordinary fecundity. Existing bony fishes of other groups lay but a modest number of eggs; among teleosts the herring, for example, may lay 30,000 in a single season and a female cod is estimated to produce up to 9,000,000 eggs. The individual counts for little; only two eggs need to grow to maturity to keep up the numbers of the race. Because of their abundance the teleosts are a major source of human food, making available to us in highly edible form the organic materials of the ocean—materials particularly plentiful on the relatively shallow "banks" of the continental shelves where the major fisheries are located.

The herrings and similar forms (Fig. 33, *A*) appear to represent a primitive group of teleosts; salmon and trout are related. The carps and catfishes are characteristic of a major fresh-water division of the teleosts. More progressive teleosts, almost all marine, are the spiny-finned forms—the perch (Figs. 32, 33, *B*)

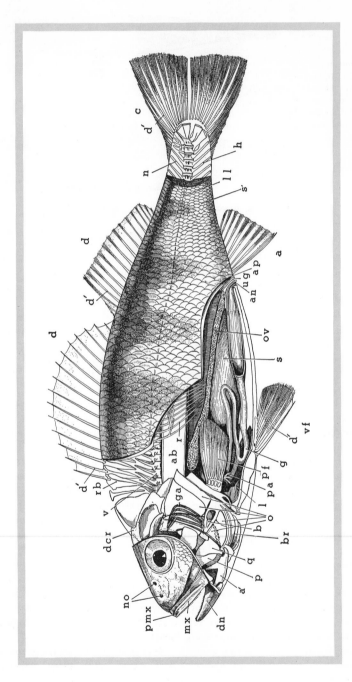

Fig. 32. Diagrammatic dissection of a teleost, the perch (Perca). *a*, Anal fin; *ab*, air bladder; *an*, anus; *ap*, abdominal pore; *a'*, articular; *b*, bulbus arteriosus (conus arteriosus); *br*, branchiostegal rays; *c*, caudal fin; *d*, dorsal fins; *d'*, dermal rays of fins; *dn*, dentary; *dcr*, dorsal crest of skull; *g*, intestine; *ga*, gill arches; *h*, hemal spines (expanded to hypurals in tail fin); *l*, liver; *ll*, lateral line; *mx*, maxilla; *n*, neural spines; *no*, nasal openings; *o*, opercular bones; *ov*, ovary; *p*, pterygoid; *pa*, pyloric appendices; *pf*, pectoral fin; *pmx*, premaxilla; *q*, quadrate; *r*, ribs; *rb*, basal fin supports; *s*, stomach; *s'*, scales; *ug*, urogenital opening; *v*, vertebral centra; *vf*, pelvic (ventral) fin. (From Dean.)

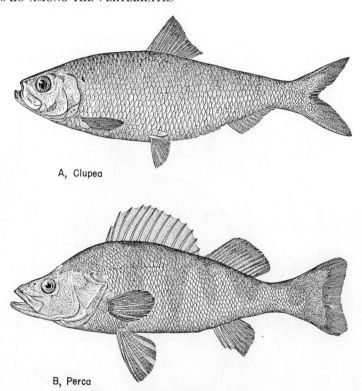

A, Clupea

B, Perca

Fig. 33. Teleosts. *A,* Primitive type, the herring; *B,* an advanced, spiny teleost, the yellow perch. (After Goode.)

is typical—in which parts, at least, of the fins are supported by stout spines rather than softer rays.

Teleosts are the most versatile of vertebrates. Within both lower and higher divisions of the teleosts there has evolved a great variety of body shapes, a few of which are shown in Figure 34. Equally diverse are their habits. In food they range from eaters of microscopic plant particles to predaceous forms which attack other fishes. And although they have not successfully invaded the land or air, some teleosts, such as the "climbing perch," can clamber about on land on stout fin spines, and "flying fishes" can glide above the water.

In any comparative study of vertebrate anatomy or physiology in which the teleosts are involved, their ecologic history must be kept in mind. Since land vertebrates come from fresh-water fishes, one tends to assume that structures or functions seen in fresh-water teleosts may be representative of those once present in the ancestors of the tetrapods. But we must remember that our common fishes belong to a different branch of the fish family tree from that which gave rise to land animals. It must, further, be kept in mind that modern fresh-water teleosts have not been, in all probability, continuous residents in that environment since the early days of fish history; between that time and the present there intervened a long marine phase.

Fig. 34. A number of teleosts, to show the variety of forms assumed by this modern fish group. *A*, The mackerel (Scomber), a fast-swimming streamlined fish. *B*, The trunk fish (Ostracion), with a stiff body and only the fins movable. *C*, The marine sunfish (Mola), a very thin, deep-bodied fish adapted to quiet waters. *D*, The globe fish (Chilomycterus), with nearly spherical contours. *E*, The sea horse (Hippocampus). *F*, A common eel (Anguilla). (From Norman, A History of Fishes.)

AMPHIBIANS

Greatest, perhaps, of all ventures made by the vertebrates during their long history was the development of tetrapods in the invasion of the land—a step which involved major changes in function and resulted in profound structural modifications. The shifts from swimming to four-footed walking, and from gill breathing to the dominance of lungs, are the most obvious of the modifications necessary in this step. But analysis shows that functional and structural changes were necessitated in almost every organ or organ system of the body.

The basic group of land vertebrates is the class Amphibia. There are three living orders (Fig. 36): the frogs and toads (*Anura*); the newts and salamanders (*Urodela*); and some wormlike burrowers (*Apoda*). Commonest are the anurans, familiar to us in temperate regions and represented in great variety in the tropics. Their specialized nature is obvious in their jumping habits, which are responsible for many modifications in their structure, particularly in the skeletal system. The salamanders are retiring but not uncommon dwellers in moist temperate zone habitats. In their external form the salamanders resemble the ancestral amphibians which first sprang from ancestral fishes. There is a fairly elongate but stoutly built body, with powerful trunk musculature, and a well-developed tail which is an aid in swimming. The median fins of fishes are gone, but the paired fins have developed into the typical land limbs which are the trademark of the tetrapods. The Apoda (or Gymnophiona) will not be familiar to many readers of this work, for they include only a few genera of small, blind tropical burrowers which look not unlike earthworms.

In salamanders, and in the other modern amphibian orders as well, we find various internal features which bridge structural gaps between the crossopterygian fishes and the higher classes of land vertebrates. Amphibian structure and func-

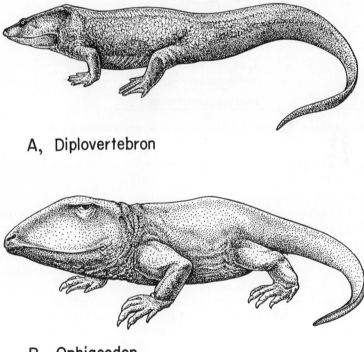

A, Diplovertebron

B, Ophiacodon

Fig. 35. *A*, Diplovertebron, a primitive Paleozoic amphibian (labyrinthodont); *B*, Ophiacodon, an early Permian reptile, representative of primitive members of that class, although showing indications of relationship to mammalian ancestry. (*A* after Gregory.)

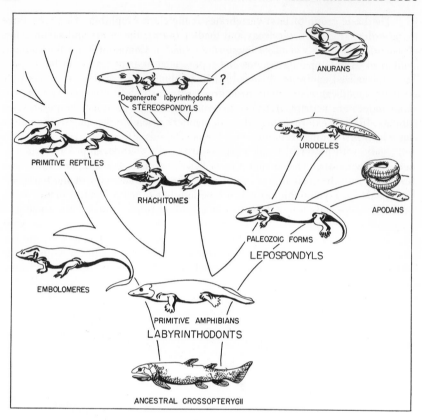

Fig. 36. A "family tree" of the Amphibia. The surviving groups are shown at the upper right. Urodeles, apodans and their fossil relatives are commonly grouped as lepospondyls, as contrasted with the labyrinthodonts; the frogs have been generally regarded as derived from labyrinthodonts, but this is far from certain. The various groups of labyrinthodonts are named from vertebral types discussed in Chapter 7.

tion are important in comparative studies. But due caution must be exercised. Frogs and salamanders and apodans are amphibians, and the amphibians are the most primitive of tetrapod classes; but we must not complete a false syllogism by concluding that these modern amphibians are really primitive tetrapods. In the modern orders the skeleton is degenerate, with considerable loss of bones from the head and, particularly in salamanders, a trend for retention of embryonic cartilages. In all, vertebral column structure is apparently quite far removed from that which was present in truly ancestral land forms, and the great shortening of the trunk and reduction of the tail in frogs shows a high degree of specialization. The limbs of newts are seemingly not too aberrant, but those of a frog are certainly highly modified; and the apodans have abolished limbs altogether. Concerning the soft anatomy, we cannot be so sure, but there are indications that here, too, many features are likewise aberrant in these modern orders. A frog is, in many ways, as far removed structurally from the oldest land vertebrates as is a man, and even a salamander must be regarded with suspicion.

For the actual ancestors of the land dwellers as a whole, we must turn to the fossil record of the late Paleozoic when, in the Carboniferous and early Permian, there lived numerous and varied amphibians of a more primitive nature. Two major groups were then distinguishable.

One included a series of small animals, termed lepospondyls, of which a diagnostic feature is the spool-shape of the central portions of the backbone segments. It seems likely that the older lepospondyls were, despite their antiquity, a side branch, if an early one, of the basal stock of land animals. The true base is to be sought among a second early group of amphibians, the *labyrinthodonts* (Fig. 35, *A*). These animals, of variable size, were in general considerably larger than contemporary lepospondyls; some attained crocodile proportions. Their vertebral construction was a diagnostic feature and was one from which that of reptiles and higher vertebrates could have been derived (cf. Figs. 104, 105, pp. 166, 168). Except for the absence of median fins and the presence of short but sturdy legs developed from paired fins, many features of the early labyrinthodonts are highly comparable with those of the crossopterygians from which they came. They were the first vertebrates to walk on land.

In the late Paleozoic and earliest Mesozoic, labyrinthodonts were abundant and varied. From them at an early stage came, presumably, the lepospondyl stock from which the salamanders and Apoda have descended. The frogs have generally been considered to be an independent offshoot from the labyrinthodonts, but it is possible that they are allied to the lepospondyls; more evidence is needed.

Before the close of the Paleozoic the labyrinthodonts had given origin to the reptiles. With the rise of that more progressive class, the amphibians rapidly dwindled in importance. The labyrinthodonts vanished at the close of the Triassic, and the surviving amphibians play but a modest role in modern vertebrate life.

One sometimes tends to think of the development of the early land vertebrates as the result of some "urge" toward terrestrial life among their fish ancestors. This is, of course, absurd; the evolution of the earliest amphibians capable of walking on land seems to have been essentially a happy accident. The amphibians appear to have evolved from crossopterygian ancestors toward the close of the Devonian, an age during which seasonal droughts were, it seems, common over much of the earth. Lungs, already present in the ancestral fishes, are an excellent adaptation for use under stagnant water conditions. But when a stream or pool dries up completely, a typical fish is rendered immobile and dies. Some further development of the fleshy fins already present in crossopterygians would give their fortunate possessor the chance of crawling up or down the stream bed (albeit with considerable pain and effort at first) and enable him to reach some surviving water body where he could resume a normal piscine existence.

Legs, the diagnostic feature of the tetrapod, may thus have been, to begin with, only another improvement for an aquatic life. The earliest amphibian was little more than a four-legged fish. Life on land would have been the farthest thing from his thoughts (had he had any). It was probably only after a long period of time that his descendants began to explore the possibilities of land existence opened out before them through their new locomotor abilities. And even today those of his descendants which have remained amphibians have never capitalized fully on these potentialities.

The term amphibian implies the double mode of life exhibited by many members of this class. Some toads spend much of their lives on good dry land, but most amphibians do not venture far from the stream banks, and some modern forms are still essentially water dwellers like their ancestors. The typical amphib-

ian mode of development, as exemplified by the familiar frogs and toads of northern temperate regions, is still essentially that of the ancestral fishes. The eggs are
laid in the water, and develop there into water-dwelling, gill-breathing tadpoles.
Only when adult size is neared do lungs replace gills, do limbs develop and mature,
and does terrestrial life become possible. An amphibian is chained to the water by
his mode of development and the necessity of returning to that element periodically for reproductive purposes. Although numerous modern amphibians have
adopted a variety of adaptations to avoid this complication, none has been a complete success as a fully terrestrial form. Indeed, some salamanders have, as it
were, abandoned the attempt; such forms as the American "mud puppy" (Necturus) never emerge onto land at any stage, retain external gills and water-breathing,
and reproduce, in paedogenetic fashion, in essentially a larval condition.

REPTILES

The reptiles are the descendants of the ancient amphibians which, happily,
solved this reproductive problem and became the first fully terrestrial vertebrates.
The "invention" of the amniote egg (with the associated developmental processes;
see Chapter 5) is the major diagnostic feature which distinguishes reptiles from
amphibians.

The reptilian egg is laid on land; thus there is avoided the necessity of any
adaptation for water existence in either young or adult. This egg type is the familiar
one preserved in the reptiles' avian descendants. The shell offers protection. A
large yolk furnishes an abundant food supply so that the reptilian young (unlike
the tadpole) can hatch out, at a fairly good size, as a miniature replica of the
adult and thus avoid the necessity of prematurely foraging for its food. Of embryonic membranes developed within the egg shell, one sheathes externally both
young and yolk. A second forms a lunglike breathing mechanism for absorption
of the oxygen which penetrates the porous shell. A third (the amnion, from which
the egg type gets its name) encloses the developing embryo in a liquid-filled space
—a miniature replica of the ancestral pond. The development of this new egg
type was so important for the later evolution of land vertebrates that, as noted
earlier, the reptiles, together with the birds and mammals which descended from
them are often styled collectively the amniotes.

It is probable that the oldest reptiles were still amphibious in their habits,
and that the amniote egg was merely an adaptation parallel to, but better than,
other adaptations seen in modern amphibians—a device which removed the eggs
from the dangers of drought, and of enemies present in the ancestral waters. Here
again, a major advance in the evolution of vertebrates may well have been a happy
accident.

Modern reptiles—mainly consisting of lizards, snakes and turtles—are moderately abundant in the tropics, but unimportant in temperate zones and absent
from cold climates where survival is difficult for these "cold-blooded" creatures.
The modern forms, however, are but sparse remnants of the great array of reptiles
which, beginning in the late Paleozoic, radiated out into a bewildering variety of
forms that long ruled the earth and caused the Mesozoic Era to be popularly known
as the Age of Reptiles (Fig. 37). The basic stock from which they sprang, the
long-extinct *Cotylosauria* or "*stem reptiles*" were, apart from reproductive improvements, still very archaic—clumsy and ungainly, with limbs sprawled out

sideways from the body, and in most regards no more advanced than their amphibian forebears and cousins. But due, no doubt, to the breaking of the chains which bound them to the water, there presently developed from them the groups which became prominent in the Mesozoic.

An early side branch of the stem reptiles were the *turtles*—order *Chelonia*. In their sprawling gait they are reminiscent of their Paleozoic forebears, but turtles have made a conspicuous advance in the development of a protective shell of bone, covered by horn, guarding both back and belly. Once encased in armor the chelonians turned conservative, and since the Triassic have advanced but little in most regards. The only later improvement of any note made by the order as a whole was the acquirement of the ability, lacking at first, to pull the head back into the shell. In all familiar types this is done by a straight backward pull, with the neck bent in an S-curve; some odd tropical forms tuck the head in sideways against the shoulder. Like the most ancient reptiles, most modern turtles are amphibious marsh and pond dwellers. Some, however, reverted to a purely aquatic life and several marine forms have developed, with paddle-like limbs for propulsion. At the other extreme, one group, the tortoises, have become purely terrestrial.

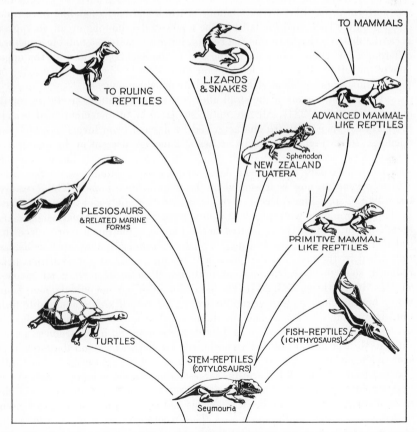

Fig. 37. A simple family tree of the reptiles (ruling reptiles not included). (From Romer, The Vertebrate Story, University of Chicago Press.)

Despite their newly-won ability to conquer the land, a number of Mesozoic reptile groups changed (like the sea turtles) to a marine existence. Two prominent Mesozoic types of this sort, now quite extinct, were the plesiosaurs and the ichthyosaurs. The *plesiosaurs* (order *Sauropterygia*) have been popularly compared to "a snake strung through the body of a turtle." Plesiosaurs were not at all related to either of these two reptiles, but the description is not inapt. They possessed a long neck or long snout or both; the body was short, broad and relatively flat. Reversion to a truly fish-like means of locomotion was impossible, for the trunk was inflexible and the tail short; instead, the limbs were developed into powerful oar-like structures, with which the creature "rowed" its way through the sea.

Even more unusual structurally were the *Ichthyosauria*, the "fish-reptiles." Possibly the plesiosaurs were able at least to waddle about on a beach in the fashion of a marine turtle or a seal. The ichthyosaurs, however, had become as completely adapted to a marine life as a porpoise or dolphin (with which there are many analogies), and there is fossil evidence indicating that egg-laying on land had been abandoned and that the young were born alive. The body shape was completely re-converted to that of a fish—the neck telescoped to give a fusiform body shape, the limbs shortened into small steering devices. Locomotion was performed, fish-like, by undulations of trunk and tail; a fish-like fin was developed on the back, and the tail became a powerful swimming organ, in appearance like that of a shark. In this last regard, however, there is a notable structural difference; for whereas in a shark the end of the backbone tilts into the upper lobe of the tail fin, that of the ichthyosaur turns sharply down at the back, the fin (as we know from excellent slabs of fossils) expanding above it.

The temple region of the skull affords diagnostic features useful in reptile classification (cf. p. 231). All the reptile stocks to be further mentioned (except the mammal ancestors) are characterized by descent from forms in which two openings, (fenestrae), bounded by arches of bone, are present in the temple and cheeks. A two-arched (i.e., diapsid) group which appeared early in the Mesozoic and has persisted to the present day, although never prominent, is the order *Rhynchocephalia*, now represented by the tuatara (*Sphenodon*). This creature, lizard-like in appearance, has survived in the relative safety and isolation of New Zealand where, once widespread, it is now preserved on a few small islands. Descended from ancient forms related to the tuatara is the much more successful order of the *Squamata*, the lizards and snakes. Technically they are readily distinguished by the fact that the cheek and temple region of the skull has been reduced, so as to leave but one temporal arch (lizards) or none at all (snakes) (cf. Figs. 160, 161, pp. 233, 234). The "scaled reptiles" are not only the most flourishing but the most modern of reptile orders, for even lizards amounted to little until late in the Cretaceous and the deployment of the various snake types did not take place until Cenozoic times. Lizards are widespread in the tropics in great variety. Most prominent of American lizards are the iguanas and their relatives, such as the collared lizard or "mountain boomer" of the Southwest and the little "horned toad." In the Old World the largest forms are the monitor lizards (Varanus), one of which, in the East Indies, may reach a length of a dozen feet. Relatives of the monitors in the late Cretaceous had a temporary success as a group of giant marine lizards, the mosasaurs. The (true) chameleons of the Old World tropics, with peculiar grasping feet and highly protrusible tongue, are a specialized side branch of the lizard stock. In several lines of lizards there have developed burrowing types, with limbs reduced or absent.

Derived from lizards are the snakes, which are highly modified in two major regards. As in some lizards, the limbs have been reduced and generally lost completely, and locomotion is accomplished by sinuous undulations of the body and tail, the projecting horny scales preventing backslipping; essentially, a snake swims on dry land. More distinctive is the fact that skull parts and jaw apparatus are markedly altered in the direction of flexibility and as a result allow the swallowing of the prey whole. Some snakes of primitive type are burrowers, and it is possible that snake evolution began with such forms, but even among such primitive types as the constrictors—the boas and pythons, some of great size—most now live above the surface. The great majority of snakes belong to a family of which the common harmless forms of northern temperate regions are representative. But even within this family many tropical genera have developed poison glands. These, however, are generally small and inoffensive and the fangs, situated in the back of the mouth, present little danger to man and other large animals. Three further families include the major poisonous snakes, with highly developed fangs and with powerful and varied venoms which attack the nervous system or cause destruction of tissues: (1) a group, mainly Old World, which consists of the cobras and their kin, and the coral snakes as well; (2) venomous sea snakes, found in the Indian and Pacific Oceans; (3) the vipers, with erectile fangs, including the adders and other vipers of the Old World, and the pit vipers, mainly American, with such representatives as the rattlesnakes, copperhead and water moccasin.

An exceedingly important reptile group with the same two-arched type of skull build as Sphenodon is the great subclass *Archosauria*, the ruling reptiles (Fig. 38). Today they survive only in the form of the rather aberrant crocodiles and alligators; but most of the dominant land reptiles of the Mesozoic were archosaurs, and the birds are descendants of this group.

The basal stock of the archosaurs is found in the Triassic in the shape of rather small, slenderly built predaceous reptiles included in the order *Thecodontia*. Elongate hind legs, a modified hip structure and other features suggest that they were becoming adapted to a bipedal mode of life. From these modest beginnings came the dinosaurs. These are popularly considered as constituting a single group of gigantic reptiles. This concept is far from correct, for although many dinosaurs were large, some were small (one was no bigger than a rooster). There were two major dinosaur stocks, not particularly closely related to one another, although both were descended in common from thecodont ancestors.

In one group, termed the *Saurischia*, or *reptile-like dinosaurs*, the ancestral forms were bipedal carnivores. Some of the smaller and more primitive of these bipeds can scarcely be distinguished from their thecodont ancestors. Others grew to immense size; Tyrannosaurus was the most ponderous flesh eater the earth has even seen. Derived from early bipeds of this sort were the amphibious (sauropod) dinosaurs, which changed to a herbivorous mode of life, reverted from a bipedal pose to four-footed walking and grew to such giants as Brontosaurus and Diplodocus. It would appear that these great reptiles spent much of their lives in lagoons where soft vegetation abounded; such was their weight (one is estimated to have reached 50 tons) that it seems improbable that their stocky limbs could have supported them effectively on land.

A second major group was that of the *Ornithischia*, or *birdlike dinosaurs*, in which the hip girdles (but not other anatomic features) were comparable to those of birds. Like their saurischian cousins, primitive members of this group

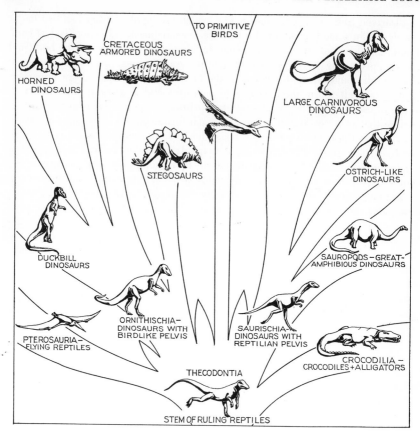

Fig. 38. A simple family tree of the ruling reptiles. (From Romer, The Vertebrate Story, University of Chicago Press.)

were bipeds; but in contrast with that other dinosaur stock, all the birdlike forms were herbivores. Best known of the bipeds of this group are the duckbills (hadrosaurs), which were abundant in the closing days of the Age of Reptiles. As in the saurischians, so in the ornithischians there was reversion to a quadrupedal pose. There were, in fact, three distinct types of quadrupeds developed in this order, all with some sort of defense against the great carnivores of the day. These types are exemplified by such popular museum exhibits as those of Stegosaurus, whose backbone is capped with defensive plates and spines; Ankylosaurus, low and flat and heavily armored on back and tail; and the horned dinosaurs, such as Triceratops, with horns—usually a trio of them—and a great frill of bone protecting the neck.

    Dinosaurs flourished greatly during the Jurassic and Cretaceous, and even in the closing phases of the latter period were present in considerable numbers and variety. Then, within a very short space of time, they disappeared completely. The reason for this abrupt end of the Age of Reptiles is far from fully understood. Geologic events are perhaps basically responsible. The Cretaceous period was one of mountain building during which great ranges, such as the American

Rockies, began to emerge from formerly flat country. Many of the low-lying marshy and lagoonal areas where dinosaurs browsed on lush vegetation disappeared. Climatic conditions were radically changed, and new types of plants appeared with which the herbivorous dinosaurs, with teeth generally none too efficient, were probably unable to cope. As the herbivores consequently dwindled and disappeared, their flesh-eating cousins, who preyed upon them, would of necessity follow them to extinction.

Still another group of extinct archosaurs was that of the order *Pterosauria*, the winged reptiles. In them the front limbs had one finger (the fourth) enormously elongated. From it there was extended, in somewhat batlike fashion, a great wing membrane. Manipulation of a wing of this sort would appear to have been an awkward matter, and it is probable that flight consisted mainly of soaring rather than active beating of the wings. Further, without any intermediate fingers extending into the wing membrane to strengthen it, the dangers of a disastrous tear would seem to have been great. The hind legs of pterosaurs, quite in contrast with those of birds, were feeble structures, and it is difficult to see how these creatures could have stood upon them, much less get a running take off, as a bird of any size must do. Probably they perched in bat-like fashion. But it is difficult to imagine what safe perch could be found for a pterosaur with a wing spread of up to 27 feet (as seen in one Cretaceous form). All in all, it is not difficult to understand why the pterosaurs became extinct once more efficient flying forms—the birds—had evolved.

Sole survivors today of the archosaurs are the alligators and crocodiles comprising the order Crocodilia. Although many of their structural features are indicative of a bipedal ancestry and descent from the thecodonts, the crocodilians, like many of their dinosaurian relatives, have reverted to a quadrupedal gait and have, further, become amphibious. The crocodiles are phylogenetically remote from the base of the reptilian family tree; their anatomic features are hardly to be considered characteristic of reptiles as a whole, and, as might be expected, they show numerous features found in the birds, whose ancestors were archosaur relatives of the crocodiles.

BIRDS

Birds have been aptly termed "glorified reptiles." We customarily treat of them as a separate class, Aves; but in many regards they are little farther removed from the general reptilian stock than are some of the ruling reptiles from which they sprang. Within that group, as we have noted, was included one series of flying forms, the pterosaurs; the birds are not descended from pterosaurs, but are a second archosaur flying type, in which, instead of membrane, feathers—diagnostic of the class—form the wing surfaces of the modified pectoral limbs. In certain respects, notably bipedal adaptations, the birds are similar to their dinosaurian relatives, but almost every notable bird character is an adaptation to flight. The maintenance of a high and constant body temperature and improvements in the circulatory system are associated with the need of a high metabolic rate for sustained flight; lightening of the body in various ways (particularly by the development of air sacs and hollow bones) is also associated with flight, as are modifications in the brain and sense organs. The birds in the course of their evolution necessarily "discovered" long ago many of the principles of aerodynamics that man has learned as a result of much scientific work and hard experience; they are "expert" in wing construction and in the utilization of winds and air currents in gaining distance or elevation. In general birds with an active beating type of flight tend to have small wings, those that rely mainly on gliding and soaring usually have relatively larger wing surfaces. Flying birds (in contrast to ostrich-like ground-dwellers) are seldom of any great size; in maintenance of flight, wing area must increase on the whole, proportionately to weight, and too great size of body would require a wingspread so great as to be difficult to manipulate.

Except in Mesozoic birds, teeth were lost and reliance placed on a bill for gathering food. Numerous variations are seen in bill structure, with such extremes as the parrot beak and the effective drilling organ of the woodpeckers. Presumably the food of primitive birds was of some relatively soft nature, and teeth were not necessary. Many modern birds, however, are eaters of grain. For this type of food mammals need highly developed "grinders"; birds have developed as a functional substitute a grinding apparatus in the muscular gizzard containing grit or small pebbles.

In the birds we see a class of vertebrates which in many regards is to be considered as on as high a level of organization as the mammals, but which (even disregarding differences in aerial vs. terrestrial locomotion) are organized in quite another fashion. Birds can, to be sure, be trained, but on the whole seem relatively much less capable of learning by experience than mammals. On the other hand they exhibit innate behavior patterns of a complexity unknown in mammals. Many of these, connected (for example) with social behavior, courtship, nest-building, and rearing of the young, are familiar to any bird-lover. Avian "knowledge" of geography is most remarkable. The homing ability of birds is great, and the ability, for example, of young golden plovers to migrate successfully from the Arctic tundras to the Chaco region of South America—unaccompanied by older birds, over a complicated course of many thousands of miles—is an accomplishment apparently verging on the supernatural.

A happy accident of preservation has given us knowledge of three skeletons of an ancestral bird, Archaeopteryx, from deposits of late Jurassic age (Fig. 39).

Fig. 39. A restoration of the primitive bird Archaeopteryx, with teeth, claws in the "hand," a long bony tail and other reptilian characters. (After Heilmann.)

In this bird teeth were still present, the wing had clawed fingers, and there persisted a long reptilian type of tail; Archaeopteryx so nearly split the differences in skeletal structure between ruling reptiles and modern birds that its systematic position would be a matter of doubt were not imprints of feathers preserved with the skeletons.

Birds, mainly owing to the delicacy of their skeletons, are relatively rare in the fossil record. However, there is evidence that before the close of the Cretaceous there had evolved forms quite modern in almost every structure.

Although taxonomists divide the birds into a considerable series of orders, the structural differences between these groups are for the most part small. There is, however, one partial exception to this; for there has been thought to be a distinction between two modern groups, representing primitive and advanced stages in bird evolution. Technically, the two have been defined by details of palatal and jaw structure (with which we need not here concern ourselves) which gave rise to the terms "palaeognathous" and "neognathous" to distinguish them. Most birds with which the reader is ordinarily familiar—indeed, the majority of all living birds—are members of the latter, higher group. To the lower assemblage (Fig. 40, *A-C, E-F*) belong the ostrich and other forms generally termed *ratites*, such as the cassowary and emu of Australia, the rhea of the South American pampas, the extinct moas and the little kiwi of New Zealand and the giant extinct birds of Madagascar.

Most of the palaeognathous birds have tiny wings and are flightless, a fact that has given rise to the claim that they represent a primitive stage in bird evolution in which flight had not been attained. But anatomic study strongly indicates that this is not the case and that the ratites are probably degenerate descendants of once flying types. (They owe their name to the reduced condition of the breastbone, to which wing muscles attach.) Most of them are found on islands where there are few terrestrial enemies, or on continents (Australia, South America)

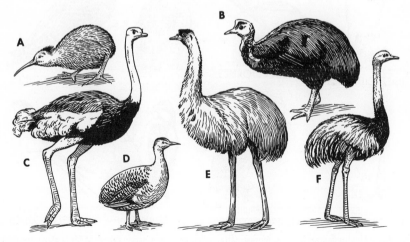

Fig. 40. Palaeognathous birds, including the ratites. *A*, The kiwi, apteryx, of New Zealand. *B*, The emu of Australia. *C*, The ostrich. *D*, The tinamou of South America. *E*, The cassowary of Australia. *F*, The rhea of South America.

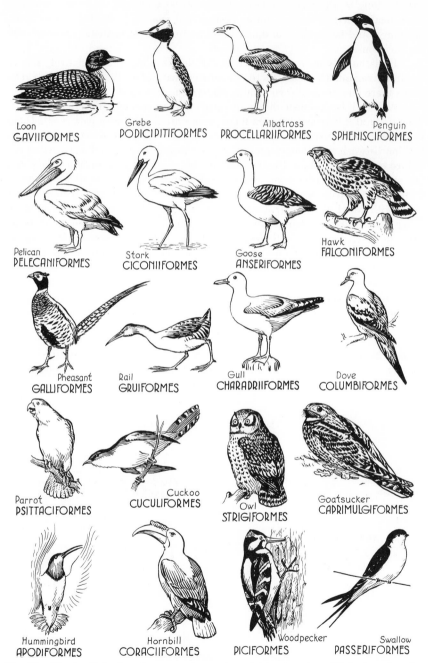

Fig. 41. Thumb-nail sketches of representative members of the major orders of birds above the ratite level. The ordinal name and the popular name of the bird representing it are given in each case.

where, the fossil record tells us, the same was true at the time that the native ratites evolved. If ground-dwelling enemies are absent, much of the "point" of flying has been lost. The tinamous of South America (Fig. 40, *D*) are birds which have the power of flight (although they are awkward flyers) and yet have the "old-fashioned" type of palate; they may represent an ancestral group from which the ratites have developed.

Apart from the ratites, most birds, as has been said above, are rather uniform in basic anatomic features, with differences between orders no greater than those which distinguish the smaller groups, termed families, among mammals. To the student of habits, songs, and plumage, the birds have much to offer; they offer little, however, to those interested in anatomic structure and function. Hence the remaining bird groups may be dismissed briefly. In Figure 41 are thumb-nail sketches of representatives of the major groups of birds other than the ratites, pictured in the sequence in which the orders are listed by many ornithologists. A majority of all birds are members of the final order, the Passeriformes or perching birds, including the song birds. These highly evolved bird types are all relatively small; the crows and ravens are giants of the order. Several orders of water birds and oceanic types are customarily placed at the beginning of the series, although there is little evidence that they are actually primitive. Of special interest here are the penguins, southern hemisphere forms which are flightless but nevertheless have powerful wings which have been transformed into swimming flippers. Here, as in the case of the ratites, it has been argued that absence of flight is primitive. It is, however, more probable that they have descended from oceanic birds of the preceding order (Procellariiformes), to which belong not only the albatross and its close kin, but diving birds, which likewise use the wings in swimming.*

MAMMALS

Mammal-like Reptiles. The mammals are descended from reptiles; but the fossil record shows that the reptilian line leading to them diverged almost at the base of the family tree of that class. Their relationship to the existing reptilian orders is exceedingly remote.

Oldest of the reptiles antecedent to mammals were the pelycosaurs (Fig. 35, *B*, p. 55), a group which flourished in the early Permian. They were in most regards exceedingly primitive reptiles, but certain characters in skull structure (such as the presence of but a single opening in the temple region of the skull) indicate that they represent a first stage in the evolution toward mammalian status. Succeeding them in late Permian and early Triassic days were the *therapsids*, progressive mammal-like forms which were the commonest animals of their day (Fig. 42). The characteristic therapsids were flesh-eaters, active four-footed runners in which, as in their mammalian descendants, elbow and knee had been swung in toward the body, making for better support and greater speed—this in contrast with the sprawled limb pose of primitive land animals. In the advanced Triassic members of the group many features of skull, jaw, dentition, and limbs approach closely the mammalian pattern.

---

* For those of literary tastes, it may be mentioned that the penguins of which Anatole France wrote are the auks of English-speaking peoples.

Fig. 42. A mammal-like reptile (Lycaenops) from the late Permian of South Africa. (After Colbert.)

The evolution of mammal-like reptiles was a major feature of early reptilian evolution. But in the Triassic period other reptile groups became prominent—notably the dinosaurs. It appears that therapsids, for the most part, could not compete successfully with them, and rapidly dwindled and disappeared from the scene. There survived, however, small therapsids from which evolved the oldest mammals, sparse remains of which are found in later Mesozoic deposits. Living as they did for tens of millions of years as contemporaries of the dinosaur dynasties, our small Mesozoic mammal ancestors were seemingly insignificant in the life of their times.

Intelligent activity may be reasonably regarded as the keynote of mammalian progress. With activity may be correlated not only the efficient locomotor apparatus characteristic of mammals, but also (as in birds) circulatory improvements and high body temperature (with which the development of hair is related). In enterprise and ingenuity even the stupidest of mammals is an intellectual giant compared with any reptile. The habit of bearing the young alive—characteristic of all except the most primitive forms—and the development of the nursing habit, with concomitant care and training of the young, are mammalian innovations which have resulted in giving a long period for the development and elaboration of delicate nervous and other mechanisms before the young are sent out into the world.

Monotremes. The monotremes, or *Prototheria*, include only the duckbill and spiny anteaters of the Australian region. So different are they from other mammals that it is believed that they must have diverged from the ancestors of other members of the class at the very beginning of mammalian history—indeed, quite possibly they sprang independently from the advanced therapsids. These curious animals possess many diagnostic mammalian characters, but retain primitive features in that, alone of mammals, they still lay shelled eggs like their reptilian ancestors. The duckbill is a semiaquatic, web-footed, fur-covered frequenter of streams in which it finds a food supply of snails and mussels. The anteater, protected from enemies by a coat of spiny hair, subsists on termites; its powerful clawed feet give it phenomenal digging ability. Both types make nests in burrows where the young are nursed after hatching. These two types are so specialized in many ways that they cannot be regarded as in themselves ancestral types. Their survival in Australia may be due to the relative isolation of that area. Unfortunately we know almost nothing of their history. Much of our knowledge of the relationships of extinct mammals is based on diagnostic characters of molar tooth pattern (discussed in a later chapter); the monotremes are, unfortunately, toothless (as adults), having instead horny bills—flat and duck-like in the one type, slender in the other.

Marsupials. Rare finds from the later Cretaceous tell us that there had by then evolved two more progressive mammal groups—the marsupials and the oldest placental mammals. The marsupials, or pouched mammals—technically termed the *Metatheria*—owe their popular name to the fact that although the young are born alive, they are born at a tiny and immature stage; typically, the female marsupial carries on her belly a pouch in which the newborn young are kept and nourished for a further period after birth. The common opossum is characteristic of the group and is a primitive mammal in many regards. In most regions of the world the marsupials have not been able to compete successfully with more progressive mammals, and even the hardy opossum failed to survive except in the Americas. South America proved a haven for many marsupials during Tertiary times, when that continent was long isolated; a variety of marsupials developed there, almost all of which became extinct when the isthmian link was reestablished and a host of more advanced mammals invaded that continent. Australia is the one region where marsupials have flourished greatly. The geologic evidence suggests that this latter continent became separated from the rest of the world at the close of the Cretaceous and has since remained isolated. No placental mammals, it appears, had reached Australia at the time of separation, and few have been able to reach it since. There the marsupials had no opposition, and expanded and diversified to fill almost every type of adaptive niche which placental mammals have occupied in other regions. Fairly directly from the ancient

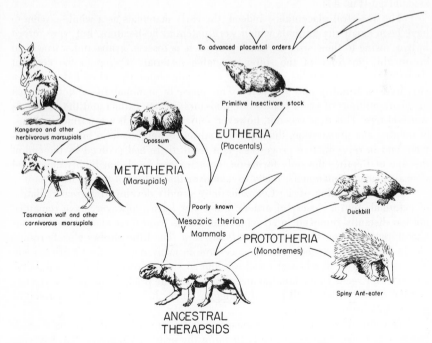

Fig. 43. Diagrammatic family tree, to show the evolution and relationship of the major groups of mammals.

opossum-like ancestors came such pouched carnivorous forms as the native "cats," the Tasmanian devil, the native "wolf," and pouched parallels to anteaters and even moles of other continents. A second branch of the Australian marsupials acquired chisel-like front teeth and developed types comparable to the rodents among placentals. There are varied native squirrel-like types, even a marsupial flying "squirrel." The wombat is analogous to the woodchucks or marmots of other regions; the native "bear," the koala, is a leaf-feeder belonging to this group. The marsupials have failed to parallel the placentals in one respect—there has been no development of hoofed forms comparable in structure to horses, cattle and antelopes. But the kangaroos—which, like the typical ungulate placentals, are speedy grass-eating plains-dwellers—fill much the same place in nature.

Placental Mammals. The major progressive group of mammals includes the host of living forms properly termed the *Eutheria*, the "true mammals," but usually called placentals. The latter name is due to the fact that, in contrast with most marsupials, there is an efficient nutritive connection, the placenta, between mother and embryo; as a result the young can develop to a much more advanced stage before birth. On the extinction of the dinosaurs, these highly developed mammals were already in existence; they rapidly expanded into a host of types, many of which have continued down to modern times. In some other groups of vertebrates the family "tree" is actually tree-like, with a main trunk or at least major branching limbs. That of the placental mammals, however, is comparable to a great bush: the various orders are difficult to assemble into groups and appear, for the most part, to have branched out independently of one another in early times. We may briefly note some of the main components of the placental assemblage (Fig. 44).

The ancestral placentals—indeed, the early mammals as a whole—seem to have been small shy animals which were potential flesh-eaters, but were forced to live, owing to their size, on small prey such as insects, grubs and worms, and presumably on some of the softer vegetable materials. Owing to the constant threat of the great reptiles which were their contemporaries, they led, of necessity, lives of timidity and obscurity. This phase of mammalian existence lasted for many millions of years before the dinosaurs became extinct and the mammals were set free. This time was not, however, entirely wasted. It was a time, it seems, of training and preparation, during which advances were made in mental development and in reproductive processes. As a result there had evolved by the end of the Age of Reptiles not only forms on the marsupial level, but highly developed if small placental mammals, ready to take over the surface of the earth.

At the beginning of the Cenozoic there rapidly developed a great radiation of mammals into a variety of orders. Some few forms, however, have remained not too distantly removed in structure and habits from their small insectivorous ancestors; these constitute the order *Insectivora*. The little shrews closely resemble, in habits at least, their remote ancestors; in many regions shrews are exceedingly abundant in woods and meadows, but so shy are their habits that they are almost never seen. Other familiar insectivores are the prickly European hedgehog and the moles, which, with powerful digging limbs, have taken up the pursuit of grubs and worms underground.

Developed from insectivore ancestors is the one group of mammals which has attained true flight—the bats, forming the order *Chiroptera*. The bat wing differs from that of pterosaurs and birds in that it is a web stiffened by four of the five "fingers." The majority of bats have remained insectivorous in habits;

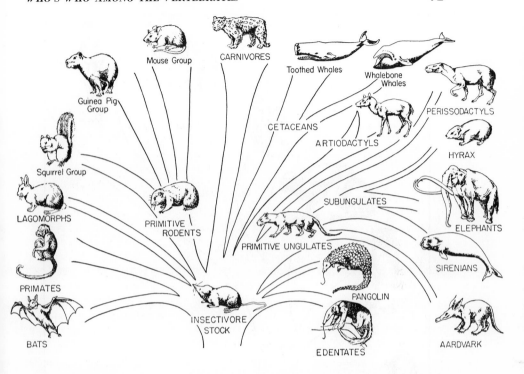

Fig. 44. Diagrammatic family tree of the orders of eutherian (placental) mammals. Separate diagrams (Figs. 45–48) give in more detail the evolution of primates, carnivores, and odd- and even-toed ungulates.

however, one major group, abundant in the tropics, consists of relatively large fruit-eaters.

Primates. This order, to which we ourselves belong, was an early offshoot of the insectivores; indeed, so close are the ties that it is an unsettled question as to which of the two orders certain fossil and living forms should be assigned. Primitive mammals are thought to have been to some degree arboreal; this mode of life was emphasized in early primates and appears to have been responsible for the development of many features of importance—general body agility and coordination; the ability to climb by grasping a limb, which has resulted in giving us that most useful of "tools," the hand; the high development of vision, so necessary for arboreal life (with a concomitant reduction in olfaction). Most important of all, the high degree of development of the brain, which is the outstanding character of higher primates, appears to have been closely correlated with the needs and opportunities found in arboreal life.

The tree shrews of the Malay region are so close to the boundary between insectivores and primates that their position is disputed (Fig. 45). Lowest of acknowledged primates are the lemurs, still flourishing today in the isolation of Madagascar and little changed from early Cenozoic ancestors. These are still four-footed arboreal forms, with thick fur, relatively poor eyesight and a nose forming a typical mammal muzzle. A step in advance is represented today by the curious little creature named Tarsius, from the East Indies. The living form is

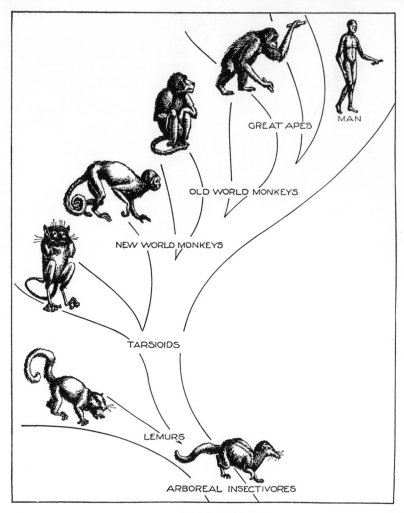

Fig. 45. A simplified family tree of the primates. (From Romer, The Vertebrate Story, University of Chicago Press.)

somewhat specialized in such characters as an elongate ankle region—a hopping adaptation to which it owes its name. But while still lemur-like in many ways, Tarsius shows advances in such features as excellent eyesight and reduction of the nose to a mere button.

The higher general level of primate evolution is that represented by the monkeys, apes and man. Although man may pride himself on mental attainments, anatomic differences between the various members of the group are few, and are mostly matters of proportions of various structures or obvious adaptations—such as the distinctive human features of vertebral posture and hind leg structure associated with upright gait. In all these higher primates the cerebral hemispheres are relatively large, eyesight highly developed, the nose reduced, the hands useful grasping organs. Two distinct groups of monkeys appear to have arisen independently from a Tarsius-like stock. One, termed the *platyrrhines,* is found in South America, where it is represented by a variety of forms such as the common organ-grinder's monkey—the Capuchin—and the little marmosets. (Incidentally, it is only in South American monkeys that a prehensile tail is to be found.) A second group of higher primates—the *catarrhines*—developed in the Old World. Primitive members are the familiar monkeys and baboons of Africa and Asia. More advanced members are the great apes including the gibbons, the orang-utan, the chimpanzee and the gorilla. All these apes are of relatively large size, in all the tail has been lost, and in the last two forms mentioned the anatomic similarities to man are close indeed, although neither is a human ancestor. The gibbon is an agile arboreal acrobat and the orang is a good traveller in the trees; but arboreal specialization is less marked in the chimpanzee, and some gorillas have become nearly completely terrestrial, although as quadrupeds. Man is essentially a fifth member of this great ape series; he has become a terrestrial biped, but has stamped deeply into his structure features acquired during his long ancestral sojourn in the trees. We do not fully know our own pedigree, but the fossil "man-apes" of South Africa (the australopithecines) structurally bridge the gap between man and his simian relatives.

Carnivores. The insectivores were potential flesh-eaters. With the development of numerous mammals of the more harmless varieties there soon arose from the primitive placental stock varied predaceous types which began the history of the order *Carnivora* (Fig. 46). Some of the first "experiments" along such lines were relatively ineffective, slow, clumsy, and it would seem, stupid, but more progressive types ancestral to the later carnivores soon evolved. The modern terrestrial carnivores may be essentially divided into two great groups, of which dog and cat are familiar examples, and the weasel tribe and civet group are, respectively, more primitive members.

The weasels and their close kin, small and short-legged in build and often purely carnivorous in habits, are seemingly primitive members of the general "dog" group (arctoids). But within the weasel family there developed a considerable series of forms variant in habits and diet—badgers, skunks, otters, even a marine member, the sea otter of the Pacific. The dog family developed into terrestrial types, adapted to running down its prey, and is represented today by a series of wolves, jackals, foxes and other doglike forms. The raccoon is related to the dog stock, but is a persistently arboreal animal with an omnivorous taste in food; there are several American relatives, and the curious panda and giant panda of Asia are allied. The bears are the members of the general dog group which have departed most widely from ancestral conditions; these clumsy fellows have (except for the polar bear) swung far away from flesh-eating to take up a mixed—but mainly herbivorous—diet.

Of the "cat" group of carnivores (aeluroids), the civets and their relatives appear to occupy a primitive position comparable to that of the weasel family in the "dog" group. These varied forms are mainly Old World tropical forest dwellers, with which the average reader will not be acquainted; the mongoose is the most familiar representative. The unattractive hyenas are an overgrown offshoot of the civets which have taken up a life of scavenging. The felids form the most highly specialized development in this sub-group of carnivores. The cats are adapted for stalking their prey and making an agile jump on to the victim, rather than running it down as do the dogs; the teeth are highly specialized for stabbing and shearing, and in nature the cats are purely flesh-eating. Most living cat types

—such as the lion, tiger, panther and so forth—are very similar to one another in structure; the extinct sabre-tooths were notable for an exaggerated development of stabbing teeth (cf. Fig. 220, *A*).

Last of the carnivores to be mentioned are the marine *pinnipeds*—the various seals, which are fish-eaters, and the grotesque walrus, with its digging tusks and blunt molars for crushing the mussels upon which it feeds. These appear to have evolved from land carnivores in mid-Tertiary times; in pinnipeds, among other adaptations, the limbs have been transformed into "flippers"; the hind limbs, turn~d backward, replace the reduced tail as a swimming organ.

Ungulates.   Notable in Tertiary history has been the development of great series of forms, often of relatively large size, which have assumed an herbivorous mode of existence and developed dentitions with good grinding molars for chewing vegetable food materials. The more advanced forms of this sort have tended to become good running types, with limb elongation, adding an extra joint to the limbs by lengthening the bones of the "palm" and "sole" region of the feet; they have tended to walk on the tips of the toes, which are generally reduced in number. The claws borne by primitive mammals have generally given place to hooves —hence the term "ungulates" applied to these herbivores.

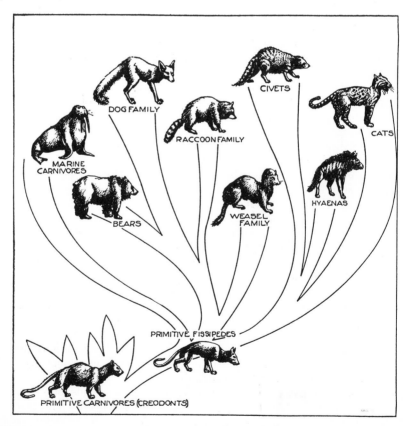

Fig. 46.   A simplified family tree of the carnivores. (From Romer, The Vertebrate Story, University of Chicago Press.)

Although the varied ungulate types have developed many common characters, it is far from certain that all ungulate stocks spring from a common source;
there has surely been considerable parallelism in their development. The statement, all too often seen in print, that "the ungulate" has such-and-such physiologic or structural features, is valueless unless it is more specifically stated just
what type of ungulate is meant; a cow is not improbably as closely related to a
lion as to a horse.

Early in the Age of Mammals there rapidly sprang into existence a host of
ungulates of varied but archaic types; most passed rapidly out of existence and
need not concern us here. The dominant ungulates of later Cenozoic and Recent
times belong to two very distinct orders, characterized by the horse and cow—
the orders Perissodactyla and Artiodactyla, respectively the odd- and even-toed
types.

In the *Perissodactyla* (Fig. 47) the key character has been the early reduction of the toes from five to three, and in the case of the later horses further reduction to a single-toed or monodactyl condition (cf. pp. 208–213). Primitive
forms such as little Eohippus (or Hyracotherium), which was not only a "dawn
horse" but close to the ancestry of the entire order, had already reached a three-
toed condition in the hind foot but in front had lost merely the thumb. Early
perissodactyls were browsers, living on relatively soft food materials in forests
and glades. In the progressive series of the horses, mid-Tertiary types had occupied the spreading grasslands, developed high-crowned teeth to cope with a diet
of grasses and grains and had reduced the toes to three on each foot. With further

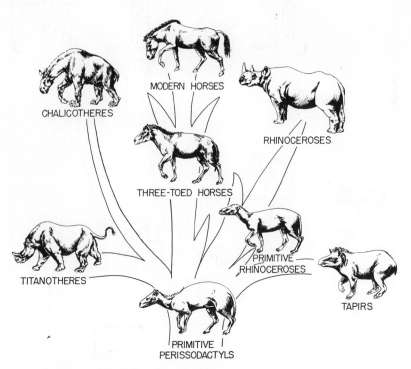

MODERN HORSES

CHALICOTHERES

RHINOCEROSES

THREE-TOED HORSES

TITANOTHERES

PRIMITIVE
RHINOCEROSES

TAPIRS

PRIMITIVE
PERISSODACTYLS

Fig. 47. A simplified family tree of the odd-toed ungulates, the perissodactyls.

approach to the modern genus Equus there was attained a single-toed pattern; the middle toe was the sole survivor. The tapirs of Old and New World tropics are persistent browsers which, although larger, have departed little from the mode of life of early perissodactyls. More divergent among extinct odd-toed ungulates were the large and ungainly horned titanotheres and the grotesque chalicotheres, which combined a somewhat horselike body with feet armed with powerful claws (perhaps used for digging tubers). More successful, despite large size and some; what clumsy build, were the rhinoceroses, which during their history developed hornlike defensive weapons; once common and widespread, they are still represented by a few species in the Old World tropics.

The perissodactyls were very successful in the earlier part of the Age of Mammals, but are now reduced to a relatively few species of three types—horses, tapirs, rhinoceroses. Quite in contrast has been the story of the order *Artiodactyla* (Fig. 48). Rare in the early Tertiary, these even-toed ungulates became increasingly abundant in later times and are widespread today. In these forms toe reduction began with the loss of "thumb" and "big toe," giving a four-

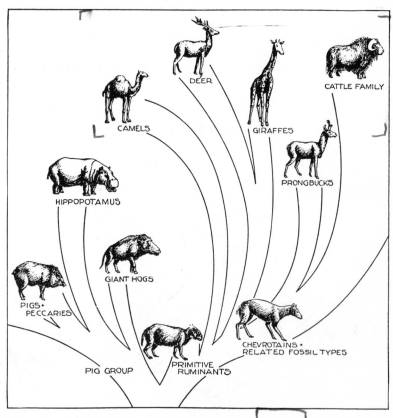

Fig. 48.   A simplified family tree of the even-toed ungulates, the artiodactyls. A major cleavage is into the pig group, to which the hippopotamus and extinct giant hogs belong, and the cud-chewing ruminants. The little chevrotains of tropical Africa and southern Asia are close to the ancestry of advanced ruminant types. (From Romer, The Vertebrate Story, University of Chicago Press.)

toed pattern. Among the four, the two side toes tended to reduction or loss, leaving toes three and four to form the so-called "cloven hoof" diagnostic of the group. The pigs of the Old World and the related peccaries of the New are relatively primitive types, omnivorous in habits. The hippopotamus is a lumbering amphibious cousin of the pigs, a vegetarian in diet. The more successful artiodactyls became purely herbivorous, developed a series of grinding cheek teeth with characteristic crescentic cusps (cf. p. 315) and perfected a multi-chambered stomach associated with the cud-chewing habit (rumination, cf. p. 353) for dealing with vegetable foods. The camels, originating in North America, but now surviving in the Old World and (as the llamas) in South America, are relatively primitive cud-chewers. The most advanced artiodactyls are the Pecora—agile, swift-running ungulates, with highly developed ruminating stomachs and with heads generally armed with some kind of horns or antlers. The deer and giraffe are relatively primitive browsers. Much more abundant are the "cow-like" forms, the bovids, most of which have become (parallel to the horses) grass-eating plains-dwellers. Cattle, sheep, and goats are familiar domesticated bovids; for a host of others, mainly inhabitants of the Old World tropics, we have no familiar specific names and tend to lump them as "antelopes." Finally, in this ruminant assemblage we may mention the prong-buck of the western American plains, survivor of a New World group paralleling the true antelopes.

Subungulates. Frequently grouped as the subungulates are a series of orders, probably originating in Africa, which are perhaps best regarded as aberrant offshoots of a primitive ungulate stock. The little hyraxes—order *Hyracoidea*, the "conies" of Scripture—are animals of rather rabbit-like size and habits, but are definitely hoofed ungulates whose pedigree goes back to the fossil records of the early African Tertiary. They have, however, never progressed structurally to any degree and have never ranged beyond Africa and the eastern Mediterranean region. Strange as it appears, these little forms appear to be related to two other quite divergent groups—the elephants and the sea cows. The *Proboscidea* (whose name derives from their trunk) are represented today only by the two elephant types proper to Africa and to southern Asia. Their history, however, has been long and varied. The older types are termed mastodons. The most primitive known form, from the Eocene of Egypt, was already large for its day—much the size of a large pig—with chisel-like front teeth and a good set of grinders in the cheek. Later mastodons increased rapidly in size and developed long jaws, with short tusks both above and below. Later the jaws diminished in length, but the upper tusks, in seeming compensation, tended to elongate and eventually there developed the characteristic head pattern of tusks and trunk seen in the modern elephants. Meanwhile, from mid-Tertiary times on, the mastodons had spread widely over Eurasia and eventually over the Americas; in the Ice Age a variety of elephants, most of them termed mammoths, roamed every continent except Australia and South America. Toward the end of the Pleistocene nearly all of the proboscideans vanished. The reasons for the sudden reduction of this seemingly flourishing order of mammals is a mystery, but no more of a mystery than the nearly simultaneous extinction of a variety of other large mammals as well.

To class the sea cows—the manatees and dugongs of the order *Sirenia*—with the ungulates would appear superficially to be a gross misuse of terms. These animals, browsers in shallow waters of the tropical Atlantic and Indian Ocean regions, are purely aquatic beasts, with front limbs transformed into paddles, hind legs reduced to concealed vestiges and the tail re-developed to form a horizontal swimming fin. Now relatively rare, they ranged widely over the world for much of the Tertiary. The oldest fossil remains—many from the Eocene of Egypt— show a number of resemblances to the most primitive conies and mastodons and add strength to the belief that all three of these curious subungulate groups are varied descendants of some common archaic ungulate ancestor who existed in Africa at the dawn of the Age of Mammals.

Whales. Although both carnivores and subungulates have developed aquatic types, none of these is as highly specialized for marine life as the whales and porpoises which constitute the order *Cetacea*. Much as in the sirenians, the front legs have been transformed into flippers, the hind legs have vanished, and the tail has become a highly developed swimming organ, with horizontal flukes. As in ichthyosaurs among the reptiles, a dorsal fish-like fin may re-develop and the neck region is shortened, so that a streamlined fusiform fish-like body is re-attained. The skull is peculiarly altered, for the external nostrils have moved upward to become the "blowhole" atop the head. Most mammals cannot survive long under water, but the physiology of whales has been so modified that some can remain submerged for the better part of an hour. The greater part of the order, including the porpoises and dolphins and most of the larger whales, are toothed forms which subsist on animal food—fishes, octopi and squids. However, the very largest of the "noble cetaceans," the whalebone whales, live on the smallest of food materials—the small marine organisms that constitute the ocean's plankton. Teeth are here absent, and instead there hang from the roof of the mouth row after row of thin sheets of cornified skin, the whalebone. The fringed edges of the whalebone sheets strain the plankton from the water and the resulting "catch" is licked down by the whale's tongue. The oldest known whales, from the Eocene, were already aquatic types, but less specialized in body and skull and suggestive of a descent from some primitive type of land carnivore.

Edentates. Extremely aberrant in many ways are the members of the order *Edentata*, mainly South American in distribution and history. The living representatives are the tree sloths, dull, sluggish arboreal leaf-eaters; the long-snouted anteaters; and the armadillos, omnivorous feeders which have a well-developed back armor. Extinct are two further types which attained large size, the glyptodonts, relatives of the armadillos, with a dome-shaped protective "shell" and an armored tail, and the great ground sloths. The anteaters are actually edentulous, but the ordinal name is a misnomer for the other forms, which have at least a good cheek-grinding series (although the enamel covering of the teeth is reduced). The group attained its development in South America, but during the Ice Age ground sloths and glyptodonts invaded North America with momentary success. However, only the armadillo has survived in the north; the reason for the extinction of the large edentates is as puzzling as in the case of the mammoths.

We shall mention here two odd types of mammals which in the past were often grouped with the South American edentates, but are now recognized as quite distinct. The aard-vark (Orycteropus) is a grotesque long-snouted African beast; the slender-snouted pangolins (Manis) of the Old World tropics are unique among mammals in that they are completely covered by overlapping horny scales which give them somewhat the appearance of animated pine cones. Both make a living by invading termite nests and are armed with powerful claws. The aard-vark has retained a few peg-like cheek teeth; the pangolin, like its South American ant-eating analogues, has lost its teeth, useless in this mode of existence. Neither animal has any close relations with any other group; the aard-vark is suspected of some remote relationship (despite its peculiarities) with the archaic ungulates; there is no clue whatever to pangolin ancestry.

Rodents.   Most successful of all mammals from the point of view of both numbers of genera and species and numbers of individuals are the gnawing animals, the order *Rodentia*. The key character of the group lies in the development of an enlarged pair of front teeth in both upper and lower jaws into an effective chisel-like gnawing apparatus. Rodents have never (we may be thankful) developed into flying forms, nor into marine types; but in almost every known terrestrial habitat rodents are the most flourishing group. Rodents have spread out into a great variety of forms, which are difficult to classify into major subgroups; three "clusters" of forms, however, stand out rather prominently. (1) A relatively small but familiar group is that of the squirrels, prairie dogs, marmots and relatives including, some believe, the beavers. (2) The guinea-pig is representative of a great group which includes most of the rodents of South America. The North American porcupine appears to be of South American origin; the Eurasian porcupine and a few other Old World rodents have been often assigned to this group, but current opinion inclines to a belief that the resemblances are due to parallelism. (3) Most flourishing of rodents are the rats and mice, ubiquitous in distribution; an indication of their versatility is the fact that they include the only terrestrial placentals that were able to reach Australia before the coming of man.

Lagomorphs.   The order *Lagomorpha* is a small one, including almost exclusively the hares and rabbits. They were at one time classed with the rodents because, as in that group, there are chisel-like front teeth. But there is no other resemblance; furthermore, the lagomorphs have two pairs of upper chisels rather than one. For decades students of recent and fossil mammals have recognized the lack of relationship, but despite this there constantly recur instances in which biologists ignorant of the animal world have described structures or functions found in the rabbits or hares as characteristic of "the rodent."

On our brief survey of the world of vertebrates we have seen the rise of many groups to prominence, followed by decline to extinction or to a point where there remain today only a few relict types, often aberrant or degenerate. Major success lies currently with the teleosts, the birds and the placental mammals. At the future we can only guess. But, apart from such damage as man may do to himself and his fellow vertebrates by his blundering utilization of major natural forces, it is likely that the progressive teleosts may long dominate the seas, the birds the air, the placentals the surface of the earth. What placentals? We fancy ourselves. But in moments of pessimistic realism one may consider the possibility that the hardy, fecund and versatile rodents may inherit the earth.

4

CELLS AND TISSUES

Although anatomic and physiologic studies of the vertebrate body generally deal with gross structures—organs and organ systems —it must never be forgotten that these structures are composed of tissues, and these in turn of cells, and that the cells are the basal living units from which and by which the entire complex body is built. A knowledge of cell and tissue structure and function is basic in the study of biology; here we shall very briefly review these familiar topics simply as a background for a better understanding of structures of greater complexity with which this work is primarily concerned. The functioning of body organs depends basically upon the activities of the cells of which they are composed; conversely, the varied organ systems are nearly all engaged, directly or indirectly, in furnishing the cells with the materials required for their vital processes and in maintaining them in a suitable environment. Each cell lives its own life; but each is dependent upon other cells and tissues for its continued existence, and each in turn makes its contribution to the welfare of the total organism.

Chemical Materials. Much of vertebrate structure and function is related to the collection, transformation, and transportation to the cells of the basic chemicals needed to form and maintain the protoplasm and enable it to play its proper part in the work of the body and, again, to the disposal of wastes formed by its activity. In consequence, it is important that we review the fundamentals of needed cellular chemical molecules, as will be done here in simple—rather, oversimplified—fashion.

WATER. Water, of course, is the major constituent of protoplasm. A vertebrate, for all its seeming solidity, is an exceedingly watery structure; perhaps three quarters of the average cell content is water (four-fifths in the case of muscle fibers). Water is a nearly universal solvent, useful in the transport of other materials and as a medium in which chemical reactions may take place; still further, water is itself utilized in various chemical reactions, or formed ("metabolic water") as a result of intracellular chemical activity.

INORGANIC SALTS. In solution in the watery portion of the protoplasm may

80

be found a variety of ions of inorganic salts. Most of these ions are identical with those found in the extracellular body fluids (but it is notable that sodium and chloride ions, abundant in those fluids, are generally in relatively low concentration in the cells themselves). Calcium, phosphorus (as phosphate), potassium, and sulfur (as sulfate) are the other common elements which may be present in inorganic form. There are further half a dozen "trace" elements generally present in minute quantities, but even so, known to be absolutely vital requisites in various vertebrates. These include the ions of iodine and the metals iron, copper, zinc, manganese, and cobalt. In addition there may be present various inorganic compounds in process of inclusion in the chemical structure of the cell, or materials such as ammonia and carbon dioxide, on their way out as end products of metabolism.

ORGANIC COMPOUNDS. But it is, of course, the numerous and varied organic compounds which are of overwhelming interest and importance in cell chemistry. Organic compounds can be variously altered and transformed in animal cells and can be to some degree manufactured by them; but in general they must be obtained, ultimately, from the plants which manufacture them, using solar energy, from carbon dioxide, water, and nitrates.

In basic chemical analysis these organic compounds all contain a considerable proportion of carbon, that versatile element which, with its four bonds for ready chemical union with other elements, is the prime feature of organic compounds. The carbon "skeleton" of these compounds may take the form of chains

of carbon atoms: $-\overset{|}{C}-\overset{|}{C}-\overset{|}{C}-\overset{|}{C}-\overset{|}{C}-\overset{|}{C}-$ to the free bonds of which hydrogen,

oxygen, or nitrogen atoms or hydroxyl groups (OH) are most commonly appended. Also characteristic are rings of carbon atoms, typically with six members, and often including oxygen or nitrogen as well as carbon:

Oxygen and hydrogen are almost as abundant in organic compounds as carbon, and nitrogen, present in smaller amounts, completes the quartet of basic organic elements. Sulfur and phosphorus are also present, to a lesser degree, in many of these compounds, and "trace" elements form complexes with organic molecules (for example iron in the hemoglobin of red blood cells and iodine in thyroid hormone).

CARBOHYDRATES. Cellular organic compounds may be for the most part grouped into four categories—carbohydrates, lipids, proteins, and nucleic acids. Simplest in structure of the four are the carbohydrates, which, as their name implies, consist of a combination of carbon with hydrogen and oxygen in the proportions of water—mostly in the form of H and OH groups attached to one or more ring-shaped "skeletons" formed by carbon and oxygen atoms. Sugars and glycogen are the characteristic animal carbohydrates. The common simple sugar found in the vertebrate body—that into which all sugars entering the body are transformed by the liver before utilization—is *glucose*, with the following structure:

This is essentially a chain of carbon atoms to each of which is attached H and OH groups, but with the chain formed into a ring by an oxygen atom. Glucose is highly important, but as such it is hardly an integral part of the "vital" materials of the protoplasm. Rather, it is to be considered a source of immediate energy supply for cell life processes; in the presence of oxygen this sugar breaks down eventually into water and carbon dioxide with a considerable release of energy. A molecule of glucose easily combines with another similar molecule (the bond forming with the elimination of a molecule of water at the point of union) to form a double-sugar or disaccharide, thus:

This process can be extended to form very large straight and branched chains of sugars, the polysaccharides or starches, in which state sugars may be stored compactly. The characteristic starch of animal cells is *glycogen*, composed of many thousands of glucose units; its name derives from the fact that it re-forms glucose on its dissolution. Carbohydrate energy is characteristically stored in cells in this form, as fuel reserves, in solid granules.

Lipids.   The lipids, or fatlike substances, include a considerable variety of materials. Most characteristic and familiar are the true *fats*. The major bulk of a fat consists of molecules of *fatty acid*. These have a monotonous structure—a chain, often long, of carbon atoms tied (except at one end) to an unvarying series of hydrogen atoms; for example, stearic acid:

$$
\begin{array}{cccccccccccccccccc}
& H & H & H & H & H & H & H & H & H & H & H & H & H & H & H & H & H \\
& | & | & | & | & | & | & | & | & | & | & | & | & | & | & | & | & | \\
H-&C-&C-&C-&C-&C-&C-&C-&C-&C-&C-&C-&C-&C-&C-&C-&C-&C-&C\diagup^{O} \\
& | & | & | & | & | & | & | & | & | & | & | & | & | & | & | & | & & \diagdown_{OH} \\
& H & H & H & H & H & H & H & H & H & H & H & H & H & H & H & H &
\end{array}
$$

(In this formula $C\diagup^{O}_{\diagdown OH}$ is the organic acid group.) These chains are stable
under most conditions, but in the presence of appropriate enzymes are oxidized
with a great release of energy. (Petroleum fuels, the hydrocarbons, seem to be
essentially "fossil" organic compounds with similar properties; gasoline is a fatty
acid minus the terminal acid group.) The various fats are formed by tying three
of these elongate molecules into a single package by uniting them with a molecule of glycerol (glycerin), a simple compound related to the carbohydrates:

$$
\begin{array}{c}
H \\
| \\
H-C-OH \\
| \\
H-C-OH \\
| \\
H-C-OH \\
| \\
H
\end{array}
$$

Fatty acid —COOH groups join with the glycerol —OH groups, with elimination of water in the process, to form fats, thus:

(In this example, tristearin, all three fatty acids are the same; in general, however, two or three different fatty acids may be present in a single fat molecule.)

Fats are a general constituent of cells and are sometmes present in great
volume in adipose tissues; but they too appear to be, in the main, fuel reserves
in storage, higher in energy content than carbohydrates but less readily oxidized,
and play a relatively small part in the living protoplasm. Related to this is the
fact that fats are insoluble in water; they are hence not an integral part of the
watery protoplasm, and tend to occur as separate droplets. Despite the seeming

inertness of the common fats, however, it is notable that the presence of very small amounts of certain "essential" fatty acids appear to be highly important to all animals; these acids cannot be synthesized but must be obtained from plant food, and so are comparable with vitamins.

The *phospholipids*, or phosphated fats, differ from true fats in that but two fatty acids are attached to the glycerin molecule; the third position is occupied by phosphoric acid bound to a nitrogen base. The phospholipids, including for example, the major constituent of egg yolk, are partially soluble in water, and are, perhaps in relation to this fact, a more integral part of the active protoplasmic materials than their fatty cousins.

Classed with the lipids as a catch-all (primarily because we do not have any other category in which to place them) are various substances broadly termed the *steroids*, important in protoplasmic activity and general vital processes. Like the fats they are composed almost exclusively of hydrogen atoms hung on a carbon "skeleton"; however, this framework is not composed merely of simple chains, but includes carbon rings in complex formations. The ubiquitous vertebrate steroid is cholesterol, the functions of which are still poorly known; many highly active substances, such as the antirachitic vitamin, male and female sex hormones, and adrenal cortex hormones also belong in this general category.

PROTEINS.   Among the most distinctive of vital materials are the proteins, which fulfill many of the most essential functions of living cells. A basic difference from the carbohydrates and fats is the presence of nitrogen. Protein molecules are giants in the chemical world. They may include many thousands of atoms and reach the limit of visibility of the electron microscope. The basic structure of proteins is well understood. They are formed by a compounding of chemical structures simple in nature and limited in number, *amino acids*. The formula of such an acid is invariably in the following pattern:

$$\begin{array}{ccccc} & \text{H} & \text{H} & & \\ & | & | & & \\ \text{H} - \text{N} - & \text{C} - & \text{C} & - \text{OH} \\ & | & \| & \\ & \text{R} & \text{O} & \end{array}$$

R designates the one variable in the system; there is found here in one amino acid simply a hydrogen atom, in all others a variety of simple atom complexes. A score of such variants is known, and hence that number of different amino acids. The bulk of the amino acids utilized by an animal are derived from protein food, and ultimately if not directly from plants. A typical vertebrate, however, can synthesize from other organic materials part—but not all—of those which it uses. Proteins are digested into their component amino acids and enter cells in this form. Within the cells of the body these building stones are combined into molecular structures of almost infinite complexity and variety. Although the number of component amino acids is limited, variations in the numbers and arrangement of these units render possible uncountable numbers of differing proteins. One common structural shape is that of linkage of a long series of amino acids (with elimination of a water molecule at each N to C link) into a long chain—termed a polypeptide chain—coiled helix-fashion, a short segment of which would be of this pattern:

The nature of the proteins present varies greatly from one animal species to another, and may even vary from tissue to tissue and from individual to individual; there is a "protein specificity."

A special category of proteins is that of the *enzymes*. These ubiquitous and absolutely essential materials are catalysts, which vastly speed up reactions, typically reversible, involving organic materials; they function much as do simpler catalysts in simpler chemical processes. All enzymes are proteins, to some of which is attached a small nonamino acid compound which may be the active agent in their catalytic activity. Some enzymes, as will be noted later, function outside the cells, in the digestive tract. But all are produced intracellularly, and each of them plays a specific part in cell metabolism.

NUCLEIC ACIDS.　Certain overwhelmingly important organic molecules belong to a further special category of nitrogen-bearing compounds, the nucleic acids, made up of units called *nucleotides*. A nucleotide includes phosphoric acid and a simple sugar (ribose or desoxyribose) combined with a nitrogen-bearing base. Simple nucleotides may carry out important functions. Thus the nucleotide adenosine triphosphate (ATP) is a major source of energy in the chemistry of the cell, most notably in muscle activity. It includes three phosphate radicals, one of which may be lost with a high release of energy utilized in major fashion in muscle and nerve activity. It is becoming increasingly clear that nucleic acids lie at the very center of living processes. They are formed as long spirals by the union of the phosphoric acid and sugar components of successive nucleotides as shown below (S = sugar, P = phosphorus, B = base):

VITAMINS.　Finally, a group of special organic molecules, the vitamins, is essential to the well-being of cells. These substances have been discovered in the course of the study of dietary deficiencies in man and higher vertebrates, and are essential, although in extremely small amounts, to the operation of the body. They do not form a single class of compounds, but are simply odds and ends of vitally needed materials which the animal itself cannot synthesize. In some cases a vitamin may be related to a specific function as, for example, vitamin A is important for functioning of the retina of the eye in vision. Many of them are needed for the formation of enzymes necessary for cellular metabolic activity. The emphasis on dietary and medical aspects of the topic obscures the general biologic picture of the vitamin story. Most studies have been made on man and other mammals (to a lesser extent on birds), and we know almost nothing of vitamin needs of lower vertebrates. But (strangely), we *do* know the nutritional needs of many microorganisms. They turn out to require, in general, most of the same vitamins as man and mammals, and we can thus infer that vitamin needs were much the same throughout the vertebrate series.

Cell Structure. The cells of the body are, of course, highly varied in their structures and functions; a liver cell and a nerve cell, for example, are very different in appearance, and have very different activities. But despite such differences all cells have in common basic structural features and basic functional activities.

The "gross" features of cell anatomy are readily visible under the microscope (Fig. 49). Centrally situated is the nucleus. Within it are amounts of readily stainable—i.e., chromatic—material, to be identified chemically with nucleic acid. Some of this chromatin may be more or less permanently consolidated into a mass termed a *nucleolus;* toward a time of cell division the chromatin is compacted into a paired series of rodlike structures, the *chromosomes;* each chromosome splits lengthwise, so that when the cell divides, each daughter cell receives a full complement of chromosomes. Except at times of division, the nucleus is generally seen to be separated by a membrane from the general cell body. The cell in turn is bounded externally by a definite cell membrane, capable of regulating to some degree the traffic in materials entering or leaving; the membrane consists of a few layers of protein and lipid molecules. To the cell materials in general the term *protoplasm* is applied; *cytoplasm* is a more restricted term, designating the contents of the cell body external to the nucleus. With the ordinary microscope certain formed structures can generally be made out in the cytoplasm. Near the nucleus there are often visible small particles, the *centrioles*, which play a part in cell division. Scattered through the cytoplasm are numerous little structures, the *mitochondria.* With the aid of the electron microscope the mitochondria, which appear as mere dots or dashes at ordinary magnification, are seen to have

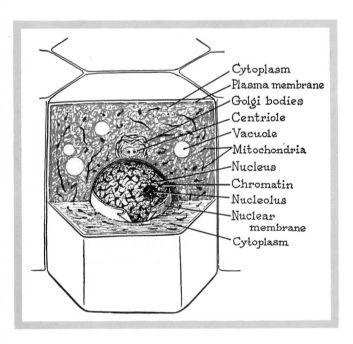

Fig. 49. Schematic drawing of a generalized animal cell. (From Villee, Walker and Smith, General Zoology.)

a definite structure as elongate spheroids or with a series of internal cross partitions. The mitochondria are centers in which take place much of the chemical activity that supplies energy for the work of the cell. It is in them that sugars and fatty acids are oxidized to yield the energy-rich compound adenosine triphosphate (ATP). Special stains reveal in many cells a *reticular apparatus* (frequently named after its discoverer, Golgi), a series of tiny vesicles whose function is little understood.

It was long thought that, apart from such structures as those just mentioned, cytoplasm was essentially an amorphous jelly-like colloid, with organic materials in solution in a fluid, watery medium. The development of electron microscopy, however, shows that, on the contrary, the cytoplasm is finely organized, with a network of delicate membranes with vesicles of more liquid material between them. The cytoplasm contains numerous tiny particles termed *ribosomes*, which are generally embedded in these membranes; the ribosomes appear to be major centers of protein synthesis.

Cell Metabolism. This complexity of cell structure gives the impression of a static condition. This is, of course, the reverse of the actual situation, for the cytoplasm is the seat of constant chemical activities of an exceedingly complex nature.

Every cell must produce energy for its particular function in the body (whether secretion, nervous conduction, muscular movement, or what not), but in addition it constantly undergoes chemical change in the maintenance of its internal economy. A cell, like a body, has, so to speak, its own "basal metabolism," necessary for the support of its vital activities.

In part these metabolic processes are constructive. Although animal cells depend on food materials (fundamentally on plants) for the elementary organic substances, they themselves have, to a high degree, the ability to manufacture from simple materials a great variety of complex organic compounds. Glucose and lipid materials are received and stored or transformed. Simple amino acids are accepted and built up into complex proteins. Further, there is considerable transformation of one into the others; of carbohydrates into fats and vice versa, and even, to some degree, an interchange of materials between the proteins and the "simpler" organic substances. Despite the seeming stability of proteins, once formed, and of fat and glycogen in reserve storage, it appears that these large molecules are constantly dropping off fractions consisting of amino acids, fatty acids, and glucose, respectively, and substituting others from "pools" of these substances present in the cell. Most important, the energy needed for the cell's own maintenance and for the performance of its role in bodily activities is gained by the oxidation and breaking down of organic materials into simpler compounds.

These processes are of an elaborately complex nature. The chemical mechanisms involved in even such a seemingly simple matter as the breaking down of glucose are highly complicated, and much of the work of the science of biochemistry is the unravelling of the complexities of cell chemistry.

Enzyme activity is of the utmost importance in these processes. Chemical activity would be exceedingly slow at the temperatures and under the physical conditions present in animal cells. The high degree of activity which actually takes place is rendered possible only through the presence in the cytoplasm (and particularly, it would seem, in cell particles in the membranes of the reticulum) of a great variety and enormous numbers of organic catalysts, the enzymes. Ultimately oxygen is needed for this work. Out of these processes, as an immediate source of energy available to the cell, come such compounds as ATP, mentioned above. A partial breakdown of ATP to a diphosphate releases a large amount of energy that can be utilized at once.

Cytoplasmic chemical action does not take place in random fashion. It is controlled and directed from the nucleus. Associated with each chromosome are large numbers of vitally essential molecules of desoxyribonucleic acid (DNA). Molecules of this nucleic acid have two highly important properties. (1) They are capable of reduplicating their own structure and passing accurate copies of themselves on to later generations of cells and individuals; these molecules, hence, may well be the genes of the geneticist. More than this, (2) a DNA molecule can act as a template in forming along its length a copy of its "pattern" in a related substance, ribonucleic acid (RNA). Ribonucleic acid is found in the nucleus (much of it often clustered in the nucleolus); passing out into the cytoplasm as messengers, so to speak, molecules of RNA in turn pattern the formation of proteins, including the enzymes. The basic structure of a DNA helix is a simple one. The sugar (whence the name of the acid) is desoxyribose, D. The nitrogenous bases are but four in number—adenine, cystosine, guanine, and thymine (A,C, G,T); these, however, may occur along a DNA strand in variable order, so that (given a very long helix) an indefinitely large number of arrangements are possible, for example:

etc.

However, this helix is not a single strand, but a double one, the two bound together by links between the bases at each step in the spiral. Most important is the fact that the bonding of the bases is not haphazard, but specific; adenine joins thymine, cystosine joins guanine only. Thus a segment of a double strand might (omitting the spiral twist) have a structure of this sort:

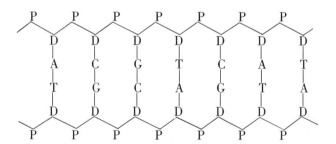

Given the specific relations between the four bases, it can be seen that each of the strands of DNA, if it could attract to itself nucleotides with appropriate bases, could reproduce the structure of its mate, and hence furnish duplicates of its complete structure to be handed on as genetic material to successive cell and organism generations. Further, a lining up along the length of the strands of nucleotides with the four essential bases and ribose sugar could cause the production of

RNA templates of DNA structure, to be carried out as "information" for protein production.

Our concerns here are not primarily with intricate cellular chemical phenomena; they have been mentioned briefly in order to give us some idea of what materials the cells must be supplied with to carry out their work, and what, in return, emerges from the cells into the body fluids for disposal.

Oxygen, obviously, is needed in constant supply as an energy source. Water must be available when needed. Inorganic ions may be needed, not only to keep up appropriate salt levels in the cell fluid but also—particularly phosphorus and sulfur ions—for utilization in the building up of organic compounds within the cell. Glucose and fats are required for consumption, for storage, and for use in "manufacture." Amino acids are absolutely necessary as building blocks in protein and enzyme synthesis. Needed too are the odds and ends of materials grouped as vitamins.

Returned to the interstitial fluid, and thence to the circulation for disposal, are the wastes from metabolic processes. Carbohydrates and fats, if completely oxidized, are returned as carbon dioxide and surplus metabolic water. More difficult for disposal purposes are the end products of the breakdown of proteins and other substances containing nitrogen and such materials as sulfur and phosphorus. Nitrogen leaves the cells as ammonia, NH_3. (This is frequently modified in the liver, to avoid toxic effects, to urea or uric acid.) Sulfur leaves the cell as sulfate; phosphorus is eliminated as phosphate (in which form it is always present intracellularly).

Cell Environment; Interstitial Fluid. A major duty of the organism is to provide the environment, physical and chemical, required by its cellular units. These requirements are rather rigidly fixed for vertebrate cells.

Although the organism as a whole may be able to exist over a fairly wide range of external temperatures, the temperature to which the cells in the interior of the body can be subjected and still survive is limited, although the optimum temperature and permissible departure from it varies considerably from form to form (cf. p. 142). In general, lower, primitively water-dwelling forms have a temperature range pitched lower in the scale than do terrestrial vertebrates. With perhaps some exceptions, even fishes are unable to stand internal temperatures much below the freezing point. Thirty degrees centigrade is about the upper limit for fish cells, 45° C. or so for the higher, terrestrial vertebrate classes. Beyond such a point "heat death" occurs; proteins undergo irreparable coagulation.

A cell can live and avoid desiccation only if bathed in a watery liquid medium. Such a material, the *interstitial fluid* (or intercellular fluid), pervades the body. But, as amply demonstrated by work on tissue cultures, water itself is not enough. This liquid must contain a considerable amount of material in solution; otherwise, through osmotic pressure, swelling and disruption of the cells which it bathes may take place. Still further, it is found that, in or out of the body, cells flourish only if the materials in solution, mainly inorganic salts, adhere rather closely to the formula actually present in interstitial fluid normally found in the body of vertebrates. This liquid contains considerable amounts of sodium and chlorine ions, lesser quantities of potassium, calcium, and magnesium ions, and small amounts of other elements.

Reasons for the requirement of this salt formula (different from that in the watery constituents of the cells themselves) are complex and poorly understood. It is of interest, however, that with two exceptions (the absence of sulfates, and the lesser amounts of magnesium), the materials in the interstitial fluid of vertebrates are similar to those found in sea water, although generally much more dilute. The suggestion has been made that this is no mere accident; that the ancestors of the vertebrates were simple animals bathed in and permeated by the waters of the early Paleozoic ocean; that their cellular physiology was evolved with this type of environment as a basic feature; and that when, as complex organisms, they developed an independent internal environment, this salty interstitial liquid persisted as, so to speak, a remnant of the ancient seas. The interstitial fluid is in relatively free communication with the similar liquid constituting the bulk of the blood plasma, and it is therefore through the blood circulation that there is accomplished the even distribution through the body of the fluid materials necessary for cell survival.

It is, of course, through the interstitial fluid bathing it that the cell is supplied with the materials which it needs for its existence and through this same liquid that it is relieved of its waste materials. The interstitial fluid must be in intimate contact with the circulatory system so that food materials may be constantly supplied and waste constantly taken away. Further, the digestive and respiratory systems must supply, directly or indirectly, the necessary "food" materials; excretory and respiratory organs must eliminate the wastes. And, indeed, in a broader view, almost every body organ is involved in some fashion in the acquisition of the food supply for the multitude of body cells and the maintenance of the proper environment for them. The cells are dependent upon the proper functioning of the body as a whole; the body is dependent for its existence upon the proper functioning of its individual cells, and labors to that end.

Osmosis.   The nature of the cell membrane, and the necessity of there being a sufficiency of materials in solution in the interstitial fluid to balance the concentration within the cell, bring to our attention for brief review the basic physical-biologic phenomenon of *osmosis*—a phenomenon of importance in a great variety of activities and hence influential in the molding of structure and function in many parts of the body.

If two bodies of liquid—say, of water with materials in solution—are separated by a membrane, man-made or organic, a variety of conditions may exist. The membrane may be so impermeable that little or no exchange of materials may take place, or so tenuous that it may be readily penetrated by all the materials of the liquids present, which may thus exchange freely. Intermediate conditions, however, may exist. It may be that the submicroscopic interstices in the membrane are so small that large molecules or even large ions cannot pass through. Such membranes, common in the vertebrate body, are termed *semipermeable.*

We conceive of the molecules and ions of a liquid, no matter how quiet it may appear to the eye, as being in rapid motion, dashing violently to and fro. If two liquids are separated by a semipermeable membrane, that membrane is constantly bombarded by particles on both sides. If both liquids consist of pure water, a large proportion of the particles will pass through the gaps in the membrane, but since the passage is equally free from both sides, no change in quantity will occur. Again, if both liquids contain in solution equal quantities of materials which cannot pass through the mesh, conditions will likewise remain stable; a given percentage of particles of the large ions or molecules strike the membrane and fail to penetrate it; but since the percentage of large particles which cannot pass, and small particles which can, is the same on both sides, quantities and qualities of the two liquids are undisturbed.

But when the two solutions are not in balance, we see a different and striking result. Let us take the extreme case where a thick solution of materials is present on one side, and pure water on the other. From the solution side, only water particles are able to penetrate the membrane, and these constitute only a fraction (if a large one) of the liquid. But from the pure water side, every particle is water and has a chance to pass. In consequence the net result is a steady, one-way flow of liquid from the pure water side into the solution. In a laboratory experiment with simple liquids it can be seen that the solution becomes increasingly diluted, owing to the incoming water, and expands, even against considerable pressure; body cells, unsuited for normal life under such conditions, are seen under the microscope to expand when placed in pure water, and, having their protoplasm diluted to a nonviable stage, may finally burst.

Cellular membranes of variable degrees of permeability, noted in later chapters, are present in numerous situations in the organs of vertebrates. It is obvious that osmosis is a phenomenon which enters notably into the determination of the architecture of the body.

Epithelia (Fig. 50).   The body cells are not isolated entities; they are part of formed *tissues*—organized associations of cells of similar origins and functions. In some cases—notably the connective tissues and skeletal structures described later—the aggregation of cells may be relatively diffuse, and sometimes ill defined or amorphous and in the case of cells in the blood stream the concept that these form a tissue is somewhat of a strain on one's mentality. In many instances, however, the cell association is that termed an *epithelium*—a regular and compact arrangement of cells in a sheet which borders on one of its aspects the surface of the body or one of its cavities.

In the embryo, most epithelia are simple and diagrammatic in appearance. Later, however, by thickening and modification they may lose much of the early epithelial appearance, as in the thick "gray matter" of the human brain, or a mass of liver tissue. This differentiation of epithelia during development roughly parallels their probable phyletic differentiation. The earliest and simplest multicellular organisms presumably had but a single epithelium, covering the surface and nec-

Fig. 50.   Types of epithelial tissue. *A*, Squamous epithelium; *B*, cuboidal epithelium; *C*, columnar epithelium; *D*, ciliated columnar epithelium; *E*, sensory epithelium (cells from the nasal mucosa); *F*, glandular epithelium, including mucus-producing goblet cells. (From Villee, Biology.)

essarily serving a variety of functions in protection, sensation reception and exchange of food and waste materials with the outside world. Later, with the development of internal cavities and internal structures, specialization could and did
occur. We may note, however, that in much of the gut and in other internal structures the epithelium, protected from external harm, may remain persistently thin
and delicate in nature, and its cells may have important properties of absorption
or secretion. Such epithelia are generally termed *mucous membranes*, since part
or all of the surface cells generally secrete mucus (cf. p. 95); as a result the
epithelium is covered and moistened by a thin film of liquid.

For convenience, various classificatory terms are used for different shapes
of epithelial cells. *Squamous cells* are those much reduced in height, appearing in
transverse section as thin lines. *Cuboidal cells* are those in which height and width
are about equal, so that in section they have a square outline. In *columnar cells*
the height is in excess of the width.

Embryologically, epithelia often consist at first of a single layer of cells, and
this arrangement is retained in various adult cases as a *simple epithelium,* frequently of the mucous membrane type; such epithelia tend to be present when
there is little wear and tear on a surface, or where there is absorption or filtration. In such an epithelium any one of the three cell types noted may be present.
Embryonic cells tend to be rounded, but when closely packed they tend to assume
a cuboidal shape in a simple epithelium; this type is not uncommon in the adult.
A thin squamous type is characteristic, for example, of the lining of blood vessels
and other areas where osmotic exchange through the membrane is of importance.
Surface cells with secretory or other important functions tend to be of a deeper,
columnar type.

When an epithelium shows two or more layers of cells, it is termed a *stratified epithelium.* The stratified types are named from the nature of the cells on
their surface; these may be squamous, columnar, or (more rarely) cuboidal. The
deeper cells of a stratified squamous epithelium may be cuboidal or columnar,
and the underlying cells of a columnar type may be much flattened.

On surface view, or in section parallel to the surface, the cell boundaries of
an epithelium may be sometimes demonstrated to be irregular, but they are typically polygonal in arrangement, frequently with the hexagonal outline, which (as
the bee knows) gives the best compromise between the ideal circular individual
shape and the necessities of a compact arrangement. The adjacent cells in an epithelium may be tightly packed together, but generally are separated by small
spaces filled by the interstitial fluid. These spaces may be bridged by numerous
tiny bars of protoplasm running from one cell to the surface of its neighbors. As
a rule blood vessels are absent in epithelia, and nutrient material reaches the
cells by passing upward in the interstitial fluid from vessels beneath the base of
the epithelium. In most cases epithelia are bounded below by connective tissues;
between the two there is typically a *basement membrane* formed by condensed
connective tissue material.

In a stratified epithelium there is frequently a constant loss or destruction
of surface cells; these are replaced from below, and the lower cells of the epithelium form a *germinative layer* capable of making replacements by cell division
(cf. Fig. 76, p. 129). The major activities of an epithelium are in general associated with its outer, free surface. As suggested by these facts, it is natural to find
that in many stratified epithelia the cells are progressively more specialized as the
surface is approached. We further find that in an epithelium of any type, the in-

dividual cells are frequently more or less polarized, the proximal (lower) and distal (upper) ends being different in nature.

The free surface of an epithelium frequently shows marked specializations. The cells may secrete a *cuticle*, a more or less solid layer of surface material covering the epithelium. More frequently, however, the surface of the cells themselves may be modified. Most specialized of surface structures are *cilia*, found on the surface of a variety of embryonic and adult columnar epithelia of vertebrates as well as invertebrates. These are slender, mobile hairlike "organs," containing as many as 11 slender filaments connected with a basal corpuscle. Cilia beat in but one direction; the beat (independent of nervous control) in a ciliated surface progresses in wavelike fashion so as to carry mucus or other materials along in a constant unidirectional stream.

In certain cases a simple epithelium may present a seemingly stratified appearance—a *pseudostratified epithelium*. If, for example, a simple but tall epithelium contains cells of two sorts, with nuclei at different levels, or with cell bodies expanded at different levels, one gets the impression that two layers are present (cf. Fig. 244, p. 338). The term is better justified in epithelia where two types of cells are present at the base of a simple epithelium, but only one type reaches the surface. (Incidentally, it will be realized that if a simple epithelium is cut at an angle, several cell layers may appear, deceptively, to be present in microscopic section.) We may here mention the poorly named *transitional epithelium* found in the amniote bladder or urinary tubes. When the cavity it surounds is empty or not greatly expanded, this type of epithelium appears to be highly stratified; with distension of the cavity the epithelium expands in area and consequently thins.

In a broad sense the term epithelium may be applied to any tissues of the sort described here, no matter where they are found in the body. By many authors, however, the term is restricted and sometimes confined to tissue layers on the outer surface of the body on the one hand, and the gut and its derivatives on the other, or to cavities obviously originating from these outer or inner surfaces. The theoretic consideration behind this is the fact that (as will be seen in the next chapter) such epithelia are derived during individual development from the surfaces of the early embryo. If such a restriction is made, one or more alternative terms are used for tissues lining cavities formed secondarily in the deeper layers of the body. The name *endothelium* is generally used for the epithelial material lining the vessels of the circulatory system. Sometimes this term is applied as well to the lining of the body cavities; *mesothelium* is here an alternative name.

Nonepithelial Tissues. Although a great series of body tissues—particularly those of the lining of the gut and derivatives and of the body surface—are in the adult clearly epithelial in nature, many others which are derived from embryonic epithelia are so greatly modified in the adult that their epithelial origin is obscured. Liver tissue, for example, is derived from the epithelium of a gut outpocketing which develops into the adult bile duct; but although the cells of the adult liver retain a connection with bile duct branches, the arrangement of the masses of liver tissue has little regard for the original epithelial arrangement. Much of the nervous system begins its history as an epithelium surrounding a neural tube; but although cavities representing the tube persist in the adult, there is little trace of typical epithelial arrangement in the nervous tissues. The striated body musculature of Amphioxus and the vertebrates can be regarded as of epithelial origin, since in Amphioxus it arises as epithelia surrounding a series of paired pouches. But in the adult vertebrate no trace of the ancestral epithelial structure

94   *THE VERTEBRATE BODY*

persists, and even in the embryo this musculature shows at the most only fleeting traces of an epithelial nature.

We can still, in a broad sense, regard these tissues as epithelial in nature, since they are ontogenetically or phylogenetically derived from true epithelia. It is quite otherwise with certain other tissues of the vertebrate body—the connective and skeletal tissues and those of the circulatory system. These arise, as will be noted in the next chapter, from a type of embryonic material known as mesenchyme —cells which may be derived from the under surfaces of epithelia, but which are themselves never arranged in a compact epithelial type of tissue. They are, instead, diffusely arranged within a ground substance—a *matrix*—which they have created. In the case of the skeletal elements the matrix becomes the hard material of cartilages or bones; in the case of connective tissue it is gelatinous in nature; in the case of the circulatory system, the matrix is a liquid—the blood plasma.

Glands (Fig. 51).   Secretory activity—the production and discharge of fluid materials—is characteristic of a variety of cells; cells in which this a dominant activity are termed *gland cells*. Frequently their nature is obvious in microscopic preparations, owing to the presence of granules of material being secreted or vacuoles filled by it in the cell body. Glands and gland cells may be classified with regard to the effect that the giving off of secreted materials may have upon the cell body. Very commonly a secretory activity may be carried on indefinitely

Fig. 51.   Diagrams of various exocrine gland types. *a–g(above)*, simple glands; *a*, tubular; *b*, coiled tubular; *c*, *d*, branched tubular; *e*, alveolar; *f*, *g*, branched acinous. *Below*, examples of compound glands. In all diagrams, ducts are in double lines, secretory portions in solid black. (From Maximow and Bloom, Histology.)

without apparent harm to the cell; this is the condition in the *merocrine* type of gland. But if the secretion is thick or viscous, the cell usually is damaged in discharging it. In the *apocrine* type the superficial part of the cell breaks down as the secretion is released, but no permanent harm is done; this part of the cell is reconstituted and secretion recurs. But in some instances (as in sebaceous glands of mammalian skin) the entire cell is destroyed with the discharge of its contents— the *holocrine* type of secretion.

In many instances gland cells may occur individually or in restricted areas of an epithelium which also serves other functions. Mucus, a thick, slimy lubricating material, moistening and protecting various membranes, may be produced by formed glands, but is frequently produced by individual cells scattered about the surface of an epithelium. The secretion frequently accumulates in the cells in the form of large droplets, causing the cells thus distended to be termed *goblet cells*.

Although gland cells or a glandular area may be simply part of the surface of an epithelium, we frequently find that in the course of embryonic development glandular tissues withdraw from the general epithelial surfaces to form discrete glands; the trend for the formation of formed glands is greater among the higher vertebrate groups. In a majority of cases these glands discharge by ducts into some cavity of the body or to the body surface, and are hence termed *exocrine glands*. Withdrawal from the surface serves a variety of purposes. The folding of the glandular epithelium allows a great increase in secretory area; the gland cells are sheltered from the vicissitudes which might be encountered on the general epithelial surface; the presence of a narrow duct (in which the cells generally are nonsecretory) may allow regulation of discharge of the secretion.

Some of the varied forms which exocrine glands may assume are shown in the accompanying figure. The secretory areas may take the shape of tubules or of rounded pockets (alveoli or acini), and may be simple or subdivided. Further, in larger glands a compound structure may be brought about by branching of the ducts as well, tending to divide the gland into lobes and lobules. The shape of glands is often quite irregular, for appropriate volume is the desideratum, and form is immaterial. The larger glands usually are surrounded by a sheath of connective tissue; generally there is an ample supply of capillaries and nerve endings.

In contrast to these "normal" glands of exocrine nature, we find in a variety of instances glands which do not discharge to any surface but, instead, pour their secretions into the blood stream. These are the *endocrine glands* (cf. Chap. 17). In some instances these can be seen in the developmental history to arise from epithelia and hence may have been originally exocrine in nature (in the case of the thyroid gland, for example, this seems certain; cf. p. 560). In other cases, however, there is no evidence of such a pedigree and the phylogenetic origin of many of the endocrines is indeed obscure. Since the secretions—the hormones— given off by endocrine glands may act, by way of the blood stream, in any part of the body, their position need have no anatomic relation to the organs which they influence, and (as described later) they are found in a variety of situations.

5

THE EARLY
DEVELOPMENT
OF VERTEBRATES

The adult phase of an organism is merely a last major stage in a long series of stages through which it passes during the lifetime of the individual. In later chapters the development of the various specific organs and tissues will be noted. Here we shall discuss briefly the early developmental history of the vertebrate from the egg to the point where the major organ systems have differentiated and the basic ground plan of the body has been established. In doing so we shall simplify the story in diagrammatic fashion, and omit many features of interest to the embryologist.

EGG TYPES

The vertebrate egg, exceedingly variable in size, is typically a spherical cell, containing, in addition to nucleus and an amount of clear cytoplasm, yolk to furnish material for the developing embryo. While embryonic development, as we customarily think of it, begins with fertilization, the egg has already made hopeful preparations for this event. The egg nucleus must be put in proper condition for union with that of the sperm, and part of the egg chromosomal materials are cast out in small polar bodies (a process generally incomplete but temporarily arrested at the time of fertilization). Further, the cytoplasmic materials of the egg cell undergo a considerable degree of organization before fertilization and much of the future pattern of symmetry appears to have been already established by that time.

The sperm supplies nuclear material which is of importance in heredity and in the later phases of development, but which has little effect on the initial phases. The egg has developed within itself all the potentialities needed for the complete development of an adult. When ripe, the egg is "set" and ready, waiting only a proper stimulus to begin the cleavage into cellular units which is the necessary first stage toward the development of the tissues and organs of the complex adult. Physical or chemical stimulation is capable in many cases of setting this process in motion. Under normal conditions, however, the trigger effect is produced by the entrance of the sperm.

The quantity of yolk present in the egg varies greatly; its amount essentially determines the size of the egg and is crucial as regards the pattern of cleavage. In some eggs—those of Amphioxus and mammals, particularly—there is little yolk, this little being somewhat more concentrated in one egg hemisphere. Such an egg may be termed *oligolecithal*. A second egg type is that which we will call *mesolecithal*. The egg is somewhat larger, containing a moderate amount of yolk which is strongly concentrated in one hemisphere of the egg—the lower hemisphere in an egg floating in water. The frog has a characteristic mesolecithal egg, and the same type is found in urodeles, lungfishes, lower actinopterygians, and lampreys; it is so widespread in lower aquatic forms that it is reasonable to conclude that the mesolecithal egg was characteristic of the ancestral vertebrates.

In the sharks and skates, on the one hand, and reptiles and birds, on the other, we find eggs of large size, the *telolecithal* type, with yolk constituting most of the volume of the cell, and with the relatively small amount of cytoplasm concentrated at one pole. So overwhelming is the yolk mass that in the kitchen the cell body of the hen's egg is simply termed the "yolk," to the neglect of the tiny amount of clear cytoplasm which it contains. In the common modern bony fishes, the teleosts, the egg is likewise heavily loaded with yolk, but is variable in size. It behaves in development somewhat like that of a shark, but has peculiarities of its own which will not be considered here.

The concentration of the yolk in one hemisphere brings to light clear evidence of organization in the egg—a polarity, with an *animal pole* in the relatively clear cytoplasmic area above, a *vegetal pole* in the yolk region below. In many invertebrates the axis connecting these two poles becomes the anteroposterior axis of the body, the vegetal pole becoming the posterior end. In the vertebrates and lower chordates this is not the case. Related to the greater complexity of development, the adult axis in Amphioxus, for example, lies about 45 degrees off the egg axis, so that (to put it crudely) the animal pole slants down beneath the prospective chin of the adult, and the vegetal pole slants upward and posteriorly toward the back of the animal. To make a bilaterally symmetric rather than a radial animal, we need, in addition to an anteroposterior axis, a medial plane separating right and left halves of the future body. In some cases, at least, this plane is known to have been established in the unfertilized egg.

To illustrate the varied patterns seen in the early development of vertebrates we shall select eggs of the three different types discussed above. For an almost diagrammatically oligolecithal egg we shall, in fact, leave the true vertebrates and resort to Amphioxus, a lower chordate relative. The frog or urodele egg is a characteristic mesolecithal type. That of the shark or skate is illustrative of an extremely heavy-yolked telolecithal type, and the bird's egg is similar in nature in early stages. We will, further, note the peculiar early development seen in the mammalian egg. This is tiny and almost devoid of yolk; but mammals have descended from reptiles with large-yolked eggs, and their developmental pattern is of a type with many "reminiscences" of that of telolecithal forms. We shall follow each of these types through three successive major processes: (1) cleavage and the formation of a blastula, (2) gastrulation, with laying down of the main body layers, and (3) formation of neural tube and mesodermal structures.

CLEAVAGE AND BLASTULA FORMATION

Amphioxus.   As a first major sequence of events in development we shall describe the process of *cleavage*, leading to the stage known as the *blastula*. This process is almost diagrammatically seen in Amphioxus.

In this form (Fig. 52) the first cleavage of the egg extends along a "meridian" from pole to pole (much as one cuts an apple into two halves) and results in the formation of two cells of equal size. In the Amphioxus egg, bilateral symmetry is already established before fertilization, and the two cells resulting from the first cleavage are destined, in normal development, to become the right and left halves of the body. The two adhere to one another, but nevertheless each tends to round up and approach a spherical shape—a tendency repeated in later divisions. A second cleavage is, like the first, from pole to pole, but at right angles, and the process is similar to that of cutting an apple into quarters.

The third division is at right angles to both those preceding, and is essentially a cut around the equator of the egg, dividing each of the four cells then present into upper and lower components and resulting in an eight-celled stage. By this time, however, it is manifestly difficult for each of these cells to maintain a spherical shape and yet remain in contact with all former neighbors. In consequence there tends to develop a central cavity inside the sphere of cells—a cavity which becomes increasingly large as division proceeds, and is known as the *segmentation cavity* or *blastocele*.

Although there is but little yolk in the Amphioxus egg its distribution is not absolutely uniform; as said above, there is a somewhat greater concentration toward the vegetal pole. A cell tends to divide, not through the center of its total mass, but through the center of its living protoplasm, without regard for such rela-

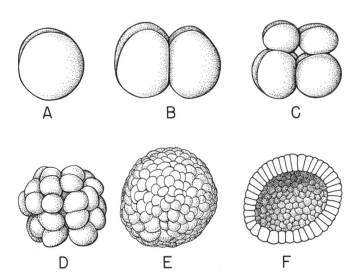

Fig. 52.   Cleavage and blastula formation in an oligolecithal egg—that of Amphioxus (cf. Figs. 53 to 55). *A*, First cleavage; animal pole of uncleaved egg is at top of figure. *B*, Second cleavage, to four-celled stage. *C*, Third cleavage; cells of animal hemisphere are somewhat smaller. *D*, After about two further cleavages. *E*, Blastula. *F*, Hemisected blastula, to show segmentation cavity in interior, and single-layered surface. (After Cerfontaine, Conklin.)

tively inert materials as yolk. In consequence the equatorial division which results in the eight-celled stage is not exactly through the equator, but slightly above this plane. Hence we find that the upper quartet of cells is slightly smaller than that below, and the concentration of yolk is slightly greater in the lower quartet.

The next set of cleavages is, as would be expected, longitudinal; each cell of both quartets is subdivided into two, to give a 16-celled stage. Then follows a paired set of cleavages in both animal and vegetal hemispheres to give a 32-celled stage with four (rather irregular) rings of cells around the circumference, and with distinct (if small) size differences between these rings as we travel from pole to pole. Beyond the 32-celled stage, since the process is a geometric progression, the number of cells increases rapidly, to about 64, 128, and so on; now, however, there is much less regularity in the divisions and a less synchronous cleavage. Within a short time the original egg cell has given rise to several hundred cells, essentially arranged as a single-layered shell about a central cavity. This sphere, the result of segmentation, is termed a *blastula*. Within is a large cavity, the blastocele, the initiation of which was noted above. For the most part the cells of the blastula are not too dissimilar from one another, but observation reveals the presence of smaller cells toward the original animal pole, larger and somewhat more yolky cells toward the vegetal pole, and still a third type occupying part of the vegetal hemisphere. In consequence there is a differentiation of types of cells which, as will be seen later, have varied destinies in the embryo.

Mesolecithal Eggs. The amphibian egg (Fig. 53) as seen in a typical frog or salamander is of the mesolecithal type, with a certain amount of granular yolk

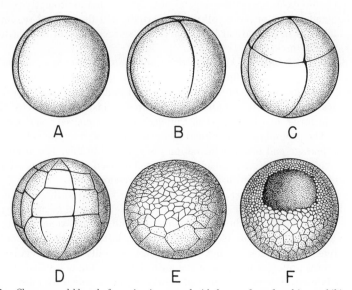

Fig. 53. Cleavage and blastula formation in a mesolecithal type of egg found in amphibians. These six figures are comparable to the six in Fig. 52 (cf. also Figs. 54 and 55). *A*, First cleavage. *B*, Second cleavage. *C*, Third—meridional—cleavage, with smaller cells in animal hemisphere. *D*, About 36-celled stage; cleavages irregular, but slower and with larger cells in vegetal hemisphere. *E*, Blastula, with strong contrast between cells at two original poles. *F*, Section of blastula, showing segmentation cavity of restricted size; blastula a number of cell layers in thickness. Yolky mass at vegetal pole has cleaved, but slowly and into a mass of large cells.

present throughout, but with a heavy concentration of it in the vegetal hemisphere. In such an egg the first two divisions are comparable to those seen in Amphioxus— longitudinal, and cutting from pole to pole at right angles to one another. In many amphibians the distribution of pigments in the egg indicates that the first cleavage here, as in Amphioxus, is a median sagittal one, separating right and left halves of the future body. There is, however, one difference between the first two cleavages here and those of Amphioxus. The great amount of yolk in the vegetal hemisphere has the effect of slowing up cleavage of this part of the egg. The first cleavage begins promptly enough in the animal hemisphere. But as the furrow progresses downward, it encounters difficulty in cleaving the inert yolk materials, and is slowed up. In consequence the second division may begin in the animal hemisphere before the first has been completed. This tendency for retardation of division in the lower portion of the egg persists through the period of cleavage.

The third division of an egg of this type is equatorial, as in Amphioxus. This cleavage tends, as there, to divide the protoplasm in each of the four cells into equal halves; but since there is considerably more yolk and less protoplasm in the vegetal hemisphere, the line of cleavage is well above the equator (almost as far north, one might say, as the Tropic of Cancer). In consequence we find in the frog or urodele egg, from this time on, a marked difference between the small cells of the animal hemisphere and the large, yolky cells of the vegetal hemisphere.

As the end result of the process of cleavage in an egg of this sort, we arrive at a blastula which in certain regards resembles that of Amphioxus, but in which there is a greater disparity between the cells of the two hemispheres in size and yolk content. Further, the blastocele is not as extensive as in Amphioxus. The yolk-filled protoplasm toward the vegetal pole fails to divide promptly in the frog or urodele and a mass of large yolky cells partially fills the internal region of the sphere, and even in the animal hemisphere the surface layer of the blastula is a number of cells thick.

Telolecithal Eggs.   Although the amphibian egg contains a considerable amount of yolk, it is, nevertheless, as is that of Amphioxus, *holoblastic;* that is, there is a complete cleavage of the entire egg in blastula formation. The *teloblastic* type of cleavage (Fig. 54) is found in such forms as the elasmobranchs, teleosts, reptiles, and birds, in which most of the egg substance consists of a great, inert yolk mass. The protoplasm is confined to a small area capping the yolk at the animal pole; cleavage and blastula formation are confined to this clear protoplasmic area. The yolk mass does not cleave at all; nuclei invade its margins adjacent to the area of cleavage, but fail to make much impression on it.

As in eggs of other types, first and second cleavages pass through the center of the animal pole. They are not, however, complete cleavages of the egg; they affect only the materials of the protoplasmic cap and do not extend into the yolk. There follow "equatorial" divisions, separating a cluster of cells at the pole from more peripheral members. Further subdivisions, generally rather irregular, occur, until the entire protoplasmic area at the animal pole region is divided into a considerable number of cells, to form a plate-like structure which we must regard as a blastula, and may be termed a *blastodisc.* In Amphioxus the blastula was only one cell thick. In a mesolecithal egg, however, the surface of the blastula is generally a thicker structure, many cells deep; and in telolecithal eggs the entire blastula region of the egg may be a thick mass of cells which tends to be slightly lifted off the underlying yolk. The "blastula" is here essentially a flat sheet, not a sphere. Its margins, bounded all about by the yolk, consists of cells which in less yolky eggs would lie in the vegetal hemisphere, but are here unable to attain such a

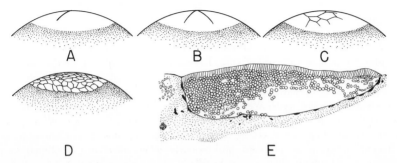

Fig. 54. Diagrams to show cleavage and blastula formation in a large-yolked egg, as that of a shark, reptile or bird (cf. Figs. 52 and 53). In *A* to *D* is figured only the animal pole of the egg, containing an area of clear protoplasm on top of the large, inert yolk mass. *A* to *D* show cleavage stages comparable to those in *A* to *D* of the two preceding figures; the result of cleavage is not a sphere, but a flattened plate of cells. In *E* is shown, at higher magnification, a section through the formed blastula of a shark. The blastula is a flat plate, a number of cells in thickness, with an irregular segmentation cavity lying below it, but above the unsegmented yolk mass. (*E* after von Kupffer.)

position. In cartographic terms, the blastula is a sphere flattened down into a two dimensional "map" on a north-polar projection.

Mammals. The early stages in mammalian development (Fig. 55) are quite specialized and unlike those of any other vertebrates. Except for the mono-tremes, mammals carry the developing young within their bodies, and nutritive materials for growth of the embryo are derived, to begin with, from uterine secre-tions and, later, from the blood stream of the mother through the *placenta*. As noted later (p. 120) this is formed by a union of maternal uterine tissues and fetal tissues which are modifications of embryonic membranes found in other amniotes.

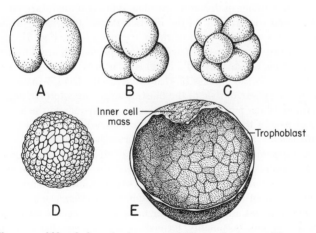

Fig. 55. Cleavage and blastula formation in a mammal. The small, almost yolkless egg cleaves (*A* to *D*) in a fashion similar to that of Amphioxus. The formed blastula (seen in section at *E*) has a deceptive resemblance to that of Amphioxus. Actually, however, the thin external sphere is the trophoblast, which forms a connection with the uterine wall, and the true blastula is merely the inner cell mass. This is a sheet of cells placed above the internal cavity much as the blastula of a telolecithal egg (Fig. 54, *E*) is situated atop the yolk mass. (After Streeter.)

The necessity for the rapid development of the placenta is responsible for early embryonic histories that are unique.

Related to the fact that food materials are to be shortly obtainable from uterine fluids and later from the maternal blood stream, the mammalian egg is a tiny object practically devoid of yolk. In consequence, total cleavage, on the mode of Amphioxus, is possible. This cleavage results presently in the production of a score or two of cells. With further division there appear marked variations between different mammalian types. We shall follow the pattern seen in primates, in which there differentiate (1) a compact cluster of cells termed the *inner cell mass*, and (2) an expanded sphere of cells external to it, the *trophoblast*. The trophoblast is to become a part of the placenta, and its early development is a functionally vital embryonic adaptation. The egg is fertilized far up the oviduct but reaches the uterus, in the walls of which it is to become embedded, within a few days, and the trophoblast develops rapidly so that contact may be made with the maternal uterine tissues when conditions are appropriate. We have here an excellent example of an embryonic adaptation, the development of a structure never present in either adult or embryo of "lower" vertebrates.

GASTRULATION AND GERM LAYER FORMATION

We have seen as the result of cleavage and blastula formation the development of the egg into an early embryonic stage which consists in most types of a single body layer in the form of a sphere or sheet of cells. In some instances (Amphioxus, for example) differences in size, pigmentation, or amount of yolk present in different parts of the blastula indicate the differentiation of specific cell areas destined to form one or another major tissue of the later embryo and adult. In other instances a real differentiation is not readily visible, but the future fate of any given area can often be discovered by applying a stain to cells in the blastula stage and following the stained area through into later stages of embryonic development. As a result of such observations and experiments it has been found in a considerable number of different chordate types that the future fate of various cell areas is already determined in the blastula stage; "fate maps" of the blastula regions can be drawn, and several of them are given here (Fig. 57, *A-H*).

There now begins a series of movements of specific cell areas toward assumption of the position which they will eventually occupy in the later embryo and adult. A major step is the process of *gastrulation*—the transformation of the surface pattern of the sphere or disc of the blastula stage into a folded, double-layered early embryo, of which part of the outer layer corresponds to the skin surface of the adult, and part of the inner layer will form the adult gut lining.

Amphioxus. In some primitive metazoans—various coelenterates, for example—gastrulation is a simple process, merely the folding of the spherical shell of cells of the blastula stage into a double-layered hemisphere, with skin outside, gut cavity lining within. All the cells of the original animal hemisphere, which form the outer layer of the gastrula, constitute the *ectoderm*, or outer germ layer of the late embryo and adult. The inner cells are the *endoderm* or inner germ layer, forming the gut, reasonably termed in the embryo, the *archenteron;* the single opening into the cavity is the *blastopore*.

The process of gastrulation in *Amphioxus* (Fig. 56) appears to be equally

simple, but is actually more complex. If there were present in the Amphioxus embryo only the materials present in the simple coelenterate cup, there would be
produced in a chordate little more than the superficial part of the skin and the
inner lining of the digestive tract and its appendages. There is needed a special
area of the superficial ectodermal layer for the formation of the complicated nervous system, a *neurectoderm*. There must be formed the materials of the third major
germ layer, the *mesoderm*, which constitutes the greater part of the bulk of the
chordate body. A distinctive mid-dorsal area of mesoderm, the *chordamesoderm*,
forms the notochord. It is of especial importance in bringing about by induction
the development of the nervous system from the overlying neurectodermal tissue.

All these areas are already laid out in Amphioxus in the blastula stage (Fig.
57, *A, B*) and are involved in the process of gastrulation. As gastrulation begins,
the large yolky cells at the vegetal pole, which are to become the endoderm, form a
flat plate and then bend inward at the ventral rim of the forming blastopore. A
crescent of mesodermal cells destined to form the notochord rolls inward over the
dorsal lip of the blastopore and pushes forward internally, lengthening in the process and tending to lengthen somewhat the gastrula as a whole. On either margin
of the blastopore, between the materials above and endoderm below, cell masses
of the mesoderm proper stream in, push forward and upward, in the inner layer,
and align themselves in a strip on either side of the forming notochord. With the
infolding of this mesodermal tissue, the future neural ectoderm comes to occupy
a large area on the dorsal surface anterior to the blastopore.

When gastrulation has been completed, we find the embryo forming a somewhat elongated spheroid, with the only entrance to its interior the posteriorly
placed blastopore, now reduced in size. On the outer surface, the future skin ectoderm forms the ventral and anterior epithelial covering; the neurectoderm the
more posterodorsal area. Internally the endoderm occupies an area essentially
comparable to that of the skin ectoderm on the outer surface, with the chordamesoderm occupying a mid-dorsal position along the roof of the archenteron between bands of typical mesodermal materials.

Although not properly a part of gastrulation, a further stage in the development of the Amphioxus mesoderm will be mentioned at this point. The cells
round up to form a lengthwise cylindrical structure as the definitive notochord.
At either side the lateral mesoderm folds outward into a pair of longitudinal
grooves. At the anterior end of each groove a pouch, more or less cubical in shape,
pinches off as a *mesodermal somite*. This contains a cavity, originally continuous
with that of the archenteron, which is destined to become part of the celom; its
walls later differentiate into mesodermal tissues. Posteriorly, successive pairs of
somites are budded off along the length of the trunk. As these pouches are formed,
the endoderm, originally lateral and ventral in position, grows upwards internally
to them and across beneath the notochord to form a continuous lining to the definitive gut. This pouch type of mesoderm formation is highly comparable to the
process seen in acorn worms and echinoderms and is a prime basis for the belief
that chordates are related in origin to the echinoderm phylum.

Mesolecithal Types (Figs. 57, *C, D*, 58, 67, *A, B*, p. 117).   In such types
as the urodeles and frogs, with mesolecithal eggs, the potential germ layer materials
are laid out over the surface of the blastula in a fashion comparable to that of
Amphioxus (except for the relative position of chorda materials and lateral meso-

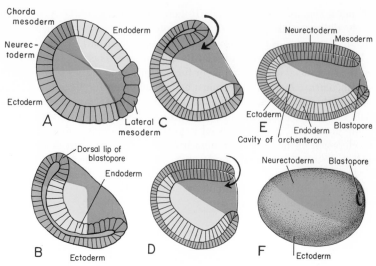

Fig. 56. Gastrulation in Amphioxus. *A* to *E*, Median sagittal sections showing successive stages. (The embryo has been rotated from the original egg position to that of the future adult, with head end at left, the former vegetal pole region postero-dorsal.) *A*, The endoderm cells are a flattened plate. In *B*, the endoderm has invaginated and the lateral mesoderm cells, originally widely separated from the notochordal materials, are moving upward to join them. In *C* this movement has been mainly accomplished, and the inturning dorsally of chorda materials (arrow) continues. *D* and *E*, Gastrula formation has been completed, and the embryo (particularly notochord and overlying neurectoderm) is elongating. *F*, Surface view of late gastrula, seen from the left. (After Hatschek, Cerfontaine, Conklin.) In this and subsequent figures in this chapter the following colors are used to distinguish germ layers: skin ectoderm, blue; neurectoderm, green; mesoderm, red; endoderm, yellow.

derm) and gastrulation takes place in a fashion basically similar. However, the presence of a large mass of yolk cells filling much of the interior of the blastula causes modification of the process. It is a physical impossibility for all of this yolky material of the vegetal hemisphere—the potential endoderm—to fold itself neatly within the mantle of cells formed from the animal portion of the egg, as is the case in Amphioxus. A furrow forms on the surface at a point corresponding to the dorsal lip of the Amphioxus blastopore. Into this pit stream cells from the exterior—at first, endoderm cells, mainly from the region below the furrow. Presently there roll inward from above and turn forward, cells destined to lie anterior to the notochord, followed by chorda tissue which places itself in the dorsal midline below the surface anterior to the blastopore. The shape of the blastopore continually changes throughout gastrulation, as the lip continues to be the site of active intucking of surface materials. At first mid-dorsal, it is added to on either side as mesodermal cells lateral to the notochord join in the inturning movement; finally mid-ventral mesodermal material is invaginated, and there is completed a circular blastopore. Correlated with these movements, there is a downward growth of the dorsal lip over the yolk, until on the surface there is visible only a small plug of yolk within a reduced blastopore.

Except that in some amphibians completion of infolding of mesoderm may be delayed beyond this point, we have now attained externally a gastrula comparable to that of Amphioxus. Externally, skin ectoderm is situated ventrally and anteriorly, and neural ectoderm occupies a posterodorsal oval area above the dor-

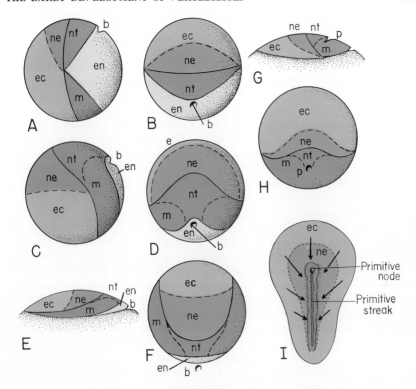

Fig. 57. Diagrams of the surface of blastulae of different types to show the presumptive fate of various regions in normal development. *A, B,* Left side and dorsal views of the blastula of Amphioxus (cf. Fig. 52, *E*). *C, D,* Similar views of an amphibian egg (cf. Fig. 53, *E*). In these figures the embryo has been rotated from the position in which the egg originally floated to that assumed by the gastrula; the shift is such that the vegetal pole region, originally ventral, has rotated posteriorly and upward to essentially the position from which the endoderm develops. The position at which the blastopore develops is arbitrarily indicated by an indentation. In *E, F,* and *G, H,* similar lateral and dorsal views are shown for the flattened blastula of telolecithal eggs of shark and bird. Note that in all forms the pattern of potential germ layer areas is similar; however, in the bird (an amniote) the blastopore is replaced, except for endoderm formation, by the primitive streak. *I,* Stage in bird development beyond *H;* the embryo is elongating, and mesoderm and neurectoderm are moving inward (as indicated by arrows) to the primitive streak. *b,* Position at which blastopore develops; *ec,* future skin ectoderm; *en,* endoderm; *m,* mesoderm; *ne,* neurectoderm; *nt,* notochordal region of mesoderm; *p,* position in which primitive node and streak make their appearance. (Data from Conklin, Vogt, Vandebroek, Pasteels.)

sal lip of the blastopore. Internally much of the endoderm is still in the form of a yolky mass of cells, but this has begun to outline an archenteron. This is of good size anteriorly, but posteriorly is a narrow tube. As in Amphioxus, the archenteron is at first roofed by the chorda and lateral mesodermal tissues. Presently the notochord—crucially important for induction of the neural tube above it—develops its distinctive structure along the mid-dorsal line; the mesoderm turns outward laterally, and the endoderm grows upward to complete the definitive gut roof. Mesodermal formation here—and, indeed, in all true vertebrates—differs

markedly from the pattern seen in Amphioxus. Never is there any pouch formation. Instead, the mesoderm pushes outward as a continuous sheet on either side
of the notochord, to grow downward between ectoderm and endoderm. Only later
do celomic cavities appear in the mesoderm, and (except in cyclostomes) only the
dorsal part of the mesodermal sheets develop a segmental pattern.

Elasmobranchs.   Obviously the geometry of movements of tissues in gastrulation must be of a different pattern in a telolecithal egg from those so far discussed, for we are dealing with a flattened blastodisc, not a spherical blastula;
the processes are, nevertheless, basically the same. Major events in more primitive modes of gastrulation are the placing in position of endoderm and mesoderm
—notably chorda tissues—by inturning at the lips of the blastopore. But where
are the blastopore lips to form on a flat disc? The most reasonable answer is that
they should be at the margins of the plate, and that the equivalent of the dorsal
lip should be the posterior end of the prospective embryo.

The surface of the blastodisc is found to be laid out in a pattern of potential
germ layers arranged in a fashion similar to that seen on the surface of an amphibian egg (Fig. 57, *E, F*). At one margin is an area of prospective endoderm
and, adjacent to it, the mesodermal area which is to form the notochord. Here
then is the region corresponding to the dorsal blastopore lip. At this point (Fig.
59), endoderm tissue rolls inward and then forward over the surface of the yolk
to underlie the central disc surface, to be followed presently by the chorda and
lateral mesoderm; these latter tissues separate from the endoderm to assume their
definitive position between ectodermal and endodermal layers.

The early elasmobranch embryo resulting from the processes just described
has attained the essential structure of an amphibian gastrula: an outer surface
composed of skin ectoderm and neurectoderm, an inner surface of endoderm and,
between, mesodermal tissues with a median band of chorda tissue. But because
of the presence of the great yolk mass beneath, the topography is radically different. Not until much later in development do the embryo germ layers completely
surround the yolk. Instead, they are at first merely spread out over its upper surface. The embryo is, so to speak, unbuttoned ventrally.

This infolding of tissues posteriorly corresponds only to the activities seen
at the dorsal lip of the blastopore of such a form as an amphibian. What are the
elasmobranch equivalents of the lateral and ventral lips of the blastopore of more
simple types, which function in infolding of further mesodermal and endodermal
materials and, finally, cover over the yolk of the vegetal pole? Their equivalents
are the margins of the blastoderm disc, curving forward on either side from the
dorsal lip homologue. The disc gradually expands over the yolk, and eventually
covers it (Fig. 71, *D*). As its ectodermal surface progresses to form a yolk sac,
there continually differentiates at the disc margins endoderm to form an internal
covering over the yolk and, between inner and outer layers, mesodermal components in which form blood vessels to carry food materials inward from yolk to
embryo.

Reptiles and Birds (Figs. 60, 61, 62, 72).   The ancestral amniotes, like the
sharks, developed a large-yolked egg and met similar problems regarding gastrulation. But the development of a telolecithal egg took place independently in the
two groups, and the solutions reached were different in nature. As seen today in
the reptiles and birds, the amniote solution differs more radically from the primitive type than that of elasmobranchs. The cartilaginous fishes infold endodermal
and mesodermal tissues at the margin of the blastodisc, utilizing this marginal area

in the fashion of the blastopore lip. The amniotes use the disc margin to form ectoderm and endoderm, but formation of the mesoderm, as we shall see, takes place only in the central part of the area of embryo formation. Further, in the pattern of distribution of presumptive areas spread over the surface of the blastodisc (Fig. 57, *F, G*), no specific endodermal area can be demonstrated experimentally. The endoderm appears to be formed by delamination—by the splitting off of a layer of cells from the under surface of the blastodisc (although beginning most prominently at the posterior end of the future embryo, where invagination occurs in less specialized forms, Fig. 60, *A*). There is, however, an infolding of mesodermal tissues by means of a peculiarly modified representative of the original blastopore, the *primitive streak* (Fig. 57, *I*). This appears on the posterior part of the clear area of the expanding blastodisc and grows forward, to form, when completed, a longitudinal groove bounded by parallel ridges; at its front end there is a raised node of tissue, with a pit extending downward and forward beneath it. Observation and experiment show that the primitive streak is not a static topographic feature; it is a region of crucial activity in the formation of the embryo, possessed of part of the functions of its predecessor, the blastopore. The primitive streak is formed within the area of the blastodisc where the potential mesodermal tissues are situated. Medially into the ridges bounding the primitive streak there is a continued movement of mesodermal cells from either side; these cells immigrate downward along the central groove and then fan out laterally to interpose themselves in proper mesodermal position between outer and endodermal layers. The chordal tissue lies, to begin with, on the surface anterior to the primitive streak. It moves backward, turns down into the anterior end of the streak, and then pushes forward in the midline, beneath its original external position. Its cells here develop into a definitive notochord, which expands in length. It grows backward beneath the surface (where neural ectoderm has come into position). As it lengthens, the notochord incorporates into its substance material from the front end of the area at first occupied by the primitive streak, while on either side of it there occurs differentiation of mesodermal tissues. The primitive streak thus tends to be more and more restricted anteriorly. However, with continued lengthening of the blastodisc, it long continues active posteriorly as further mesodermal tissues roll down into place on either side to form the posterior part of the body (Fig. 72, *B, C*).

    Mammals. Gastrula formation in mammals is a unique process. In later stages the mammal embryo comes to be identical in all major respects with its amniote relatives, but until gastrulation is completed it is still quite atypical; it has not yet recovered, so to speak, from its initial vagaries. Methods of gastrulation vary among mammalian groups; described here (as in the case of cleavage) is that characteristic of higher primates.

    The blastula, as we have seen, consisted of an external trophoblast, which makes contact with the uterine tissues, and an inner cell mass. The first stage in further development is the appearance in the inner cell mass, above and below, of cavities which expand to leave between them a flat, two-layered plate of cells (Fig. 63, *C*). The upper cavity, lined with ectoderm, is that of the amnion; the lower is a yolk sac with an endodermal lining. The cavities and the materials lining them are parts of the amniote membrane system, to be described later; the flat two-layered plate between them is a blastodisc, in which the embryo is to arise. This appears to have the same pattern of potential germ layers as the blastodisc of a reptile or bird. The cells of the upper surface are those of the future skin

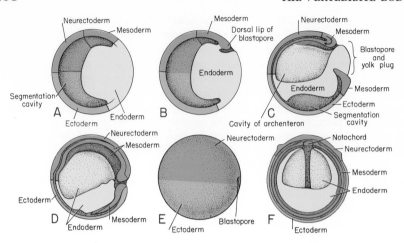

Fig. 58. Gastrulation in an amphibian type of egg. *A* to *D* are views comparable to *A* to *E* of Figure 56. The presence, however, of a large mass of yolk restricts invagination to the extent shown at *B*; the remainder of gastrulation is performed by further growth of the blastopore lips, as indicated for dorsal lip by arrow in *C*. *E*, Gastrula from left side. *F*, Transverse section, looking anteriorly. As can be seen from *C*, *D* and *F*, the mesoderm folds inward between ectoderm and endoderm (cf. Fig. 67, *A*, *B*, p. 117). (After Hamburger.)

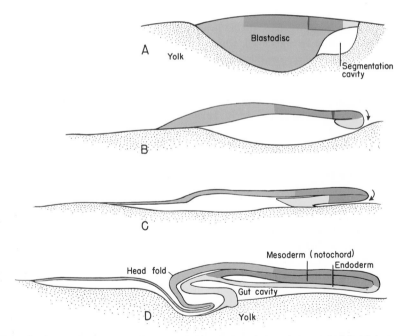

Fig. 59. Longitudinal sections of successive stages in gastrulation of an egg of telolecithal type, as seen in an elasmobranch. Only the disc of the blastula and the neighboring part of the yolk are shown. Anterior end at left. *A*, Blastula (cf. Fig. 54, *E*); *B*, involution of endoderm at posterior end of disc, corresponding to blastopore; *C*, continued process of inturning of mesoderm; *D*, mesoderm separated from endoderm; gut cavity formed, open below, roofed by endoderm. (After Vandebroek.)

Fig. 60. Two successive longitudinal sections of bird embryos at successive stages to show gastrulation. *A*, Figure comparable to the shark, of Figure 59, *B*, but the endoderm is delaminating rather than involuting posteriorly to form a roof to the archenteron. *B*, Later stage, comparable to Figure 57, *I*; from the primitive pit backward, cells are turning down inward from the surface (in the plane of the paper) and rolling laterally to form typical mesoderm, and are moving forward from the pit to form the notochord ("head process").

Fig. 61. A cross section of the primitive streak at the stage shown in Figures 57, *I* and 60, *B*. Mesoderm, as indicated by arrows, is rolling medially, downward in the primitive streak, and then outward laterally on either side; above, the presumptive neural ectoderm is moving inward toward the midline. (After R. Bellairs, in Marshall, Biology and Comparative Physiology of Birds, Academic Press.)

ectoderm, neurectoderm, and mesoderm, both chordal and lateral. Its under surface, facing the yolk sac, is endoderm, formed here, as in reptiles and birds without benefit of blastopore or inrolling of cells. As in other amniotes, a primitive streak now arises on the blastodisc (Fig. 73, *A*, *B*); chordamesoderm and lateral mesoderm roll inward and downward along the course of the primitive streak to push forward and outward below, between ectoderm and endoderm, just as in birds and reptiles.

NEURAL TUBE AND MESODERM DEVELOPMENT

Neural Tube Formation. When gastrulation has been completed, with movements which place in proper position the various major tissues of the body—neurectoderm, chordamesoderm, and lateral mesoderm in addition to skin ectoderm and endoderm—there begin processes of organ formation. Early stages in structural development bring the embryo to a stage termed the *neurula*.

Prominent on the outer surface is the formation of a neural tube; stimulus for its formation is the presence of chordamesodermal tissues beneath this area of the ectoderm. In Amphioxus the potential neurectoderm occupies a large oval area on the dorsal and posterior surface of the gastrula (Fig. 56, *E, F,* p. 104). We presently find on either side a folding upward of tissue at the junction of the future body ectoderm and neurectoderm areas (Fig. 65). In Amphioxus (not in true vertebrates) the two tissues separate as this fold forms. The ectodermal margins from right and left sides grow over the neural region, beginning posteriorly, and finally meet to form a complete layer of "skin" over the top of the body. Beneath this layer the lateral margins of the neurectoderm sheet gradually roll upward, meet, and form a circular tube—the neural tube (Figs. 65, *F;* 66). The tube in Amphioxus first closes midway of its length; the process gradually progresses both forward and backward. For some time the anterior end still opens to the surface as a *neuropore*. More curious is the situation at the posterior end of the canal. Here the folds cover over the blastopore (Fig. 66). This remains open, but now opens, not onto the surface, but into the posterior end of the neural tube. The primitive gut thus remains in connection with the surface; but the connection is indirect, running up into the neural canal and then forward to the neuropore. The connecting piece between gut and neural tube is termed the *neurenteric canal.* In later development, as the tail sprouts out, this canal closes, and neural and gut tubes become discrete structures.

Most vertebrates show a type of neurectoderm differentiation differing somewhat from that seen in Amphioxus (Figs. 62, *C, D;* 64; 70, *B;* 71, *B;* 72, *C*). The ectoderm tissues fold upward on either side as a *neural fold.* Eventually the two folds meet one another mid-dorsally; ectodermal and neural tissues in each fold separate and meet their "other numbers" from the opposite side, and skin surface and neural tube are jointly completed. The end result is much the same as in Amphioxus, although attained in different fashion. During the folding process, high crests are formed on either side, from which masses of cells are pinched off into the interior. Most of these *neural crest* cells are destined to become part of the nervous tissues; but others, as noted in later chapters, have an exceedingly varied history. In the head region still other future nervous system elements and sensory structures may arise as *placodes*—thickenings of the embryonic ectoderm lateral to the neural tube region, which detach themselves from the under surface of the future skin.

Mesoderm Development.   The mesoderm forms the greater part of the bulk of the body. Except for the brain and spinal cord, the ectoderm forms little but the superficial portion of the skin. Except for a mass of liver and pancreas tissue, the endoderm forms little but a thin film of epithelium lining the gut and its outgrowths. Practically all the rest of the body is derived from the mesoderm —muscles, connective tissues, most of the skeleton, circulatory, urinary, and genital tissues. If comparison be made with a house, the ectoderm corresponds to the paint on the outside and the wiring system; the endoderm to the floor varnish, wall paper and perhaps the kitchen stove and stovepipes. All the rest—frame, plumbing, sheathing, flooring, even the floor boards, lath, and plaster—is comparable to the mesoderm derivatives.

We have here considered the notochord as part of the mesoderm, in a broad sense of that term. Many, however, would regard the chordamesoderm as a quite separate tissue; it certainly becomes distinct at a very early stage, as a long band of cells lying lengthwise along the roof of the archenteron. This rapidly separates from the sheets of mesoderm on either side and rounds up in section to gain its characteristic cylindric shape (Figs. 62, *C, D;* 65, *C–F;* 66; 69). It is much reduced in the adult of most vertebrates, but forms a center about which vertebral formation takes place. Exceedingly important is the fact that, as noted earlier, presence of the underlying notochordal tissue is responsible for the induction of the neural tube.

Apart from the notochord, the mesoderm forms in Amphioxus a paired series of segmentally arranged somites, which from the beginning contain a celomic cavity (Fig. 65). In true vertebrates, as we have seen, there is a marked modification of this pattern. There is at first no segmentation in the mesoderm, which pushes out on each side as a longitudinally continuous sheet between ectoderm and endoderm; nor does the mesoderm at first contain any cavities of celomic type. In mesolecithal eggs the mesoderm of either side grows as a hemicylinder, following the curve of the formed body wall downward and then inward to the ventral midline of the belly (Figs. 58, p. 108; 67, 69). In telolecithal eggs, where the body is at first spread out flat above the yolk mass (and in mammals where the same pattern is followed despite the absence of yolk), the mesoderm is spread out laterally as a flat plate (Fig. 62, p. 112) and continues beyond the region of the body proper to contribute to the development of the extra-embryonic membranes. In these latter types, we noted, the body is at first "unbuttoned" ventrally, so that it is only at a late stage that the mesoderm growths of the two sides gain contact ventrally, and the contours of the body (and those of the mesoderm within) come to resemble those of mesolecithal forms.

There presently appears, in all vertebrates, a differentiation, from the dorsal midline outward, of three divisions of the mesoderm, each extending the length of the trunk (in head and tail, mesoderm is more restricted in its development). Next to the neural tube and notochord the mesoderm thickens and subdivides on either side into a longitudinal row of cubical blocklike structures—the mesodermal somites (Figs. 62, *C, D;* 67; 69; 72, *C, D;* 73, *C*, pp. 117–120), comparable to the somites of Amphioxus. These are the first indications of true segmentation in the vertebrate body, and it appears that (apart from the independently derived serial arrangement of the gill structures) the segmentation seen in other vertebrate organs is basically due to the influence of the segmental arrangement of the mesodermal somites.

Within each somite there is generally, for a short time, a development of a small celomic cavity comparable to that which exists from the very first in Amphioxus. Soon differentiation appears within the somite, with a loss of its epithelial nature (Fig. 68). There is a great proliferation of cells from its ventral medial corner. These cells form an area of loose embryonic tissue which expands around the nerve cord and notochord and forms much of the axial skeletal structures, particularly the vertebrae and at least the proximal part of the ribs; in relation to this, the medial part of the somite is termed the *sclerotome*. The epithelial layer on the outer side of the somite disintegrates, and proliferates mesenchyme cells which appear to form part of the connective tissues of the skin; hence the name *dermatome* given to that part of the somite. After the loss of these two areas, medial and lateral, the remaining portion of the somite, termed the *myotome*, gradually differentiates and expands to form striated axial musculature, the history of which we shall follow in a later chapter.

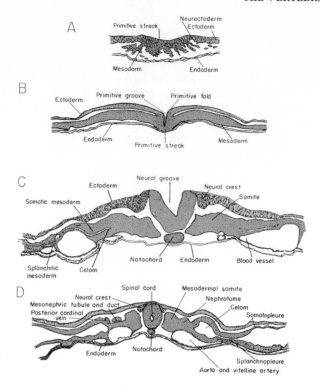

Fig. 62.   Cross sections of chick embryos to show successive stages in development of mesoderm and neural tube. *A*, Stage in which the inturning of mesoderm in the primitive streak has begun. *B*, The mesoderm has spread widely on either side between ectoderm and endoderm, but has not differentiated further (cf. Fig. 61). *C*, The celom has begun to appear, splitting the lateral part of the mesoderm into outer—somatic—and inner—splanchnic—parts. Centrally, the notochord has separated from the remainder of the mesoderm, and neural folds and crests are appearing on either side of a neural groove. *D*, The neural folds have closed to form a tube, the spinal cord. The mesoderm has divided into somites, nephrotomes, and a lateral plate in which a celom separates inner and outer layers of the body—splanchnopleure and somatopleure. (From Arey.)

Lateral or ventral to the somites a relatively small intermediate region of the mesoderm develops in the trunk into materials, the *nephrogenic tissues,* from which are derived the kidney tubules and their ducts, and the deeper tissues of the gonads as well. This region may exhibit a segmentation comparable to that of the somites adjacent to them and form *nephrotomes,* but frequently the kidney forming tissue develops for most or all of the length of the trunk as a continuous band (Fig. 67, *C*).

Beyond the nephrogenic region—curving ventrally in mesolecithal forms, but at first extending straight laterally in other types—is a great sheet of mesoderm termed the *lateral plate* (Figs. 67, *C;* 69). Apart from the cyclostomes there is never any segmentation in this plate. At first it is a solid sheet; later, however, it cleaves, and a *celomic cavity,* the cavity which in adult life surrounds most of the viscera, develops within it (Figs. 62, *C, D;* 69, p. 118). The mesoderm external to the celom, plus the adjacent ectoderm, is termed the *somatopleure;* the inner mesodermal layer plus endoderm is the *splanchnopleure.*

During much of embryonic development there exist, between the epithelia and tissue masses of the major organs, relatively empty spaces filled with fluid. Scattered through these spaces, however, we find a diffused network of star-shaped cells which are believed to have in many cases the properties of ameboid movement. These cells compose the *mesenchyme,* the embryonic connective tissue. Much of it is formed by proliferation from the somites, but in addition the lateral plate is a source of mesenchyme. These areas of origin are both from the mesoderm, and certainly most mesenchyme is of mesodermal origin. But the ectoderm

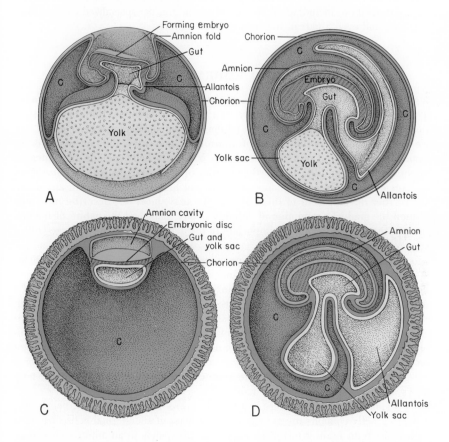

Fig. 63. *A, B,* Formation of embryonic membranes in reptile or bird. Anterior end at left. *A,* An early stage. The embryo has been lifted somewhat off the yolk, but gut cavity proper and yolk sac are broadly connected. Yolk sac incompletely formed; amnion folds and chorion incomplete; allantois barely indicated. *B.* Later stage; embryonic membranes formed and yolk already partially reduced. *C, D,* Comparable views of mammalian type of development as seen in primates. *C,* Stage beyond the blastula seen in Figure 55, *E.* The inner cell mass has split ventrally to produce a gut cavity—constituting the major act of gastrulation—and split dorsally to produce an amnion cavity. Between the two cavities the embryo forms a disc in which primitive streak formation occurs much as in a reptile or bird. Mesoderm has already appeared, and chorionic villi are establishing connections with the surrounding uterine wall. *D,* Later stage in mammalian development, corresponding to *B. c,* Celomic cavity.

in certain instances gives rise to materials of a mesenchyme-like nature, as does the neural crest; the endoderm, too, it seems, may produce tissues of a sort normally derived from mesenchyme; its production is not confined to one region or one germ layer alone.

Though the mesenchyme acts as an embryonic connective tissue, its activities are not confined to such an essentially passive and transient function. It is a most versatile material. It gives rise to the connective tissues of the adult. Vertebrate skeletal materials, both cartilage and bone, are of mesenchymal derivation; they are essentially modified and strengthened types of connective tissue. The mesenchyme gives rise to the circulatory system *in toto*—to the blood vessels and to the blood corpuscles as well. Much of the musculature of the body is of mesenchyme derivation, including all smooth musculature, the specialized cardiac musculature, and even a part of the striated musculature.

BODY FORM AND EMBRYONIC MEMBRANES

In earlier sections we have seen that development from the egg through cleavage and gastrulation takes place in a variety of fashions. But once gastrulation has occurred and mesodermal and neural components have been sorted out, we find that, much as the means of attaining it may vary, the end result is the same—the laying out of a rather uniform pattern of body regions and potential organ systems (Fig. 69). The further history of these systems will be considered in later chapters. In consequence we shall not here carry onward in any detail the further development of the embryo. We may, however, describe in simple fashion the gradual assumption of definitive body shape and the nature of the embryonic membranes which are important in the development of many large-yolked eggs.

Primitive Types.   In Amphioxus we left the embryo at the neurula stage as a rather short cylinder. The remainder of the developmental story is, superficially, mainly one of bodily elongation. Anteriorly, there is a development of a mouth opening and of a complex gill region; posteriorly, the neurenteric canal closes, and there buds out a tail in which develops a continuation of spinal cord and notochord and numerous mesodermal somites. (The mouth and gills of Amphioxus develop in a quite unique asymmetric fashion which, however, need not be considered here.)

In vertebrates with a moderate amount of yolk, such as amphibians, lampreys, and less specialized bony fishes (Fig. 70), the neurula is likewise essentially a spheroid. Dorsally, there is a rapidly growing nervous system; below this, a bulging belly contains the gut cavity and a mass of endodermal cells distended with yolk. With brain growth, the head region expands in an anterior direction; posteriorly, there is a major development of a tail beyond the anal region, much as in Amphioxus. Soon there is attained a body shape not far removed from that of the later fish or amphibian larva, except for a distended gut region which is gradually reduced as the yolk material is absorbed.

Cartilaginous Fishes.   Body form is slower of attainment in large-yolked eggs. In the elasmobranchs (Fig. 71) the neurula is little more than a flat sheet overlying a thick yolk mass, with the neural tube, above the notochord, marking out the "main line" of body organization. Anteriorly, the growing brain comes to extend forward over the yolk surface, with the ectoderm folded about it, and the anterior end of the digestive tract assumes a tubular form, separate from the yolk cavity. At the posterior end, too, the body lifts off the yolk as the tail buds out; only near the midlength of the body does the gut long remain connected with the yolk mass. Meanwhile the margins of the blastodisc continue to expand over the yolk and eventually completely enclose it in a *yolk sac,* the cavity of which is essentially an extra-embryonic part of the gut. As the blastodisc rim advances over the yolk, it continually differentiates to extend the ectodermal covering superficially, an entodermal sheet facing the yolk, and, between the two, mesoderm with forming blood vessels. The yolk is gradually digested and carried to the embryo by these vessels; the sac dwindles and is eventually resorbed. (In addition there may be, in viviparous elasmobranchs, provisions for supplying the uterine young with food materials from the mother.)

Reptiles and Birds.   The shelled amniote egg has evolved as a structure in which, in contrast to the egg of lower vertebrates, development can take place on land rather than in the water. Apart from the protection of the shell, we find that the embryo becomes surrounded by a series of membranes which afford it protection and aid its metabolic activities. These membranes include a yolk sac, amnion, chorion, and allantois (Fig. 63, *A, B,* p. 113).

There is in reptiles and birds a development of a yolk sac somewhat as in sharks. The endoderm, to begin with, is a flat sheet of cells capping the yolk; it gradually grows downward to enclose the yolk in a nearly complete sac, followed in its growth by mesoderm, spreading outward and developing vessels for yolk sac circulation. The connection of the sac with the growing embryo is eventually constricted to a stalk.

In sharks the ectoderm lying outside the region of the embryo grows downward around the yolk sac, the only structure external to the embryo proper. In amniotes the situation is more complicated; this extra-embryonic ectoderm (with accompanying mesoderm) does not directly envelop the yolk sac, but gives rise to other important membranes. Folds grow upward over the developing embryo to form a closed sac, the *amnion;* its liquid-filled cavity furnishes a miniature replica of the former aquatic environment for development of the embryo. Externally, the ectoderm sheet, with mesodermal reinforcement, expands to enclose almost the entire set of embryonic structures in a protective membrane, the *chorion.*

With the constriction of the yolk sac connection to a stalk, the remaining part of the gut cavity assumes a tubular form. However, there soon grows out ventrally from the posterior end of the gut a stalk of endoderm plus mesoderm. This rapidly expands into a large sac which underlies and is attached to the chorion over much of its extent. This is the *allantois.* The kidneys of the embryo begin to function at an early stage, and the expanding allantoic cavity becomes an embryonic bladder; indeed, the allantois seems to have arisen as a "precocious" embryonic development of a bladder such as is present in the adult amphibian but not notably developed in the embryo in that class. Much more important, however, in an embryo reptile or bird is the function of the allantois as a breathing organ. The combined chorionic and allantoic membranes operate as a lung surface for absorbing the oxygen which enters through the porous shell; blood vessels in the allantoic walls carry oxygen in to the embryo and carry outward carbon dioxide in exchange. With these membranes formed, the embryo takes shape and grows within the expanding cavity of the amnion (Fig. 63, *B*).

Mammals (Figs. 63, *C, D;* 73, 74, p. 120).   We have previously noted that there are many variants among mammals in early developmental processes. In

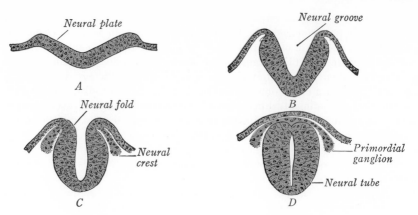

Fig. 64. Formation of the neural tube and crest as seen in a typical vertebrate (mammal); a series of transverse sections at successive embryonic stages. (From Arey.)

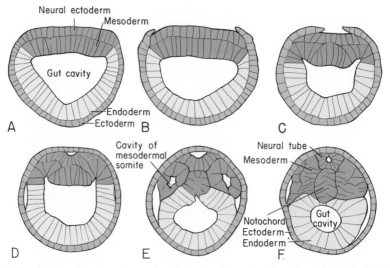

Fig. 65. A series of cross sections to show formation of mesodermal pouches and neural tube in Amphioxus. (Sections *E, F* somewhat diagrammatic, since the somites of the two sides are alternating in position.) (After Cerfontaine.)

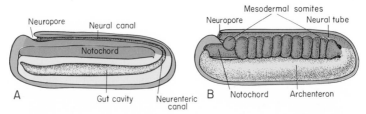

Fig. 66. Amphioxus embryos at a stage in which the neural tube has formed and mesoderm is differentiating. *A*, Sagittal section. *B*, Longitudinal view with skin ectoderm sectioned medially, but internal structures preserved intact. (After Cerfontaine and Conklin.)

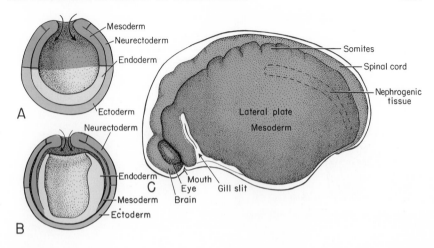

Fig. 67. Mesoderm formation in an amphibian. *A*, Section of a urodele gastrula, cut transversely through the blastopore, showing involution of mesoderm into the lateral walls of the archenteron. This is essentially similar to the situation in Amphioxus at the stage of Figure 56, *C* or *D*. *B*, Later stage; the mesoderm, instead of forming hollow pockets, as in Amphioxus (Fig. 65), attains its intermediate position by pushing downward and forward between ectoderm and endoderm. *C*, A later embryo of an amphibian, after the neural tube is formed, seen in side view; the skin has been removed. The mesoderm forms a long, continuous sheet on either side of the body. The dorsal part is beginning to subdivide into somites. The part of the mesoderm which will later form kidney tissue is indicated by broken lines. The lateral plate is being broken up anteriorly by the formation of gill clefts. (*A* and *B* after Hamburger; *C* after Adelman.)

primates, which we chose as a "sample," there appear, as a preliminary to gastrulation, cavities lying above and below the embryonic disc within the inner cell mass of the developing egg. These cavities are comparable to those of the amnion and yolk sac of reptiles and birds, but because of a precocious development of the trophoblast, the order of events is here quite different. The blastodisc, present between amniotic and yolk sac cavities, is connected posteriorly with the superficially placed trophoblast by a stalk of mesodermal cells. Along this stalk there pushes a gut outgrowth which expands beneath the trophoblast into an allantoic sac. Mesodermal tissues, in which develop blood vessels for the embryonic circulation, come to reinforce the endoderm in its extension as a yolk sac and in its allantoic development; mesoderm reinforces the ectoderm in formation of a stout amnion, and sheathes the trophoblast internally to form a chorion comparable to that of reptiles. As an end result we find that the mammal has, by a different route, arrived at the formation of a series of embryonic membranes highly comparable to that of its reptilian forebears.

There are, of course, notable differences; the yolk sac contains no yolk in any but the most primitive of mammals, and, a placenta, as noted below, is formed by the external membranes. As in reptiles and birds, the growing embryo gradually takes form, and in this process separates its body from the yolk sac (Fig. 74). Eventually its only connection with other structures is by a narrow ventral area, the *umbilical cord.* This cord is surrounded by the ectoderm of the amnion and contains stalks connecting embryo with yolk sac and allantois, together with mesodermal tissues and blood vessels associated with those structures.

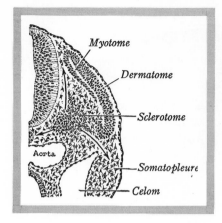

Fig. 68. Hemisection through a mammalian embryo to show the subdivision of the somite into myotome, dermatome, and sclerotome. Arrows show directions in which mesenchyme grows from sclerotome to form vertebra and rib. The small notochord is present above the aorta, and part of the gut wall is shown below that large vessel. (From Arey.)

Fig. 69. Stereogram of the front part of an embryo (particularly of a mesolecithal type) after partial differentiation of mesodermal components and nervous system. (After Waddington, Principles of Embryology, George Allen and Unwin.)

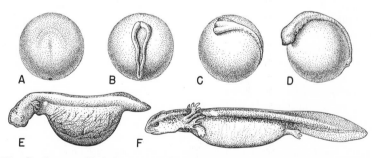

Fig. 70. Development of body form in a mesolecithal egg type—the urodele Necturus (the mud puppy). *A,* Late gastrula, seen from above, head end at top. *B,* Neural folds forming. *C,* View from left side, neural tube formed, brain bulging upward above sac partly filled with yolk. *D,* Head and trunk taking shape dorsally. *E, F,* Steps in reduction of yolk-filled belly sac and assumption of normal form. External gills and eye appear in *E,* limbs in *F.* (After Keibel.)

Fig. 71. Development of body form in a shark. *A* to *C* are dorsal views of the cellular disc from which the embryo forms; the underlying yolk is omitted in these figures. *A*, The embryonic disc at gastrulation; the endoderm is rolling under at the thickened posterior and lateral margins (cf. Fig. 59, *B*, p. 108). *B*, The disc is enlarging, and the neural folds are developing on the upper surface. *C*, The neural folds are closed except at the growing posterior end; the body of the embryo is lifting off the yolk, and head region and somites are visible. *D*, The yolk sac is completely formed and the embryo connected with it by a stalk; eyes and gill slits are visible. *E*, Nearly normal shape has developed except for retention of a relatively small yolk sac. (After Ziegler, Dean.)

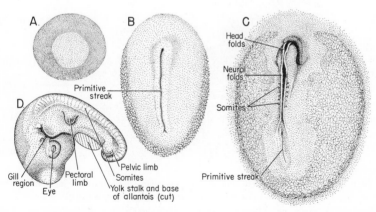

Fig. 72. Some stages in amniote development as seen in reptile or bird. *A*, Small germinal disc situated on the upper surface of the yolk. *B*, Formation of primitive streak and elongation of germ disc (cf. Figs. 57, *I*, 60, *B*, 61, and 62). *C*, The embryo is enlarging to cover more of yolk; the head region is lifting off the yolk surface; neural folds and somites are appearing; the primitive streak, now relatively small, is still active in formation of posterior part of body. *D*, Side view of a considerably later stage, comparable to Figure 63, *B*. The embryo is separated from the yolk except by a stalk (cut). Many head and body structures are formed, and limb buds are appearing. (*B* and *C* after Huettner.)

Fig. 73. A series of early human embryos, to illustrate stages in mammalian development. All three are dorsal views of the embryo, with the embryonic membranes cut away. *A*, Primitive streak stage, comparable to Figure 72, *B*, for a bird or reptile. *B*, Later stage in which the primitive streak is still active posteriorly, but the neural tube is forming more anteriorly. This stage is comparable to Figure 71, *C*, for the shark, not quite so advanced as Figure 72, *C*, for the bird. *C*, More advanced stage, with neural tube nearly completely closed and somite formation well advanced. (After Heuser, West, Corner.)

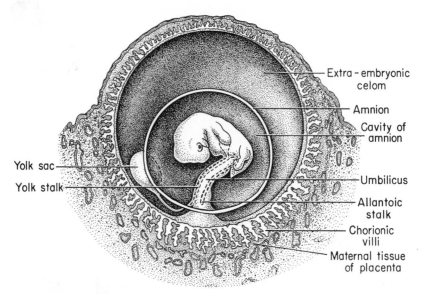

Fig. 74. Diagram to show the development of a mammalian embryo inside its membranes. The stage represented is one at which the embryo, though well formed, is still of small size.

A major difference between a typical mammal and its amniote relatives is the development of a *placenta*, through which the embryo receives food and oxygen from the mother and sends back waste materials in return. This characteristic mammalian structure is formed by an intimate union of the embryonic membranes with the surrounding maternal uterine tissues. A primary embryonic component of the placenta is the chorion, formed from the trophoblast plus the mesodermal tissues which come to reinforce it. On its outer surface there develop finger-like processes, which project into the maternal tissues. These are highly variable in size, disposition, and the fashion in which they interlock with the uterine walls. A number of different placental types, which need not concern us here, are found in the various mammalian groups.

The placenta increases in size and complexity during the growth of the embryo. It is richly supplied with blood vessels from both mother and embryo, and in it there is a constant exchange of materials between the two organisms. It is, however, important to note that the two blood streams are never in contact; they are everywhere separated by a membrane through which small molecules may pass readily, but never larger bodies such as blood proteins or blood corpuscles.

The chorion, however, is only part of the placental structure supplied by the embryo (and, in fact, may disappear during late stages of development). This membrane is not in direct communication with the embryo within; some means must be supplied through which the blood may freely flow from embryo to placenta and return. In most marsupials the yolk sac adheres to the inner surface of the chorion and its mesoderm develops blood vessels which serve this purpose; to some extent a yolk sac type of placenta persists in some higher mammal groups. In nearly all higher forms, however, the dominant structure is an allantoic placenta. In reptiles and birds the allantois extends far around the outer surface beneath the chorion and becomes closely attached to that structure, and allantoic blood vessels are important in those groups in carrying oxygen and carbon dioxide from surface to embryo, and vice versa. In most mammals the allantois is similarly developed beneath the chorion as an integral part of the placenta; its vessels here are vital as carriers of food materials as well as oxygen to the embryo and in carrying carbon dioxide and wastes back to the mother's blood stream.

Larvae. In amniotes and the sharklike fishes with large-yolked eggs, in which an abundant food supply is available to the embryo, development proceeds rather directly toward adult structure; the young, at birth, is essentially a sturdy little replica of the adult, soon capable, in a modest way of setting about its business of making a livelihood in the fashion of its elders. Not so in many water-dwelling lower vertebrates—lampreys, many bony fishes, amphibians. In these forms the supply of yolk available for embryonic growth is limited; the young, when hatched, is of tiny size. At such a stage it is in many cases unable to take up adult habits and is liable, because of its size, to dangers to which the adult is not subjected. Under such conditions it is to be expected that frequently the young of such forms assumes a mode of life quite different from that of the adult, often lives in a different environment, eats a different type of food and develops, temporarily, structures suited to its livelihood which may differ markedly from those of the adult. A *larval stage* is thus interjected into the life history. With growth, larval features are eventually lost and adult structures and habits assumed—the process of *metamorphosis* (in which thyroid gland activity plays an important part.) The tadpole stage of the frog or toad is a familiar larval form. Aquatic water-breathing larvae are found in the Urodela; most metamorphose into a somewhat more terrestrial gill-less adult stage, but some fail, partially or entirely to metamorphose—the common mud puppy, Necturus, of Midwest streams and the axolotl of Mexico are examples. Many teleosts have larval stages; an extreme type is the translucent, leaf-shaped larva of the eel, found in midocean, whose relationship to the adult was long unsuspected. The adult marine lamprey is a large predaceous form; the larva is a tiny food strainer, sessile in the mud of stream bottoms.

Regeneration. In the description of developmental processes given above it has been more or less tacitly assumed that organs and tissues, when finally differentiated, are permanent, that they are made once and for all. But this is, of course, far from true in many instances. In even the most normal of existences blood cells are constantly replaced; hairs, feathers, skin cells, teeth and other structures may be discarded and renewed. Further, accident and disease may cause destruction of essential tissues or organs. In such cases regeneration and reformation of lost parts often occur; development is thus not only characteristic of embryonic and youthful stages, but is to some degree a lifelong process.

Mammals and birds are not notable for regenerative powers, but even so we find, for example, that large epidermal areas may regenerate after damage; injured blood vessels and nerves (but not whole nerve cells) may redevelop, and destroyed liver tissues may be regrown. Lower tetrapods tend to have greater regenerative powers. In many lizards much of the tail is readily shed and as readily regrown (although never fully reattaining its former structure). Most labile of all vertebrates are the urodele amphibians, which exhibit remarkable regenerative powers; a complete limb may be redeveloped following amputation.

DEVELOPMENTAL MECHANICS

In the earlier sections of this chapter we have given a description of the orderly series of events which take place during the development of a vertebrate, but have said little as to the "why" of these occurrences.

The answer to this question is a major interest of embryologists today. The development of the individual from seemingly simple egg to complex adult is a miracle so common that we regard it as commonplace. When some accident occurs in the normally well-regulated process, we tend to be puzzled or disturbed over the abnormality that results. Rather, we should marvel that the processes of development normally proceed so effectively; that development takes place at all. Most of the major events in vertebrate embryology are well known, but the mechanisms of development are in many regards still a mystery, and the solution of the chemical and physical problems involved is the chief concern of modern embryology.

The external environment is, of course, influential in development. It is, for example, obvious that a typical anamniote egg must have for proper development water of appropriate salinity; that mammalian development depends upon the reception of proper nutritive materials through the placenta. The hereditary factors carried by the chromosomes can be considered basically responsible for the entire developmental story. But their influence is not, in general, direct; it can, for example, be proved in certain cases that the sperm nuclear material introducing half the hereditary factors for the new individual has little effect on the embryo until a relatively late stage in its development. The hereditary materials from the female are presumably responsible for the organization of the egg. When organized, however, the egg is essentially beyond their control; the nature and distribution of its cytoplasmic materials are the factors mainly responsible for development. Once development is "triggered" by the entrance of the sperm, growth and differentiation proceed inexorably toward their determined goal.

A certain degree of organization is already present in the ripe egg. We have noted the polarity associated with yolk distribution; and that in certain cases it can be shown that, despite its seemingly radial symmetry, the chordate egg already has an established median plane, with the consequent attainment of bilateral symmetry.

The successive cleavages of the egg appear to depend upon mechanical factors. For example: a cell tends to divide, as noted earlier, through the middle of its protoplasmic mass; the orientation of the plane of cleavage is correlated with the position of the mitotic spindle on which the chromosomes divide. As differentiation progresses, chemical and physical conditions in the various areas may be responsible for differences in the rate of cell division and consequent differences in the number or sizes of cells in these areas.

In some invertebrate groups the fate of the various cells into which the egg divides is determined at an early stage in cleavage, or even before cleavage occurs; each cell is destined to form one particular part of the adult and can form no other. In the vertebrates the pattern is much less rigid. For example, each of the two cells formed by the first cleavage normally forms half the body, but in various types, from Amphioxus to mammals, it has been found that either of the two, if separated from its fellow, can alter its normal destiny and form a complete embryo. However, every embryonic cell or region sooner or later loses its original broad capacities and becomes increasingly limited to a more and more narrow range of potentialities.

In the amphibians, in which studies of this sort have been most extensively carried out, this determination of the future fate of cell areas becomes marked during the process of gastrulation. We have noted, for example, that future skin ectoderm and neurectoderm areas can be marked out at the blastula stage (Fig. 57, p. 105). The cells of these areas, however, appear to be exactly the same in nature at this time, and their fates are as yet undetermined; if bits of tissue are exchanged between the two regions, they follow the fate of their new locations. The same holds true for an exchange at an early gastrula stage. But by the end of gastrulation these two areas are irrevocably determined as to their general fate; potential neural tissue will remain such if transplanted into the future skin area; potential skin will develop as skin even when included in the neural tube. Still later, narrower areas of potentiality may be determined. It is as if each cell passed along a series of ever-branching pathways; at each fork it must take one path or the other, and its future possible goals are constantly more and more narrowly restricted.

This progressive determination appears to be induced through a variety of influences. Cells may be influenced by their topographic position in a "field" in which specific processes are occurring, or differentiation may be evolved by the presence of adjacent tissues or structures. For example, the formation of the neural tube is induced by the presence of the chordamesoderm beneath it, and, at a later stage of development, the formation of an eye lens may be dependent in certain cases on the presence of an eye vescicle (cf. Chap. 15). The competence to respond to such chemical or physical influences may be qualified by the degree of histologic or chemical specialization already undergone by the cells or tissue concerned; the changes induced may be further histologic differentiation of the cells concerned, regional differentiation of special tissues, or the formation of definite organ structures.

ONTOGENY AND PHYLOGENY

Even in the early days of the scientific study of embryology, a century and more ago, it was noticed that animals vastly different as adults are similar in structure and appearance as embryos and that the embryos of "higher" vertebrates often exhibit conditions quite different from those of the adult, but similar to those seen in the adults of "lower" groups. From such observations came the idea of a biogenetic "law," which proclaimed that individual development—*ontogeny*—repeats the history of the race—*phylogeny;* that, in other words, an animal in its development climbs its own family tree, successive embryonic stages representing the adult stages of ancestral types.

This "law" was for decades an important factor in the stimulation of embryologic work and in the study of homology. But further consideration has shown that it is only a half truth. A mammalian embryo at an early stage is fishlike in many regards; it has, for example, prominent "gills" which are, of course, later reduced or modified. But there is actually little resemblance to an adult fish. The "gills" are the gill pouches seen in the fish embryo; they may fail to open to the surface as do the gill slits in the mature fish, and gill membranes never develop. Actually, it is the fish embryo, not the adult fish, which the mammalian embryo resembles. As evolution has progressed, there has been no progression ontogenetically of piling one adult stage on top of another. New forms, it would seem, have arisen by diverging at some point from old developmental sequences and thus arriving at new goals in the adult.

Development tends to be a conservative process, for departure from the old, tried and true methods will usually result in failure and death. In consequence, much of the developmental pattern in forms only remotely related to each other may be similar, and the mode of development may follow a devious course, with indications of structures which were once present in the adult of ancestors, but which now never reach maturity. Ontogeny repeats many important steps in the developmental pattern of ancestral forms; it is especially likely to repeat them when they are structurally or functionally necessary or useful in the derived type's own development.

But embryos as well as adults may be modified in relation to their environment, and such modifications may result in the creation of embryonic structures never seen in adults at any lower level. Larval types, as noted earlier, possess many features of this sort. Again, early amniotes developed a shelled egg with a large yolk mass as food and with embryonic membranes as devices for improved development; no amniote ancestor ever had, of course, an adult stage with a pendant yolk sac, nor was there ever an adult amniote ancestor enclosed in a "caul" —the amnion.

Although, in general, ancestral developmental patterns are conservatively followed or are at the most subject to gradual modifications, there may be drastic modifications of the pattern, and later embryonic stages may be reached by a different route from that followed by ancestral types—presumably in relation to powerful adaptive requirements. We have seen that large yolked amniotes have radically modified the older methods of gastrulation and endoderm formation, although reaching the same goal by another path. A further striking example is seen in the early development of the mammal. Other amniotes have a neat, "logical" method of forming the embryonic membranes. The mammal departs radically from its reptilian ancestors in the process of membrane formation, but arrives at the same end result.

THE GERM LAYERS

In our account of development we have laid emphasis upon the early differentiation and segregation of the major structural elements of which the adult body has been built. The theory of the germ layers was an early concept in embryology and a most useful and fruitful one. In the early embryo two layers, ectoderm and endoderm, already potentially determined in the egg, may be distinguished as comparable in general to the outer and inner layers which alone constitute the entire body of a coelenterate; soon there becomes distinct a third, intermediate, germ layer, the mesoderm, from which in vertebrates, as in all invertebrates above the coelenterate level, the greater part of the body substance is derived. We have in this chapter adhered to the germ layer concept, although emphasizing the early separation between body and neural portions of the ectoderm.

In the adult vertebrate, tissue components of organs and organ systems can for the most part be sorted out readily as regards their derivation from these germ layers. Details and exceptions will be found in later chapters; major derivatives are listed here.

From the body ectoderm: the superficial portion (epidermis) of the skin of the body surface together with its extensions into both ends of the digestive canal (mouth, cloacal region); epidermal skin structures, such as hairs, feathers, skin glands; sensory epithelia of nose and internal ear; eye lens.

From the neural ectoderm: the entire nervous system; the eye retina; and from the neural crest certain non-neural structures (gill cartilages, pigment cells).

From the mesoderm: connective and skeletal tissues; the musculature; the vascular system; most of the urinary and genital systems; the lining of the celomic cavities; the notochord.

From the endoderm: the lining of the major part of the digestive tract and the substance of organs (liver, pancreas) connected with it; much of the gill membranes of lower vertebrates and all the lining of the lung-breathing apparatus of higher forms; terminal parts of the urinary and reproductive tracts.

So generally do the patterns of origin of various adult tissues adhere to tabulations of this sort that beliefs as to the absolute specificity or origin of such tissues completely dominated the minds of many embryologists for many decades. In more recent times, however, further observation and experimental work have shattered such a faith. It is found, for example, that though most skeletal material arises in orthodox fashion from mesodermal mesenchyme, certain cartilages in the head and throat come from cells of the neural crest, otherwise mainly devoted to the development of nervous system structures; that the gill lining may come from either ectoderm or endoderm; that cell areas which normally produce nerve cord will, if transplanted, produce skin, and vice versa. There has been, in consequence, a tendency on the part of some to abandon the germ layer concept as meaningless. This, however, is a counsel of despair. What a cell becomes depends, as we have noted, on the potentialities present in it at any given stage of development and on the influences to which it is subjected. But in general we find that in normal development the embryonic cells and tissues do follow a consistent pattern of regional movement and arrangement of components. If nothing more, the germ layer terminology is useful as a description of the topography of development. It is, however, more than this. Experimental work has shown that, although in early stages there may be little differentiation between various regions of the embryonic germ layers, there is increasingly, in later stages, a limitation of capacities in different regions. The prospective fate in normal development of the germ layers and subsidiary areas of these layers is in general accord with the experimentally deduced story of their prospective potencies.

6

THE SKIN

Skin Functions. Forming a covering for the entire body, the *integument*—the skin with its accessory structures—is an organ system performing varied and important functions, many of which are protective. The tough "hide" of many vertebrates—often reinforced with dermal scales or bones—is a protection against mechanical injury and against the attack of predaceous enemies. The skin is a continuous unbroken line of defense against the invasion of bacteria and other micro-organisms. As a sheath of tissue isolating the internal structures from the exterior, the skin may ward off physical or chemical influences disturbing the inner economy. It may aid in regulation of the water content of the body, preventing too great a loss of water in marine or terrestrial vertebrates, too great an influx of water in fresh-water dwellers. Skin pigment prevents the intake of injurious amounts of light. The skin itself, in addition to auxiliary structures such as hair or feathers, insulates the body against too great a loss (or gain) of heat and plays a major part in temperature regulation in mammals.

The skin may further play an active physiologic role in the absorption or elimination of materials through moist skin membranes or glandular structures. Breathing—the absorption of oxygen and release of carbon dioxide—is a function of the skin in many forms, and in some vertebrates the skin is a major breathing organ. The skin may, through its glands, function as an accessory to the kidney in the elimination of wastes.

As the region of the body in immediate contact with the outer world, the skin would appear to have been the area of origin of sensory and nervous structures in ancestral metazoans. In the vertebrates the nervous tissues have tended to become a separate organ system withdrawn from the surface; but embryologically, we have seen, the nervous system still arises in continuity with the skin ectoderm, and the skin is still the seat of abundant sensory structures.

The skin is not a single structural entity, but consists of two parts, *epidermis* and *dermis,* closely united but differing greatly in their nature and origins. The epidermis is superficial in position and is an essentially cellular material, an epithelium derived from the ectoderm of the embryo; the deep-lying dermis has primarily a fibrous structure, with relatively few cells, and is derived from embryonic mesenchyme, mainly of mesodermal origin. The epidermis is relatively thin, the dermis usually much thicker. The epidermis gives rise to a host of differen-

127

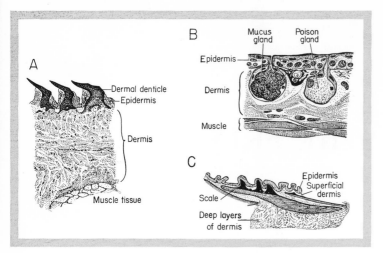

B   Mucus   Poison
    gland   gland

Epidermis

Dermis

Muscle

A

Dermal denticle
Epidermis

Dermis

Muscle tissue

C

Epidermis
Superficial
dermis

Scale

Deep layers
of dermis

Fig. 75. Sections of the skin of *A*, a shark; *B*, a salamander; *C*, a teleost. (After Rabl.)

tiated structures, such as hair, feathers, various glands; the dermis, on the other hand, has (except for bone and scale formation) a relatively simple and uniform composition.

Epidermis. This, the superficial body covering, is usually much the thinner of the two skin layers. Derived directly from the embryonic ectoderm, it forms a continuous epithelium over the entire body. It tends to give rise in higher groups to varied special skin structures (described in later sections).

In Amphioxus the epidermis is in the simplest possible condition; it consists merely of a single layer of columnar cells, without glandular elements; it is ciliated in the young but in the adult is covered by a thin film of cuticle which the cells have secreted. Except for the cyclostomes, the cuticle is absent in the adult vertebrate, and in every case the epidermis of true vertebrates is a stratified epithelium.

In fishes and in water-dwelling amphibians the epidermis (Fig. 75) remains in general a simple structure, apart from the presence of glandular elements. Blood vessels are seldom present. Pigment may be present in the vertebrate epidermis in the form of *melanin,* an organic compound which in various concentrations gives shades of brown and black. However, in lower vertebrates coloration is mainly due to color-bearing cells situated in the dermis (described later), and the melanin of the epidermis is derived, by cellular transfer, from pigment cells situated in the dermis.

In fishes and amphibians generally the entire thickness of the epidermis consists of "live" cells, containing a normal protoplasm. The superficial cells, however, include a certain amount—usually small—of *keratin,* a protein material abundant in the horn sheaths of cattle, fingernails, and like surface structures.* These outer cells tend to be lost by wear or injury, and there is a constant replacement from below. The basal layer of cells, usually more or less columnar in shape, is the vitally important part of the epidermis in any vertebrate. This is the "matrix" of the epidermis, the layer from which successive generations of cells are budded off to form the outer portions of the epithelium. Superficial dam-

---

* *Keratos* and *cornu* are, respectively, the Greek and Latin words for horn, whence are derived English words for this substance.

age to the epithelium is readily repaired. But if, through major injury, such as serious burns, a large area of this basal matrix is destroyed, a re-covering of the flesh by skin becomes difficult, if not impossible. The skin of a fish or water-dwelling amphibian is permeable to some degree, and in most modern amphibians, in default of any backing-up of the epidermis (as in fishes) by bone or dense connective tissue, this permeability is availed of to make the skin a major breathing organ, supplied by special blood vessels beneath the epidermis.

With the assumption of a definitely terrestrial life by certain of the amphibians and the amniotes, the nature of the epidermis is changed. In land dwellers, where water loss through the skin is a serious matter, the outer part of the epidermis becomes differentiated from that beneath. As the surface is approached, the layers of cells are successively flatter, the protoplasm becomes increasingly modified and lifeless and the cells are mainly filled with keratin. The surface of the skin is dry and covered by thin, "dead" cells. These may be rubbed off and lost piecemeal (dandruff is a familiar example) or shed seasonally in reptiles and amphibians.

The transition between the inner and outer portions may be gradual, as in amphibians, reptiles, and birds (in which last group, incidentally, keratin is mainly concentrated in the feather covering), but in mammals (Fig. 76) there is a sharp contrast between the lower zone of "live" cells, the *stratum germinativum,* and the flattened, deadened and cornified cells of the *stratum corneum.*

Keratin Skin Structures. Throughout the higher vertebrates keratin-filled epithelium develops into a variety of special structures. Simplest perhaps are thickenings or swellings of the stratum corneum, such as in the "warts" of toads. Such thickenings are frequently present on surfaces subject to wear, as the under surface of the feet. In mammals generally we find a characteristic arrangement of *foot pads* (Fig. 77, *A*), including, in five-toed types, a pair of pads on the proximal part of palm and sole, one on the base of "thumb" or big toe, a series between the bases of the other toes, and one on each toe tip. In higher primates, where the hand and foot grasp the tree limb in locomotion, we find palm and sole covered instead by a pattern of *friction ridges* (Fig. 77, *B*) which aid in obtaining a firm grip. These epidermal ridges, in the position of the pads of other groups, form complex series of loops and whorls. As is well known, the pattern of the fingertips is almost infinitely varied and affords a ready means of individual identification in man.

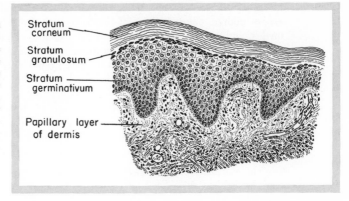

Fig. 76. Section of the skin of the human shoulder, × 125. In addition to the germinative layer and stratum corneum, there is (as here) in many areas of the skin in mammals an intermediate granular layer in the epidermis; in some situations there is further a transparent layer (stratum lucidum) between horny and granular levels. (After Maximow and Bloom.)

Stratum corneum

Stratum granulosum

Stratum germinativum

Papillary layer of dermis

Fig. 77. Palm surface of the manus of *A*, an insectivore; and *B*, a monkey (macaque). The insectivore shows a presumably primitive mammalian structure, with thick pads on either side at the proximal end of the palm (III¹, III²), pads between the bases of successive digits (II¹ to II⁴) and pads at the tip of each toe (I¹ to I⁵). In higher primates these pads are replaced by patterns of friction ridges. (After Whipple.)

In reptiles, thickening and hardening of the cornified epidermis results in the formation of *horny scales* or *scutes*. In crocodiles and most turtles they form a pattern of flat plates; in the latter (as the tortoise "shell" of commerce) they overlie the bony dermal skeleton of the back and belly. In lizards and snakes (Fig. 78) overlapping scales are commonly present, and these are in snakes highly developed as aids to locomotion, giving a "hold-fast" in the absence of limbs. Though such structures are termed scales, it cannot be too strongly emphasized that these horny epidermal scales of reptiles (and other amniotes) are not at all homologous with the bony dermal scales most characteristically developed in fishes.* A reptilian horny scale develops embryologically as an outpushing of the epidermis containing a papilla of mesodermal tissue; the broad upper surface of the papilla becomes the intensely cornified scale.

In mammals and birds the horny scales once present in their ancestors have for the most part disappeared. They persist, however, on the legs of birds, and are present on the legs and tails of a variety of mammals, notably certain rodents, insectivores, and marsupials. The pangolin of the Old World tropics is notable as a mammal which has redeveloped a complete body covering of large horny scales.

In many amniotes in which teeth are reduced or absent, the skin on the jaw margins may cornify as a substitute, producing a *bill* or *beak*. Such structures are, of course, characteristic of the birds as a group, are well developed in the turtles, and are found in a few mammals, such as the monotremes.

Claws, nails, and hoofs are keratinized epidermal structures tipping the digits of amniotes (Fig. 79). The claw is the basal type; nails and hoofs are mammalian modifications. A typical *claw* forms a protection for the top, sides, and tip of a terminal toe joint; an inverted V in cross section, the claw becomes increasingly narrow distally and curves downward beyond the tip of the toe. Beneath the claw (except for its projecting tip) there is a germinative layer, protected at its base by a fold of skin; from this matrix the keratinized claw epithelium continually grows outward over the dermis to be as continually worn away at the claw tip.

---

* In some lizards bony scales may be present as well as horny scales, the latter, of course, being more superficial in position (Fig. 78, *C*).

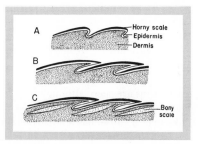

Fig. 78. Diagrammatic sections of reptile skin to show scale types. *A*, Lizard skin with simple, horny epidermal scales, gently overlapping; *B*, deeply overlapping horny scales of snake type; *C*, type of scale present in many lizards, with bony scale underlying horny element. (After Boas.)

On the under surface, distally, is a pad of softer, less cornified tissue, a *subunguis*, which effects a transition between claw and normal epidermis.

A *nail*, as developed in the arboreal, grasping type of locomotion of the primates, is essentially a broadened and flattened claw restricted to the upper surface of the finger or toe. In a mammal claw the germinative "nail bed" is confined to the proximal end of the structure (seen as a white area in the translucent human nail, for example). *Hoofs* are characteristic of the various ungulate mammals, which have undergone toe reduction and walk on the tips of the remaining digits. The original claw has shortened and broadened to become essentially a hemicylinder sheathing the toe tip; it is the curved or V-shaped distal end of the hoof which rests on the ground, the subunguis forming a pad within the curve of the hooftip.

Horns and hornlike structures are widespread in distribution, particularly among mammals. Though actual horn—i.e., keratin—is not always present in these structures, the general picture may be discussed here.

A true *horn* is seen in cattle and present in other members of the cattle family—sheep, goats, and antelopes. The core of the horn is a spike of bone arising from the skull. Sheathing and extending this, however, is a hollow cone of true horn substance, formed by keratinization of skin epidermis. Neither core nor sheath is ever shed, and it will be noted that these typical horns, variously curved, are never branched.

Fig. 79. Longitudinal sections and ventral views of terminal phalanges of mammals to show the build of claw, nail, and hoof. Toe phalanges, stippled; subunguis, fine stipple; epidermis of ventral surface of foot, hatched; epidermis of upper surface and horny material of claw, clear. *A*, Claw of carnivore type; *B*, a horse's hoof; *C*, a nail of a typical primate; *D*, a human nail. (After Boas.)

Although often called a horn, the *antler* of the deer is quite a different structure. When matured it consists solely of bone; only during growth is it covered by skin in the form of "velvet"; no actual horn substance is present. As further points of contrast we may note that an antler is usually branched, and is shed annually.

Still other types of "horns" are found among mammals, and comparable structures are seen, although less commonly, in reptiles and even in birds. Among mammals, for example, may be mentioned the horn of the prongbuck, which, like that of cattle, has a horn-sheathed bony core; but in contrast, the horny sheath is branched and is shed annually. The giraffe has short "horns" which are bony ossicles permanently covered by skin and hair. Again, the "horn" of a rhinoceros is formed entirely of keratinized epidermis, but this is a fused mass of long modified hairlike epidermal papillae, rather than a typical horn.

Feathers.　The possession of feathers is the distinguishing mark of the bird. They are primarily horny epidermal structures derived, it is believed, from reptilian scales, and perform two major functions in the avian economy. As a body covering they form an effective insulation, aiding in the maintenance of the high body temperature which is as characteristic of birds as of mammals. Bird flight is rendered possible through the development of large feathers which form the wing surface and the tail "rudder."

Three types of feathers may be distinguished (Fig. 80): the down feather, the contour feather, and the filoplume. As the most familiar (if the most complicated) type, *contour feathers* may be first described. These are the large feathers which sheathe the body surface and (as the term will be used here) include as well the feathers of the wing and tail. A mature feather is formed entirely from greatly modified and cornified epithelial cells. The basal portion of the feather is the *quill* or *calamus*, a hollow cylinder with its cavity more or less filled by a pithy material—the remains of mesodermal tissue which was present here during the development of the feather. At the base of the feather is a small opening into this cavity, an *inferior umbilicus*, and a similar *superior umbilicus* is present at the distal end of the quill. The quill lies in a *follicle*, a deep cylindric pit surrounded by a sheath of epidermal tissue, sunken into the dermis of the skin.

Beyond the quill lies the exposed and expanded portion of the feather, the *vane*. The axis is continued by the *shaft* or *rachis* (there is in some feathers a smaller, secondary axis at the plume base, an *aftershaft*). Unlike the quill, the shaft is a solid rather than a hollow structure, its interior filled with a sponge of horny, air-filled cells. Obliquely out from either side of the shaft extend the major shaft branches, *barbs*. These are so closely connected with one another as to appear to the naked eye to form a continuous sheet. Closer inspection, however, shows that the continuity of the feather surface is effected by tertiary elements, *barbules*, which arise in rows on either side of each barb. By a complicated system of hooks and notches each barbule interlocks with neighbors on the next barb. Any disruption of this arrangement can be repaired by the bird's preening action. In nonflying ostrich-like birds, where smooth feather contours are unnecessary for wing surfaces or for streamlining of the body, there is little development of barbule hooks, and the contour feathers may be fluffy plumes.

Basically similar, but simpler in build, are *down feathers* or *plumules*. These make an entire body covering for the chick and underlie the contour feathers over much of the body of the adult, forming the main insulation. A proximal quill region is present in these small feathers as in the contour type. Distally, however,

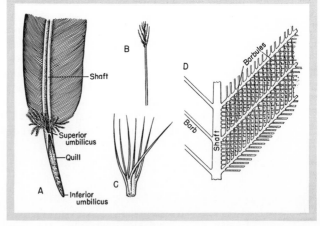

Fig. 80. Feathers. *A*, Proximal part of a contour feather; *B*, filoplume; *C*, down feather; *D*, diagram of part of a contour feather, to show interlocking arrangement of barbules. (After Gadow, Bütschli.)

beyond the quill termination, there is no shaft, but, instead, a spray of slender simple branches.

Filoplumes, "pinfeathers," are still simpler in appearance. These are small, hairlike feathers with a slender shaft continuing out from the body; they may terminate in a tiny tuft of barbs.

Much of the beauty of birds lies in their varied and attractive coloration. In part this is due to pigments present in the feathers. Dark colors may be due here, as in the mammal or bird epidermis, to pigment transferred from special color cells in the dermis (described later in this chapter); brighter hues are in part brought about by pigments obtained from the blood stream by the cells of the developing feather. However much of the color and the iridescent sheen of feathers are not attributable to pigments, but to the refraction of light from the horny feather substances.

Feathers are not, of course, uniformly distributed over the bird body. Contour feathers occur in definite feather tracts, *pterylae*. Most prominent is a long row of large feathers along the back of the "forearm" and "hand," the *remiges*, which form the wing surface; another group of large feathers, the *retrices*, forms the tail. Over a number of body areas no contour feathers arise, but the arrangement of the pterylae is such that the entire body is completely and smoothly ensheathed. In ratites neither plumules nor filoplumes are present.

In its initial stages the development of a feather is comparable to that of a reptilian scale (Fig. 81). Mesodermal tissues, including small blood vessels, gather beneath the site of the prospective feather to form a feather papilla. Above this the epidermis extends outward into a cone-shaped structure with an epithelial surface and a pulp-filled center.

From this point onward, development diverges from that of the horny reptilian scale. The papilla does not remain on the surface; instead, the epidermis surrounding it sinks inward to form the feather follicle, out of which the papilla grows in further development into a mature feather.

Taking up first the development of a down feather, we find that the papilla becomes a greatly elongated tubular structure. The living mesodermal tissues of the papilla, a nutritive pulp, extend the length of the tube during development. The epidermal surface gradually takes on a horny character. Proximally, in the future quill region, the epidermal tube is a simple cylinder. Distally, however, a thin outer layer separates as a conical sheath from the inner regions of the epithelium. The inner mass develops as a series of thickened longitudinal ridges. When feather growth is completed, the mesodermal tissue of the distal part of the feather is resorbed, the thin sheath breaks down, and the ridges are freed to become the spreading distal filaments of the down feather. Proximally, however, the tube remains intact as the quill sector. The mesodermal tissue filling it dries to a pith; the two umbilici of a mature feather are the original proximal and distal openings of this tube segment.

More complicated, but basically similar, is the development of a contour feather. As in a down plumule, the feather rudiment takes the form of an epi-

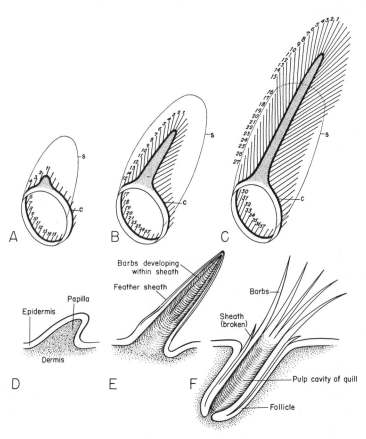

Fig. 81.   Feather development. *D, E, F,* Diagrammatic sections through successive stages in the development of a down feather. Development begins in the form of a mesodermal papilla; later the structure sinks into a follicle. An outer layer of the ectodermal covering separates as a thin feather sheath. The remainder of the ectoderm forms basally a hollow tube which becomes the quill. More distally it divides into a number of parallel columns. With rupture of the sheath these are freed as the barbs. *A, B, C,* Diagrams to show the development of a replacement contour feather; the basic pattern is comparable to that of a down feather. Feather growth begins at a basal ectodermal collar (*c*), from which develop, as in the down feather, parallel columns of tissue within the feather sheath (*s*). One exceptionally strong upgrowth (stippled) becomes the shaft; the parallel columns of tissue migrate successively (as shown by the numbering) on to this to become the barbs. (*A* to *C* from Lillie and Juhn.)

dermal cone, mesoderm-filled, in the distal part of which a surface layer separates as a thin sheath. One might expect the complicated branching structure of the mature feather to grow in treelike fashion. This is not at all the case, for the entire process of differentiation takes place within the feather sheath (Fig. 81, *A–C*). The future barbs arise, like those of a down feather, as parallel outgrowths from a basal "collar." At one point, however, an especially strong process grows out to form the shaft. The barbs gradually migrate onto this shaft as it develops, and further barbs form from the collar and continue the migratory process. At a later stage the barbules form from the barbs. When the feather is completely formed within the sheath, this ruptures, and the feather has simply to unroll to attain its mature state. Feathers, as we have said, are considered to be a modification and elaboration of the horny scales of the birds' reptilian ancestors. The early stages of development are in agreement with this conclusion, but the later phases of development and the adult structure are far different and much more complex.

Feather replacement continues throughout life. At the base of each follicle the papilla and its epidermal covering persist as a feather matrix; from these materials new feathers form. In many birds, particularly those of temperate and arctic regions, feather replacement is the seasonal phenomenon of *moulting*; in others there may be a gradual replacement throughout the year. At the base of contour feathers muscle fibers may be present. Sensory nerve endings at the feather base may register touch, and in night-flying birds, such as the owls, hairlike sensory feathers may be present on the face.

Hair. As an insulating device formed of keratinized epidermis, hair is a mammalian analogue to the avian feather. In other regards, however, the two structures are in contrast. As will be seen, they develop in different fashion, and, unlike a feather, a hair is a purely epidermal structure, without the mesodermal component seen within the feather during its development. Hairs, unlike feathers, are not modifications of horny scales, but are new structural elements of the skin. It is probable that hairs had developed before scales were lost by our reptilian forebears. In certain instances where horny scales are retained in mammals, hairs are found growing in definite patterns between the scales; even when (as usual) scales are absent, the same arrangement of hairs may persist (Fig. 82).

A typical hair (Fig. 83) includes two portions, the projecting *shaft*, and the *root*, which lies in a pit sunk, usually at a slant, within the dermis, termed the *hair follicle*. Both shaft and root consist (except at the very base) of essentially dead and heavily keratinized epidermal cells. At its base, however, the root expands into a hollow bulb. Beneath is a dermal *papilla* containing connective tissue and blood vessels. Through the latter come nutrient materials for the sustenance of the bulb cells and thus for the growth of the hair.

Fig. 82. Hair patterns of mammals to show presumed derivation from structures developed in the interstices between scales. *A*, Part of the scaly tail of a tree shrew, with the hair (represented by dots) in this position; *B*, skin of a marmoset, with the hairs arranged in a similar pattern despite the absence of scales. (After De Meijere.)

Epidermis

Dermal papillae
Nerve endings
Capillaries

Arrector pili m.

Sebaceous gland

Blood vessels

Hair root

Sweat gland

Epidermis

Dermis

Group of fat cells

Fig. 83.   Section of mammalian skin, to show particularly hair, glands and accessory structures.

In the bulb alone the hair includes typical "living" cells, with a normal protoplasmic content—the hair *matrix.* Growth and division of these cells results in the development of the hair. As cells are budded off distally in the bulb region and pushed outward by the development of further cells beneath, they become part of the root, and eventually of the shaft section of the hair, and gradually assume a "dead" keratinized structure as typical hair cells.

Within the hair two or three layers may be distinguished in section. Externally is a thin *cuticle,* consisting of a single layer of transparent cells which often overlap in scale-like fashion. Beneath the cuticle is the main substance of the hair, a dense horny material of modified cells containing a variable amount of pigment and air vacuoles. In stout hairs, a thin central area of shrunken cells and large air spaces may be distinguished; when present, this is considered a *medulla,* and the main mass of the hair substance termed a *cortex.* Lining the follicle is the hair sheath, which includes several layers.

Adjacent to the follicle and emptying its oily lubricating material into it, may be found a sebaceous gland (cf. p. 139). Each hair is further provided with a small *arrector pili muscle,* composed generally of smooth muscle fibers. Attached at one end to the superficial part of the dermis, the muscle slants inward to insert into the hair follicle deep down at the side toward which the hair inclines. Contraction of such a hair muscle (under the control of the "involuntary" autonomic nervous system) erects the hair (and by its pull on the skin causes "gooseflesh"). Of little avail in such a thinly haired form as man, this potentiality of raising and depressing the hair can bring about, in a thickly furred animal, marked changes in the insulating powers of the coat.

In the development of a hair in the mammalian embryo (Fig. 84) there is no formation of a mesoderm-filled papilla such as we find initially in feather development. Instead, we see the growth of a solid column of epidermal cells downward into the dermis. At the bottom of this column a thick mass of these epithelial cells develops as a hair germ; a hollowing of its base allows the development of a vascular papilla. Above, the column of epithelial cells which had descended from the surface hollows out to form the epithelial walls of the follicle, and growth of the hair upward from its germinal base takes place in this tube.

Once developed, a hair is not (any more than a feather) a permanent structure; throughout life most hairs are cast off and replaced, either as a gradual process or as a seasonal shedding of much or all of the entire coat. Resorption takes place at the bulb, and a new hair develops in the same follicle from the matrix cells surrounding the papilla.

Although hair may serve a variety of special functions, its primary use is as an insulating and thermal regulating material. It is perhaps difficult for us, as members of a mammal group in which hair is much reduced, to appreciate this fact fully; but it must be remembered that in mammals generally the hair forms a thick covering over almost the entire body. It is a furry coat, containing numerous "dead" air spaces which give it many of the attributes of commercial rockwool insulating material. In connection with its insulating qualities we may note the seasonal shedding of hair in mammals of temperate and arctic regions, whereby a thicker coat is grown for winter, a thinner one for milder summer weather.

All hairs contain pigment to some degree, and hair color may be independent of that of the skin. Melanin, taken over from dermal pigment cells, is the common substance, producing in various concentrations various shades of brown and black; a related pigment is responsible for reddish tinges. Air bubbles present in the hair will lighten the intensity of coloration; when abundant, air spaces will turn darker colors to gray and in the absence of pigment will produce a silvery white.

Loss of hair color with age in an animal is due to reduced pigmentation and to increase in the air content of the hair. Coat color may change notably with the seasons when the hair is shed and replaced, as is witnessed by the white win-

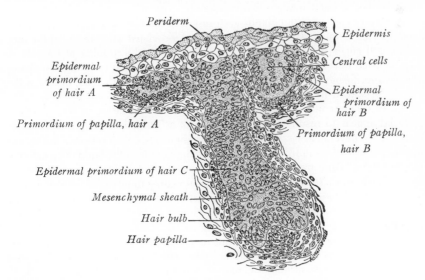

Fig. 84. Hair follicles from a 3-months human embryo, showing successive stages of development at *A*, *B*, and *C*. (From Arey.)

ter coats of various arctic animals, admirably adapted to concealment in the snowy landscape and contrasting sharply with the dark summer pelage of the same species.

Mammalian hair is, of course, highly variable in a number of regards. It varies from form to form, between one area of the body and another, from one season to another, from youth to old age. The hairy covering in many mammals is a thick fur. In others, such as the higher primates, which are primarily tropical forms, it is a much thinner and uneven coat. In whales, which depend on fat rather than hair for insulation against the cold of sea waters, it may be entirely absent in the adult, and sea cows are nearly hairless. An animal may have a double pelage, consisting of a sparse outer set of long coarse hairs and an insulating undercoat of much more numerous finer hairs. Hair is generally arranged in tracts, in which all hairs have a slope in the same direction; these directions appear to be related in various cases, to the manner in which the animal combs or scratches its pelage, or to the better shedding of water.

Specialized types of hair are found in many instances. All hairs have a nerve plexus at their base, but various mammals may develop *vibrissae*, special tactile organs such as the cat's "whiskers" on the face and—particularly in arboreal types—near the carpus and tarsus. Hairs which are rounded in cross section tend to be straight and erect, and if stoutly built may develop as bristles or protective spines as in hedgehog or porcupine. Hairs which have an oval or flattened section are more readily bent; their presence may result in the production of a curly or woolly covering.

Skin Glands.   Glandular structures are developed in the epidermis in every vertebrate class. In fishes they occur mainly as discrete, mucus-secreting cells widely distributed over the surface of the body, but serous cells, secreting a watery material, are common in elasmobranchs and are found in a few teleosts. The mucous cells are responsible for the slimy feel of fish skin and aid in insulation and in a sealing off of the body surface. In the hagfishes mucus-forming glands are abundant and it is said that a single one of these animals can turn a whole bucket of water into a jelly of slime.

In some cases formed glands are present in the fish skin, generally serving some special function. *Poison glands* are found associated with spines on the fins, tail, or gill cover in several sharks and chimaeras and a number of teleosts. A most unusual development in various deep sea fishes is that of luminous organs, *photophores*, formed by modified mucous glands (Fig. 85). In some instances the light is produced by the symbiotic presence of phosphorescent bacteria in the organ; in others complicated chemical processes of oxidation in the glandular material appear to result in the production of a "cold light." In many teleosts these organs develop accessories, including a pigment-backed reflector behind the light organ and a lens in front, giving the photophore much the build of an automobile headlight. They are not, however, to be considered as designed to illuminate the fish's pathway. Recognition, particularly at mating time, in the depths, may be important. Frightening enemies, on the one hand, and luring food on the other, may enter the picture (one deep sea angler fish dangles a phosphorescent lure, formed from the dorsal fin, above its gaping mouth).

In water-dwelling amphibians, mucus production persists. Here, however, we are dealing not with individual mucous cells, as in most fishes, but with formed *mucus glands*, although glands of a simple alveolar nature (Fig. 75, *B*, p. 128). A second type of gland is also frequently present in amphibians: the *granular glands* owe their name to the granulation of the protoplasm of the se-

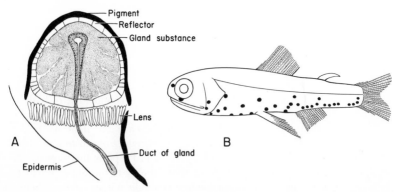

Fig. 85. *A*, Section through a light organ of a teleost (Cyclothone). Part of the duct leading in from the body surface is seen. *B*, Light organs of a small teleost (Myctophum). The organs are in black. (After Brauer.)

creting cells. The varied product is poisonous, ranging from mildly irritating substances to alkaloids which may be highly toxic. The common toad, for example, has a large gland of this type on either shoulder.

When the reptilian stage is reached, the primitive mucous cells have disappeared, and glands of any kind are rare in the hard dry skin. In birds, too, skin glands are rare; the only conspicuous gland is the *uropygial* or *preen gland*, a large, compound holocrine alveolar structure present in most birds on the back above the base of the tail. Its function appears to be the supplying of an oily "water-proofing" material used by the bird in preening its plumage.

In mammals, other gland types make their appearance, seemingly *de novo*. Wax-producing glands are developed within the mammalian ear pinna. Alveolar *sebaceous glands* typically are associated with hair follicles (Fig. 83), but may persist in regions where hair is absent; their oily secretion, produced through cell break-down, is a protection and lubricant for hair and skin. Perhaps derived from the sebaceous type are *scent glands* found in a variety of mammals, particularly in the anal region; they serve for recognition, particularly in mating. *Sweat glands* have a simple tubular structure; a much elongated tube coils in complicated fashion in the dermis (Oliver Wendell Holmes, Sr., who was an anatomy professor as well as author, compared them to fairies' intestines). The exocrine secretion of the sweat glands contains salt, urea, and other waste products. These structures thus act as accessory kidneys, and we are familiar with the fact that excessive sweating results in a considerable loss of salt from the body. Two types of sweat glands may be found. The smaller type, predominant in human skin, gives off a watery secretion; larger sweat glands, common in many mammal groups, produce a thicker, milky fluid. The evaporation of sweat on the skin surface is a cooling device important in mammalian temperature regulation. The excretion of sweat is aided by the contraction about the gland of small cells which function like smooth muscle but appear to be of ectodermal origin. In climbing forms, high development of sweat glands on palm and sole aids the grip. In carnivores, generally, sweat glands are much reduced in number; the panting of a dog utilizes salivary evaporation on the tongue as a substitute. Skin glands are reduced in many aquatic animals and are absent in whales and sirenians.

Still another mammalian gland type—one to which, in fact, the class owes its name—is that of the *mammary glands,* inactive in males but in females secreting a nourishing milk, of casein, lactose, fats, and salts, for the young. No antecedents for these are found in lower classes; it is thought, from their construction, that they are specialized derivatives of the sweat glands.

There is considerable variation in the structure of mammary glands. In monotremes there are simply two bundles of discrete glands in the abdominal wall which discharge a sticky secretion into depressions on the belly surface, to be licked off by the young. (They are functional, exceptionally, in both sexes.) In all higher mammalian groups there are well-formed mammae, the gland openings concentrated in projecting nipples or teats whence the fluid is sucked by the young. Active milk glands typically have the structure of clusters of alveoli, from each one of which ducts lead toward the surface. Properly the term nipple should be applied to types in which the ducts lead directly to the tip; in a teat (as in the familiar cow), the gland ducts open into a common storage cavity, whence a large duct leads to the surface. Embryonic development of these glands begins with the appearance of a pair of longitudinal swellings, *mammary ridges* (Fig. 86), running along the length of the trunk on either side. Concentration of tissue at specific points on the lines results in the eventual development of the mammary glands. They develop further in the female when sexual maturity is reached and become functional at the time of parturition, the development being under hormonal control. The number is generally correlated with the number of young produced at a birth; they range from a single pair up to half a dozen pairs or more. Their position is likewise variable. In marsupials they are generally enclosed within an abdominal pouch in which the young are carried after birth, each one tightly clamped to a nipple. In many ungulates the mammae are abdominal in position; in higher primates, on the other hand, they are in the pectoral region; forms with large litters (as pigs, many carnivores) usually develop two long rows of nipples.

Dermis. Thicker but less varied in structure than the epidermis is the deeper skin component, the dermis. Basically this consists, in most vertebrate

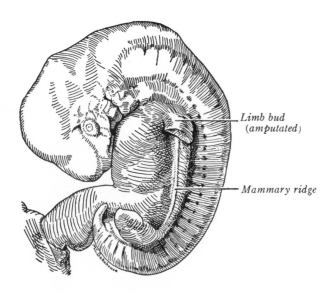

Limb bud (amputated)

Mammary ridge

Fig. 86. Mammalian embryo, to show mammary ridge or "milk line." (From Arey.)

groups, of a tightly felted fibrous mass of connective tissue, derived from embryonic mesenchyme (Fig. 83). It is this part of the skin of various animals which, after treatment, becomes commercial leather (a fact which the alternative name of *corium* for this layer implies). The dermis is an effective insulating material, and its flexible yet unyielding nature makes it a major defense against injury. The deeper part of the dermis is generally loose in texture, frequently containing fatty deposits; there is often a practically imperceptible transition to the connective tissues covering the muscles or other deeper organs. The skin may thus be closely bound to the underlying structures; in other cases the skin may be quite loose, as in birds, in which the dermis is thin.

In Amphioxus the dermis is, however, of a different (and perhaps more primitive) nature; it consists mainly of a layer of gelatinous material containing few fibers except on its inner and outer borders. In most bony fishes, too, we find a different kind of dermis from that described above. A certain amount of connective tissue is present, but in considerable measure it is replaced by mesenchyme derivatives of a more specialized sort in the form of bony dermal scales or plates (Fig. 75, *C*, p. 128). These structures, forming a defensive armor of a harder and stiffer type than that offered by the normal connective tissues, are part of the external skeleton, and as such are described in the chapter following. Except for the skull region, this dermal armor is much reduced or absent in most land vertebrates (turtles form a conspicuous exception), and it is likewise absent in the cyclostomes and sharklike fishes (except for the small, toothlike denticles embedded in the skin of the latter).

Offhand, one would assume that the more common condition of the dermis in modern vertebrates—that in which it is fibrous—is primitive and that the presence of bone in the dermis is secondary. The history of vertebrates shows, however, that the reverse is the case. The evidence is definite in the land vertebrates; tetrapods are descended from fishes in which the dermis was occupied by thick bony scales, and stages in the reduction of the bony armor to the modern fibrous condition of the skin are observed in the paleontologic record of early amphibians and reptiles. For lower fish groups, the evidence, although not absolutely conclusive, indicates that here too the ancestors had bony dermal scales, for the oldest vertebrates had an armored skin. A bone-filled dermis was, it would seem, the primitive vertebrate condition; the leathery type prevalent today has been arrived at as the result of dermal degeneration.

Though connective tissue fibers form the main bulk of the typical dermis, other materials are present here as well. A certain (though small) percentage of the fibers are of the elastic type. Cellular components are present among the fibers, notably fibroblasts (p. 147), by which the tissue is formed. The deeper layers of the dermis are a major locus for the development of fat tissues. Fat is an excellent insulating material; in whales, as the thick "blubber," it substitutes for the absent hair in this regard. Down into the dermis projects, in higher vertebrates, the basal portion of glands and of feather or hair follicles. Smooth muscle fibers may develop in the dermis, and striated muscle tissues, derived from underlying body muscles, may attach to the under surface of the skin. The sensitivity of the skin is due to the presence in the dermis (less commonly in the epidermis) of nerve fibers; some end freely, others—most notably in mammals—terminate in sensory corpuscles, often numerous, generally situated in the outer part of the dermal layer.

Circulatory vessels are, in general, abundant—lymphatics, small arteries and veins, and capillary networks of complicated pattern. The blood vessels supply nutriment not merely to the dermis, but also, by diffusion of materials through the tissues, to the overlying epidermal cells. In vertebrates with a thick epidermis, its under surface is irregular and may be deeply indented by an out-pushing of *dermal papillae* (cf. Fig. 76) which bring blood vessels in closer relation to the epidermis as well as effecting a closer union of dermis and epidermis. In forms with moist skins the presence of this rich vascular supply gives the possibility of exchange of materials with the surrounding medium. Notable is the utilization of the skin as an auxiliary breathing organ in many amphibians and some bony fishes; certain salamanders and eels, indeed, are able to supply their entire oxygen need in this way.

Temperature Regulation.   Proper functioning of the body in vertebrates can take place only over a restricted internal temperature range. In fishes, amphibians and reptiles internal temperature tends to vary with the external, with consequent climatic restriction of situations in which many of these forms can live. But even in such groups, notably reptiles, there is a tendency for regulation, partly perhaps by internal mechanisms of which we know little, partly by the animals taking advantage of environmental variations—as the way in which reptiles seek shade and sunlight, for example. Among mammals the internal temperature is highly irregular in the archaic monotremes, and somewhat variable in marsupials, edentates, and bats, but in mammals generally body temperatures are so regulated that the internal temperature varies little from a norm which is generally somewhat below 100° F.; in birds temperatures range between 100° F. and 105° F. Mammals and birds are said to have a *homoiothermous* condition, contrasted with the varying *poikilothermous* state of lower vertebrate groups. Regulation is under the control of a center in the hypothalamic region of the brain stem which is sensitive to heat and acts as a neural "thermostat." Internal temperature depends upon the amount of heat created by metabolic processes and upon the amount lost (or gained) by the body. Most of the heat lost in mammals (some 70 per cent in man) is lost through the skin, which is thus of the greatest importance in regulation. It may be noted that in a small animal the skin surface is relatively larger in proportion to body bulk than in a larger form; size, therefore, is a factor in heat conservation. In general the larger members of any mammalian group are those which live in colder climates, and hair tends to be reduced, as little needed for insulation, in such large mammals as elephants and rhinoceroses. On the other hand, such forms as shrews and small bats find it difficult, even with the best of fur, to maintain body temperatures without great expenditures of energy. In mammalian hibernation the hypothalamic thermostat ceases to function and body temperatures drop sharply.

The skin is to some extent a static insulating material in every vertebrate, but in birds and mammals the heat loss can be regulated by various devices. We have already noted that feathers and hair are adjustable insulators produced by the epidermis, and evaporation of liquid from the sweat glands produces a cooling effect. The dermis supplies an important factor in regulation in its abundant blood vessels. Under control of the autonomic nervous system, the skin arterioles can be dilated, the skin flushed, and heat lost rapidly; with constriction of the arterioles (and a blanched skin) a major saving in heat is effected. Color changes between light and dark shades aid in the limited heat control available to lower vertebrate classes.

Chromatophores. The functional "reasons" for the varied colors and color patterns of animals, and the relative importance in their development of camouflage, warning, mating, attraction, or even pure evolutionary "accident" have been warmly debated and need not be rehearsed here. In birds and mammals feathers and fur are mainly responsible for surface coloration. In lower vertebrate groups, however, skin color is due almost entirely to special color-bearing cells, the *chromatophores*, located in the outer part of the dermis (Fig. 87). The chromatophores contain numerous granular elements. They are typically stellate, with elongate cell processes, and are capable of amoeboid movement. Common types include (1) *melanophores,* with the dark brownish pigment melanin, (2) *lipophores,* with red to yellow carotenoid pigments, (3) *guanophores* (or *iridocytes*). The last contain not pigment, but crystals of an organic substance, guanine, which by reflection may alter the effect of the pigmented materials present. Nearly all the varied colorations seen in fishes, amphibians, and reptiles are due to chromatophores of these three types, present in varied numbers and in varied arrangements. Lying as they do in the dermis, the chromatophores were once regarded as derivatives of the embryonic mesenchyme. It is now known, however, that (curiously) chromatophores are derived as migrant cells from the neural crest.

The chromatophores are capable of producing striking color changes in a variety of fishes, amphibians, and reptiles (particularly lizards). The chameleon is proverbial in this regard, and the flounders are equally remarkable in the variety of color and color patterns which they are able to display. In part the color changes are attributable to shifts in the relative position of the chromatophore types in the skin, one or another becoming more broadly exposed at the dermal surface or more fully masked by neighboring cells. In the main, however, the color changes are due to changes in the distribution of the color granules within the individual cell. If the granules are dispersed throughout the cell, the effect is maximum; if they are concentrated in a tight cluster, little color appears.

Chromatophore changes may result from the direct stimulus of light or heat, but for the most part appear to be changes toward the color scheme of the environment, based on information reaching the brain through the eyes. The paths through which this stimulus reaches the chromatophores are varied. In sharks,

Fig. 87. Enlarged surface view of a piece of the skin of a flounder, seen by transmitted light, to show the three types of chromatophores present—pigmented melanophores, lipophores, and crystalline guanophores (or iridocytes). (After Norman.)

Black chromatophore
Yellow chromatophore
Iridocyte

amphibians and some reptiles the control is by hormones from the pituitary gland (cf. p. 559); in teleosts and some reptiles change is influenced by diffusion through the skin of chemical material given off by the tips of associated nerve fibers—a type of substance which has been termed a *neurohumor* (cf. pp. 502, 511). Again, in some teleosts and reptiles both types of action are effective.

In addition to their role in pigmentation of the dermis, the melanophores are responsible for dark pigments in the epidermis of birds and mammals and in feathers. The melanophore cell bodies remain in the dermis but send outward long slender processes which gain contact with cells in the epidermis or in developing feathers and transfer pigment particles to them.

7

SUPPORTING TISSUES— THE SKELETON

Most of the functionally "active" tissues of the body are epithelia or (as in the case of the central nervous system, liver or muscles) tissues derived from epithelia. But were the vertebrate body to be composed solely of epithelia and epithelial derivatives, it would be a flabby and amorphous mass. Materials are needed to back up and reinforce epithelia, to weld them together into a formed body, to protect this body and—particularly in nonaquatic forms—to give strength and support. Such materials are described in the present chapter. The notochord is a distinctive structure of this sort. Connective tissues are widespread and important. Most prominent in vertebrates are the cartilages and bones that compose the skeleton.

NOTOCHORD

The notochord is an ancient structure, present even in such lower chordates as Amphioxus and the tunicates. As has been seen, it is derived from cells which fold in at the dorsal lips of the blastopore or at the corresponding position at the anterior end of the primitive streak, and, pushing forward, come to lie beneath the neurectoderm. It soon differentiates, along the median axis, from adjacent regions of the mesoderm.

The notochord is always well developed in the embryo, and in many lower vertebrates it continues little changed throughout life. It is prominent in adult cyclostomes (where vertebrae are little developed) and there performs, as in Amphioxus, the function of preserving body shape during locomotion, acting as an anti-telescoping device (Figs. 17, 106, pp. 37, 169). Anteriorly in all vertebrate embryos it extends to the region just behind the hypophysis and infundibulum of the brain; posteriorly it extends to the terminus of the fleshy part of the tail. Its cells are soft and gelatinous; the notochord, however, is surrounded and made firm by a cylindric sheath and an external membrane, apparently of its own

145

making. In lower vertebrates with a large and persistent notochord this sheath is of considerable thickness; it renders the whole a relatively strong yet flexible structure, resembling a slender, elongate sausage.

In more advanced vertebrate groups the notochord is progressively replaced functionally by the central elements of the vertebrae, which develop around it and give greater strength, if lessened flexibility, to the back. As this replacement occurs, we find a correlated reduction of the adult notochord. In many fishes and in ancient fossil amphibians and reptiles the notochord is present in the adult as a continuous, unbroken structure running the length of the body. It is, however, generally greatly restricted by the vertebrae; it may expand between successive vertebral centra, but constrict within each segment, so that its contours resemble those of a series of hour glasses set end to end. In most tetrapods even this tenuous connection between successive segments fails, and the notochord is represented in the adult only by gelatinous materials which may persist in intervertebral discs between successive centra of the vertebral column. In amniotes the notochord is still a large and prominent structure in early stages of the embryo; later, however, it ceases to grow and hence becomes relatively smaller and smaller.

CONNECTIVE TISSUES

Even in such lowly invertebrates as the coelenterates, which lack a true mesoderm, there is generally interposed between inner and outer layers an intermediate zone of more or less gelatinous material, sometimes fibrous, and containing sparsely distributed cells; this material aids in filling out the form of the body. Such materials are comparable in a sense to the mesenchyme of the vertebrate embryo. In the adult vertebrate the most direct products of the mesenchyme are the connective tissues, which form the "stuffing" of the body and reinforce the epithelia of many of the body organs. The simplest form of connective tissue is a loose, *areolar* type (Fig. 88). Much of it is a gelatinous protein ground substance. It contains a loose network of small branching *reticular fibers* and, more prominently, long and slender white *collagenous fibers*, flexible but inelastic structures which are formed by the spindle-shaped or stellate connective tissue

Fig. 88. Loose (areolar) connective tissues. (After Millard, King and Showers, Human Anatomy and Physiology.)

Fig. 89. Fatty (adipose) tissue under low magnification. Lobules of fat cells are separated from one another by partitions of fibrous connective tissue. (From Millard, King and Showers, Human Anatomy and Physiology.)

cells, the *fibroblasts;* each fiber is made up of a bundle of very small fibrils which are polypeptide chains. A more abundant form of connective tissue is a *compact* type, such as the dermis, in which there is a densely packed mass of interlacing fibers, producing a feltlike structure. Most connective tissues contain a small percentage of coarse, yellow *elastic fibers;* in some instances the elastic type of fiber is dominant, producing *elastic tissues. Tendons,* forming the attachment of many muscles, consist of parallel bundles of connective tissue fibers which at one end are tightly bound to the connective tissue of the muscle and at the other may be closely attached to cartilage or bone, into which the fibers may penetrate. Some actively moving tendons are, further, surrounded by a fibrous connective tissue sheath. Where tendons play over the surface of a bone a *bursa,* a liquid-filled sac, may be formed beneath the tendon by the connective tissues. *Ligaments* are comparable to tendons but unite skeletal elements; *fasciae* are sheets of connective tissue investing muscles or other objects. Fatty or *adipose* tissue (Fig. 89) is a variant of connective tissue most commonly developed beneath the skin or in mesenteric folds among the abdominal organs. Fat droplets form and flow together within modified mesenchyme cells to fill most of their distended volume. We may further note the presence in connective tissues of *mast cells,* irregularly oval in shape with deeply staining granules. They contain supplies of the anticoagulant heparin and the basic amine histamine, but their function is little understood. Still further, there may be found macrophages (histiocytes), which will be discussed in connection with the circulatory system (p. 415).

SKELETAL TISSUES

From a physiologic or biochemical point of view the skeleton is sometimes thought of as a relatively inert organ system. From a broad functional viewpoint, however, it is of the greatest importance. Evolved, in ontogeny and in phylogeny, from the connective tissues, or the mesenchyme which precedes them in the embryo, the hard skeletal structures are vital in welding together and protecting the softer organs and helping in support and maintenance of proper body form. Almost all the striated musculature attaches to the skeleton, which is hence the agent through which bodily movement is accomplished. Still further, the seemingly inert nature of bones and cartilages as viewed in a skeletal preparation is deceptive, for studies show that not only the cellular materials but the apparently "dead" matrix surrounding them are centers of continual biochemical action; and bones undergo constant remodeling throughout life, both internally and externally, in correlation with mechanical strains and stresses.

Cartilage.   Two skeletal tissues are characteristic of vertebrates—cartilage and bone. Although both are specialized derivatives of the connective tissues and arise from mesenchyme, they differ markedly in nature, in mode of origin, and (frequently) in position.

Typical *hyaline cartilage* (Fig. 90) is a flexible, rather elastic material, with a translucent, glasslike appearance. Its ground substance, or matrix, is mainly a sulfated polysaccharide which forms a firm gel; through this is spread a network of connective tissue fibers. Throughout are spaces, lacunae, containing cartilage cells, *chondrocytes;* except in some lower vertebrates or in early stages in formation in higher forms, these are typically rounded and without the branching processes characteristic of bone cells. They are isolated within the matrix which they have secreted. Blood vessels are absent except in very large cartilages; the nutriment supplied to the cells must thus reach them by diffusing through the ground substance. The outer surface of a cartilage is covered by a layer of dense, cell-containing connective tissue, the *perichondrium.*

There are numerous variants from ordinary, hyaline cartilage. In fishes there may be present a type of cartilage in which there is little matrix between the cells. At the opposite extreme, in animals such as sharks in which the adult skeleton is largely cartilaginous, there is a strong tendency for the development of *calcified cartilage.* A deposition of calcium salts in the matrix produces a relatively hard, brittle, and opaque substance superficially somewhat similar to bone; calcification prevents nutriment from reaching the enclosed cells, resulting in their death. Calcification precedes the replacement of cartilage by bone during the ossification of deep-lying bones. *Elastic cartilage* (seen characteristically in the ex-

Fig. 90.   Section through part of a cartilage (from the sternum of a rat). The surface layers (at the top) show a fibrous condition transitional to the perichondrium. (After Maximow.)

ternal ear of mammals) gains flexibility through the presence of many elastic fibers in the ground substance. *Fibrocartilage* is a form of material transitional between a dense connective tissue and cartilage, and is often present in the neighborhood of joints and the attachments of ligaments and tendons. *Mucous cartilage,* found in larval lampreys and to some degree in sharks, is relatively soft and gelatinous, with branching cells.

In cartilage formation the irregularly shaped mesenchyme cells round up, and develop between themselves the interstitial ground substance and fibers. At first closely packed, the cells tend to separate as more material is laid down. Frequent cell divisions are seen in growing cartilage; we may find cells grouped in pairs or quartets, indicating their origin by division from a single parent cell. A cartilage may grow by the addition of new materials to its outer surface, formed by cells derived from the perichondrium. But it is also capable of growth, particularly when newly formed, by internal expansion—a very important character of cartilage as contrasted with bone.

Cartilage is essentially an *internal* skeletal structure. With few exceptions (as the mammalian ear pinna) it is never present in the skin or near the surface of the body but is, rather, characteristic of deep-lying parts of the skeleton. It is always abundant in the embryo and young of vertebrates. In the higher groups of living vertebrates and in many of the older fossil types of lower vertebrates, however, the adult skeleton is in great measure bony, and cartilage is relatively reduced. Only in living lower groups—cyclostomes, Chondrichthyes and a few degenerate Osteichthyes—is cartilage the major skeletal material in the adult.

Cartilage is a deep tissue, an embryonic tissue, a relatively soft and pliable and readily expandable tissue.

Bone (Fig. 91). Bone is the dominant skeletal material of the adult in most vertebrate groups. Like cartilage, it is a derivative of the mesenchyme and consists of transformed mesenchyme cells enclosed in a ground substance, containing connective tissue fibers. The two materials differ, however, in numerous regards. The bone matrix rapidly becomes a hard, opaque, calcified material. Laid down in it are salts in which phosphate and carbonate are combined with calcium in complex fashion, forming the type of mineral termed apatite, the principal substance being calcium phosphate. (It may be noted that bones serve as a storage of calcium for other body needs.) Enclosed within the matrix are the bone cells—the *osteocytes*—which have secreted it. They differ markedly from cartilage cells, for they (and the lacunae in the bone in which they are situated) are irregular, star-shaped structures.* In early stages the bone cells have long branching processes which continue outward from the lacunae in all directions, in tiny *canaliculi* which reach neighboring bone cell spaces; later the protoplasmic processes disappear, but the canaliculi persist. In contrast with cartilage, bones are penetrated by blood vessels. The solid matrix of the bone is impervious to nutritive materials, and the cells receive sustenance by the transfer of food materials from the blood vessels via the canaliculi. The external surface of bone is covered (like that of a cartilage) by a layer of dense connective tissue, the *periosteum,* the deeper portion of which may, when required, furnish cells for additional bone formation.

Whereas a cartilage is generally rather uniform in appearance when seen in section, bones have a complicated internal structure. Many areas (particularly

---

* In many teleosts, particularly the advanced spiny-finned forms, cells may be lacking in the bony tissue.

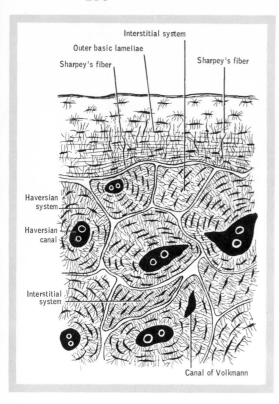

Fig. 91. Bone structure. A ground thin section through a mammalian metacarpal. Toward the top (outer) margin are parallel lamellae of bone formed from the periosteum; within are a number of haversian systems cut at various angles. The "interstitial system" includes remains of earlier formed bone layers not destroyed when the present haversian systems were created. A cementing substance binds the different bone areas together. "Volkmann's canals" carry blood vessels from the surface or bone marrow cavity to haversian systems. Sharpey's fibers are connective tissue fibers which run from the periosteum inward through the bone substance. (After Maximow and Bloom.)

the outer portions of bony elements) consist of *compact bone,* which forms a hard mass in which openings of microscopic size only are present. *Spongy* (*cancellous*) *bone,* generally present in the interior of large skeletal elements, contains a framework of bars of bony material, enough to preserve the shape and rigidity of the structure; but much of its area is occupied by vascular, fatty, or other tissues which may form a *bone marrow.* The development of this type of bone aids in lightening the skeleton, and the marrow itself has positive functions (fat storage, blood cell formation).

Much of the substance of any bone is laid down during development in the form of layers—*lamellae*—and a lamellar arrangement is common in much adult bone, particularly surface layers. However, bones are reworked throughout life by resorption of material and redeposition of new bone, so that the histologic pattern is often highly complicated. Large multinucleate cells—*osteoclasts*—are found in areas of resorption and are the destructive agents. Characteristic in bone remodeling is the usual development of *haversian systems,* consisting of small *haversian canals* containing blood vessels and nerves, which branch through the bone. Surrounding them are concentric cylinders of bone, the cells of which obtain their nutriment from the canal. The formation of haversian systems is preceded by the destruction of the bone materials present in a given region; tubular channels are formed, and bone is redeposited in concentric layers inside their walls.

BONE DEVELOPMENT.   Bone arises through the activity of mesenchyme cells termed *osteoblasts,* which form about themselves a thick matrix containing numerous fiber bundles. The rapid deposition of calcium salts in this intercellular material completes the formation of bone, and the osteoblasts, their main activity over, become the osteocytes.

Two radically different modes of bone formation—i.e., *ossification*—are to be seen in the embryos and young of vertebrates. The simpler of the two is the formation of *membrane bone* or *dermal bone* (Fig. 92), in which the bone forms directly from mesenchyme. Membrane bone formation is seen in the dermal bones formed in the skin. A group of mesenchyme cells in the dermis take on the properties of osteoblasts and lay down between them thin, irregular membranes or plates of dense fibrous interstitial substance in which bone salts are presently deposited. Such plates gradually expand at their margins and become thickened by the deposition of successive layers of additional bone on inner and outer surfaces. In bony fishes dermal bones are usually formed over nearly the whole of the body (including the mouth cavity), in the form of large plates anteriorly, and of bony scales over most of the trunk. In higher vertebrates the extent of dermal bone formation is much restricted, for bony scales tend to disappear, and in birds and mammals dermal bones are normally found only in the skull, jaws, and shoulder girdle. In adult form, platelike membrane bones usually consist of inner and outer layers of compact bone with an intervening reworked layer of spongy bone.

Quite different and much more complicated is the formation of *endochondral bone* (Figs. 93, 94). This is primarily the replacement of an embryonic

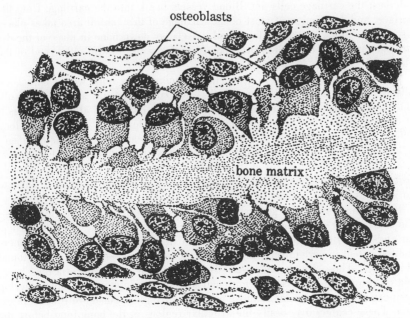

Fig. 92. Section through a dermal bone of the skull at an early stage of development. A thin sheet of bone matrix has already formed, surrounded by bone forming cells—osteoblasts—some of which will presently be enclosed, as osteocytes, in the growing bone. (From Windle, Textbook of Histology, McGraw-Hill Book Company.)

Fig. 93.   Section of a mammalian embryonic metapodial, in which ossification is taking place in the shaft (bone in black). Perichondral ossification is taking place superficially. At either end is normal cartilage; toward the center of the shaft the cartilage becomes "hypertrophic"; the cells are swollen and arranged in rows; calcification occurs, followed by their replacement with dermal bone.

cartilage by an adult bony structure. But, as will be seen below, actual replacement of cartilage by bone is only part of the process; a good fraction of the bone is really laid down directly in intramembranous fashion external to the embryonic cartilage.

In such typical internal structures as the long bones of the limbs of tetrapods the cartilage tends to assume the definitive form of the adult bone at an early stage and tiny size. Presently the cartilage begins to undergo modification and degeneration near the middle of its length; the cartilage cells swell and arrange themselves in longitudinal columns; the material between these columns calcifies; the cartilage cells die. Blood vessels break into the cartilage from the surface, and destruction of most of the cartilage of this central area takes place. Osteoblasts which enter with the blood vessels lay down bone in place of the destroyed cartilage. Ossification proceeds from the center toward either end of the element.

If the cartilage failed to grow, its replacement by bone would be accomplished in a short time, and a completely ossified bone of tiny size would result. But this does not occur, for the cartilage grows at either end about as fast as it is destroyed centrally. The cartilage, so to speak, leads the osteoblasts a long "stern chase"; the process of ossification does not catch up with the cartilages at either end of the element until adult size has been attained. With complete ossification, growth stops; for at their ends, internal skeletal elements are usually articulated with their neighbors, and bone cannot be readily added to the articular surfaces without damage to the joint areas.

In lower vertebrates, generally, internal bones ossify from a single center—the shaft region of a long bone, for example—and even in the adult the articular ends are often largely cartilaginous. But in mammals (and to a much more limited extent in certain reptiles) accessory ossifications—*epiphyses*—are found (Fig. 94).* These are characteristically developed at either end of a long bone, and on prominent processes for muscular attachment. In epiphyses there develop ossification centers similar to those of the shaft region, but more limited in extent. These centers may ossify the articular regions of the bone long before the growth of the shaft—the *diaphysis*—is completed and thus allow the element to

*The term "epiphysis" is sometimes applied in a broader sense, to include terminal cartilages without accessory ossifications.

Fig. 94. Ossification and growth in a long bone of a mammal. *A*, Cartilaginous stage. *B, C,* Deposit of spongy, endochondral bone (stippled) and compact, perichondral bone (black). *D,* Appearance of an epiphysis at either end. *E,* Appearance of the marrow cavity (sparse stipple) owing to resorption of endochondral bone. The growth of the bone is confined to the thin strips of actively growing cartilage between shaft and epiphyses. *F,* Union of epiphysis with shaft, leaving articular cartilages on end surfaces; enlargement of marrow cavity by resorption of periosteal bone, centrally, as deposition continues peripherally. (From Arey.)

function despite incomplete ossification. Between epiphysis and shaft there is a long-persistent band of cartilage. This would seem at first sight to be a relatively inert and functionless region. Actually, of course, it is highly important. This is a zone of growth; the cartilage here is continually growing, and as continually being replaced by bone from shaft and epiphysis. Once ossification eliminates this band of cartilage, shaft and epiphysis unite; bone growth is over, and definitive adult size has been attained.

Though much of the growth of an internal "cartilage bone" takes place by the replacement of cartilage, this is not, as one will readily see upon reflection, the whole story. When the center of the shaft of a long bone is first ossified, the bone has a small diameter. As the cartilage grows at either end, these ends gradually expand in width toward adult size; but the bone, if formed solely by internal replacement, would be shaped rather like an hour glass, with a constricted middle portion. With the result of rectifying this imperfection, we find that, in addition to internal replacement, cartilage bones have a major increment produced by the direct formation of bone on the surface of the cartilage as *perichondral bone,* formed in successive concentric layers rather after the fashion of membrane bone. These layers are thickest in the originally thin middle part of the shaft. This process of superficial addition of bony material may continue after the underlying shaft region has been ossified; at this stage the term *periosteal bone* rather than perichondral is more appropriate.

The process of endochondral bone formation in higher vertebrates was long believed to be an example of the ontogenetic recapitulation of phylogenetic history. The replacement of cartilage by bone in embryonic development was thought to repeat the phylogenetic story of the vertebrate skeleton, under the assumption that the cartilaginous condition found in the adult cyclostome or shark was a truly primitive one. However, the fossil evidence strongly suggests that this is not the case; that, on the contrary, the living lower vertebrates are skeletally degenerate and that cartilage in the adult is a retention of an embryonic condition.

The question may, however, be fairly asked: Why this roundabout way of forming bones if there is no phylogenetic story concerned?

The answer may be deduced from the fact that not all bones are preformed in cartilage. It is significant that the dermal elements, which lack that stage, are usually simple and platelike and are capable of free growth at every surface until adult size is reached, whereas most of the deeper elements, which are preformed in cartilage, have complicated articulations with their neighbors and important muscular attachments. The vertebrate skeleton at an early embryonic stage is an almost perfect if tiny model of that of the adult. If the internal elements, with their complicated articular relations, were formed directly in bone, growth to adult size would be impossible; for bone can grow only at its surface, and surface growth would disrupt the relations of the bone with surrounding structures. Some type of moldable material, capable of growth without disturbance of surface relations, is needed for the growth of deep-lying elements. Cartilage, with its capability of growth by internal expansion, is an ideal embryonic adaptation for this purpose. Except where degeneration has occurred—in various fishes and amphibians—bone is the normal adult skeletal material in a vertebrate, cartilage its indispensable embryonic auxiliary.

Joints.   Bones and cartilages are joined to one another by structures of varied types. In such cases as the bones of the skull, where one abuts directly against another, there is usually little possibility, or desirability, of movement. The connection between such elements—termed a *synarthrosis*—may be formed by thin intervening sheets of cartilage or connective tissue, the visible line of apposition being termed a *suture*. If the union is completely immovable, because of actual fusion of bone with bone, we speak of *ankylosis*.

A freely movable joint between adjacent elements is termed a *diarthrosis* (Fig. 95); the adjacent surfaces are typically covered by a film of cartilage even if the articulating elements are bony in major structure, and are bound together by stout connective tissues; frequently there is a liquid-filled joint cavity, surrounded by a *synovial membrane*.

Classification of Skeletal Elements.   The skeleton includes a wide variety of elements of varied form, structure, function, position, and embryonic origin, associated in variable combinations and showing major modifications

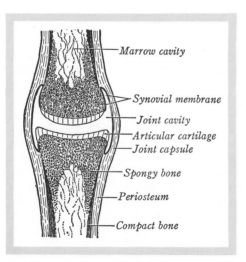

Marrow cavity

Synovial membrane

Joint cavity

Articular cartilage
Joint capsule

Spongy bone

Periosteum

Compact bone

Fig. 95.   A typical diarthrodial joint. (From Arey.)

from group to group. Classification of skeletal elements is difficult, and no classification is absolutely satisfactory. We here adopt the following scheme of major subdivision:

Dermal skeleton

A primary distinction may be made between the *dermal skeleton,* consisting of bony structures—plates and scales—developed in the skin and never preformed in cartilage, and the more deeply placed skeletal parts, the *endoskeleton,* in which the elements are preformed in cartilage (particularly in lower vertebrate groups) and may remain cartilaginous throughout life.

Within the class of endoskeletal elements, a distinction may be made between two categories of unequal size, the somatic and visceral groups (as noted in Chapter 9, the associated muscular system may be similarly subdivided). As the *visceral skeleton* we may classify the elements which lie between and operate the gill openings, and structures (such as the jaw cartilages and ear ossicles) derived from them. The *somatic skeleton* includes all the remaining internal structures. As further discussed in other sections, the gill region is distinctive as regards its musculature and nerve supply. Its skeleton is equally distinctive, and, as will be seen, its embryologic origin is radically different from that of most other skeletal elements. We are here dealing with structures associated with the theoretic "visceral animal" discussed in an earlier chapter on chordate history. The remaining skeletal structures are those of the theoretic "somatic animal." This somatic skeleton includes in its more primitive, axial portions the vertebrae, the ribs, and other related elements of the trunk and tail segments, and, anteriorly, the braincase, which forms a major element of the skull. These structures constitute the *axial skeleton.* The limb girdles and the elements of the free appendages, forming the *appendicular skeleton,* may be considered derivatives of the axial skeleton.

In certain instances we find that structural units of the adult skeleton contain elements derived from two or more categories. Thus, for example, the shoulder girdle of many vertebrates contains both dermal and endoskeletal components; the lower jaw of several vertebrate classes includes both visceral and dermal elements. Most complex of all is the skull, which in bony fishes and land vertebrates includes dermal, somatic, and visceral structures in its formation.

DERMAL SKELETON

Fishes. The skin over most of the body of many living vertebrates contains no hard skeletal parts; but dermal bony structures are usually present in the head region, at least, and the fossil evidence leads to the conclusion that ancestral vertebrates were completely ensheathed in a bony armor. Although there may be a superficial covering of other hard skeletal materials, the major component of skin plates and scales is bone, formed directly in membrane. Body armor of this sort was present in the most ancient vertebrates, the jawless ostracoderms, was present over part or all of the body of the extinct placoderms, most primitive of jawed vertebrates, and is present in varied and sometimes reduced form in nearly all of the great group of Osteichthyes. Armor is absent in the living lampreys and present only as skin denticles in the sharklike fishes. This condition, once thought to be primitive, now seems quite surely to be a degenerate one.

In the ostracoderms and many placoderms a pattern of microscopic structure in scales and plates was present which, with variations, persisted into the primitive bony fish stage (Fig. 96). The inner layer consisted of lamellae of compact bone. Above this was a layer of spongy bone, with numerous spaces presumably containing blood vessels. Toward the outside was a further compact layer. The surface of the plates and scales was frequently ornamented with tubercles or ridges. The surface of each "denticle" and, indeed, of the whole plate or scale, was covered with a hard shiny material resembling the enamel of a tooth. Beneath was a "pulp" of blood vessels. Between enamel and pulp cavity, the substance of the tubercle was formed of a bonelike material. In some presumably very primitive cases this appears to have been typical bone, with starshaped bone cell spaces. In more advanced types, however, the cells had retreated to the pulp cavity, but tiny canals, presumably filled in life by cell processes, penetrated the bony material—the structure now resembling the dentine of a tooth. It seems clear that this primitive armor was of a type from which the scales of more modern fishes have been derived, and that the surface tubercles were structures from which were evolved both shark dermal denticles and true teeth.

In the Osteichthyes the body is generally covered with an overlapping series of scales arranged in diagonal rows and either rectangular in shape or with a curved external border. Among early bony fishes two types of plate and scale structures were present. In primitive sarcopterygians the *cosmoid* scale (Fig. 96,

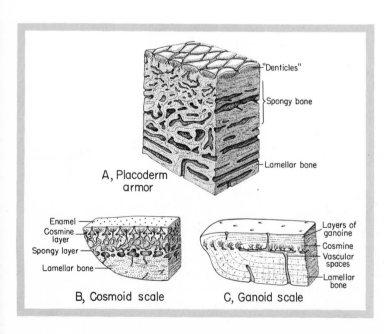

Fig. 96. The structure of dermal plates and scales in primitive vertebrates. *A*, Devonian placoderm. *B*, Primitive crossopterygian with a cosmoid scale. *C*, A Paleozoic ray-finned fish with a ganoid scale. (After Kiaer, Goodrich.)

B) was characteristic. The general arrangement of the three layers was that just described, but the main substance of the tubercles was not typical dentine, but a variant termed *cosmine*, differing in that the tiny canals penetrating it from the pulp cavity were branching structures rather than simple tubes. Scales of this sort were characteristic of the typical crossopterygians and the very earliest lungfish. In coelacanths, however, the scales became simpler in nature and in the lungfishes are reduced to a rather fibrous and leathery type of bony structure— true cosmoid scales are nonexistent in living animals.

In primitive actinopterygians there was present quite a different sort of scale, the *ganoid* type (Fig. 96, *C*). This differs from the cosmoid type in that, instead of a single layer of enamel above the cosmine, there is laid down, during scale growth, layer after layer of a shiny enamel-like material termed *ganoine*, and, correspondingly, successive layers of compact bone are formed on the lower surface of the scale. Hosts of Paleozoic and early Mesozoic ray-finned fishes, the palaeoniscoids, had scales of this type. However, actinopterygians, like the sarcopterygians, have tended to simplify scale structure. Ganoid scales are present today only in Polypterus and the gar pikes, and even in the latter are in somewhat simplified form, for the cosmine is lost; in most Mesozoic actinopterygians the ganoine was reduced or lost, and the cosmine layer as well. By the time the teleosts were developed there remained only the basal layer of the originally thick armor, in the form of relatively thin, pliable scales, formed of a thin sheet of bonelike material (but usually lacking cells) and an underlying fibrous layer (Fig. 75, *C*, p. 128); even these reduced structures may be lost, leaving (as in catfish) a naked skin over the trunk and tail. Teleost scales are typically translucent and overlapping—imbricating. The "free" margins may be smoothly rounded—the "cyloid" type—or this margin may be frayed out—the "ctenoid" scale. The distinction between these two teleost scale types was once thought to be important for classification, but is now seen to be of little significance. Teleost scales frequently show annual growth rings—of practical value in determining the age of a fish in life history studies.

No dermal scales or bones are preserved in the degenerate lampreys and hagfishes. In the Chondrichthyes there are in some instances fin-spines of a dentine-like material, but the skin is otherwise naked except for the *dermal denticles*, or placoid "scales" (Figs. 75, *A*, p. 128; 97). These are small isolated structures, often conical in form, which resemble simple teeth (cf. Fig. 178, p. 256). The base is bonelike in substance and contains a pulp cavity; a mass of dentine forms the bulk of the tubercle; there is a shiny surface film of enamel-like material which is, however, a hard external layer of dentine—*vitrodentine*. It was formerly assumed that the presence of these dermal denticles in sharks marked

Fig. 97. Shark dermal denticles. *A*, Section through a denticle; *B*, Side and surface views of denticle. Abbreviations: *D*, dentine; *D'*, dermis; *E*, hard, enamel-like surface of denticle—vitrodentine; *E'*, epidermis; *PC*, pulp cavity. (From Dean.)

the first phylogenetic appearance of dermal armor and that bony scales and plates appeared later in world history as the result of the fusion of such denticles. It now seems, however, that the reverse is the case. Dermal denticles are the last remnants of an ancestral armor; the bone proper has, so to speak, melted away, leaving only its superficial tubercles.

The anterior portion of the body in fishes with dermal armor is generally covered, not with discrete scales, but with bony plates, sheathing the head and gill region and extending down over the "shoulder" region. In many ostracoderms we find these regions covered by armor plates of varied patterns which are difficult to compare with those of higher groups. In placoderms we can distinguish plates in the pectoral region which roughly correspond to shoulder girdle elements of higher fishes, and anterior to this a "head" shield. In bony fishes we find, at last, a more familiar pattern in the arrangement of head plates, although individual bones are highly variable. There is a well defined cranial shield which forms part of a typical skull; dermal bony plates are further associated with the lower jaw and the inner surfaces of the mouth, and there is a dermal shoulder girdle. These structures will be discussed later. We may here, however, note briefly the presence, between head and shoulder, of a series of *opercular elements* lying in the flap of skin over the gill region (Figs. 154, 156, 157, pp. 226, 228, 229). There is typically a major plate, the *operculum,* on either side behind the cheek region of the skull, and other, smaller elements may be present adjacent to the main operculum (preoperculum, suboperculum). The opercular structures follow the contours of the gill chamber downward and forward beneath the jaws. Here there was primitively a series of plates termed *gulars;* in teleosts these have been reduced to a series of parallel rods as *branchiostegal rays* (Figs. 32, 108, 156; pp. 52, 170, 228).

We may here (parenthetically) discuss the nature of the rays which stiffen the peripheral portions of fish fins, median or paired (Fig. 98). In some more primitive fishes scales like those of the body sheathe the fins, but become smaller and more attenuate distally. In higher bony fishes these fin scales tend to be modified into elongated rays, termed *lepidotrichia,* each of which represents a row of slender scales. The very tip of the fin in bony fishes may be additionally stiffened by tiny horny rods developed in the dermis of the skin—*actinotrichia*—and larger rays of this sort—termed *ceratotrichia*—are the sole support of the shark fin web.

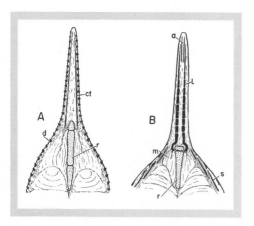

Fig. 98.   Sections through the dorsal fin of *A,* a shark; *B,* a ray-finned fish; to show the nature of the fin supports. *a,* Actinotrichia; *ct,* ceratotrichia; *d,* dermal denticle; *l,* lepidotrichia; *m,* muscle tissue at fin base; *r,* skeletal supports of fin; *s,* bony scales. (From Goodrich.)

Tetrapods. Land vertebrates are descended from fishes with a complete bony covering of plates and scales. The dermal bones of the head are retained as part of the skull and jaw structures, and a dermal shoulder girdle generally persists. The remainder of the dermal armor, however, has tended strongly to reduction and loss.

With the reduction of the gills in land vertebrates, the series of opercular bones vanishes. The bony body scales may persist, but only in a much reduced or modified fashion. In the older fossil amphibians part of the original fish scaly covering was retained in the form of V-shaped rows on the belly and flanks, perhaps as a protection to the low-slung body in land locomotion; more rarely are bony scales found over the back. In modern amphibians scales are completely lacking except for functionless vestiges buried in the skin of the Apoda.

In some of the oldest reptiles the ventral bony scales persisted in the shape of a series of jointed V-shaped rods beneath the skin of the belly—abdominal ribs or *gastralia*. These structures are dermal and should not be confused with ventral extensions of the true ribs, which may lie deep to them, but are, of course, part of the endoskeleton. Abdominal ribs persist today in lizards, crocodilians, and Sphenodon; but in birds and mammals these last representatives of the old fish bony scale system have vanished.

The skin, however, retains its potentialities of forming dermal bone, and in many reptiles and a few mammals we find a redevelopment of bony nodules, scales, or plates as a protective armor. Examples of this sort are common in extinct reptiles; in lizards there is frequently a development, probably secondary, of bony scales underlying the horny scales in the epidermis (Fig. 78, *C*, p. 131); in some crocodilians there is an armor of subquadrate bony plates covered by horny skin. Most mammals which have armor belong to the edentate stocks native to South America. Extinct ground sloths reinforced their tough hide with lumps of dermal bone buried in the dermis; in the armadillos and their extinct relatives, the glyptodonts, bony plates form a complete carapace covering the back and the top of the head and in glyptodonts sheathe the tail as well.

Turtle Armor (Fig. 99). Although in extinct reptiles there are many interesting examples of armor, that of the living chelonians is unequalled for completeness and efficiency. We have noted earlier the presence of horny scutes over the surface of the turtle body; beneath these scutes there is in most chelonians a stout and effective bony shell. This consists of a convex oval dorsal shield, the *carapace*, and a flat belly slab, the *plastron*. At the sides the two parts are connected by a bony bridge; front and back, the shell is open for the head, limbs, and tail.

The carapace consists essentially of three sets of plates. (1) Circling the margin is a set of *peripheral* (marginal) plates. (2) From front to back in the midline is a series of subquadrate plates, most of which are fused to the vertebrae beneath them and termed *neurals* (anterior and posterior members of the median series have special names). (3) Transversely placed between peripherals and neurals are eight paired *pleural* (costal) plates, bound to underlying ribs. The elements of the carapace are firmly fused in many cases, with obliteration of sutures; the lines of separation of the horny surface scutes, however, are often impressed on the surface of the bony carapace. In part the boundaries between the horny scutes of the carapace (and of the plastron as well) alternate with the sutures between the bony plates, a condition which lends strength to the shell structure as a whole.

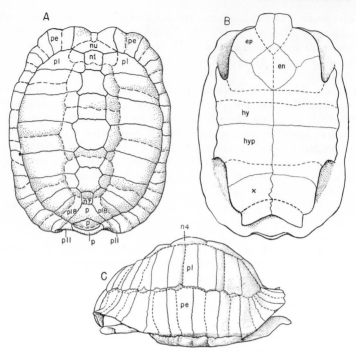

Fig. 99. *A,* Dorsal, *B,* ventral and *C,* lateral views of the shell of a tortoise (Testudo). Sutures between bony plates in solid line, outlines of horny scutes in broken line. Abbreviations: *en,* entoplastron; *ep,* epiplastron; *hy,* hyoplastron; *hyp,* hypoplastron; *nu,* nuchal; *n1-n7,* neurals; *p,* pygal plates (postneurals); *pe,* peripheral plates; *p11,* most posterior (eleventh) peripheral; *pl,* pleural plates; *x,* xiphiplastron.

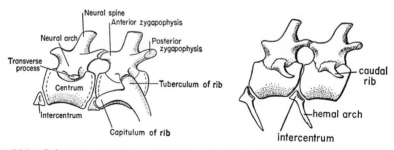

Fig. 100. *Left,* two trunk vertebrae of an early generalized reptile (anterior end to the left). *Right,* two caudal vertebrae.

The plastron of typical chelonians consists of four paired plates and an anterior median element; their nomenclature is given in the accompanying Figure 99. (In primitive types additional paired plates may be present.) The three plates at the anterior margin are actually elements (clavicles and interclavicle) of the dermal shoulder girdle described later in this chapter; the remaining plastral elements, and all the carapace plates, appear to be new developments in turtles, although there is some evidence suggesting that dermal abdominal ribs have been incorporated in the plastron structure.

AXIAL SKELETON

Vertebrae—Amniote. The host of skeletal structures remaining for description are endoskeletal, lying (in contrast to those of the dermal skeleton) in the interior of the body; they are first formed in the embryo as cartilages, the cartilage being usually replaced and supplemented by bone. The great majority of endoskeletal elements belong to the system here termed somatic; they are formed (in contrast to those of the visceral system) from mesenchyme of mesodermal origin. Apart from the special category of limb supports, the somatic skeletal elements can be classed as axial.

The major axial structure is the vertebral column, which replaces the notochord as the main longitudinal girder of the vertebrate body. The greater flexibility given by the notochord is sacrificed for greater strength, and need for the strength given by bony elements is especially great in land vertebrates in which the back must suspend the weight of the body. As an additional function, the vertebral elements extend upward from the notochordal region to surround and protect the spinal cord adjacent to it.

As an introduction to vertebral structure we may first consider the relatively simple situation seen in typical vertebrae of amniotes (Fig. 100) before considering the wild assortment of variants seen in lower vertebrate classes. Each vertebra, formed of bone in these forms, includes two principal portions, a neural arch and a centrum. Ventrally placed is the *centrum,* which functionally replaces the notochord. In many vertebrate groups this is a spool-shaped cylinder articulated at either end with the adjacent centra. In some reptiles the centrum may be hollowed at both ends, a condition termed *amphicelous* (Fig. 101, *A*). The cavity thus present between successive centra is filled with soft material which may be, in part at least, derived from the embryonic notochord, and in early fossil reptiles and in Sphenodon and the gecko lizards today there is a tiny hole, piercing the centrum lengthwise, through which the notochord extends as a continuous (though much constricted) structure.

In most living amniotes, however, the notochord has disappeared except for, at the most, thin pads of tissue lying between successive centra, and the centra have become solid structures, whose end faces are closely apposed to those of their neighbors. Those vertebrae which have flat terminal faces, as is common in mammals, are termed *acelous* (Fig. 101, *D*). In many cases one end of the centrum expands in spherical fashion, to be received in a hollowed socket in the neighboring centrum. If the concave socket is at the anterior end of the centrum (a condition found in most living reptiles) the vertebra is termed *procelous* (Fig. 101, *C*); if posteriorly placed, *opisthocelous* (Fig. 101, *B*). Since the nature of the articular faces may change regionally along the column, various irregularities and combinations of structure may occur, and there are numerous variants from these orthodox types. Notable is the development in the neck region of birds of *heterocelous* vertebrae, with saddle-shaped articular faces between the centra, and the development of complicated central connections in the retractable neck of turtles.

In reptiles, and in the tail of mammals, there may be present a series of small elements, crescentic in end view, which are wedged in ventrally between successive centra. These are *intercentra* (or hypocentra), remnants of "central" elements important, as we shall see, in lower tetrapods and their crossopterygian ancestors. Fused to the intercentra in the tail are the *hemal arches* or chevrons,

Fig. 101. Longitudinal sections through amniote vertebrae of various types (anterior end to the left). *A,* Primitive amphicelous type; the form represented is pierced through the centrum by an opening for a continuous notochord. *B,* The opisthocelous type. *C,* The procelous type. *D,* Essentially an acelous type, but with centra slightly biconcave and with room for an intervertebral disc. (After Gregory.)

which extend downward in the septum between the muscles of either side. The base of each hemal arch consists of a pair of processes which descend from the intercentrum to enclose a space in which lie the major blood vessels of the tail; usually the two branches join below the vessels to give a V or Y shape as seen in end view. As will be seen later, the hemal arches are represented in fishes not only in the tail, but in the trunk as a type of rib—the ventral rib—not present in land vertebrates.

In most cases a rib attachment is present in the central region. Primitively this was with the intercentrum, but in amniotes this point of attachment shifts to the centrum, where there may develop a special process, the *parapophysis,* or it may come to lie, in the trunk of mammals, at the point of junction between two successive centra.

The upper surface of the centrum forms the floor of the canal carrying the spinal cord. At either side rises the broad base of a *neural arch,* firmly bound to the centrum in most adults. Above the spinal cord the two arches fuse to form a *neural spine,* which runs upward between the dorsal muscles of the two sides; successive spines are usually bound together by an elastic ligament. At the base of the arch on either side there is frequently a stout *transverse process* (*diapophysis*) as a rib attachment.

In land vertebrates (and in a few bony fishes) strength is added to the column by the presence of articulations, paired "yoking" processes, or *zygapophyses,* between successive neural arches; these allow a degree of vertical and horizontal movement of the column but aid in the prevention of undue torsion. The anterior zygapophyses terminate in rounded surfaces which generally face upward and inward; to them are opposed surfaces facing downward and outward on the posterior zygapophyses of the next anterior arch (for mnemonic purposes one may recall that in any procession, those at the front of the parade are up and in —those at the rear, down and out). There are sometimes additional articulating processes for firmer vertebral union.

The structures described are those normally found in the higher vertebrate classes; in amphibians and the various fish groups there is a great variety of vertebral types. Before discussing them, however, we should briefly consider the embryologic development of vertebrae as seen in amniotes.

In the discussion of mesoderm differentiation it was noted that a considerable amount of mesenchyme proliferates from the medial side of each somite— the area known as the sclerotome (Fig. 68, p. 118). Its major function is the formation of vertebrae; the sclerotome cells spread out in a sheet applied to the sides of both notochord and spinal cord opposite each somite.

Fig. 102. Diagrams to illustrate the manner of utilization of mesenchyme in the formation of amniote vertebrae. *A* is a diagrammatic vertical section of the sclerotomes of two somites; nerve cord and notochord are shown behind them, and below is arbitrarily figured a portion of the musculature belonging to these somites. In *B* the sclerotomes have split into anterior and posterior halves, which move apart and in *C* have fused with the adjacent halves of neighboring sclerotomes. These newly formed sclerotome masses are the materials from which successive vertebrae are derived, and in *D* is diagrammatically represented (by differences in stippling) the dual origin—from parts of two segments—of an adult vertebra. As a result of this seemingly odd developmental process, the vertebrae (as is seen by reference to the blocks of segmental origin) are inter-segmental rather than segmental in position.

The number of vertebrae in the adult corresponds to the number of somites from which their materials are derived, and one might assume that in consequence each vertebra would correspond in position to the muscle segment likewise produced by each somite. Actually this is not the case; in amniotes, at any rate the vertebrae alternate with the muscle segments, and the mesenchyme from which a vertebra is composed is derived, half and half, from each of two adjacent somites. In many amniotes there early appears a distinction between the anterior and posterior portions of the mesenchyme sheets produced by each segment. As development proceeds it is found that the front half of a vertebra is formed from the posterior part of one segmental mesenchyme sheet, the back half from the anterior part of the mesenchyme of the next segment (Fig. 102).

On reflection it is seen that this mode of vertebral formation is not a senseless developmental complication, but a functionally useful one. In lower vertebrates, particularly, the segmentally arranged axial muscles are powerful and are important in locomotion. To exert their force they depend in great measure on attachment to the vertebrae and ribs. But these attachments, to be effective, must be to two successive vertebrae; in consequence, vertebral structures must alternate with muscular ones. It will be noted that the primary segmentation, that of the somites, is retained by the axial muscles; the vertebral segmentation, developing later in both phylogeny and ontogeny, is subsequent to that of the muscles and alternating with it.

Anamniote Vertebrae (Figs. 103, 104).   In considering the highly vari-able structure of the vertebrae in fishes and amphibians we may first consider the history of the neural arches. The story is fairly straightforward. Such arches are present in every case (apart from the hagfishes, which are destitute of vertebral structures of any sort). In lampreys a small arch cartilage is present on either

Fig. 103.   *A–F*, fish trunk vertebrae. *A*, Cross-section of a vertebra of the shark Lamna, showing arch bases wedged into centrum. The dark areas are calcified. *B*, Lateral view of two segments of the column of the same shark. Elements between the neural arches complete a closed tube for the spinal cord; a complex of small elements represents short ventral ribs (= hemal arches). The dorsal arch bases are covered by the base of the neural arches. *C*, A cross-section of a vertebra of a teleost, Esox; the structure is comparable to that of a shark. *D*, Lateral view of two vertebrae of a young Amia; both dorsal and ventral arch bases are visible and distinct from the centrum proper. *E*, Adult vertebrae of the same; the arch bases are incorporated in the centrum. *F*, Side view of vertebrae of Esox (cf. *C*). The ventral arch bases are distinct; as in the shark the dorsal arch bases are concealed by the neural arches. *G*, Vertebrae of the urodele Necturus. *H*, Two vertebrae of a frog in which short ribs are present. *dab*, Dorsal arch base; *dr*, dorsal rib; *na*, neural arch; *r*, rib; *t*, transverse process; *vab*, ventral arch base; *vr*, ventral rib (= hemal arch). (Mainly after Goodrich.)

side in the more anterior trunk segments; posteriorly two small paired cartilages may be present in each segment, and a continuous median sheet of cartilage bounds the tail both above and below. In the Chondrichthyes (Fig. 103) there are, in addition to the neural arches proper, accessory neural elements which fill out the gaps between them and enclose the spinal cord in a continuous cartilaginous sheath. The presence of "extra" neural arches is quite surely secondary, for in all older fossil groups in which the column is preserved (including the primitive placoderms and older sharks) there is never more than one arch per segment. In bony fishes and amphibians, characteristic single neural arches are present throughout.

The story of hemal arches in lower vertebrates is likewise a simple one. They are essentially comparable to those of amniotes except that their attachment to central structures is variable. They are not developed in cyclostomes, but are present in the caudal region of all higher types; in elasmobranchs there are here (as in the case of neural arches) accessory cartilages.

In the history of the centrum great diversity is to be found. No such structure is present in the cyclostomes (which hence can be called vertebrates only by courtesy). In sharks (Fig. 103, *A, B*) the centra are short amphicoelous cylinders. Their structure is far from simple. In part they are formed of concentric layers of cartilage around the notochord and even within the notochordal sheath; in these layers calcification usually occurs, often in complicated and characteristic patterns. But this continuity of structure is interrupted, above and below on either side, by plugs of cartilage of a different texture. These lie beneath the areas of attachment of neural and hemal arches (the latter represented by ventral ribs), function as bases for the arches, and are frequently in continuity with them. In the bony fishes these same *arch bases* are present as distinct structures during development and in lungfish, Latimeria, sturgeons, and paddlefishes cartilaginous arch bases are the only skeletal elements in the adult, the notochord persisting as a large unconstricted structure. But in most actinopterygians—Polypterus, Amia, the garpikes and all teleosts—the whole region of the centrum is ossified and the arch bases are fused with or buried within the remainder of the centrum at maturity (Fig. 103, *C-F*).

The fossil record gives us a series of stages leading from the vertebrae of crossopterygian fishes to those present in varied form in the great extinct group of amphibians, the labyrinthodonts, and on to the amniote structure (Figs. 104, 105).

In the crossopterygian vertebrae two sets of ossifications are present in the central region. The notochord is, of course, not preserved in the fossils, but appears to have been persistently large. On either side, just below the neural arch, is a small plate of bone. This is surely the element called a *pleurocentrum* in fossil Amphibia, and which we believe to have expanded and developed into the true centrum of amniotes. Below the curve of the notochord is a single median element, wedge-shaped in side view, crescentic if seen from the end. This, although much larger than in reptiles, is certainly the intercentrum, as is shown by the attachment to it (as in reptiles) of the hemal arches of the tail.

If we wish to compare these crossopterygian structures with those of other fishes (Fig. 105), a reasonable assumption is that the pleurocentra correspond to the basal elements beneath the neural arch, the intercentra to a fusion of the pair of ventral arch bases. But in contrast to the more "advanced" bony fishes, there is no further ossification in the crossopterygian centrum. The arch bases, it would seem, have (so to speak) absorbed all the potentialities for ossification present in the centrum as a whole.

Fig. 104. The evolution of vertebral structures from crossopterygians to primitive tetrapods and reptiles. *A*, Two vertebrae of a crossopterygian; the principal central element is a large intercentrum, wedge-shaped in side view, crescentic if seen in end view; there are small paired pleurocentra. *B*, Vertebrae of the most primitive known amphibian type, of similar construction. *C*, The typical rhachitomous type, common in Paleozoic labyrinthodonts. *D*, The stereospondylous type of vertebra, found in late labyrinthodonts; the pleurocentra have disappeared and the intercentrum forms the entire centrum. *E*, The embolomerous type, found in extinct forms related to reptile ancestors; the pleurocentra have expanded and fused to form a complete ring-shaped centrum and the intercentrum forms a similar but thinner structure. *F*, The primitive reptilian type in which (as in *E*) the pleurocentra have expanded to form a large true centrum, but the intercentra are reduced. Abbreviations: *c*, centrum; *ca*, capitular attachment of rib to intercentrum; *ic*, intercentrum; *n*, neural arch; *p*, pleurocentrum (paired); *t*, transverse process on neural arch for attachment of tuberculum of rib. (*A*, *B*, after Jarvik.)

This pattern of centrum is basically that known as the *rhachitomous* type; it is seen not only in the crossopterygians, but (as recently discovered) in the very oldest and most primitive amphibians and has long been known in a great percentage of later labyrinthodonts. Among these amphibians and the reptiles descended from them, however, there is a trend toward a more solid and better ossified condition of the centrum, brought about by an expansion of either the pleurocentrum, the intercentrum, or both. Among the labyrinthodonts themselves, late members tend to reduce the pleurocentra and to expand the intercentrum until it comes to form by itself a completely cylindric central structure—the *stereospondylous* condition. In forms closer to the reptile pedigree the two pleurocentra, on the contrary, tend to expand and form a complete ring. In one somewhat aberrant group we find an *embolomerous* structure in which both pleurocentrum and intercentrum are rings, giving a double centrum in each segment.*

* In some fishes—notably the holostean Amia—"duplex" caudal centra are developed, and in chimaeras there may be several discs representing one centrum; however, these are formed in ways that do not appear to be closely comparable to that seen in embolomere vertebrae.

However, in the true reptilian ancestors the intercentra are, in contrast, reduced to the small ventral crescents described earlier, while the pleurocentra are enlarged and fused to take over practically the entire ossification as the true centrum.

In this description we have said nothing as yet of the centrum in the modern amphibian orders (Fig. 103, *G, H*) because of the embarrassing fact that we cannot fit them into the seemingly clear story just given of the evolution of other tetrapod vertebrae. In urodeles and apodans the centra are essentially simple cylinders (despite irregularities in outlines) in which there is no evidence of structures corresponding to separate pleurocentra and intercentra; they ossify directly from mesenchyme with little or no cartilaginous preformation. In some frogs and toads there develops a simple cylinder of cartilage which ossifies in continuity with the neural arch; in others the centrum is represented in the adult only by ossification in the upper half of the cylinder. Unless (quite improbably) the modern amphibians have developed independently of all other land vertebrates, it is reasonable to believe that these structures of modern amphibians have developed from the conditions seen in crossopterygians and early labyrinthodonts; but there is at present little evidence to connect these modern amphibian vertebral types with those of any other group.

Regional Variations in Vertebrae. It is obvious that there may be considerable variation along the length of the vertebral column. In higher vertebrates vertebral regions may be defined according to the variations in the nature and presence or absence of ribs; but in many fishes, early amphibians, and various reptiles ribs may be present without a break on every vertebra from neck to tail base. In fishes a *caudal* series of vertebrae can be distinguished from that of the "neck" and trunk by the presence of hemal arches in the tail; in land vertebrates specialized ribs, as noted later, develop for attachment of the pelvic girdle and this distinguishes a *sacral* region separating more distinctly *presacral* and tail segments. In the neck of land forms (as noted later) the ribs tend to be short, fused or absent and hence a *cervical* region can be distinguished from the *dorsal* region, that of the trunk. Even in primitive tetrapods the posterior ribs of the trunk tend to be relatively short, and in mammals there develops here a ribless region, so that in the mammal trunk we may distinguish *thoracic* and *lumbar* divisions. Thus there can be established, progressively as we "climb the tree" of vertebrates, a series of column subdivisions as follows:

$$\left\{ \begin{array}{l} \text{presacral} \left\{ \begin{array}{l} \text{cervical} \\ \text{dorsal} \left\{ \begin{array}{l} \text{thoracic} \\ \text{lumbar} \end{array} \right. \end{array} \right. \\ \\ \text{sacral} \\ \\ \text{caudal} \end{array} \right.$$

In primitive land vertebrates there is a variable vertebral count, but thirty or so presacrals, of which about seven were cervicals, appears to have been a fairly common number in early tetrapods. In amphibians there is normally but a single sacral. Primitively the tail was long, with perhaps half a hundred or more caudals. There is great variation in modern amphibian vertebral numbers: the elongated Apoda may have 200 or so vertebrae; typical frogs, on the other

Fig. 105. Diagrams to show possible evolutionary sequence in the structure of vertebral centra. *d* and *v* are the dorsal and ventral arch bases found in many fishes, parts of the centrum structure supporting neural arches and hemal arches or ventral ribs, respectively. In crossopterygians and many tetrapods the arch bases appear to be represented by pleurocentra (*p*) and intercentra (*i*). Cartilage stippled; arch base cartilages, heavy stipple; pleurocentra hatched; intercentra cross-hatched; parts of central ossifications not included in arch bases, plain white. Part or all of the neural arch is shown as well as the central structures. Front end of vertebrae to left. *A*, Shark condition; arch bases incorporated in cartilaginous centrum. *B*, Embryonic Amia vertebra, showing presumed basic actinopterygian condition, with arch bases forming separately from rest of cartilaginous centrum. *C*, Teleost condition; centrum ossified, and incorporates dorsal arch base and in some cases ventral arch base as well. *D*, Crossopterygian condition, probably basic for tetrapods; much of the centrum was persistently cartilaginous, but small paired dorsal arch bases ossify as pleurocentra, and ventral elements fuse as a wedge-shaped structure. *E*, Oldest known amphibians, similar in structure to crossopterygians. *F*, Type leading toward reptiles among fossil labyrinthodonts; the pleurocentra have grown and fused to form a ring-shaped "true" centrum. *G*, Primitive reptiles; the centrum has grown at the expense of the intercentrum, which is much reduced. *H*, Advanced reptiles, birds, mammals. The intercentrum disappears, and the whole centrum corresponds to the expanded pleurocentra. *I*, Modern amphibians; the centrum ossifies as a simple spool-shaped structure, with no evidence of arch bases. *J*, Structure in rhachitomous labyrinthodonts; the intercentrum is a large wedge-shaped structure, the pleurocentra persistently small. *K*, Late, stereospondylous labyrinthodonts; the pleurocentra vanish, and the intercentrum constitutes the entire centrum. *L*, Extinct embolomere labyrinthodonts; both pleurocentra and intercentrum form complete rings.

hand, have reduced their backbone to nine vertebrae plus a rodlike *urostyle* representing a number of fused caudals. The primitive reptiles appear to have had about twenty-seven presacrals and a long tail; two or more sacrals are generally present. There is great variation within the reptiles in vertebral counts, for snakes may have several hundred vertebrae, turtles a very short column.

A curious condition is seen in the tail of Sphenodon, some lizards, and certain ancient reptiles, in which there is a "breaking point" in the middle of each caudal at which the tail may be shed. The appearance is like that of some fishes with double caudal centra or the embolomerous amphibians, but the structure here is surely a specialized, not a primitive, one.

Fig. 106. Skeleton of the lamprey, Petromyzon. *A*, Otic capsule; *AN*, ring cartilage surrounding mouth; *BB*, cartilages of branchial basket; *DC*, dorsal cartilages of mouth region; *FR*, dermal fin rays; *HFS*, fibrous sheath around dorsal aorta; *LL*, longitudinal ligament connecting tips of neural processes; *N*, notochord; *NA*, openings of nasal capsule; *NFS*, fibrous sheath of spinal cord; *NP*, neural processes; *O*, openings of gill chambers; *SOA*, cartilaginous arch around orbit; *TC*, tongue cartilage. (From Dean.)

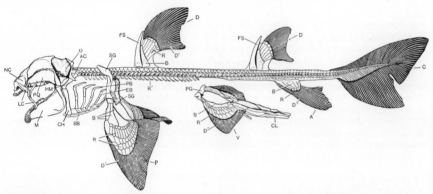

Fig. 107. Skeleton of a shark (Cestracion). *A*, Anal fin; *AC*, auditory capsule; *B*, basal elements of fin; *BB*, basibranchial; *C*, caudal fin; *CH*, ceratohyal; *CL*, claspers of male; *D*, dorsal fins; *D'*, dermal rays of fin; *EB*, epibranchial; *FS*, fin spines; *HM*, hyomandibular; *LC*, labial cartilages; *M*, mandible; *NC*, nasal capsule; *O*, orbit; *P*, pectoral fin; *PB*, pharyngobranchial; *PG*, pelvic girdle; *PQ*, palatoquadrate; *R*, radial elements of fin; *R'*, ribs; *SG*, pectoral girdle; *V*, pelvic (ventral) fin. (From Dean.)

In birds the distinct cervical region has a highly variable number of vertebrae. Most of the thoracic vertebrae tend to be fused together, as an aid to the effective bracing of the wings in flight. The posterior thoracic, lumbar, and proximal caudal vertebrae are generally fused with the original sacrals into an elongated *synsacrum* supporting the pelvic girdle; there is thus almost no motility in the avian column back of the neck region. The bony tail is much shortened, and is capped by a *pygostyle* formed of fused vertebrae.

Ancestral mammals appear to have had, much like early reptiles, about twenty-seven presacral vertebrae, two or three sacrals, and a tail which, however, tended to become relatively short and weak. With remarkable consistency the number of cervicals, which lack free ribs, remains at seven. Only in a few instances (tree sloths, manatees) is this rule violated, and a neckless whale and a giraffe both have seven cervicals, appropriately abbreviated or elongated. The number of dorsal vertebrae is usually in the twenties and tends to remain rather constant within the limits of many mammalian families or orders. However, the number of ribs—and hence the proportion of thoracics to lumbars—is variable. Thus, in the cow-antelope family of ungulates, the number of dorsal vertebrae is almost always nineteen, but thoracics may vary from twelve up to fourteen, and

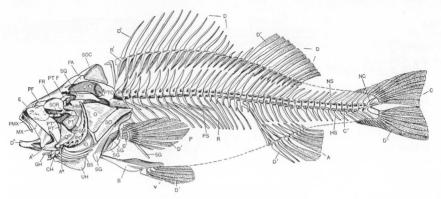

Fig. 108.   Skeleton of a teleost (Perca). The interpretation of certain skull elements differs from that used in Figure 157, but is one commonly used in works on teleosts. *A*, Anal fin; *A'*, articular; *A''*, angular; *B*, pelvic girdle; *B'*, skeleton of pectoral fin; *BS*, branchiostegal rays; *C*, caudal fin; *C'*, centrum of vertebra; *CH*, ceratohyal; *D*, dorsal fins (anterior one supported by stout dermal spines); *D'*, dermal rays of fins; *D''*, dentary; *E*, ethmoid; *EPO*, epiotic; *FR*, frontal; *GH*, hypobranchial (glossohyal); *HM*, hyomandibular; *HS*, hemal spine; *IO*, interopercular (part of opercular series); *MX*, maxilla; *NC*, tip of notochord in tail; *NS*, neural spine; *O*, opercular; *P*, pectoral fin; *PA*, parietal; *PF*, prefrontal; *PMX*, premaxilla; *PO*, preopercular (part of opercular series); *PS*, supporting processes of ribs; *PT*, *PT'*, *PT''*, bones of palatal region; *PTF*, postfrontal; *PTO*, pterotic; *Q*, quadrate; *R*, ribs; *R'*, supports of dorsal fins; *SG*, various portions of shoulder girdle; *SM*, symplectic (binding hyomandibular to skull); *SO*, subopercular; *SOC*, supraoccipital; *SOR*, suborbitals; *SQ*, squamosal; *UH*, urohyal (ventral element of branchial skeleton); *V*, pelvic fin. (From Dean.)

Fig. 109.   The skeleton of a salamander, as seen from above. (From Schaeffer.)

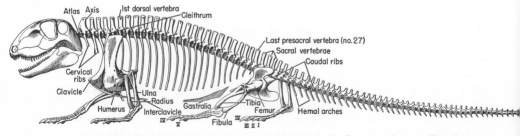

Fig. 110.   The skeleton of a generalized primitive reptile (the Permian pelycosaur Haptodus).

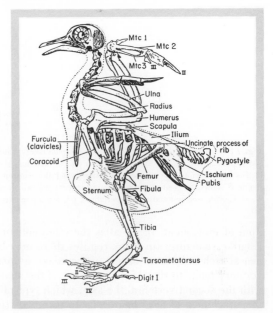

Fig. 111. The skeleton of a bird (the pigeon). (After Heilmann.)

Fig. 112. The skeleton of a generalized mammal, the tree-shrew, Tupaia. (After Gregory.)

the lumbars, correspondingly, from seven down to five. Mammalian sacrals are generally three to five in number.

Atlas-Axis Complex (Fig. 113). In fishes, head and trunk move as a unit. In land vertebrates independent movement of the head is important, and modifications of the most anterior vertebrae and their skull articulations facilitate this. The articular surface at the back of the skull, the condyle, is in fishes a single rounded structure, comparable to the end of a centrum, and the oldest amphibians still retained this type. In most amphibians, living or fossil, the single condyle has divided into a pair, one at either side, and the articular surface of the first vertebra has become correspondingly divided. This allows the head to swing up and down in hinge fashion, but gives little scope for lateral movement. In most reptiles and in birds the condyle remains single, but the first two vertebrae, termed the *atlas* and *axis*, have been modified to permit considerable free-

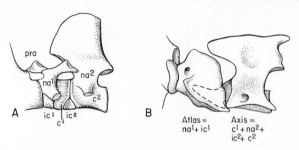

Fig. 113. The atlas-axis complex. *A*, The occipital condyle and first two vertebrae in a primitive reptile (Ophiacodon). *B*, The same region in a typical mammal, showing fusion of elements. The proatlas in *A* is the neural arch of a "lost" vertebra of which the centrum has fused with the occiput. The broken line in *B* shows the position of the odontoid process (c^1), which runs forward inside the ring of the atlas. c^1, c^2, Centrum of first and second vertebrae; ic^1, ic^2, intercentra; na^1, na^2, neural arches; *pra*, proatlas.

dom of movement. In the atlas the intercentrum and neural arch may form a ringlike structure; (in many reptiles there may be, incidentally, a small, extra neural arch in advance of that of the atlas—a *proatlas*). The centrum of the first vertebra tends to remain independent of the atlas proper and to associate itself with the second vertebra, the axis, which typically has a large neural spine for the attachment of head ligaments. In mammals (in which as in amphibians, the condylar articulations with the skull are double) the axis bears anteriorly a process projecting from its centrum into the ventral part of the atlas ring; the embryologic story shows that this *odontoid process* includes the centrum of the atlas segment as well as the intercentrum of the axis itself. The head may move upward and downward on the atlas; the major component in sideways and rotary movements of the head is movement of atlas on axis.

Ribs in Fishes. Although the vertebral column is the main skeletal structure upon which the powerful fish axial muscles play, little musculature is directly attached to the vertebrae. For the most part muscular force is exerted, in fishes, upon the connective tissue septa—*myocommata*—between successive muscle segments; ribs, formed at strategic points in these septa, connect with the vertebrae and render the muscular effort more effective.

In most fishes each muscle segment in both embryo and adult is divided into dorsal and ventral parts by a longitudinal septum running the length of the flank (Figs. 2, p. 6, and 114). A logical place for rib formation is at the intersection of this septum with successive myocommata; in many fishes *dorsal ribs* are present at these points. A second position in which ribs may develop is that where the myocommata reach the walls of the celomic cavity ventrally and internally. Ribs in this position, common in fishes, are termed pleural or *ventral ribs* and are serially identical with the structures termed hemal arches in the tail of both fishes and tetrapods; at the back end of the body cavity, the ventral ribs of the two sides approach one another and then, a bit farther back, fuse to form a V-shaped chevron structure. In addition to these two types of characteristic ribs, riblike intermuscular bones may be found in teleosts (the shad is all too good an example) at other points in the myocommata, making for greater muscular efficiency. The ribs, like the connective tissues in which they are found, are derived from mesenchyme and usually are preformed in cartilage even if later ossified. Proximally, close to the vertebrae, rib mesenchyme may be derived from the sclerotomes, more distally from the lateral plate of the mesoderm.

There are no ribs in cyclostomes. In sharks, short ribs may be present which appear to be members of the ventral series. In many bony fishes only ventral ribs are present, but in Polypterus, on the one hand, and in numerous teleosts on the other, both dorsal and ventral ribs are to be found.

Tetrapod Ribs. In tetrapods but one type of rib is present in the much reduced muscular wall of the body. Although doubts have been expressed, it is fairly generally agreed that these ribs correspond to the dorsal ribs of fishes. As in fishes, ribs were borne in ancestral tetrapods by every vertebra from the atlas to the base of the tail (cf. Fig. 110). The more anterior—cervical—ribs are short, in relation to the development of a flexible neck region. The thoracic region is typically characterized by stout and elongated ribs which are, through muscular connections, concerned in supporting the trunk on the pectoral limb girdles. These thoracic ribs are in most groups of tetrapods bound to a median ventral structure, the sternum. In primitive tetrapods the vertebrae of the lumbar region may bear ribs, but these are relatively short. One or more highly developed sacral ribs, not present in fish, connect the backbone with the pelvic girdle. Beyond the pelvis, ribs, diminishing in size posteriorly, may be present in the lateral muscle septum of the tail.

In ancestral tetrapods the ribs were characteristically double-headed structures on the anterior vertebrae at least, although the two heads may be connected by a thin web of bone (Fig. 100, p. 160). The *capitulum*—the head proper— was attached, in early forms, to the intercentrum. With reduction of the intercentrum in advanced tetrapods this attachment tends to shift to the anterior edge of the adjacent centrum or to the intercentral space. The second head, the *tuberculum*, is essentially a short process from the curved proximal part of the rib, and primitively attached to the transverse process of the neural arch. In the posterior part of the column the two heads tend to come close to one another and may fuse, the capitular attachment shifting upward and backward. The sacral rib or ribs are powerfully built, with a broad head, a short shaft, and a distal expan-

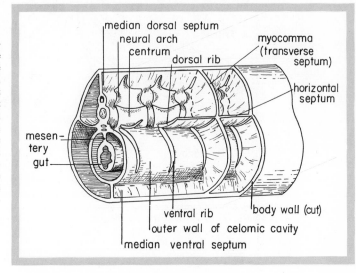

Fig. 114. Diagram of a section of the trunk of a vertebrate to show the connective tissue system and the axial skeletal elements. A view from the left side, as if partially dissected out and the muscles removed from between the septa. Vertebral elements develop in the tissue sheath surrounding the spinal cord and notochord; ribs, dorsal or ventral, develop where the transverse septum intersects the horizontal septum or celomic wall. (After Goodrich.)

sion applied to the inner surface of the dorsal element of the pelvic girdle. The sacral ribs are immovably attached to the vertebrae, and the lumbar and caudal ribs, where present, tend likewise to be incapable of movement.

In modern amphibians the ribs (like the vertebrae) have departed more radically than those of early reptiles from the primitive tetrapod type. They are always much reduced and never reach the sternum. In most frogs and toads they are entirely absent except for a sacral. In urodeles they are present but short, sometimes forked distally, and proximally attach by two heads to a transverse process of a peculiar type, not comparable to that in any other group.

Within the reptiles there is much variation in rib structure. Particularly notable is the variation in vertebral attachment, with either a single or double head; either or both heads may attach to transverse process or centrum. In the Squamata the single-headed ribs articulate with the centrum. In the crocodiles the ribs are two-headed; in the cervical region the capitulum arises from the centrum, but in the trunk both heads attach to the transverse process. Each thoracic rib in reptiles is typically formed in two segments, a proximal, ossified, rib proper, and a distal *sternal rib* (Fig. 115) which almost always remains cartilaginous. A joint between the two segments allows for flexibility necessary in the expansion and contraction of the chest and consequent filling and emptying of the lungs. In turtles the ribs are reduced in number; eight of them are firmly fused to the overlying costal plates of the carapace.

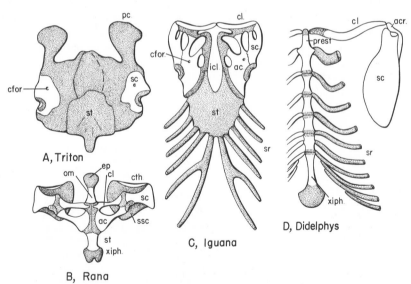

Fig. 115. Ventral views of the shoulder girdle and sternal apparatus in various tetrapods. For lateral views, cf. Figures 123 and 124 (pp. 186, 189). *A*, Salamander; *B*, a frog; *C*, a lizard; *D*, a mammal (opossum). Anterior end at the top of the figures. In *A* and *C* the dorsally turned scapulae are invisible. In *A* the two coracoid cartilages overlap, as indicated by the broken line. *ac*, Anterior coracoid element; *acr*, acromion; *cfor*, coracoid foramen; *cl*, clavicle; *cth*, cleithrum; *ep*, episternum; *icl*, interclavicle; *om*, omosternum; *pc*, precoracoid region of coracoid plate; *prest*, presternum; *sc*, scapula (in salamanders this ossification extends down into the place of the absent coracoid); *sr*, sternal ribs; *ssc*, suprascapula; *st*, sternum; *xiph*, xiphisternum. Cartilage stippled. (*A*, *C*, and *D* after Parker.)

In birds the cervical ribs are fused to the vertebrae; free ribs, with ossified sternal segments, are confined to the compact thoracic region. These carry, as do those of some living reptiles and early fossil tetrapods, expansions in the form of *uncinate processes* for the attachment of muscles supporting the shoulder blade. In mammals generally cervical ribs appear to be absent, but the embryologic story shows that the so-called transverse processes of the cervical vertebrae actually include short, fused, two-headed ribs; a foramen piercing the process represents the gap between capitulum and tuberculum of the rib. Distinct although immovable cervical ribs are present in monotremes. Ribs are present on all the thoracic vertebrae in mammals and are, indeed, diagnostic of that region; most curve forward ventrally to reach the sternum through cartilaginous sternal rib segments, but the shorter posterior "floating ribs" are bound to that structure only via ligamentous connections with their longer anterior neighbors. The lumbar vertebrae have long transverse processes, but no ribs, and caudal ribs are never developed in mammals.

Sternum (Figs. 115, 124, p. 189). As seen in many reptiles the sternum is a ventrally placed, shield-shaped cartilage which articulates anteriorly with the shoulder girdle, and posterolaterally connects on either side with the ventral ends of thoracic ribs to form a complete enclosure of the chest region, the thorax. Although there is (owing to the usually cartilaginous nature of the structure) little fossil evidence, the sternum was probably developed in early tetrapods; no such structure is found in fishes.

In modern amphibians, most urodeles have a typical sternal plate of cartilage; in frogs there is found a sternal plate or rod posterior to the girdle ventrally, and in some forms, a second element anterior to the girdle. Among reptiles the sternum has been lost in turtles and in snakes and certain snakelike lizards. In birds (Fig. 124, *F*, p. 189) the sternum is an enormous ossified structure, its size being due to the attachment to it of most of the mass of the chest muscles, important in flight; except in the ostrich-like birds, in which flight has been lost, the bone bears a huge keel for additional muscle attachment. In typical mammals the sternum, usually ossified, has a different type of structure from that of either reptiles or birds. It has the form of an elongated, jointed rod with which the ribs are articulated at the "nodes."

Although the sternum is associated topographically with the shoulder girdle, it is generally considered part of the axial skeleton because of its close association with the rib system. Its embryologic development, however, shows that in both reptiles and mammals it arises independently of the ribs.

Braincase. The braincase, of cartilage or replacement bone, forms the anterior end of the axial skeletal system, here greatly modified in relation to the brain and specialized sense organs of the head region. In most vertebrates the braincase is fused with dermal and visceral arch skeletal materials to form a definitive skull structure of compound nature. In cyclostomes and Chondrichthyes, however, the braincase, owing to the absence of dermal bones—presumably a secondary condition—is a discrete skeletal element. The shark braincase shows a structure which, with modification, is repeated in all the lower jawed vertebrates, and in further modified form is represented in the skull of even the highest of vertebrate groups. In sharks, cyclostomes and modern lungfish, it retains its embryonic cartilaginous nature; in most other forms it is more or less replaced by bony elements.

As seen in sharks, the braincase (Fig. 116) is a troughlike structure which

Fig. 116. The braincase of the shark Chlamydoselache; *A*, dorsal, *B*, ventral and *C*, lateral views, and *D*, sagittal section. Nerve exits in Roman numerals. (After Allis.)

forms a floor and side walls for the brain and a partial roof. The roof, however, is never complete; one or more dorsal gaps, *fontanelles*, may be present. This lack of a complete roof is repeated in most other vertebrates; in forms with an ossified dermal skeleton (as presumably in the shark's ancestors) a bony roof was present overhead, and a complete braincase roof was unnecessary.

As seen in adult sharks and in at least the embryo of many other forms, four major braincase regions may be distinguished, from back to front: occipital, otic, orbital, and ethmoidal. The most posterior part of the braincase, the *occipital region,* is of relatively narrow width. Posteriorly there is an opening, the *foramen magnum,* through which passes the spinal cord. Below this is a rounded *occipital condyle* which abuts against the first vertebra. The notochord in the embryo, and sometimes in the adult, may extend forward in the floor of the braincase from the condyle to a point just back of the pituitary body pendant from the brain. Anterior to the occipital region the braincase expands laterally in the otic region; there is here incorporated on either side an *otic capsule* enclosing the sacs and canals of the internal ear. Still farther forward the braincase narrows in the *orbital region* to aid in forming sockets, the orbits, for the eyeballs and their musculature. Here a median depression in the braincase floor may mark the position of the pituitary. Still farther forward the braincase expands in an *ethmoid region* to terminate in a rostrum; on either side, in front of a preorbital ridge (antorbital process) are the *nasal capsules* which enclose the olfactory organs.

Numerous openings—*foramina*—are present in the braincase for the cranial nerves and blood vessels. Into the orbit emerge the optic nerve (II) of the eye, and in variable fashion, three smaller nerves (III, IV, and VI) for the eyeball muscles. Near the posterior end of the orbit there is typically a large foramen or gap for the trigeminal nerve (V), and the facial nerve (VII) usually leaves the braincase close by. Behind the otic capsule there are openings for nerves associated with the gill region, the glossopharyngeal (IX) and vagus (X), and, in fishes, posterior to the last, for small occipital nerves. (Nerves I and VIII, connecting with nasal pocket and internal ear, do not, of course, show superficially.) In sharks the endolymphatic ducts from the internal ear (cf. Chap. 15) open to the surface, typically into a median depression, or fossa, in the braincase roof. Ventrally, in the pituitary region, an opening is present for the carotid arteries, which supply blood to the brain, and other arterial and venous openings are present laterally.

A specialized gill bar element, propping the jaws—the hyomandibular— articulates rather loosely with the outer surface of the otic capsule, and the cartilages which form the shark upper jaws also articulate with the braincase (Fig. 150, p. 217). The common jaw connection in sharks is one in which they are loosely joined anteriorly with the under surface of the braincase; in primitive sharks there is an additional articulation with a braincase process posterior to the orbit. In higher fishes and early land vertebrates this last connection tends to be reduced or absent, and there is instead a strong *basal articulation* of the upper jaw structures with the base of the braincase in the orbital region (Figs. 117, *E*; 151, p. 220; 157, p. 229; 170, p. 242).

In the embryo vertebrate (Fig. 117) the brain, and the notochord extending forward beneath it to the pituitary region, are already far advanced in development before skeletal structures appear. Braincase development begins ventrally, then continues laterally; because of the "precocious" growth of the brain to large size, it is difficult, so to speak, for the braincase to surround it, and the roof, as we have noted, often remains incomplete. The two basic embryologic braincase structures are the parachordals and trabeculae. The *parachordals* are a pair of cartilages which develop beneath the posterior part of the brain on either side of the notochord; farther forward there is in lower vertebrates a similar pair, the *trabeculae* (in mammals, however, a single median structure represents the trabeculae).* Presently these paired elements fuse with their mates and with each other to form a nearly solid braincase floor. There may, however, be a long-persistent median opening for the hypophyseal sac, which grows upward from the roof of the mouth to form part of the pituitary body, as well as openings for the carotid arteries.

---

* As noted later, the trabeculae appear to have been originally part of the gill bar system, but have been "borrowed" by the axial skeleton to complete enclosure of the brain.

Fig. 117. Stages in the embryonic development of the braincase of a lizard. In *A* the outlines of the head, brain, and notochord are given for orientation. The main elements of the braincase structure are appearing—trabeculae, parachordals, otic capsule, and occipital arches (the nasal capsule appears later); further development consists in great measure of the growth and fusion of these elements. In the lizard the orbital region grows as a complicated latticework, rather than a plate. Nerve positions are indicated by Roman numerals. *bap,* Basal articular process with upper jaw cartilage; *fo,* fenestra ovalis (for stapes); *nc,* nasal capsule; *oa,* occipital arch; *oc,* otic capsule; *pc,* parachordal; *tr,* trabecula. (After DeBeer.)

Alongside the posterior part of the brain, the sacs and canals of the internal ear develop at an early stage. A shell of cartilage, the *otic capsule,* forms around the outer surface of these structures and tends to enclose them nearly completely. Farther forward, the eye, of course, is not enclosed, but there soon appears, in one fashion or another, a plate or latticework of cartilage internal to the eye socket, which often forms an *orbital plate.* The nasal region is relatively slow to develop, but there eventually appears a *nasal capsule* of complicated structure. The posterior boundary of the skull is somewhat variable from group to group. The occipital region appears to be formed from one or several modified vertebrae. In agreement with this, we find that in the embryo there appears behind the otic capsule a variable number of *occipital arches* somewhat resembling the vertebrae behind them.

As development proceeds, the ventral elements of the braincase fuse with the lateral structures and with the occipital arches to form side walls as well as a floor to the brain (cf. Fig. 147, *D, F,* p. 214). Most of the openings for nerves and vessels lie in spaces between the major components. Thus nerves V and VII have their exits in openings in front of the otic capsule; nerves IX, X and XI emerge between otic capsule and occipital region. Although a roof is slow to form, there is always a union of the two otic capsules above the foramen magnum.

The description above of the adult braincase was mainly based on that of sharks. In the other lower vertebrates in which the braincase is a separate entity —cyclostomes and chimaeras—its structure is degenerate or highly modified and need not be considered in detail. In cyclostomes (Figs. 106, p. 169; 147, *A,* p. 214) it consists of little more than a rather simple brain trough, a pair of otic

Fig. 118. Diagram to illustrate the main embryonic components in the formation of a braincase. Trabeculae and parachordals are the main ventral elements to which an occipital arch (or arches) is added posteriorly. Usually later in development are more dorsal elements: otic capsule, nasal capsule and orbital plate (the last, as in Fig. 117, often develops merely as a latticework). These primary elements are later bound together by a further growth of cartilage, leaving, however, gaps for nerves and blood vessels.

capsules, and a capsule for the single nostril. The chimaera braincase (Fig. 119) is short and high, and specialized in various features, of which the most noticeable is the fusion of the short upper jaw cartilages to the braincase. This peculiarity (repeated in lungfishes and in modified fashion in various land vertebrates) is here associated, apparently, with the stronger support necessary for the shell-crushing activity of these mollusc-eating fishes.

The braincase of more highly developed fishes and tetrapods, described later as part of the skull structure, is usually well ossified in the adult, but always develops in cartilage in a fashion similar to that of sharks. In sharks the braincase floor is flat, and the same is true of the degenerate modern amphibians; in most other vertebrates, however, the braincase tends to be relatively high and more constricted ventrally in the orbital and ethmoidal regions.

Median Fins. The primitive vertebrate was a water dweller. As the builder of ships is aware, the most efficient propulsive shape, that offering the least resistance to the water, is a fusiform one, in which the surfaces are as smoothly contoured as possible—"streamlined"—and in which, following a pointed anterior tip, the greatest width is not far from the anterior end of the body. A majority of fishes approximate this shape, although there are conspicuous variations. In general, the posterior part of the body tends to be flattened from side to side. This flattening is associated with the nature of the propulsive force; forward movement is due to lateral muscular movements of the body, which effect a backward pressure of trunk and tail upon the surrounding water (Fig. 120, *A*). Tension of the muscles on one side of the body produces lateral curvature in a given region; such curves, successively produced on opposite sides, travel back along the trunk and tail, pushing the body forward as a result of their backward thrust. The "snap" of this whiplike motion is accentuated at the posterior tip of the body, and an expanded caudal fin gives the maximum effect from the push at this point.

These propulsive movements would tend to be unregulated (as are those of a tadpole) in the absence of fins as aids in stabilization and steering. Rotary, rolling motions are checked in part by the development of median fins in addition to the caudal: dorsal fins—usually one or two of them—above, and an anal fin below, posterior to the anus. Some believe that originally all the median fins formed a continuous fold down the back, around the tail, and forward to the anal region. Certain fish larvae do exhibit a continuous median fin, and dorsals and

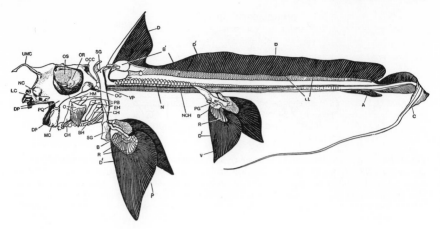

Fig. 119.   The skeleton of a female chimaera. *A*, Anal fin; *B*, fin basals; *B'*, dorsal fin supports; *BH*, basibranchial; *C*, caudal fin; *CH*, ceratohyal, ceratobranchial; *D*, dorsal fin, with spine; *D'*, dermal fin rays; *DP*, dental plates; *EH*, epibranchial; *HM*, hyomandibular; *LC*, cartilages in nasal region of "lips"; *LL*, ligament connecting fin supports; *MC*, lower jaw (Meckel's cartilage); *N*, cartilages of neural arch regions; *NC*, nasal capsule; *NCH*, notochord, with ring calcifications of sheath; *O*, cartilages in operculum; *OC*, occipital condyle; *OCC*, crest on occiput; *OR*, orbit; *OS*, interorbital septum; *P*, pectoral fin; *PB*, pharyngobranchial; *PG*, pelvic girdle; *PQ*, palatoquadrate, fused with skull; *R*, radial fin supports; *SG*, shoulder girdle; *UMC*, upper median cartilage of snout (this is not the clasper of the male); *V*, pelvic fin; *VP*, plate formed of fused anterior vertebrae. (From Dean.)

anals are often more broadly based in the embryo than in the adult. These facts tend to support such a theory; but the oldest known fossil vertebrates, with a few exceptions, show just as discrete median fin structures as any modern fish.

The skeleton of median fins is formed in the median dorsal septum above the neural spines, and in the tail also in the ventral septum in which the hemal arches occur. In the tail region neural and hemal spines may themselves contribute directly to the support of the caudal fin (Fig. 121, *A*). This, however, is never the case with the other median fins—the dorsals and anal (Figs. 107, 108, pp. 169–170; 119). Here the fin supports are commonly rods of cartilage or bone, the *radials* (sometimes in two rows), which may articulate with neural or hemal elements of the column, but are often separated by a gap from these structures. It is probable that the radials originally corresponded in number to the body segments, but frequently in teleosts double the number is present. Primitively, it appears, the radials extended well into the fin, as is the case today in sharks; in actinopterygians, however, they hardly extend at all into the free fin, which is supported mainly by fin rays (lepidotrichia) articulating with the ends of the bony radials (cf. p. 158). There may be, as in many sharks, a concentration of elements at the fin base. With such concentration there may appear larger elements termed *basals* (Fig. 107), presumably representing a fusion of radials.

In a number of sharks and the chimaeras the median fins carry anteriorly spines which act as cutwaters, and spines were present on nearly all the fins in the fossil acanthodians (Fig. 20, *A*, p. 40). In some of the lowly placoderms and in ostracoderms we find rows of spines as stabilizers in the absence of fins. It is not impossible that spines were the basic structures from which dorsal and anal fins evolved; a web of skin may have developed behind projecting spines, with a later strengthening of the structure by skeletal elements and fin rays.

Dorsal fins are normally one or two in number. Ostracoderms, placoderms, and Chondrichthyes all show both conditions in various cases; among bony fishes the actinopterygians primitively have a single dorsal (Fig. 29, *A*, p. 49), early sarcopterygians two (Fig. 27, p. 47). Dorsal fins may be reduced, or fused with the caudal as in modern lungfishes; on the other hand, there may be a secondary increase in numbers, as in the "many-winged" Polypterus (Fig. 29, *B*). A single *anal fin* is almost always present ventrally behind the anus, but may be lost in such forms as the bottom-dwelling skates and rays, and in lungfishes it fuses with the caudal.

Caudal Fin.   In the caudal fin (Fig. 121) the major skeletal supports are the arches, neural and hemal, of the distal elements of the vertebral column. Additional radial elements are sometimes present, but these are seldom well developed; the fin proper consists of a stout web of skin supported by powerful fin rays.

Three main types of caudal fins are to be found in fishes—heterocercal, diphycercal, and homocercal. The *heterocercal fin* type is that familiar in sharks (Figs. 22, *B*, p. 42; 107); the tip of the vertebral column turns upward distally, and the greater part of the fin membrane is developed below this axis.

Fig. 120.   *A*, Dorsal views of a fish swimming, to show the essential method of progression by the backward thrust of the body on the water, resulting from successive waves of curvature traveling backward along trunk and tail. The curve giving the thrust (indicated by arrow) in *1* has passed down the tail in *2* and is replaced by a succeeding wave of curvature; the thrust of this wave carries the fish forward to the position seen in *3*, and so on. *B*, Dorsal views of locomotion in a salamander. Although limbs are present, much of the forward progress is still accomplished by throwing the body into successive waves of curvature. In position *1*, the right front and left hind feet are kept on the ground, the opposite feet raised; a swing of the body in *2* carries the free feet forward, as indicated by arrows. If these feet are now planted and the other two raised, a following reversed swing of the body will carry them forward another step, as seen in *3*.

In the *diphycercal fin* the vertebral column extends straight back to the tip of the body, with the fin developed symmetrically above and below it; the living lung-fishes and Polypterus are examples of fishes with fins of this type (Figs. 28, *B*, 29, *B*). The *homocercal fin* is characteristic of teleosts (Figs. 32, p. 52; 108). It is superficially symmetric, but dissection shows that the backbone tilts strongly upward at the tip; the fin expanse is purely a ventral structure, despite its appearance, and is supported by enlarged hemal spines known as *hypurals*.

With seeming logic one tends to arrive at the conclusion that the symmetric diphycercal caudal fin is the primitive type, from which the others have been derived. This is not the case. The ancestral vertebrate may, like Amphioxus, have had a simple straight tapering tail, but in nearly every ancient fish known the tail is strongly asymmetric. In most instances diphycercal tails are shown by fossil history to have arisen from heterocercal ones, and the homocercal type is likewise of heterocercal origin. The oldest of vertebrates, the ostracoderms, have tails generally of a "reversed heterocercal" type (Fig. 18, *B*, p. 38), in which the backbone tilts downward rather than upward posteriorly. The modern cyclostomes have as adults a diphycercal type of tail, but the larval lamprey shows some development of the reversed heterocercal condition. In the oldest jawed vertebrates of the Devonian in which the tail structure is known, the heterocercal type is dominant (Figs. 20, p. 40; 22, *A*, p. 42; 27, *A*, p. 47; 28, *A*, p. 48; 29, *A*, p. 49). The tails of all well known placoderms had this structure; the heterocercal type is found in the oldest Chondrichthyes and in the oldest bony fishes of all types as well; it is clearly the ancestral form in all these fish groups.

In later Chondrichthyes the heterocercal tail remains dominant and is seen in typical form in modern sharks. However, skates and rays, with depressed bodies, and chimaeras (Figs. 22, *C*, p. 42; 119) tend to reduce the tail to a rather whiplike structure, although the basal fin pattern is that of an attenuated heterocercal form; swimming in skates and rays is mainly accomplished by undulations of the enormous pectoral fins, and a caudal fin is redundant.

Among the actinopterygians the typical Paleozoic forms, the palaeoniscoids (Fig. 29, *A*), had a good heterocercal tail fin. The sturgeons and paddlefishes have retained it (Fig. 30, p. 50), but Polypterus, although primitive in other ways, has modified the tail to a diphycercal type (Fig. 29, *B*). In Mesozoic days the holosteans, which form the middle group of ray-finned fishes, exhibit a tail technically heterocercal, but an abbreviate modification; the distal extension of the column into the fin is much shortened. This condition is retained in the gar pikes and Amia, the modern holostean representatives (Fig. 31, p. 51). Their tails are superficially symmetric and appear much like those of teleosts; but it is not until we reach this last group that further shortening of the tip of the column and development of large hypural bones gives us the true homocercal type with its deceptively simple and seemingly primitive appearance (Figs. 33, p. 53; 108).

In the Sarcopterygii, the earliest lungfishes had typical heterocercal caudals (Fig. 28, *A*, p. 48). Soon, however, in geologic history the tip of the tail tended to straighten and the dorsal and anal fins to lengthen out in the direction of the caudal. In modern genera (Fig. 28, *B*) the tail fin is diphycercal; it reaches far anteriorly both dorsally and ventrally, owing to the incorporation in it of dorsal and anal fins. The most primitive of Devonian crossopterygians likewise had a heterocercal tail fin (Fig. 27, *A*, p. 47). In this group, however, there was a rapid trend toward straightening of the tip of the vertebral column, and most crossopterygians show a characteristic type of three-lobed, diphycercal caudal (Fig. 27, *B*).

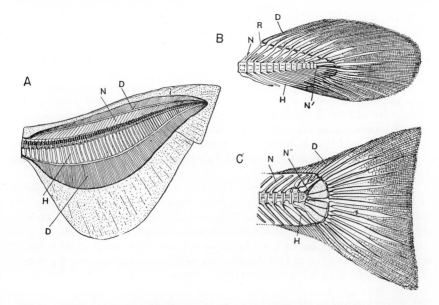

Fig. 121. Caudal fins. *A,* Heterocercal type seen in sharks, sturgeons, paddlefish; *B,* diphycercal type, as seen in Polypterus; *C,* homocercal type of teleosts. Abbreviations: *D,* Dermal fin rays; *H,* hemal spines; *N,* neural arches; *N',* tip of notochord; *R,* fin radials. In *C,* enlarged elements beyond *H* are hypural bones. (From Dean.)

It is to be noted that the development of symmetric tails, of both homocercal and diphycercal types, has taken place mainly among bony fishes with either lungs or an air bladder. The heterocercal tail facilitates swimming with the body in a tilted position and thus counteracts gravity effects; this is not as greatly needed in fishes which have air sacs capable of functioning as hydrostatic organs.

In land vertebrates (except for a few very ancient fossil amphibians) the original fish median structures have been completely abandoned; a tadpole or salamander exhibits a tail expanded dorsoventrally as a good swimming organ, but we fail to find any evidence of internal structures characteristic of fish fins. Many amniotes have returned to an aquatic mode of life. Some, such as the turtles, the extinct plesiosaurs, and the seals, have never redeveloped the tail as a propulsive organ, and rely instead upon limbs for locomotion. The extinct ichthyosaurs among reptiles and the whales and sea cows among mammals have redeveloped caudal fins, but these are never the same as those of their fish ancestors, long since lost. The caudal fins of whales and sirenians are expanded transversely, not vertically, and have fibrous rather than true skeletal supports. The ichthyosaurs have come closest to the redevelopment of a fish type of caudal fin supported by the axial skeleton; the backbone extends into the sharklike fin, but extends into its lower, not into its upper, lobe. Ichthyosaurs and cetaceans also redeveloped dorsal fins, but skeletal supports are absent.

Heterotopic Elements. Besides the normal cartilages and bones which are welded into the comprehensive pattern of the vertebrate skeleton, there may be mentioned here a variety of bones and cartilages which are not part of the proper skeleton, but arise as accessories to body organs in one vertebrate group or another. Generally these elements take the place of fibrous connective tissues

Fig. 122. Baculum of an otter.

otherwise present in the same situation; bone may form directly from such tissues or pass through an intermediate cartilaginous stage. Common, particularly in mammals, are small bones or cartilages formed in connection with muscle tendons at points of potential friction where, for example, a tendon passes over a bony ridge or joint. Such structures (frequently found in the manus or pes) are termed *sesamoids;* the knee-cap of mammals, the patella, is an "overgrown" sesamoid structure. Other bones which are found here and there in one vertebrate type or another and seem to be skeletal "afterthoughts," late in development, are termed *heterotopic bones.*

A *baculum* (os priapi, os penis, Fig. 122) is a heterotopic bone, a skeleton of the penis, found in all insectivores, bats, rodents, and carnivores, and in primates except man; its widespread distribution suggests that it developed early in the evolution of mammals. It forms in the fibrous septum between the corpora cavernosa and above the urethra. In shape it is the most varied of all bones; it may be a plate or a rod of varied form—straight, bent, or doubly curved; round, triangular, square, or flat in section; simple, pronged, spoon-shaped, or perforated; long or short.

Other heterotopic elements have a more limited distribution in special groups. We may mention, as examples, the *os palpebrae* of crocodilians, a plate embedded in the eyelid; the *os cordis* formed in the heart of deer and bovids; *rostral bones* found in the muzzles of some mammals; the *os falciforme,* a sickle-shaped element in the digging "hand" of moles, functioning as the skeleton of a supernumerary digit.

APPENDICULAR SKELETON

The girdle and limb elements constituting the appendicular skeleton definitely belong to the general somatic system of endoskeletal structures; their history, however, has been distinctive. Normally two pairs of appendages are present, as fins in fishes and as the limbs of tetrapods. The anterior, *pectoral appendages* are situated just behind the gills in fishes; in land vertebrates in an equivalent position at the border of neck and chest regions. The posterior, *pelvic appendages* are typically placed at the back end of the trunk region, just anterior to anus or cloaca.

Origin of Paired Fins. Paired appendages were not present in the ancestral vertebrates; they were developed during the course of early fish evolution. They are absent in the living jawless vertebrates, and were rarely present in the ancient ostracoderms; the only known case is that of pectoral "paddles" in cephalaspids (Fig. 18, *C*, p. 38)—structures difficult to compare with normal vertebrate limbs.

The origin of paired fins has been much debated. Many decades ago a famous anatomist of the day suggested, ingeniously, that these fins are modified gill structures. The limb girdles were compared with gill bars; the fin was regarded as developed from the flap of skin which, in a shark, forms the outer margin of the gill structure; its skeleton was supposed to have been derived from a concentration and extension of the small cartilages which may stiffen the shark gill flap. A host of embryologic and morphologic facts show that this idea is purely fanciful, but a reminiscence of this theory remains in the name archipterygium (p. 195) given to a leaf-shaped fin type (Figs. 129, *H*, p. 196; 130, *D*, p. 197) which was supposed, under this theory, to be primitive (but apparently is not).

In reaction against this theory arose a rival *fin fold theory* of the origin of paired fins. Its advocates pointed out that paired fins are similar to median fins in essential structure. In both there is a fold of skin extending outward from the body, a centrally placed set of skeletal supports, and, on each surface of the skeletal structures, a sheet of musculature which moves the fin. If the structure of median and paired fins is similar, may they not have had a similar origin? If, as we believe, median fins have evolved in simple fashion as keels growing outward dorsally or ventrally from the trunk, may not the paired fins have developed from the flanks in a comparable way? *

The functional aspect of paired appendages may be considered in relation to this problem. From the viewpoint of tetrapods we tend to think of paired limbs as active propulsive organs. This is, however, not a function of the paired fins in most fish groups. In many modern fishes they have relatively narrow bases and are capable of a free movement which is of aid in steering, but generally has little to do with propulsion. In fins which seem to be of relatively ancient patterns there is generally, in contrast, a broad base which makes the fin relatively immobile. Primitively, it would seem, the paired fins were little more than horizontal stabilizing keels, which aided, as do the median fins, in the prevention of rolling movements, and had the further function of preventing fore and aft pitching. Both structure and function suggest that, like the median fins, the paired fins were developed as stabilizing aids in the aquatic locomotion of early vertebrates.

Since the extinct placoderms are the oldest of gnathostomes, one would, a priori, expect in them paired fins of diagrammatically simple structure. This is the exact opposite of the actual findings. The fins of placoderms were "experimental models," most of which differed as much from the more orthodox paired fins of later date as did many early (and unsuccessful) flying machines from the modern airplane. Notable is the frequent presence of spinous structures as the main element in placoderm fins. In some placoderms (Fig. 20, *C*, p. 40) the entire paired "fin" is a bony structure; in the acanthodians (Figs. 20, *A*; 129, *A*, p. 196) the fins are more normal in appearance, but are supported by a stout (and fixed) spine. We have noted earlier the possibility that median fins may have developed in connection with spinous structures; the placoderm story suggests that the same may have been true of paired fins.

Typical living vertebrates have two pairs of appendages; but other phyla of animals may have other numbers of limbs, and there is no reason to think that there is anything sacrosanct about four as a limb count. In this regard, as in others, the placoderms experimented. Some had well developed pectorals, but no pelvic fins. Some acanthodians went to the other extreme and show additional fin pairs (Fig. 20, *A*); in one "spiny shark" as many as seven pairs are present. Above the placoderm level, however, supernumerary appendages are never seen; it is vain (if amusing) to speculate as to the possible results had they survived in higher vertebrates.

---

* In an extreme form of this theory it was suggested that the paired fins developed out of a pair of long folds running the length of either flank, and that these folds were continuous with a median fold running along the back and tail. There is little evidence to support this.

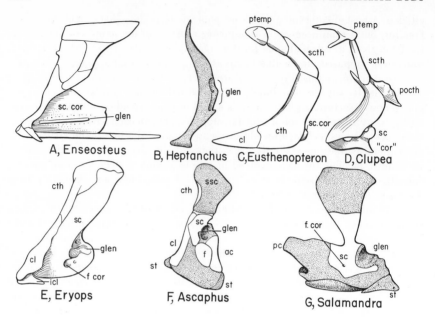

Fig. 123.   The shoulder girdle in fishes and amphibians. *A*, Devonian placoderm; *B*, a shark; *C*, a Devonian crossopterygian; *D*, a teleost (herring); *E*, a Paleozoic primitive amphibian; *F*, a frog; *G*, a salamander. Cartilage stippled. In all except *B* and *G* a dermal girdle is present; in fishes *A*, *C*, *D*, this is the most prominent part of the girdle, including all parts except that labeled scapula and coracoid, and in the placoderm (*A*) the dermal girdle is the lateral part of an extensive thoracic armor. In amphibians the dermal girdle is reduced or absent. Except in the shark the endoskeletal girdle is relatively small in fishes and partially hidden beneath the dermal elements. In amphibians the endoskeletal girdle is expanded, but generally ossifies from a single center, comparable to the scapula of amniotes; the frog, however, has a coracoid element. Much of the endoskeletal girdle is cartilaginous in living amphibians. *ac*, Anterior coracoid element; *cl*, clavicle; *"cor"*, coracoid of teleost (homology with that of land forms doubtful); *cth*, cleithrum; *f*, foramen in coracoid plate of frog; *f.cor*, coracoid foramen for nerve and blood vessels; *glen*, glenoid cavity, point of fin attachment in fishes; *icl*, interclavicle; *pc*, precoracoid process of coracoid plate; *pocth*, postcleithrum; *ptemp*, posttemporal; *sc*, scapula; *sc. cor*, single scapulo-coracoid ossification of fishes; *scth*, supracleithrum; *ssc*, suprascapula; *st*, sternum. Cartilage stippled. (*A* after Stensiö; *C* after Jarvik; *D* and *F* after Parker.)

Pectoral Girdle—Dermal Elements (Figs. 123, 124).   Each vertebrate limb includes not only skeletal elements lying within the free portion of the appendage, but a basal supporting structure, the limb girdle. This lies within the substance of the trunk, acts as a stable base for the motions of the fin, and, in land vertebrates, forms an intermediary through which the weight of the body is transferred to the limb.

The pectoral girdle is, in all major groups except the Chondrichthyes, a duplex structure including both dermal and endoskeletal elements. The latter form the fin supports; the dermal bones, however, give added strength and help to tie the endoskeletal girdle to the body.

As we have noted, the anterior part of the fish body was early armored by solid plates of bone, in contrast to the flexible scale system found more posteriorly. In varied placoderms, particularly the arthrodires, this armor extended backward to enclose part of the trunk (Figs. 20, *B*, p. 40; 123, *A*). The side walls of the thoracic "chest" armor, behind the gill opening, can be considered a *dermal shoulder girdle*, although differing greatly from that in higher fishes (an endoskeletal girdle was present within and behind the dermal girdle). The Chondrichthyes lack dermal elements, in correlation with the general reduction of the bony skeleton in that group.

In the more primitive bony fishes (Fig. 123, *C*) we find a dermal pectoral girdle with a pattern basic to that of all remaining vertebrate types. On either side is a vertical band of superficially placed dermal bone extending dorsoventrally along the back edge of the gill opening; the endoskeletal girdle, usually of modest dimensions in fishes, is bound to its inner and posterior surfaces. The main element in the fish dermal girdle is a vertically placed paired *cleithrum;* below it is the smaller *clavicle,* which curves downward and forward beneath the gill chamber and is expanded ventrally, where the two clavicles have a union— a symphysis—with one another. Above each cleithrum there are additional elements which curve upward and forward above the gill chamber and anchor the dermal girdle to the skull.

This general type of structure is found in a great variety of fishes—all known crossopterygians and lungfishes and all chondrosteans, living and extinct. In the holosteans and teleosts (Fig. 123, *D*), however, the clavicle is lost.

In early fossil amphibians (Fig. 123, *E*) the dermal girdle is retained, but with notable changes. Dorsally, the connection with the skull is lost, a condition which allows the head to move more freely on the trunk. For part of their length cleithrum and clavicle are rather slender dermal rods lying along the front margin of the much enlarged endoskeletal girdle. The upper end of the cleithrum may expand to cap the shoulder blade; ventrally, the clavicles typically expand in triangular shape; between them there is a diamond-shaped median *interclavicle* —a new element, although foreshadowed in some crossopterygians by an enlarged scale in this position.

Among modern amphibians (Fig. 123, *F, G*) the dermal girdle has disappeared completely in the skeletally degenerate urodeles. In the frogs it is much modified. There is no interclavicle, but a cleithrum rudiment may be present in the scapular region. The clavicle forms a bar connecting scapula and sternum. In some frogs the clavicle is developed in connection with a bar of cartilage. This is a highly unorthodox procedure, of course, for a dermal bone; it appears that this cartilage is an intrusion from the underlying endoskeletal girdle.

In primitive fossil reptiles (Fig. 124, *A*) the dermal girdle was like that of early amphibians; the cleithrum, however, disappeared at an early reptilian stage and is not present in any living amniote. Clavicles and interclavicle are found little changed today in Sphenodon and lizards (Fig. 124, *B, C*), but have been subject to change and loss in other groups. In turtles (Fig. 99, p. 160) they are incorporated in the plastron; in crocodilians the clavicles have disappeared, but the interclavicle persists ventrally (Fig. 124, *E*). In birds the clavicles and interclavicle are present (Fig. 124, *F*) in fused form as the *furcula,* the wishbone.

As witnessed by the living monotremes, the primitive mammals retained the general reptilian pattern of interclavicle and paired clavicles (Fig. 124, *I*), but above the monotreme level the former has vanished (Fig. 124, *J*). The clavicles remain in many of the more generalized marsupials and placentals, articulating ventrally with the sternum. They are, however, frequently lost or reduced (as in the cat), particularly in running or bounding types where complete freedom of the shoulder blade from the body skeleton is desirable to relieve the jars otherwise transmitted from front legs to body.

Endoskeletal Shoulder Girdle (Figs. 123, 124).   Functionally, the endoskeletal girdle is much more important than the dermal girdle, for it always carries the limb articulation and is used as the major base of attachment of limb muscles. It is cartilaginous in the Chondrichthyes and partly or entirely cartilaginous in some of the more degenerate bony fishes; otherwise it is an ossified structure, although cartilage may persist in peripheral areas in many fishes, amphibians, and reptiles.

Centrally situated on the endoskeletal girdle on either side is the limb articulation. In land animals with but a single proximal appendicular element this is an articular socket termed the *glenoid fossa;* in most fishes, however, a number of skeletal fin elements articulate with the girdle. An area above the limb articulation, affording attachment to limb muscles, may be termed in general the *scapular blade;* a similar area below it, the *coracoid plate.* (These regional names are derived from those of bony elements found in these areas in land vertebrates, but we shall use the terms here merely as descriptive of girdle regions, without reference to ossifications.)

In the Chondrichthyes, as we have noted, the dermal girdle is not developed, and in compensation, apparently, the endoskeletal cartilages (Fig. 123, *B*) are enlarged, those of the two sides fusing ventrally to produce a U-shaped structure. In bony fishes the endoskeletal girdle is relatively small; it is generally ossified, with, in teleosts, as many as three small bony elements present.

In land vertebrates, in which the dermal girdle tends to undergo reduction, the endoskeletal girdle is, in contrast with bony fishes, much expanded. This expansion is obviously related to the larger size of the land limb, as compared to the fish fin, and the more massive nature of the limb musculature attaching to the girdle. Above the glenoid fossa there is in primitive tetrapods (Fig. 123, *E*) an elongate yet broad scapular blade; below, an expanded coracoid plate with a characteristic *coracoid foramen* for a nerve and blood vessels. In primitive amphibians the entire endochondral girdle may be ossified, but each half ossifies as a single element which corresponds to the scapular ossification of amniotes. The modern urodeles (Fig. 123, *G*) also have but a single ossification; much of the girdle remains unossified, and there is an elongate cartilaginous anterior process from the coracoid plate region. In urodeles and primitive frogs the lower margins of the two coracoid plates may overlap ventrally. In some frogs a *firmisternal* condition develops (Fig. 115, *B*, p. 174) in which the margins of the two coracoid plates are butted together ventrally, bracing the animal against the jar of landing in its leaping mode of progression. In frogs (Fig. 123, *F*) and in all early reptiles there are two ossifications on either side. One, the *scapula*, centers in the scapular blade. The other, a ventral ossification, is sometimes called the coracoid, but, since it is not homologous with the mammalian bone of that name, is better termed *procoracoid* or *anterior coracoid.*

In many reptiles (Fig. 124, *A–C*) there persists a girdle pattern highly comparable to that of primitive tetrapods. However, chelonians (Fig. 124, *D*) show a triradiate girdle structure, with two ventral prongs. It is sometimes said that there are here two coracoid bones; but actually the anterior ventral process is a downward extension of the scapula, which thus retains its connection with the clavicle (here a plate situated ventrally in the plastron). In crocodilians (Fig. 124, *E*) and dinosaurs both scapula and coracoid are rather elongate elements which meet at an angle at the glenoid fossa. This construction is in general retained in birds (Fig. 124, *F*); the coracoids brace the wing on the sternum.

The earliest of mammal-like reptiles, the pelycosaurs (Fig. 124, *G*), added a third ossification not present in other reptiles. Most of the coracoid plate was still ossified as an anterior coracoid, but behind it there appeared a new element, equivalent to the true *coracoid* of mammals. This bone was small in pelycosaurs;

Fig. 124. The shoulder girdle in reptiles and mammals. *A*, "Stem reptile" (cotylosaur); *B*, Sphenodon; *C*, a lizard; *D*, a turtle; *E*, a crocodile; *F*, a bird; *G*, a pelycosaur (primitive mammal-like reptile); *H*, a therapsid; *I*, a monotreme (duckbill); *J*, opossum. In *B*, *E*, and *F* the sternum is shown. In most reptiles and birds only one (anterior) coracoid element is present; in mammal-like forms the true coracoid appears and persists, despite the loss of the coracoid plate area. The borders of the scapula and coracoid are often cartilaginous in reptiles. In lizards, scapula and coracoid are often fenestrated at points of muscular origins. The cleithrum has vanished in all living amniotes, but persisted long in mammal-like forms (*G*, *H*); its position is represented by the scapular spine, which lies at the front edge of the scapula in monotremes, but back of the new supraspinous fossa in higher mammals. *ac*, Anterior coracoid bone of reptiles, birds, monotremes; *acr*, acromion; *c. for*, coracoid foramen; *cl*, clavicle; *cor*, true coracoid; *cth*, cleithrum; *icl*, interclavicle; *isp*, infraspinous fossa; *sc*, scapula; *sp*, spine of scapula; *ssp*, supraspinous fossa; *st*, sternum. (*C* and *I* partly after Parker; *H* after Pearson.)

in therapsids (Fig. 124, *H*) it grew forward at the expense of the anterior coracoid to occupy the greater part of this ventral plate. Meanwhile, excavation of the front edge of the coracoid plate had the result that the point of attachment of the clavicle to the scapula became a distinct process, the *acromion*.

In the most primitive of living mammals, the monotremes, the endoskeletal girdle (Fig. 124, *I*) greatly resembles that of the therapsids. With the step upward from monotremes to marsupials and placentals, however, there is a major change (Fig. 124, *J*). The entire coracoid plate has vanished; the anterior coracoid has disappeared, and the coracoid has dwindled to a process like a crow's beak (as its name implies), attached to the lower margin of the scapula. The girdle is thus practically reduced to a dorsally situated scapular blade, with the glenoid cavity below it. But even the scapula has radically changed, for, instead of being a simple plate, it has a ridge, the *scapular spine*, running down its length which separates *supraspinous* and *infraspinous fossae*; the acromion is situated not at the front end of the bone, but at the base of the spine.

This major change in girdle structure is related to the shift in limb posture in mammals as compared to reptiles, and consequent major changes in limb musculature (cf. p. 268). Much of the musculature which once arose from the coracoid plate has shifted upward to the scapula, rendering this plate useless. The spine and acromion on the scapula actually represent the original anterior margin of that bone; the supraspinous part of the bone is a new shelf built out in front of the erstwhile front margin, to accommodate part of the musculature which has migrated upward.

Pelvic Girdle (Figs. 126; 127, p. 193; 128, p. 194). The pelvic girdle, a purely endochondral structure, differs markedly from the pectoral throughout the vertebrate series—even more markedly, perhaps, in lower than in higher types. In fishes (Fig. 130, p. 197) each half of the girdle is a small and simple ventral plate, often triangular, embedded in the muscles and connective tissues of the abdomen, typically just anterior to the cloaca. Never is there in fishes any connection with the vertebral column; the ventral tissues seem to be sufficient to anchor girdle and limb in place. The half-girdles of the two sides are usually in contact anteromedially. This contact, a primitive *pelvic symphysis*, affords further mutual support, and in the sharks and lungfishes the two half-girdles are fused to form a single element. Along its posterolateral margin the girdle affords a point of attachment for the fin skeleton. Although the half-girdle of either side is usually a single, compact structure, the sturgeons and the early shark Cladodus show evidence of subdivision, suggesting that the pelvis arose from a fusion of originally independent basal fin elements. In the Chondrichthyes, lungfishes, and a few ray-finned forms the girdle remains in a cartilaginous condition in the adult; in other fish groups each half of the girdle ossifies as a single element.

With the presence, in tetrapods, of large limbs which support much of the weight of the body, the pelvic girdle changes in radical fashion. Greater areas are needed on the girdle—particularly ventrally—for the attachment of the limb musculature; the problems of support necessitate that the girdle be tied more closely into the body (Fig. 125).

In the process of tetrapod development the original, ventral part of the girdle on either side becomes a large plate of bone lying in a tilted position in the flank. This ossifies from two centers, the *pubis* anteriorly and the *ischium* posteriorly, and may be termed the *pubo-ischiadic plate*. Externally, it offers an area of origin for limb muscles; it is pierced by the *obturator foramen*, carrying a nerve

Fig. 125. Diagrams to show the development of the pelvic girdle and sacrum in the evolution of amphibians from fishes. *A*, Left lateral view of the pelvic region of a fish, with the vertebral column and ribs above, the small pelvic girdle placed ventrally. *B*, Primitive tetrapod stage, found in some early fossil amphibians. The girdle has expanded, with the three typical bony elements. The ilium extends upward, but was presumably connected with the column only through ligaments binding it to the neighboring ribs. *C*, The girdle has grown further, and the ilium is firmly attached to an enlarged sacral rib.

supply to part of these muscles. Above the pubo-ischiadic plate there develops the *acetabulum,* a large rounded socket which receives the head of the proximal limb bone, the femur. Pubis and ischium enter into the formation of the acetabulum; its upper margin is occupied by the third of the pelvic elements, the *ilium,* which forms the dorsal part of the girdle. In fishes there is sometimes a small dorsal girdle process; in even the most primitive of known amphibians this process, as the ilium, had grown to be a large rodlike structure, and there early developed an iliac blade in addition to the primitive rod; beneath this blade lies an expanded sacral rib, which ties girdle and body together and is the major factor in the support of the body on the limbs.

The two halves of the pelvic girdle are broadly apposed ventrally in a symphysis. The cloaca lies posterior to the pelvic girdle; hence the girdle and the ribs and vertebrae with which it joins form a ring of bone bounding a *pelvic outlet,* through which materials in genital, urinary, and digestive systems must pass before leaving the body; the size of the outlet is an important factor in forms laying large eggs or bearing young alive.

There are marked variations among amphibians in the structure of the pelvic girdle (Fig. 126). The posterior projection of the ilium was usually reduced

Fig. 126. The pelvic girdle in amphibians. *A*, A primitive fossil labyrinthodont; *B*, a typical later labyrinthodont; *C*, a frog; *D*, a urodele. A posterior process of the ilium, present primitively, is retained in many reptiles (cf. Figs. 127 and 128), but is lost in most Amphibia (represented by a prong in *B*). In the anurans the ilium is a specialized and elongate rod. The pubis was primitively well ossified, but remains cartilaginous in many fossil forms and all modern amphibians.

even in ancient times, and this bone became only a narrow vertical blade apposed to the sacral rib. In many of the older amphibians the pubis failed to ossify, and it is never ossified in modern forms. The urodele pelvis (Fig. 126, *D*) is basically similar to that of older types except for the development anteriorly of a median cartilaginous prepubic process (not figured), which serves as an added support for the belly wall. In the anurans (Fig. 126, *C*) in correlation with the hopping gait and shortening of the vertebral column, the ilium is a long slender bone extending far forward as well as upward from the acetabulum.

In reptiles (Fig. 127, *A*) the blade of the ilium tends to be expanded for the attachment of more extensive limb muscles on the outer surface, and for the attachment medially of two or more sacral ribs rather than the single rib usual in amphibians. Within this class there occurs great variation in pelvic structure.

Much of the outer surface of the pubo-ischiadic plate was primitively occupied by the broad, fleshy origin of a muscle (obturator externus; cf. Fig. 187, p. 271) running to the under side of the femur. An opening, or fenestra, covered by a membrane, tends to develop beneath the origin of the muscle, separating pubis and ischium and turning the pelvic girdle into a tripartite structure; this *pubo-ischiadic fenestra* (or *thyroid fenestra*) is present in turtles, Sphenodon, and lizards (Fig. 127, *B*).

In the archosaurians (Fig. 127, *C–E*) the girdle becomes highly modified in relation to the development of bipedal habits. In these reptiles and their avian

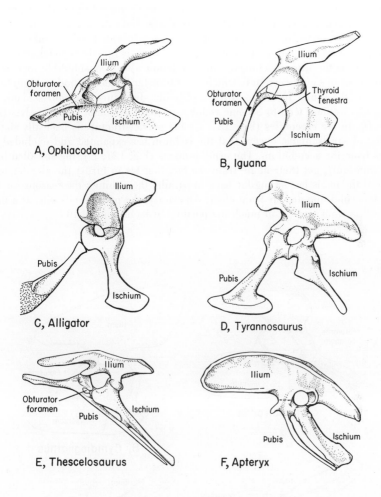

Fig. 127. The pelvic girdle in reptiles and birds. *A*, Primitive reptile; *B*, a lizard; *C*, a crocodilian; *D*, a reptile-like dinosaur (Saurischia); *E*, a birdlike dinosaur (Ornithischia);—*F*, a bird (the kiwi). In *A* the ilium is a low blade, and the same is true in lizards; in other forms this structure is more expanded. In the dinosaurs and birds, with a bipedal type of locomotion, the ilium has grown forward somewhat as in mammals (cf. Fig. 128). In the archosaurs (*C*, *D*, *E*) and the birds descended from them there is typically an open bottom to the acetabulum for the better reception of the head of the femur. In the primitive reptile the pubo-ischium is a solid plate. In lizards there is a large thyroid fenestra developed between pubis and ischium, from which a large muscle to the femur takes origin (Sphenodon and turtles are similar). This fenestra is comparable to one seen in mammals, but there the obturator foramen is concerned in the development of the fenestra. In such archosaurs as the alligators and saurischians there appears at first sight to be a similar structure. Actually, however, this is not the case; the pubis and ischium are twisted downward, and the true ventral margin of the girdle is the curving lower margin of pubis and ischium. In *C* and *D* the pelvis is triradiate, with a simply-built pubis; in *E* the pubis is two-pronged, and the pelvis tetraradiate. In the bird the anterior process of the pubis is reduced or absent. In the alligator the pubis is excluded from the acetabulum by the ischium; the pubic region of the girdle extends forward along the belly as a fibrous cartilage.

descendants the acetabulum usually becomes open at its base for the better reception of the head of the femur. The ventral plate tends to be reduced, and the ventral limb muscle attachments moved fore or aft toward the ends of pubis or ischium, gaining a more advantageous leverage. Both these bones curve downward at their ends, and in all except the most primitive fossil members of the Archosauria the symphysis becomes restricted to their tips. In bipedal archosaurs and in birds the ilium is elongate, in correlation with a considerable increase in the number of sacral vertebrae which must transfer the entire body weight to the limbs via the ilium. In the so-called reptile-like dinosaurs, the saurischians, the pubis and ischium tend to become rodlike, giving a triradiate type of pelvis (Fig. 127, *D*). In the crocodiles (Fig. 127, *C*) the pelvic structure is basically similar to that of saurischians, except that the ischium has expanded and excluded the pubis from the acetabulum. The ornithischians (Fig. 127, *E*), the so-called bird-like dinosaurs, get their name from the fact that (as in birds) the slender main shaft of the pubis has swung far back to parallel the ischium; the reasons for this peculiar condition are far from clear. Anteriorly, the pubis sends out, as a belly support, a stout process in much the position of its original shaft.

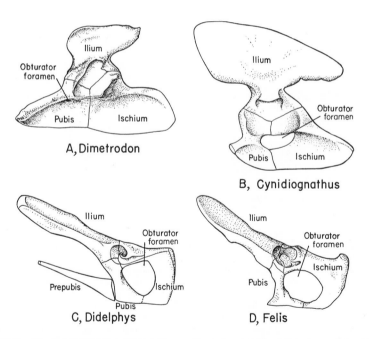

Fig. 128. The pelvic girdle in mammal-like reptiles and mammals. *A*, Primitive pelycosaur; *B*, a therapsid; *C*, opossum; *D*, cat. The Dimetrodon pelvis is of a primitive reptilian type. In the therapsid the ilium has grown forward dorsally, pubis and ischium have swung back ventrally, and the obturator foramen has expanded (comparable to the situation in many modern reptiles) into an obturator (or thyroid) fenestra. The opossum and cat show a typical mammalian structure, with a large obturator fenestra, a shortened ischium and a slender ilium (secondarily broadened in many heavy mammals, however). The opossum, like other marsupials and the monotremes, has a pair of "marsupial bones" not found in other groups. (In the cat, as in certain other mammals, an accessory element is seen in the acetabulum.)

In birds (Fig. 127, *F*), as in ornithischians, the pubis has swung back to a posterior position. There is, however, little development of an anterior pubic process; the greatly developed sternum forms a bony sheath over most of the ventral surface of the body, and belly support by such a process is little needed. Except in the ostrich, the pelvic symphysis has disappeared, and the two halves of the girdle are widely separated ventrally, a situation correlated with the relatively large size of the bird egg and the consequent necessity for a large pelvic outlet. Some strengthening of the ventral parts of the girdle is, however, afforded by a fusion between the posterior ends of the three elements of either side in many birds.

In the mammal-like reptiles and mammals (Fig. 128) marked changes associated with changed limb posture and changed musculature have occurred. The muscles and the bones from which they originate undergo a marked rotation, counter-clockwise as seen from the left side. The ilium, which primitively grew mainly backward dorsally, comes to extend anteriorly as it reaches upward to the sacrum. The pubis and ischium, on the contrary, have moved posteriorly so that the ventral plate of the girdle extends hardly at all anteriorly to the acetabulum.

The mammalian ilium is primitively a rather slender rod, triangular in section; however, in heavy-bodied ungulates (as horses, cattle, elephants) or bipeds (as man), in which there are powerful gluteal muscles running from ilium to femur, this bone may be much expanded. As in many reptiles, the pubo-ischiadic plate is fenestrated. Here, however, in contrast to reptiles, the foramen for the obturator nerve is included in this opening, termed the *obturator fenestra*. In connection with viviparity, the pelvic opening is often broader in the female, and in some forms the symphysis (mainly between the pubes) is loosened under hormonal control at the time of parturition. In monotremes and marsupials there is a pair of "marsupial bones" (prepubes), extending forward from the pubis and supporting the body wall. They were not present in the ancestral reptiles and are absent in placentals; the reason for their appearance in these two groups of primitive mammals is not clear (although they serve to a degree in support of abdominal muscles and the pouch for the young).

Paired Fins in Fishes (Figs. 129, 130). We noted earlier some of the theories and problems connected with the origin and nature of fish fins. Apart from various peculiar early patterns, we see in the general run of living and fossil fishes two basic types of paired fin skeletons, together with various intermediates. One type is the *archipterygium*, typically developed in the lungfish Epiceratodus (Figs. 129, *H*; 130, *D*). The skeleton of the leaf-shaped, narrow-based fin consists of a jointed central axis and side branches which are usually better developed on the anterior (preaxial) margin of the fin. Typical archipterygia are found in fossil lungfishes and in some early crossopterygians; hence the archipterygium may be a basic type in the sarcopterygians. But except for an aberrant family of extinct sharks it is unknown in other fish groups, ancient or modern, and hence is unlikely to have been antecedent to other fin types. In most crossopterygians we find an abbreviated type of archipterygium (Figs. 129, *I*; 130, *E*) in which the axis is short and the branches are generally confined to the anterior margin—a fin pattern of great interest as one antecedent to the skeletal plan of the tetrapod limb.

In strong contrast to the archipterygium is the finfold type of fin seen in ancient Paleozoic sharks such as Cladoselache (Figs. 129, *B*, 130, *A*, Cladodus). Here the fin has a broad base, and hence was little more than a fixed horizontal stabilizer; there is no projecting fin axis, and the skeleton consisted of parallel bars of cartilage. This type of fin persists with modification in modern cartilaginous fishes (Figs. 129, *C, D;* 130, *B, C, F*). The major change is that the base of the fin has generally become much narrowed, making it more movable and a more effective steering device. With this constriction of the base, the fin cartilages have, of necessity, become crowded together; there is a tendency for one of the most posterior cartilages to become particularly prominent and act as an axis on to which many of the other bars articulate. This axial element is frequently

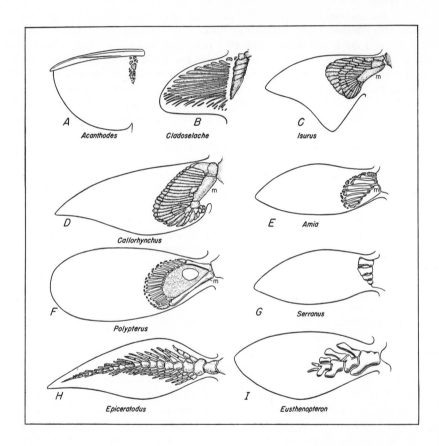

Fig. 129. Pectoral fins of fishes. All are fins of the left side, viewed from the upper surface, so oriented that the long axis of the body is vertical on the page, the anterior end above. The outline of the complete fin is indicated, and (except for *A*) the articular region of the girdle is included at the right. *A*, Fossil acanthodian, with the fin skeleton little developed, and a spine forming a cutwater and main fin support. *B*, Primitive fossil shark, with a parallel-bar type of fin. *C*, Modern shark with a narrow-based flexible fin and a basal concentration of bars with formation of a metapterygial axis (the metapterygium is the elongate posterior basal element, *m*). *D*, Comparable type found in chimaeras. *E*, Primitive actinopterygian type, with parallel-bar construction, but metapterygial axis present. *F*, An aberrant modification of the last, found in the archaic actinopterygian, Polypterus. *G*, Teleost (sea bass) with a much reduced skeleton. *H*, The typical archipterygium of the Australian lungfish. *I*, The abbreviate archipterygium of a fossil crossopterygian. (*A* after Watson; *B* after Dean; *C* and *D* after Mivart.)

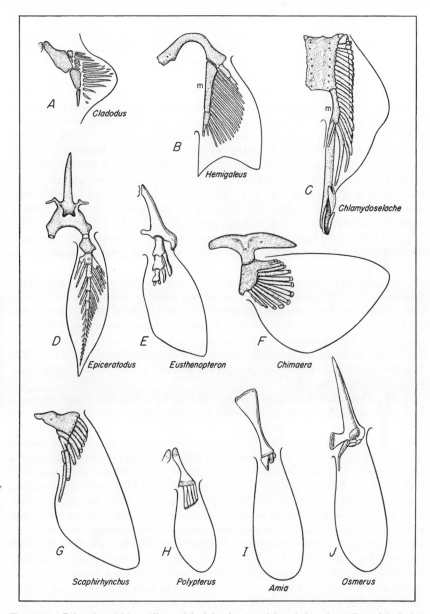

Fig. 130. Pelvic fins of fishes. All are of the left side, viewed from below, the midline of the body is at the left, the anterior end above. The fin outline is indicated in each case. The left half of the pelvic girdle is included, or the whole girdle if the halves are fused. *A,* Primitive Carboniferous shark, with a broad-based fin and parallel bars as fin support. *B,* Modern female shark, with similar construction. *C,* Male shark, with additional cartilages supporting the clasper. *D,* The archipterygium of the Australian lungfish. *E,* The abbreviate archipterygium of an ancient crossopterygian. *F,* Female chimaera fin, essentially similar to that of sharks. *G,* The sturgeon, also with a sharklike construction. *H,* Polypterus; *I,* the bow-fin; *J,* a teleost; showing nearly complete reduction of the bony fin skeleton. *m,* Metapterygium. (*A* after Jaekel; *B* after Garman; *C* after Goode; *D, H, I* after Davidoff; *E* after Gregory.)

termed the *metapterygium.** It is obvious that the modern type of shark fin shows
a condition intermediate between the finfold type and the archipterygium; there
is here a main fin axis with side branches, although the branches are almost all
on the exterior or anterior margin of the axis. In the shark group, at least, the
parallel-barred finfold type is primitive, suggesting that the archipterygial type is
a secondary, not a primitive, type of fin.

The actinopterygians are by definition a group of fishes in which, in general,
skeleton and flesh extends hardly at all into the fin, which is mainly a web of
skin supported by horny rays. Consideration of a series of actinopterygian fins
indicates rather surely that they have been derived from the finfold type, and
have evolved in a fashion comparable to that of sharks. The basic structure is a
series of parallel bars; in such a primitive ray-finned form as the sturgeon, the
pelvic fin (Fig. 130, *G*) is broadbased, with numerous bars extending into the fin
much as in a primitive shark. As in later sharks, there is in ray-finned forms a
trend toward a narrow fin base and greater flexibility, with a consequent development of a metapterygial axis in some cases (Fig. 129, *E*).† In teleosts (Figs.
129, *G;* 130, *J*) the bony elements are much reduced; there typically remain in
the pectoral fin only a few short parallel bars, and in the pelvic fin these may be
further reduced to nubbins of bone or cartilage.

In fishes generally the pectoral fins are more important as steering devices
than the pelvics; they are the larger of the two pairs and have a more highly developed skeleton. Pectorals are practically universal in jawed fishes of every sort,
but the pelvics may be reduced or may, in many teleosts, move forward to a position beneath the shoulder region (Fig. 33, *B*, p. 53) or even forward beneath
the "chin." In the Chondrichthyes, associated with internal fertilization (cf. Chap.
13), the finger-like *claspers* are supported by extra posterior cartilages on the
pelvic fins (Fig. 130, *C*).

The Primitive Tetrapod Limb. The limbs of land vertebrates appear at
first sight strikingly different from fish fins, but although the greater size and
greater complexity of the land limb tend to obscure the relationship, the two
are readily comparable in basic structure. The numerous muscles that sheathe
the tetrapod appendage can be resolved on comparative and embryologic grounds
into two series comparable to the simpler muscle masses on the upper and lower
surfaces of the fish fin, and the limb elements of land forms are comparable in
essence to the fin supports of crossopterygian fishes with abbreviate archipterygia.

The limb of a primitive land vertebrate is composed of three major segments (Fig. 131). In both front and hind limbs—corresponding, respectively, to
pectoral and pelvic fins—the proximal segment projects laterally from the body
and includes but a single bony element, humerus or femur, which primitively
moves fore and aft in an essentially horizontal plane. Beyond the elbow or knee
region a second segment is present which lifts the body off the ground. (Track-
ways of ancient amphibians, by the way, prove erroneous the popular belief that
these ancient tetrapods crawled on their bellies.) Here movement in a vertical
plane parallel to the long axis of the body is capable of increasing the progression caused by the fore and aft movement of the proximal elements. Two bones

* It is sometimes stated that the shark fin has three elements attaching basally, termed the pro-,
meso-, and metapterygium. This situation is seen at times, but actually there is great variation in elements other than the metapterygium.

† Polypterus (Fig. 129, *F*) shows a peculiar and overelaborated development of the pectoral fin
skeleton, but the primary structure is nevertheless one of parallel bars.

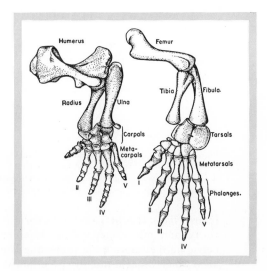

Fig. 131. Left front and hind limbs of a primitive reptile (Ophiacodon), to show the general pattern of limb construction in early tetrapods.

are present in this segment—radius and ulna in the forelimb, tibia and fibula in the hind, the first named in each case being the anterior or medial element of the pair.

The third segment in either pectoral or pelvic limb is that of the foot, termed the manus in the pectoral, pes in the pelvic, limb. This includes proximally the wrist or ankle region—carpus or tarsus—which forms a more or less flexible adjustment between the foot and the more proximal part of the limb, and distally the toes, or digits, placed upon the ground. The proximal element of a toe (contained in palm or sole) is a metapodial—a metacarpal or metatarsal; the remaining joints form the phalanges.

This pattern of limb skeletal construction is, as mentioned, comparable basically to that found in crossopterygian relatives of the tetrapods (Fig. 132). In such fishes there is a single proximal element articulating with the shoulder girdle and equivalent to humerus or femur; in a second segment are two elements comparable to the radius and ulna of pectoral limb or tibia and fibula of the hind leg. Beyond this point the fin skeleton of known crossopterygians shows an irregular and variable branching arrangement; attempts at detailed homologies of these distal elements with particular bones of the manus or pes seem for the most part to be valueless.

From the first there were notable differences between the front and hind legs of land vertebrates, despite the basic similarity of their bony patterns, and many of these differences are retained in later tetrapods. We note particularly the differences in the major joints between limb segments. Below the elbow, radius and ulna rotate rather freely on the humerus, but the comparable knee joint is invariably a simple untwistable hinge. Wrist articulations are essentially hingelike; but although the ankle in mammals is a hinge, the foot could be readily rotated on the shin in reptiles and early amphibians. This contrast in joint structure can, it seems, be traced back to a contrast in the position of the pectoral and pelvic fins in the ancestors of the tetrapods (Fig. 133). Presumably, as in living lungfishes, the fins of the fish forebears of tetrapods extended outward and backward from the body. For the pectoral fin a major forward twist occurred at the

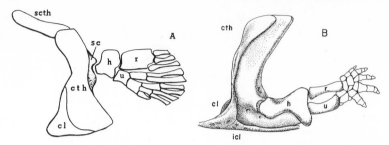

Fig. 132. The shoulder girdle and pectoral fin of a crossopterygian, *A*, and the same structures in an ancient fossil amphibian, *B*, placed in a comparable pose to show the basic similarity in limb pattern. *h*, *r*, and *u*, Humerus, radius, and ulna of the tetrapod and obvious homologues in the fish fin. *cl*, Clavicle; *cth*, cleithrum; *icl*, interclavicle; *sc*, scapula; *scth*, supracleithrum. (*A* after Gregory.)

future elbow; this brought the forearm forward, with the "hand" directed anteriorly, and only a simple hinge was needed in the future wrist region. In the pelvic fin the future limb, projecting laterally, developed a simple hinge at the knee which brought the lower leg into vertical position; this segment, however, faced more or less outward and hence sharp rotation at the future ankle was needed to bring the foot into a fore and aft position.

LIMB FUNCTION AND POSTURE.   The development of terrestrial habits brought about a major revolution in vertebrate locomotion. In fishes, propulsion was accomplished by undulatory movements of the trunk and tail. Undulatory movement appears to have long remained important in early land animals and is still important today in salamanders (Fig. 120, p. 181). Here the feeble limbs play only a minor role as positive propulsive agents; they are in great measure stationary organs through which the push of body undulations may be exerted on the ground. In tetrapods generally, however, the limbs have taken over a positive and dominant role in progression.

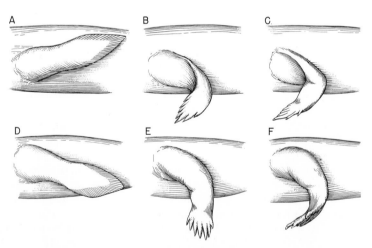

Fig. 133. Diagrams to show the postural shift in the paired limbs in the transition from fish to amphibian. *A* to *C*, Pectoral limb; *D* to *F*, pelvic limb; *A*, *D*, fish position; *B*, *E*, transitional stage; *C*, *F*, amphibian position (cf. text).

Primitive land vertebrates, both amphibians and reptiles, had a sprawling posture, with the limbs extending far out from the side of the body. This pose is still preserved in living urodeles, and with little modification in turtles, lizards, and Sphenodon. But it is wasteful of energy, for much muscular effort is used up in merely keeping the body off the ground, and most land vertebrates have modified this primitive structure in various ways. The frogs have become specialized for a hopping gait, with highly modified hind legs. In early Ruling Reptiles a strong trend toward a bipedal mode of life occurred, and there existed in Mesozoic days a variety of bipedal dinosaurs. The front legs were little modified but hind limbs were strengthened and lengthened, and the knees brought around forward to a position essentially beneath the body, thus transferring much of the burden of weight support directly to the limb bones. Many of these giant reptiles reverted to a quadrupedal gait, and the living archosaurs, the crocodilians, are likewise quadrupedal. With the front limbs freed from ground locomotor function, the development of wings and flight became possible among Ruling Reptiles. One group, the pterosaurs, evolved a wing membrane supported by one elongate finger. Birds, with feathered wings, developed from another group of bipedal archosaurs.

A second type of major improvement in land locomotion, one in contrast with bipedalism, was the development of the efficient four-footed gait characteristic of mammals. The knee is turned forward as in bipedal reptiles and birds, but in addition the elbow was turned backwards and brought in close to the body. In this pose the entire limb movement is a fore and aft swing, making for a longer stride and greater speed; further efficiency is gained through the fact that the body is supported directly by the bones of the four limbs, without the constant muscular effort needed in the old-fashioned sprawled position. This pattern of locomotion was developed by the therapsids and remains relatively unchanged in most modern mammals. There are, however, many variations, such as the flying mechanisms of the bats, the digging specializations of moles, the bipedalism of man, and so forth.

Many amniotes, despite their fitness for terrestrial life, have returned to the water, with consequent modification of limb structure. In general, the limbs of aquatic tetrapods tend to reassume a finlike shape, with shortened proximal segments and an expanded "foot" area. In less specialized aquatic types, such as seals, the proximal elements may remain little modified, but in advanced types, such as the whales and the extinct ichthyosaurs and plesiosaurs, the whole limb may be modified into a flipper-like structure (Fig. 134). Aquatic birds usually use webbed feet for swimming, but penguins and auks use the powerful wings as swimming organs.

The Apoda among amphibians, the snakes, and certain lizards, have abandoned limbs and reverted to an essentially eel-like piscine type of locomotion based on body undulation. In whales and sirenians the pelvic limbs are reduced or absent, and among bipedal forms the "arm" is reduced in certain dinosaurs and nonflying birds.

Humerus (Fig. 135). In many tetrapods the two ends of the humerus are much expanded and seemingly "twisted" on one another. This apparent twist is, however, a primitive feature; the proximal end of the bone is essentially horizontal, the distal end tilted so that its lower surface faces the forward-slanting forearm. Proximally, stout processes are developed on the humerus for the pectoralis, deltoid, and subscapular muscles, the insertion of the last represented in mam-

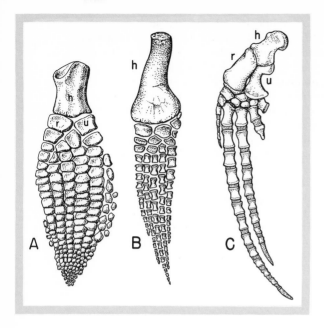

Fig. 134. Examples of tetrapod appendages retransformed into fishlike paddles in
marine forms. Pectoral limbs of *A*, an
ichthyosaur; *B*, a plesiosaur; *C*, a whale.
In all there has been a shortening and
broadening of the proximal bones and a
multiplication of the phalanges. *h*, Humerus; *r*, radius; *u*, ulna. (*A* after Huene;
B after Williston; *C* after Flower.)

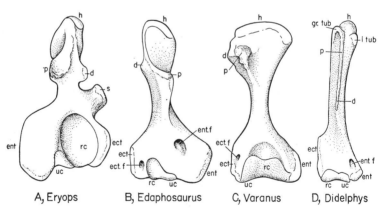

A, Eryops   B, Edaphosaurus   C, Varanus   D, Didelphys

Fig. 135. Humeri of *A*, a Paleozoic amphibian; *B*, a primitive fossil reptile; *C*, a lizard; *D*, the opossum, all from the under surface. Primitive humeri were short, practically without a shaft, and much expanded at both ends (in *A* and *B* the proximal end is twisted about 90 degrees with the distal and hence
appears thin). In all a prominent crest is present to which is attached the pectoralis and deltoid muscles.
In later types the bone became relatively long and slender, particularly in small animals. In primitive
reptiles, foramina developed distally on the inner or posterior side (entepicondylar foramen, *ent. f*) and
on the outer or anterior margin (ectepicondylar foramen, *ect. f*). The former foramen persists in various
mammals and in Sphenodon, the latter in many reptiles. *d*, Deltoid crest; *ect*, ectepicondyle, for attachment of extensor muscles of forearm; *ent*, entepicondyle, for attachment of flexor muscles of forearm;
gr. tub, greater tuberosity, for attachment of supraspinatus and infraspinatus muscles; *h*, head; *l tub*,
lesser tuberosity, for attachment of subscapular muscle; *p*, pectoral crest; *rc*, radial condyle; *s*, process
(supinator) which in reptiles aids in formation of ectepicondylar foramen; *uc*, ulnar condyle, or trochlea.

mals by the *lesser tuberosity*. In the mammalian humerus the *greater tuberosity* affords attachment for muscles from the scapula. In primitive forms the proximal articular surface is an elongate oval capping the end of the bone; in later types there tends to develop a spherical head distinct from the shaft. Primitively little if any shaft was present between proximal and distal expansions, but in many small reptiles and in most birds and mammals the bone is more slenderly built and elongate.

Distally, the humerus bears on its under surface a rounded condyle for the radius; posterior to this the end of the bone is notched for a pulley-like ulnar articulation. Expansions on either side distally, for forearm muscle attachment, are the *ectepicondyle* on the front (or outer) side, and the larger *entepicondyle* on the back (or inner) margin, Universally in early reptiles (seldom in amphibians) there is a large *entepicondylar foramen* for a nerve and blood vessels. Proximal to the ectepicondyle there is primitively a separate projecting process which in some reptiles fuses with the ectepicondyle, bridging a foramen. This *ectepicondylar foramen* persists in many turtles and lizards and in Sphenodon, and the entepicondylar opening is present in the last form and in many of the more primitive mammals; but in many reptiles and mammals, and in birds as a whole, both foramina have disappeared.

Radius (Fig. 136).   The radius is a stout columnar bone which supports the body on the front foot, and articulates at its upper and lower ends with humerus and carpus, respectively. Except in extreme aquatic specialization, there is little variation in its structure.

Ulna (Fig. 136).   The ulna lies lateral to the radius in the forearm. It seldom bears any notable part of the weight, but is important for muscular attachment. Below, it articulates with the carpus; above, at the elbow, it articulates by a notch with the distal edge of the humerus. Above this notch the ulna projects as the *olecranon*, the "funny bone"; to this attaches the main extensor muscle of the upper arm, and the pull of this muscle on the olecranon is the major force extending (i.e., opening out) the forearm. Particularly among mammals the shaft of the ulna may fuse with the radius or may be entirely lost, but the olecranon is persistently present.

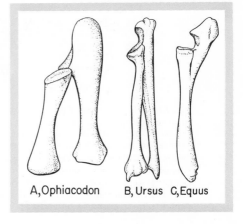

Fig. 136.   Radius and ulna, seen from the anterior or extensor surface in *A*, a primitive reptile; *B*, a bear, representing a typical mammalian condition; and *C*, a horse. The humerus articulates with the curved surface of the notch in the ulna and the adjacent head of the radius; above, the projecting olecranon of the ulna serves for the attachment of the powerful triceps muscle, which extends the forearm. In many mammals, as in the horse, the lower part of the ulna is reduced and fused with the radius.

A,Ophiacodon   B,Ursus C,Equus

Manus (Figs. 137–141).   The proximal part of the hand, or manus, consists of a series of small elements which form the *carpus*, a region of flexible
adjustment between the arm region and the digits. Primitively, as seen in early
tetrapods, there appear to have been twelve elements in the carpus, arranged in
three series:

1. Three proximal elements, beneath the two forearm bones, are reasonably
termed *radiale, intermedium,* and *ulnare.*

2. A series of central carpals or *centralia,* wedged in between this proximal
set and a distal one; four were primitively present.

3. A row of *distal carpals,* one typically lying opposite the head of each toe,
or digit.

It is impossible in any limited space to recount all the variations undergone
by the carpal elements in the history of land vertebrates. There are numerous
reductions and fusions. The three proximal elements persist in most cases. The
centralia, on the other hand, are almost always reduced. Even in the most primitive reptiles there are never more than two; a single centrale is a common reptilian and mammalian condition. Distally, there is a general trend for the loss of
a fifth distal carpal, even when the fifth digit is retained, and with toe reduction
there is generally further loss. In reptiles and mammals there is found an additional small bone, the *pisiform,* attached to the outer margin of the carpus and
forming a point of attachment for the tendons of muscles along this aspect of the
limb.

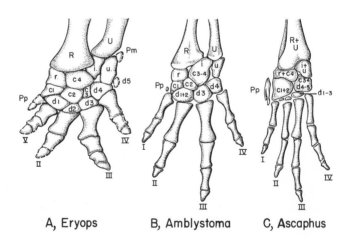

A, Eryops   B, Amblystoma   C, Ascaphus

Fig. 137.   The left manus of amphibians, including an early labyrinthodont, a urodele, and an anuran.
Restored elements in *A* in broken line. All twelve elements thought to have been present in the primitive carpus are found in Eryops; in modern amphibians fusions of various sorts have occurred. As in
most amphibians, four toes are present in the forms figured, although all have some development of a
digit medial to the pollex, and an element in Eryops may have been the stub of an extra toe beyond the
reduced fifth digit. The phalangeal count of two or three is usual in amphibians. *cl* to *c4,* Centralia; *cu.,*
cuneiform; *d1–d5,* distal carpals; *i,* intermedium; *l,* lunare; *m,* magnum; *m1, 3, 5,* metacarpals; *p,* pisiform; *Pm,* postminimum digit; *Pp,* prepollex; *R,* radius; *r,* radiale; *s,* scaphoid; *td,* trapezoid; *tm,* trapezium; *U,* ulna; *u,* ulnare; *un,* unciform; *I* to *V,* digits. (After Gregory, Miner, and Noble.)

Fig. 138. The manus in *A*, a turtle; *B*, the alligator; *C*, a carnivorous dinosaur; *D*, the goose. Abbreviations as in Figure 137. The bird manus includes the fused elements of the first three digits only; a somewhat comparable structure is seen in certain dinosaurs. (*A* after Williston; *C* after Gilmore; *D* after Steiner.)

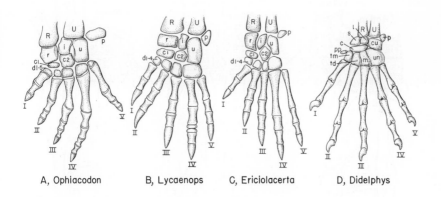

Fig. 139. Evolution of the mammalian manus. *A*, Primitive reptile; *B*, a primitive therapsid; *C*, an advanced therapsid; *D*, a primitive mammal, the opossum. Abbreviations as in Figure 137. In the carpus there is a loss of the fifth distal element, a reduction from two centralia to one; distally, "supernumerary" phalanges are lost from digits III and IV. (*B* after Broom; *C* after Watson.)

The terminology of the carpals in lower tetrapods is relatively simple. In mammalian anatomy, unfortunately, this is not the case; each was early given a distinct name, still used in comparative studies (Fig. 140); and (to make matters worse) still other names, not useful elsewhere, have been applied to some of these elements in the medical school dissecting room. We list this plethora of terms without comment:

General Terminology	Mammalian Anatomy	Human Anatomy
Radiale	Scaphoid	Os scaphoideum (naviculare)
Intermedium	Lunar (or semilunar)	Os lunatum
Ulnare	Cuneiform	Os triquetrum
Pisiform	Pisiforme	Os pisiforme
Centrale	Centrale	(Absent)
Distal carpal 1	Trapezium	Os trapezium (multangulum majus)
Distal carpal 2	Trapezoid	Os trapezoideum (multangulum minus)
Distal carpal 3	Magnum	Os capitatum
Distal carpal 4	Unciform	Os hamatum

Beyond the carpus lie the toes, or *digits*. For each toe there is a proximal segment contained in the flesh of the "palm." These elements in either limb are termed *metapodials;* more specifically the term *metacarpal* applies to those of the forefoot. In mammals with speedy locomotion, particularly the ungulates, there may be a considerable increase in the length of the metapodials of such toes as are present, with the effect of adding essentially an extra functional segment to the limb. Distal to the metapodials are the elements of the free toes, the *phalanges;* distal *ungual phalanges* may be much modified to bear claws, nails, or hoofs.

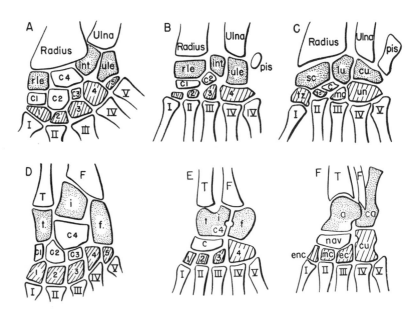

Fig. 140. Diagram of carpus (*A* to *C*) and tarsus (*D* to *F*) to show essential homologies between primitive tetrapod (*A, D*), primitive reptile (*B, E*), and mammal (*C, F*). Proximal row of elements stippled; central row (and pisiform) unshaded; distal row hatched. Digits indicated by Roman numerals; distal carpals and tarsals by Arabic numerals. *a,* Astragalus; *c, c1* to *c4,* centralia; *ca,* calcaneum; *cu,* cuneiform in carpus, cuboid in tarsus; *ec,* external cuneiform (ectocuneiform); *enc,* internal cuneiform (entocuneiform); *f,* fibulare; *F, Fib,* fibula; *i, int,* intermedium; *lu,* lunar; *mc,* middle cuneiform (mesocuneiform); *mg,* magnum; *nav,* navicular; *pis,* pisiform; *rle,* radiale; *sc,* scaphoid; *t,* tibiale; *T, Tib,* tibia; *td,* trapezoid; *tz,* trapezium; *ule,* ulnare; *un,* unciform.

Fig. 141. Left front feet of ungulates—in order, camel, pig, horse, rhinoceros, and tapir. The first two are artiodactyls, in which the axis of symmetry lies between the third and four toes. In the pig (*B*) lateral toes, 2 and 5, are complete but small. In most artiodactyls, as in the camel (*A*), the two main metapodials are fused into a cannon bone. The three remaining forms are perissodactyls, in which the axis runs through the third toe. In the tapir (*E*) the pollex is lost, but the other four toes remain; in modern rhinoceroses (*D*) the fifth toe has disappeared; in modern horses (*C*) the second and fourth are reduced to splints. (After Flower.)

Since the complicated foot pattern had no fixed antecedents in the ancestral fish fin, it is probable that considerable variation occurred in foot structure in the earliest land vertebrates. Unfortunately, however, complete feet are seldom preserved in fossil form. The presence of five toes in both front and hind feet is a condition primitive and common in amniotes and is found as well in some of the oldest amphibians. However, there are never more than four toes in the front foot of living amphibians, and the same number is found in many fossil forms.

In ichthyosaurs (Fig. 134, *A*, p. 202) there is great variation in the number of digits present in the "fin"; there may be as few as three or as many as eight longitudinal rows of disc-shaped phalanges. In the bipedal archosaurs the "arms" are partly or completely freed from duty as locomotor organs, and there may be much modification of the hand (Fig. 133, *B*, *C*), with reduction of the outer elements; in some dinosaurs only the three inner fingers remain, and in an extreme case only two. The flying reptiles, the pterosaurs, lost the fifth digit; the three inner ones are feeble, clawed structures, but the fourth is enormously elongated as a support for the wing membrane. The birds appear to have descended from Ruling Reptiles in which only the three inner fingers remained; these three digits are preserved, in modified fashion, in the bird wing (Fig. 138, *D*).

Five toes were present in the manus in the ancestral mammals and are found in many forms today (Fig. 139). Early mammals, many believe, were more or less arboreal, and the first digit, as a thumb or *pollex*, became more or less opposable to the others to give a grasping power useful in tree locomotion. Most mammals abandoned arboreal life, however, at an early day; this divergent digit was of little use in terrestrial locomotion and is frequently reduced or lost.

Further digital reduction or modification occurs in a great variety of mammals. We may note, for example, the development in bats of a wing membrane which, in contrast to that of pterosaurs, is supported by all the digits except the "thumb," and on the other hand the modification of the whale manus into a structure somewhat comparable to that of ichthyosaurs (Fig. 134, *C*).

The development of the ungulate foot is accompanied by a reduction and elimination of digits (Fig. 141). In most ungulates the "thumb" was early lost, and a four-toed manus was characteristic of forms as dissimilar as ancestral horses and cows. Further reduction, however, followed two different paths. In one group the main axis of the limb extends down into the third digit, which enlarges at the expense of the others. This is the pattern followed by the Perissodactyla, the horses and their relatives—the odd-toed ungulates; the outer toe tends to be lost, giving a three-toed foot, and in the modern horses there is a functionally one-toed condition, with toe 3 the survivor in the elimination contest. The Artiodactyla, or even-toed ungulates, followed another pattern. In them the primitive manus was four-toed, with the axis of the limb passing down between toes 3 and 4. These two toes tend to dominate jointly, and become the so-called "cloven hoof" of pigs, camels, and numerous familiar ruminating animals. The side toes (2 and 5) may persist, but are usually reduced to vestiges; the two major metapodials may fuse to form a "cannon bone."

A *phalangeal formula* indicates the number of phalanges in each digit in succession from inner to outer toes. In amphibians the number of phalanges is in general low, usually two or three per toe. In primitive reptiles, however, there was established a formula of 2.3.4.5.3 for the manus. This persists with little change through a great variety of reptilian groups. As stated in this formula, the number of phalanges (and the length of the toes) increases steadily from pollex to fourth toe; the fifth toe is reduced in size and phalangeal count, and tends to diverge laterally from the other four. This situation is perhaps due to the fact that in the sprawling limb posture of primitive tetrapods the foot strikes the ground at an angle. The toes toward the higher, outer side must be longer to get a proper "footing"; the fifth toe abandons the attempt, so to speak, of gaining sufficient length and extends out sideways as a lateral prop. In chelonians there is frequently a reduction in phalangeal formula (Fig. 138, *A*). On the other hand, the extinct marine plesiosaurs and ichthyosaurs greatly increased the number of phalanges in each toe; each individual phalanx was, however, much abbreviated (Fig. 134, *A, B*).

In the mammal-like reptiles the earlier types (Fig. 139, *A, B*) retained the reptilian formula. Advanced forms, however, reduced to 2.3.3.3.3, which is the generalized formula for primitive mammals (Fig. 139, *C, D*). One joint has been lost from the third toe, two joints from the fourth; some therapsid genera show a transitional stage in which the joints to be lost are present but vestigial. This change in formula may be related to the changed limb posture; with the limb in a straight fore and aft plane, all the toes strike the ground equally well and hence tend to be subequal in length. Among mammals, as we have noted, there is frequently a loss of digits, but seldom a reduction in phalangeal count in any persisting toe. In the Cetacea, alone among mammals, we find an increase in the phalangeal count to as high as thirteen or fourteen in a digit; the whales here parallel the extinct marine reptiles (Fig. 134, *C*).

Femur (Fig. 142).   The thighbone in primitive land vertebrates is essentially a cylindric structure with expanded ends. Proximally there is a terminal head fitting into the acetabulum. Beneath the head is a cavity, or fossa, into which some of the short ventral muscles insert, and at the anterior (or inner) margin of this fossa is seen ventrally in primitive types a strong *internal trochanter* for further ventral muscle attachment. Along the length of the shaft ventrally is an *adductor crest* for the attachment of strong adductor muscles. Near the proximal

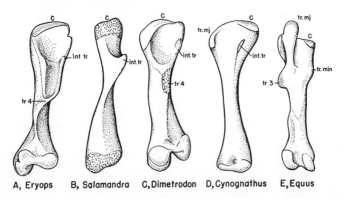

A, Eryops   B, Salamandra   C,Dimetrodon   D,Cynognathus   E,Equus

Fig. 142. Femora seen from the ventral surface. *A*, Primitive fossil amphibian; *B*, a urodele; *C*, a primitive reptile; *D*, a mammal-like reptile; *E*, the horse. The proximal end above; distally, the articular surfaces for the tibia. *c*, Head (capitulum); *int. tr.*, internal trochanter of primitive forms, for attachment of obturator externus muscle or equivalent; *tr. 3*, third trochanter of perissodactyls for part of gluteal muscles; *tr. 4*, fourth trochanter, to which are attached tail muscles pulling the femur backward in many amphibians and reptiles; *tr. min.*, lesser (minor) trochanter for iliopsoas muscles of mammal; *tr. mj.*, greater (major) trochanter of mammals, for gluteal muscles.

end of this ridge is frequently seen the so-called *fourth trochanter,* to which attach powerful muscles running onto the thigh from the tail. Distally, the femur expands, with rugosities on either side for shank muscle origins; there is a deep groove along the dorsal midline distally for the tendon of the extensor muscle of the thigh, which extends to the tibia. Below, at the distal end, there is a broad, double articular surface for the head of the tibia, and along the posterior (or lateral) margin of the femur an adjacent area for the fibular articulation.

The general nature of the femur remains little modified in a majority of tetrapod groups except for the head of the bone. This usually develops into a more or less spherical structure set off from the shaft. In forms in which the hind limbs are rotated forward (archosaurs, birds, mammals) the femur head faces inward for better reception in the acetabulum, and a *greater trochanter* for iliac muscle attachment may develop on the upper end of the shaft. In mammals the internal trochanter disappears, and a new *lesser trochanter* develops in much the same region, but for different muscular attachments. The fourth trochanter is absent in mammals, where the muscles once attaching to it have dwindled or disappeared. The adductor crest may persist or be represented by rugose lines, the *linea aspera.*

Tibia (Fig. 143). The tibia, corresponding to the radius in the front limb, is the main supporting element of the lower leg segment; it is always stoutly developed, articulating broadly below with the inner side of the tarsus, and above by a much expanded head, triangular in section, with almost the entire under surface of the distal end of the femur. The front margin of the head bears a strong ridge, the *cnemial crest,* to which attaches the terminal tendon of the main extensor muscle of the thigh. Primitively the attachment of the tendon was a direct one. However, the sharp curve which this tendon must make down over the end of the femur is disadvantageous. In mammals there generally develops the *patella,* a nubbin of bone which rides over the knee joint with functions comparable to those

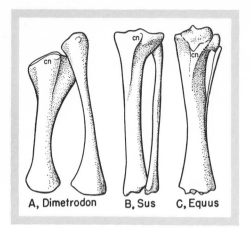

Fig. 143. The left tibia and fibula, seen from the extensor (dorsal) surface, of *A*, a primitive reptile (a Permian pelycosaur) with a fibula of good size; *B*, the pig, showing a primitive mammalian condition, with the fibula complete, although slender; *C*, the horse, exemplifying a type with reduced fibula. *cn*, Cnemial crest.

A, Dimetrodon   B, Sus   C, Equus

of the ulnar head in the front limb; the extensor tendon inserts into this ossification which is, in turn, tied to the cnemial crest.

Fibula (Fig. 143). This bone is in some respects comparable to the ulna in the forearm; it bears little weight and, in consequence, tends to undergo reduction. Since in the hind leg the extensor tendon attaches to the inner element, the tibia, the fibula has no development comparable to the olecranon. The fibula is articulated proximally with the posterior (or outer) aspect of the end of the femur, distally with the outer side of the tarsus. In many living groups the fibula has lost its femoral articulation, and the tarsal attachment may be much reduced or lost. It usually persists, although as a slender structure, its ends may fuse with the tibia, or the shaft may be lost.

Pes (Figs. 140, p. 206; 144–146). The structure of the ankle region, the *tarsus*, was primitively quite similar to that of the carpus; the same number of bones was present in much the same arrangement, and a terminology similar to that of the carpus may be used. A proximal series of three elements are termed *tibiale*, *intermedium*, and *fibulare*. There were, as in the manus, four *centralia* in primitive types and five *distal tarsals*. As in the carpus, free central elements are reduced to two in primitive reptiles and to one in mammals, and the fifth distal element tends early to be reduced and to disappear.

There are, however, notable differences in the history of the tarsus as compared with the carpus. There is no development of any element corresponding to the pisiform. More important, however, is the change which occurs in reptiles in the proximal row. There are here in reptiles but two elements which are often called by their mammalian names of *astragalus* and *calcaneum*. The latter is simply the fibulare under another name. The astragalus, however, appears to be a fusion of tibiale with intermedium and a central element. We have noted that in the original limb position the hind foot would tend to project out laterally from the body if it were not twisted sharply forward on the leg. The fusion of elements to form the astragalus appears to give a firmer support to the tibia in the twisted position; there is in primitive reptiles free movement between tibia and astragalus.

In reptiles there has tended to develop an "intratarsal" joint where there occurs the major movement of lower leg on foot. In archosaurs astragalus and calcaneum are closely applied to tibia and fibula, and reduced distal tarsals are

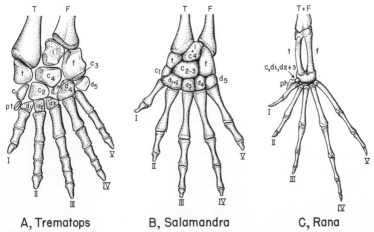

A, Trematops   B, Salamandra   C, Rana

Fig. 144. The pes of amphibians, including *A*, an early labyrinthodont; *B*, a salamander; and *C*, a frog. The tarsus of Trematops includes all elements presumed to be present in ancestral tetrapods, as well as an additional pretarsal bone. In the urodele some fusion of tarsal elements has occurred. In the frog, tibiale and fibulare are so elongated as to constitute an additional limb segment; except for a few small distal elements, the fate of the other tarsal bones is not clear. Five toes are typically present, as contrasted with four in the manus, and the count of phalanges is generally higher in the pes than in the amphibian manus (cf. Fig. 137). The frog has a developed prehallux. *c1* to *c4*, Centralia; *d1* to *d5*, distal tarsals; *F*, fibula; *f*, fibulare; *i*, intermedium; *ph*, prehallux; *pt*, pretarsal element; *T*, tibia; *t*, tibiale. (*A* after Schaeffer; *B* after Schmalhausen; *C* after Gaupp.)

A, Sphenodon   B, Alligator   C, Allosaurus   D, Columba

Fig. 145. The pes in reptiles and birds. *A*, Sphenodon; *B*, the alligator; *C*, a carnivorous dinosaur; *D*, the pigeon. In all forms there have been various types of reduction and fusion of the tarsal elements and a trend toward the development of a main joint within the tarsus between proximal and distal elements. In the birds all the tarsals are fused with the tibia proximally or with the fused metatarsals distally. In archosaurs, such as the alligator and dinosaurs, there is a strong trend toward the loss of the fifth toe, and it has disappeared in the dinosaur figured and in the bird. Except for the lack of fusion of the metatarsals, the Allosaurus foot is quite similar to that of birds. *a*, Astragalus; *c*, calcaneum; other abbreviations as in Figure 144. (*B* after Williston: *C* after Gilmore.)

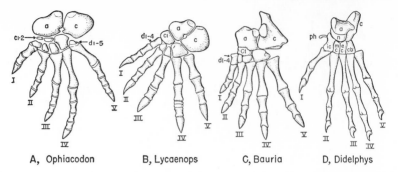

Fig. 146. Evolution of the mammalian type of pes. *A*, Primitive reptile (of the early Permian); *B*, a primitive therapsid (of the late Permian); *C*, an advanced Triassic mammal-like reptile; *D*, the opossum. Principal changes include development of a pulley surface on the mammalian astragalus, development of a heel on the calcaneum (in *C* and *D*), loss of two small tarsal elements, and reduction in phalangeal count (a transitional stage in *B*). *a*, Astragalus; *c*, calcaneum; *c1* to *c4*, centralia; *cb*, cuboid; *d1* to *d5*, distal tarsals; *ec*, external cuneiform; *ic*, internal cuneiform; *mc*, middle cuneiform; *ph*, prehallux (exceptional in mammals). (*B* and *C* after Schaeffer.)

functionally joined to metatarsals. In birds, actual fusion of bones has taken place, so that we speak of a *tibiotarsus* as a single limb element, succeeded distally by a *tarsometatarsus*; there are no free tarsals at all.

In mammals, astragalus and calcaneum are much modified. The astragalus develops a head as a keeled rolling surface which fits into a corresponding set of grooves in the distal end of the tibia. The joint is a hinge, without possibility of any degree of twisting, but allowing a great amount of extension and flexion of the foot. Characteristic of artiodactyls is an astragalus in which the lower end also has a keeled rolling surface, so that an extreme amount of backward and forward movement of the foot in running is possible. The calcaneum has little or no articulation with the more proximal limb elements in mammals, but develops a powerful heel projection to which attach the calf muscles through the "tendon of Achilles."

In the tarsus, as in the carpus, we find (unfortunately) a complicated series of names applied to the mammalian elements:

General Terminology	Mammalian Anatomy	Human Anatomy
Tibiale + Intermedium....	Astragalus	Talus
Fibulare	Calcaneum	Calcaneus (Os calcis)
Centrale..................	Navicular (or scaphoid)	Os naviculare (pedis)
Distal tarsal 1	Internal cuneiform	Os cuneiforme mediale (primum)
Distal tarsal 2	Middle cuneiform	Os cuneiforme intermedium (secundum)
Distal tarsal 3	External cuneiform	Os cuneiforme laterale (tertium)
Distal tarsal 4	Cuboid	Os cuboideum

The description given for the digits of the manus applies in general to the pes, but the proximal elements are, of course, termed *metatarsals* rather than metacarpals. The phalangeal formula of the pes in amphibians and reptiles frequently corresponds closely to that for the manus, except that in reptiles there is usually a fourth phalanx in the last toe. In bipedal archosaurs there was often, in relation to speedier locomotion, an elongation of the metapodials comparable to that noted in ungulate mammals. There was, further, a reduction in the number of digits in these reptiles; the divergent fifth toe often disappeared, and the first toe, or *hallux*, was turned back as a prop for the foot. There remained, in the more advanced bipedal types, three forwardly turned toes, symmetrically disposed, the center one the longest; these toes were, of course, the second, third, and fourth. Despite the modification seen here in their comparative length, the primitive phalangeal count had been retained; the second and fourth toes, although subequal in length, had three and five phalanges, respectively; the middle (third) toe, four. The birds, as descendants of bipedal archosaurs, have exactly the same toe structure; it is thus natural that dinosaur footprints when first discovered were thought to be those of gigantic birds.

In mammals the history of the hind foot is comparable in general to that of the manus. We may note, however, that in the horses and their relatives digital reduction proceeded more rapidly in the hind foot than in the forefoot; the earliest known fossil horses had already attained a functional three-toed stage.

VISCERAL SKELETON

Between the gill openings of lower vertebrates is a series of cartilaginous or bony bars—arches which aid in the support and movements of the gill apparatus. These gill arches are the basic components of a set of structures termed the visceral skeleton. Except in agnathous forms, the elements of the visceral system never form more than a small proportion of the skeletal materials of the body; they are, however, notable for their versatility, the degree of modification of form and function which they have undergone in the course of vertebrate history. Primitively, to be sure, they were merely gill supports. But early in fish history they played a leading role in the development of the jaws; and although gills as such have disappeared in amniotes, persistently surviving visceral skeletal elements are to be found even in mammals in such varied areas as the skull, the auditory ossicles, and the larynx.

At first sight it seems difficult to justify classifying these usually modest structures in a special category contrasting with all other endoskeletal elements. Consideration, however, shows that such distinction is well warranted. The gill region, or pharynx, although relatively insignificant in land vertebrates, is, if traced downward in the chordate series, increasingly prominent, important, and in every way distinctive. In the nature of its muscles and nerve supply the gill region is in strong contrast, primitively, with any other body region, and its skeleton is likewise unique.

Other endoskeletal structures form in the "outer tube" of the body, the "somatic animal"; those of the gill region are formed in the walls of the gut, and are truly visceral in position. In addition, they are unusual in their embryologic origin. The visceral cartilages are derived from mesenchyme; but this mesenchyme is not of mesodermal origin—a situation embarrassing to the embryologist who lays down rules for embryos to follow. It is, instead, derived from the ectoderm.

We have noted in our embryologic review the development of the neural crest—cell masses from which elements of the nervous system are major derivatives. But part of the neural crest cells of the head have a different fate. They migrate downward and inward, form a mesenchyme material similar to that elsewhere derived from the mesoderm, and ultimately form skeletal structures. This mesenchyme, sometimes termed *"mesectoderm,"* is primarily concerned with the formation of the gill bar system and its derivatives. It is thus associated with the pharynx, the most prominent structure of the "visceral animal" component of the vertebrate, and it is hence not surprising that it should have a mode of origin different from that of the "somatic" skeleton. The one seeming exception to the clear-cut distinction in origin between visceral and somatic skeletal structures is that (as noted earlier) the front part of the braincase—otherwise a somatic endochondral structure—is derived from the neural crest. But it is probable that this area was originally part of the skeleton of an anterior gill, long since lost.

The Gill Skeleton. In the cyclostomes (Figs. 106, p. 169; 147, *A*) certain of the gill structures are highly specialized, serving to stiffen the rasping

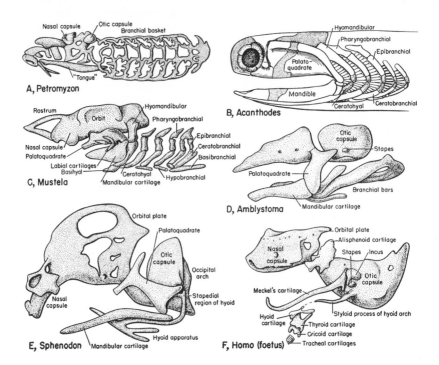

Fig. 147. Visceral skeleton and braincase in representatives of six vertebrate classes; *A* to *C*, adult forms, *D* to *F*, embryos; cartilage stippled, bone unstippled. *A*, The lamprey, with a peculiar braincase and associated cartilages not readily comparable to those of other groups; the branchial basket is fused anteriorly to the braincase. *B*, Paleozoic spiny "shark," a placoderm in which jaws are developed, but the hyomandibular is unspecialized (the sclerotic plates of the orbit are figured, as is a slender dermal bone below the mandible). *C*, Shark, with hyostylic jaw suspension. *D*, Salamander; the palatoquadrate is reduced, and the branchial arches are reduced even in the embryo or larva. *E*, The reptile Sphenodon. The braincase is incompletely formed (cf. lizard in Fig. 117 *D*), and hyoid and branchial bars are reduced to a hyoid apparatus and stapedial cartilage. *F*, Human foetus. The braincase develops only ventrally and anteriorly around the brain. The palatoquadrate is reduced to alisphenoid and incus (= quadrate). The lower jaw (Meckel's cartilage) is reduced, the proximal part becoming the malleus in the adult. Other visceral elements include the hyoid and its styloid process, stapes, laryngeal and tracheal cartilages. (*A* and *C* after Goodrich; *B* after Watson; *D* after Hörstadius and Sellman; *E* after Howes and Swinnerton; *F* after Gaupp, Macklin.)

"tongue" which has evolved in these predaceous forms as a jaw substitute. The remainder of the visceral skeleton forms a continuous latticework surrounding the gill region and connecting in lampreys with the braincase. In the cephalaspid ostracoderms, some of the oldest of fossil vertebrates, the skeleton of the gill pouches, as far as preserved, is fused with the rest of the "cranial" skeleton (Fig. 232, p. 326). These facts suggest the probability that in the ancestral vertebrates the gill supports were not discrete elements, but were fused with one another and with the cranial region. Our knowledge is, however, too imperfect as yet to be certain of the true ancestral situation, and in all gnathostomes, at any rate, the gill skeleton consists (except for cases of secondary fusion) of numerous separate movable structures.

The gill skeleton in jaw-bearing fishes consists of jointed bars which follow one another in sequence along the walls of the pharynx, forming arches between successive gill slits. These *visceral arches* are serially arranged structures, as are the gill openings themselves and the muscles and nerves of the gill region. It must, however, be emphasized that no proof has been found, despite many attempts, that this segmentation is in any way related to the segmentation present in other parts of the body, which is founded on the segmentation of the mesodermal somites. The pharyngeal segmentation is based, it seems sure, on the seriation of the endodermal gill pouches, and this has no proved relationship to the series of mesodermal somites seen in the trunk or head.

Each typical gill bar of a jawed fish (Figs. 147, *C;* 148, *A;* 190, p. 277)

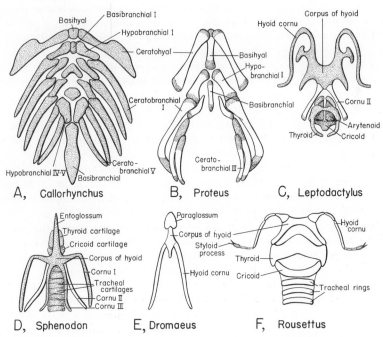

Fig. 148. Gill bars and tetrapod derivatives, in ventral view, in *A,* a chimaera; *B,* a water-dwelling salamander; *C,* a frog; *D,* a reptile, Sphenodon; *E,* the cassowary; and *F,* a bat. In *A* the dorsal arch elements are not included. In *C, D,* and *F* laryngeal cartilages are included. The entoglossum of *D* and paraglossum of *E* are tongue-supporting anterior developments from the body of the hyoid.

includes on either side a major dorsal and a major ventral element, the two bent somewhat forward on each other. The dorsal elements are the *epibranchials;* the ventral ones, *ceratobranchials.* There are generally *pharyngobranchials,* turned inward over the pharynx, at the upper end of each normal arch. Below, the successive arches are tied to one another and with their mates of the opposite side by elements which extend downward, forward, and inward to the midline; there is a great variation here, but frequently there are short paired *hypobranchials* below the ceratobranchials, and median ventral structures—*basibranchials* or *copulae.* The gill bars generally bear on their inner margins *gill rakers,* and on their outer surfaces a row of *gill rays* which stiffen the gill septum or gills (Fig. 227, p. 319). In most jawed fishes five sets of typical gill bars are present, in addition to the specialized jaw and hyoid arches now to be described.

Jaw Development. Perhaps the greatest of all advances in vertebrate history was the development of jaws and the consequent revolution in the mode of life of early fishes. In this process the visceral skeleton played a leading role, for transformed gill bars are basic structures in jaw formation and, indeed, form the entire jaw structure in the Chondrichthyes.

In the sharks (where there is no complication of investing dermal bones) both upper and lower jaws are formed solely of paired cartilages which seem surely to represent transformed gill arch elements (Figs. 147, *C*, p. 214; 150). The shark upper jaw element, running fore and aft below and beside the braincase, is the *palatoquadrate* (or pterygoquadrate) *cartilage;* it is comparable to the epibranchial of a normal gill arch. Posteriorly, it articulates with a lower jaw or *mandibular cartilage,* presumably derived from the ceratobranchial of the same arch as the upper jaw. It appears that in the development of jaws, a pair of gill bars lying adjacent to the expanding mouth cavity became armed with teeth and enlarged to function in a new capacity as biting jaws (Fig. 149). That the gill arch which became modified into jaws in the ancestral gnathostome was the most anterior one present in the jawless ancestor is doubtful; it is more than probable that one or two anterior arches were destroyed in the expansion of the mouth cavity. (It has been suggested that the small *labial cartilages* present in the angle of the mouth in sharks [Fig. 150] represent such arches, but this is doubtful; again, the trabeculae, we have noted, are thought to represent an arch otherwise lost.)

In forms other than sharklike fishes, dermal elements are also present in the complex structure of upper and lower jaws, and the part played in jaw formation by gill arch elements is much reduced. The jaw articulation, however, remains persistently that between upper and lower visceral bars in every group except the mammals, in which (as discussed later) the entire structure of the jaws and palate is taken over by dermal elements. Even in mammals, however, relics of the gill-bar jaw structures persist, although, as will be seen, in curiously transformed fashion, as ear ossicles and a component of the brain capsule.

JAW SUSPENSION. In most fishes (Figs. 149, *C;* 150), the second or *hyoid arch,* lying behind the first gill opening (the spiracle) is specialized as an aid to jaw support. The ventral part of this arch is normal; there is here on either side a major element termed the *ceratohyal* and usually a smaller *basihyal.* In the upper part of this arch, however, the epibranchial segment is an element, often of considerable size, termed the *hyomandibular.* This is braced dorsally against the otic region of the braincase; below, it runs to the region of the jaw articulation and is bound by ligaments to the jaw structures. This mechanism is an effec-

Fig. 149. Diagrams to show evolution of jaw and hyoid region. Gill openings in black. *H*, Hyomandibular; *S*, spiracular gill slit. In *A*, a primitive jawless condition. *B*, Jaws formed from a pair of gill arches (two anterior arches and slits may have been lost in the process); spiracular gill slit unreduced, and hyomandibular not specialized. This condition may have prevailed in the extinct placoderms. *C*, Condition seen in most jawed fishes; the hyomandibular has become a jaw support, and the intervening gill slit reduced to a spiracle.

tive support for the jaws, propping them on the braincase. In tetrapods where the addition of dermal bones makes for a compact skull structure, the upper jaw and the palatal structures are satisfactorily bound to the remainder of the skull without the aid of the hyomandibular support. In relation to this we find that the hyomandibular has been transformed into an auditory bone, the stapes; its history is discussed in connection with the ear.

The nature of the hyomandibular serves to introduce the general problem of the suspension of the jaws on the skull in fishes. If, as is the case in most modern fishes, the upper jaw structure has no direct connection with the braincase (except for anteriorly) and the jaw joint is braced entirely by the hyomandibular (with the effect of widening the gape) the condition is said to be *hyostylic*. In a few sharks, however, there is support both from the hyomandibular and from a direct articulation of upper jaw and braincase; this is an *amphistylic* condition. In still other fishes the hyomandibular is nonfunctional as a supporting structure, and the upper jaw region is entirely responsible for its own suspension; this is termed *autostylic*. In chimaeras (Fig. 119, p. 180) and lungfishes the autostylic condition is associated with the fact that the upper jaw itself is fused tightly to the braincase. Land vertebrates are all autostylic, of course, in a broad sense of this term, since the hyomandibular never functions as a jaw support.

Tetrapod Gill Arch Derivatives (Figs. 147, *D-F*, p. 214; 148, *B-F*, p. 215). In larval amphibians gills are still functional, and in relation to this fact the gill bars remain prominently developed. There is already, however, some tendency toward reduction; there never are more than four arches present behind

Fig. 150. The cranial skeleton of a shark, Chlamydoselache: braincase, jaws, hyoid arch. (After Allis.)

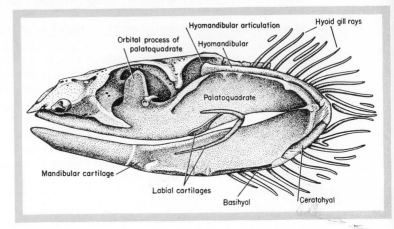

the hyoid arch, instead of the five customary in fishes, and these are often continuous bars, without clear-cut divisions into the various elements typical of their fish ancestors.

In metamorphosed amphibians and in amniotes functional gills have been done away with; visceral arches nevertheless persist (apart from the jaw and ear ossicles) as two sets of structures formed in connection with new tetrapod developments in the former gill region. (*a*) A tongue, never characteristically present in fishes, arises in the floor of the mouth where there once lay the more anterior and ventral parts of the visceral bars; reduced and transformed remnants of the anterior gill bars serve, as the hyoid apparatus, to support the tongue. (*b*) With increased importance of the lungs, skeletal structures derived from or related to the more posterior part of the visceral skeleton are developed about the larynx and trachea which form the lung entrance. These structures consist of a laryngeal skeleton, the "Adam's apple" of man, and ring-shaped tracheal cartilages.

The tetrapod *hyoid apparatus* typically includes a main body, the *corpus*, formed from one or more of the median ventral arch elements (copulae or basals), and remnants of the hyoid arch and of one or two branchial arches extending outward and upward as "horns" or *cornua* (singular, cornu). The body of the hyoid is situated in the floor of the throat in the base of the tongue, ventral to the anterior end of the windpipe. In some reptiles and in birds the corpus of the hyoid develops a long anterior process for better tongue support. The horns extend upward on either side of the windpipe, and although the most anterior—"principal"—horns represent only the lower half of the original hyoid arch (the upper part forms the stapes), they may nevertheless gain a slender secondary connection with the otic region of the skull, either directly or by ligaments. In mature amphibians and in reptiles there are frequently three pairs of cornua; in birds generally a single pair; in mammals typically two pairs, representing the hyoid and first branchial arch. In mammals additional ossifications may occur in the slender process of the hyoid horn, reaching up to the ear region, and in some mammals, including man, the distal end of this horn may fuse with the skull as a *styloid process*.

But the hyoid apparatus is only one part of the tetrapod derivatives of the fish gill supports; skeletal structures supporting the windpipe itself have developed. Just beyond the entrance to the windpipe, the glottis, there typically develops in tetrapods an enlargement in the tube as the larynx (cf. Chap. 11). The basal part of the hyoid apparatus generally lies close to the front end of the floor of this expansion; additional cartilages, at least part of which appear to be modified visceral arch structures, tend to form a complex *laryngeal skeleton*. When fully developed, these include unpaired *thyroid** and *cricoid cartilages* in line ventrally behind the body of the hyoid and, dorsally, paired *arytenoids;* these cartilages are not infrequently ossified. In salamanders only the arytenoids are developed; in anurans a cricoid is present as well. The thyroid is present only in mammals; the *epiglottis*, found in the flap of skin covering the windpipe opening (glottis) is present in mammals, but may be represented in reptiles by a cartilage in this position in some members of that class. In most tetrapods the windpipe (trachea), running down from the larynx, tends to be strengthened by ring-shaped *tracheal cartilages*. These last structures are not readily comparable to any specific fish elements, but are reasonably to be regarded as new developments of the visceral skeletal system.

* The term "thyroid" means simply shield-shaped; the thyroid gland, also shield-shaped, happens to lie in this general region of the throat, but the topographic juxtaposition is pure coincidence.

8

THE SKULL

The term "skull" is used in somewhat variable fashion. In a broad way it refers to any type of skeletal structure found in the head region. In this sense one may consider the lamprey as having a skull composed of a braincase and the peculiar tongue cartilages, the shark as having a skull consisting of braincase and isolated jaw bars. But in common parlance, and as we shall use it here, the term has a somewhat different meaning. The familiar skull of every form from a bony fish to a mammal is a fused, unit structure, in which braincase and endoskeletal upper jaws are welded together by series of dermal bones; the lower jaw is not included.

In the older Agnatha and in the extinct placoderms there appears to have been present a fused head skeleton which included dermal as well as endoskeletal materials and is hence to be considered a skull in the present sense. But in most of those archaic fishes the structures seem to have been aberrant, and they are as yet too incompletely known to warrant their being considered here; further, in these ancient forms, the gill region is frequently included as well as proper head structures. In the higher bony fishes and all tetrapods there is a well-constructed skull, with many common features present throughout these groups. Even so, it is difficult to give a generalized description which will hold in all cases. And the task is further complicated by the fact that in most living groups considerable degeneration and specialization have taken place, obscuring the true phylogenetic story.

In the study of soft anatomy we suffer under the handicap of knowing nothing of the actual ancestral types from which the organs of modern animals have been derived; we can, at the best, merely make guesses (which we hope are intelligent) at the structural conditions in such ancestors, extinct these many millions—or hundreds of millions—of years. In the case of skeletal history, however, we are better off, for there are frequently preserved as fossils the bones of actual forebears. As regards the skull, we have a fairly complete knowledge of the structure of the head in the ancient labyrinthodont amphibians of the later Paleozoic, whose skulls are of the very type from which those of all later tetrapods have been derived. Further, though bony fish history is still obscure in some respects, the skull pattern of the higher fishes—particularly fossil crossopterygians—is not far removed from that of the ancient amphibians. We shall, therefore, give at this

219

Fig. 151. The skull of an ancestral land vertebrate, based primarily on the Carboniferous labyrintho-dont, *Palaeogyrinus*. *A*, Dorsal view of dermal skull roof; *B*, palate; *C*, lateral view; *D*, lateral view with dermal skull roof removed (outline in broken line); palatal bones—dermal and endoskeletal—of left side are shown; deep to them, the braincase. The hatched area is the sutural surface of palatal bones against maxilla. *E*, Lateral view of braincase; *F*, posterior view. (Partly after Watson.)

Abbreviations: *bart*, basal articulation of braincase and palate; *bo*, basioccipital; *bs*, basisphenoid; *con*, condyle; *e*, epipterygoid; *ec*, ectopterygoid; *en*, external naris; *eo*, exoccipital; *eth*, ethmoid region; *f*, frontal; *fo*, fenestra ovalis, *ic*, foramen for internal carotid; *in*, internal naris; *iptv*, interpterygoid vacuity; *it*, intertemporal; *j*, jugal; *l*, lacrimal; *m*, maxilla; *n*, nasal; *nc*, nasal capsule; *on*, otic notch; *op*, opisthotic; *or*, orbit; *p*, parietal; *paf*, parietal foramen; *pf*, postfrontal; *pl*, palatine; *pm*, premaxilla; *po*, postorbital; *pp*, postparietal; *pr*, prootic; *prf*, prefrontal; *ps*, parasphenoid; *pt*, pterygoid; *ptf*, posttemporal fenestra; *pv*, pituitary vein; *q*, quadrate; *qj*, quadratojugal; *sm*, septomaxilla; *soc*, supraoccipital; *sph*, sphenethmoid; *sq*, squamosal; *st*, supratemporal; *stf*, subtemporal fossa; *t*, tabular; *v*, vomer. Roman numerals, foramina for cranial nerves.

point a rather full account of this central skull pattern of the early amphibians and then discuss the major modifications seen in the various fish and tetrapod groups. The roof pattern and general proportions of the skull figured (Fig. 151) are those of Carboniferous embolomerous labyrinthodonts; the internal structures, not fully known in these forms, are restored after the pattern of certain other primitive labyrinthodonts.

Skull Components. To avoid (as far as can be) mental indigestion in treating of this complex structure, it is best that it be resolved into components (Fig. 152). The skull includes dermal bones and cartilages or their bony replacements, of both somatic and visceral nature (cf. p. 155). One possible method of treatment would be to consider as units the elements derived from each of these three embryologic sources. It is, however, preferable to recognize that a primitive skull seems to be composed of three major functional units, one purely dermal, the other two composites, as follows:

A. A *dermal skull roof*—a shield of membrane bone covering thoroughly the top and sides of the head, and extending down to the jaw rims where shield elements bear the marginal row of teeth. The roof is unbroken save by openings for the nostrils (*external nares*), eyes (*orbits*), and a small *parietal foramen* for a third, median eye. On either side, the shield is primitively notched behind the orbit for the eardrum opening, which replaces the spiracle present here in bony fishes.

B. A *palatal complex*. This includes ossifications in a palatoquadrate cartilage of visceral origin (which in sharks forms the entire jaw) and in addition a series of membrane bones formed below this cartilage in the roof of the mouth and in great measure replacing it. The anterior portion of this complex forms a broad palatal plate with, anteriorly, lateral gaps for the *internal nares,* or *choanae.* Posteriorly the palatal complex on either side is separated from the edge of the shield by the *subtemporal fossae;* through these descend the temporal muscles which close the jaws.

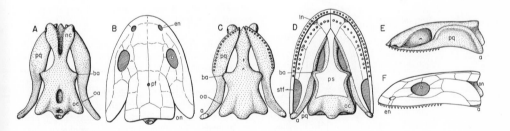

Fig 152. Diagrams to show the components of the skull. *A, C, E,* Dorsal, ventral, and lateral views of endoskeletal structures of braincase and palate (or upper jaw) as present in a shark or an embryo of higher jawed vertebrates; *B, D, F,* similar views with dermal elements added. In *B* and *F* a dermal roof shield binds together and covers braincase and endoskeletal jaw structures; in *D,* dermal palatal structures are seen reinforcing the endoskeletal palate, and a further dermal element underlies the braincase. *a,* Articulation with lower jaw; *ba,* basal articulation of braincase with palatoquadrate; *en,* external naris; *in,* internal naris; *nc,* nasal capsule; *o,* orbit; *oa,* otic articulation of palatoquadrate; *oc,* otic capsule; *on,* otic notch; *pf,* parietal foramen; *pq,* palatoquadrate; *ps,* parasphenoid; *s,* notch in skull for spiracle or ear drum; *stf,* subtemporal fossa for jaw muscle.

C. The *braincase*, formed in cartilage, mainly of somatic endochondral origin but usually ossified to a considerable degree; to its lower surface, in early tetrapods and bony fishes, is applied a sheet of dermal bone formed in the central area of the mouth vault.

The Primitive Amphibian Skull.   Dermal Roof.   In a primitive tetrapod the dermal skull roof includes a considerable number of elements, suturally connected to form a practically solid armor. In general these bones are paired; occasionally we find as variants unpaired median ossifications of little importance. It is a strain to commit to memory the names of the many elements present. Many of them, however, occur in bony fishes and in all tetrapods and are important to the student of osteology, of taxonomy, of evolution, and of paleontology. As an aid to memory we may arbitrarily group them into several series (Fig. 153):

(*a*) Tooth-bearing marginal bones. At the tip of the skull there is on either side a small *premaxilla* bearing the most anterior teeth. The remaining marginal teeth are carried on the elongate *maxilla*. The suture between premaxilla and maxilla lies below the external naris.

(*b*) A longitudinal series along the dorsal midline. From the premaxilla back to the occipital end of the skull we find in order the following bones: nasal, frontal, parietal, postparietal. The *nasals* lie medial and posteromedial to the external nares. The *frontals* lie between the orbits, but primitively do not enter into their margins. The *parietals* are generally large and occupy the central part of the skull table—the flattened roof area behind and between the orbits; the parietal foramen is situated here. The *postparietals* (dermal supraoccipitals) are at the back rim of the roof and may descend as flanges on to the posterior surface of the braincase.

(*c*) A circumorbital series of five bones—prefrontal, postfrontal, postorbital, jugal, and lacrimal—which in many early tetrapods form a complete ring around

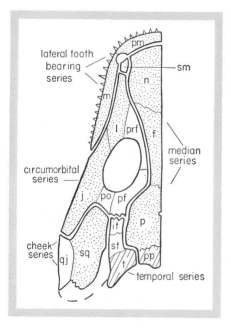

Fig. 153.   A diagram of the skull roof of a primitive tetrapod with the elements grouped (rather arbitrarily) into regional series. (The little septomaxilla does not readily fit into any series.) The stippled elements are retained as such in the skull of typical mammals; hatched elements at back appear to be fused into the mammalian occipital bone. *f,* Frontal; *it,* intertemporal; *j,* jugal; *l,* lacrimal; *m,* maxilla; *n,* nasal; *p,* parietal; *pf,* postfrontal; *pm,* premaxilla; *po,* postorbital; *pp,* postparietal; *prf,* prefrontal; *qj,* quadratojugal; *sm,* septomaxilla; *sq,* squamosal; *st,* supratemporal; *t,* tabular.

each orbit. *Prefrontal* and *postfrontal* form the upper rim of the orbit; the *post-orbital* occupies a place at the upper back orbital margin. The *jugal* is usually a large bone centered beneath the orbit. The *lacrimal* lies between the orbit and the external naris, and may enter the margin of either or both of these openings; the lacrimal (tear) duct lies in this area in tetrapods, and the bone derives its name from the fact that in amniotes it carries a canal for this duct on its inner surface. (We may mention here in passing the *septomaxilla*, a small and obscure dermal element which may be present at the back margin of the external naris adjacent to the lacrimal, or appear as a small shell of bone within the nasal cavity; it is described occasionally in tetrapods of one group or another, but its history is poorly known.)

(*d*) Temporal series. The notch in the skull behind the orbit is known as the *otic notch* in early tetrapods, since the eardrum is believed to have been placed here. Extending back above the notch at the margin of the skull table is a row of three small bones—*intertemporal, supratemporal,* and *tabular*—which tend to be reduced and lost in most later tetrapods.

(*e*) Cheek bones. Most of the cheek region, behind the orbit and below the otic notch, is occupied by a broad, platelike bone, the *squamosal;* below it there is primitively a smaller marginal element, the *quadratojugal.*

In primitive tetrapods the skull shield usually had a "sculptured" surface pattern of ridges or pits to which the dermis was strongly attached. This pattern is repeated in primitive bony fish skulls, but is generally replaced by a smooth surface in living types. Fishes and water-dwelling amphibians bear sensory lateral line organs (cf. Chap. 15) in a pattern of canals or grooves on the head. In fishes the canals are usually sunken into the substance of the roofing bones as closed tubes with occasional pores opening to the surface; in amphibians they are more superficial and in the roofing bones are indicated, at the most, by grooves. Similar canals or grooves are found in the lower jaws and in the operculars of fishes.

PALATAL COMPLEX (Fig. 151, *B, D*). In sharks, lacking dermal bones, the only "skull" structure lateral to the braincase is the cartilage which functions as an upper jaw. This, however, is not comparable to the jaw margins of bony fishes or tetrapods, for in them the homologue of the shark jaw cartilage is combined with dermal bones to form a complex palatal structure (Fig. 147, *D*), and the jaw margins are formed by bones of the skull shield.

The major part of the palatal complex consists of four pairs of dermal bones developed in the skin lining the roof of the mouth. The largest and most medially situated is the *pterygoid*, which primitively runs the greater part of the length of the skull; it is applied to the superficial—that is, lower—surface of the palatal cartilage or the ossifications formed in it, and in part replaces that structure as an element of strength in palatal construction. Lateral to the pterygoid is a row of three further dermal elements: the *vomer*, which meets its partner anteriorly and extends back medial to the internal naris; the *palatine*, extending back from that opening along the palatal margin; and the *ectopterygoid*, terminating at the subtemporal fossa. Teeth may be present on any or all of the four dermal elements of the palatal complex in bony fishes and early tetrapods, and the three lateral bones sometimes carry a series of teeth even larger than those of the jaw margins (shark teeth are perhaps comparable to this set, rather than to the marginal teeth of bony types).

These dermal palatal bones serve many of the functions performed by the shark upper jaw cartilage; but that structure, or bones replacing it, persists, although in somewhat reduced form, in the embryonic skull of bony fishes and tetrapods as the *palatoquadrate* (or pterygoquadrate) *cartilage.* In bony fishes a number of ossifications, variously named, may be found in the adult along the length of this bar; in tetrapods but two ossifications are found. Posteriorly, the *quadrate* bone forms the articular surface for the lower jaw. More anteriorly a second ossification, the *epipterygoid,* lies, as the name implies, above the ptery-goid. This bone connects at the basal articulation with the sphenoid region of the braincase; a movable articulation at this point between palate and braincase was characteristic, it would seem, of early bony fishes and early land vertebrates. A vertical bar of the epipterygoid extends upward toward the skull roof; more pos-teriorly, the epipterygoid sometimes extends backward to meet the quadrate. An-teriorly, the palatoquadrate cartilage originally extended, it seems, on toward the nasal region, but this area is reduced and cartilaginous in early tetrapods.

The anterior part of the palatal complex is an essentially horizontal plate of dermal bone, notched laterally by the internal nares, but otherwise tightly ap-posed to the marginal tooth-bearing dermal bones. The palatal plates of the two sides meet anteriorly; posteriorly, they separate, leaving *interpterygoid vacuities* and exposing the ventral surface of the braincase. The posterior half of the palatal complex is, by contrast with the anterior part, a vertical sheet of bone, bounding medially the subtemporal fossa for the jaw muscles. At the junction of anterior and posterior parts of the palatal complex is the basal articulation with the brain-case, in which the pterygoid as well as the epipterygoid may take part. Behind this point there is an open cleft between the vertical palatal plate and the side walls of the braincase. Through this cleft pass important blood vessels and nerves; through it also passes in primitive bony fishes the spiracular gill slit, and in am-phibians the ear passage which replaces the spiracle.

THE BRAINCASE (Fig. 151, *B, E, F*).   In bony fishes and all lower tetrapods a median dermal element, the *parasphenoid,* forms in the skin of the roof of the mouth beneath the braincase and is applied closely, sometimes indistinguishably, to its lower surface. Anteriorly, it is a slender and sometimes rodlike structure; more posteriorly, it spreads broadly over the expanded ventral surface of the braincase.

The braincase is well ossified in most bony fishes and tetrapods. However, the region of the nasal capsules never ossifies in typical land vertebrates, and in the skeletally degenerate living amphibians braincase ossification is greatly re-duced. In the better ossified forms the bony elements are frequently fused in the adult, so that it is difficult to delimit the areas of the individual bones.

In the occipital region a ring of four bones—median *basioccipital* and *supra-occipital* elements, and paired *exoccipitals*—surrounds the foramen magnum. In fishes and primitive tetrapods the occipital condyle is a single concave circular structure, mainly formed by the basioccipital, but with the exoccipitals entering into its upper and lateral borders. Basioccipitals and exoccipitals are formed, embryologically, from fused occipital arch elements and hence (not unexpectedly) tend to resemble the centrum and neural arches of a vertebra. The supraoccipi-tal, on the other hand, arises in a cartilage connecting the otic capsules of the two sides (it is unossified in some bony fishes and amphibians). The basioccipital may extend well forward beneath the floor of the brain cavity. The exoccipitals, however, are relatively small. Except in the degenerate modern amphibians, they are pierced in all tetrapods—and in crossopterygian fishes as well—by openings for the twelfth (hypoglossal) nerve. The vagus and accessory nerves (X and XI) and usually a vein draining part of the brain pass through a large foramen (jugular) lying anterior to the exoccipital and representing the embryologic gap between occipital arch and ear capsule; nerve IX may use this exit or pierce, more anteriorly, the ear capsule.

The roof of the braincase is generally open between the two otic capsules, but the region is, of course, protected by overlying dermal elements. Two ossifications are present in the otic region, the *prootic* and *opisthotic,* but the two are generally firmly fused and difficult to distinguish in the adult. The sacs and canals of the internal ear are buried within these ossifications of the capsule and may extend into the supraoccipital as well. In fishes there is no external opening from the otic region, but the head of the hyomandibular bone abuts against its outer surface; in land animals the *fenestra ovalis* is present at this point to receive the footplate of the sound-transmitting stapes (evolved from the hyomandibular). Nerve VIII, for the reception of sensory stimuli, enters the auditory capsule from within; nerve VII usually pierces the prootic near the anterior end; and the large trigeminal nerve (V) emerges through one or more openings at the anterior margin of the prootic. There is frequently an opening, the *posttemporal fenestra,* running in forward from the back surface of the skull above the otic capsule and below the dermal bones of the skull roof.

Forward from the otic region the braincase rapidly contracts in width to the interorbital or sphenoid region. A major element here is the *basisphenoid,* an unpaired bone which has its center of ossification in the braincase floor and is nearly completely sheathed ventrally by the parasphenoid. At either side the basisphenoid sends out a *basipterygoid process,* which forms the basal articulation with the palatal complex. A pocket, the *pituitary fossa* (or sella turcica, not seen in Figure 151) extends down into this element from the floor of the brain cavity, and contains the pituitary body. Nearby there is, ventrally, an opening from below on either side through which the internal carotid artery enters the braincase, and just behind the pituitary there is primitively a canal containing a vein which crosses from one orbit to the other. The lateral walls of the interorbital region are pierced by an opening for the optic nerve (II) and tiny foramina for the eye muscle nerves (III, IV, VI).

A median ossification, the *sphenethmoid,* sheathed below by the anterior process of the parasphenoid, is present in the narrow ethmoid region. Within it the two olfactory nerves diverge toward the nasal capsules. The more anterior part of the ethmoid area and the nasal capsules remain unossified in almost all tetrapods; they are ossified in various fishes, but the nature of the ossification centers here is unknown.

The Skull Roof in Bony Fishes.   Before following through the story of skull evolution in later tetrapods, we shall first compare the skull pattern seen in early tetrapods with that of their bony fish relatives.

Paleontologic work makes it increasingly evident that the ancestors of the tetrapods are to be sought among the Paleozoic crossopterygians. We have considerable knowledge of their cranial structure; this shows a resemblance to the early tetrapods in many features.

The dermal shield of these forms (Fig. 154, *A, C*) is as a whole comparable to that of tetrapods, and, despite considerable confusion in past interpretations, many of the individual dermal elements can be directly homologized. It is, however, interesting to note the marked evolutionary change in proportions between front and back regions of the skull. In crossopterygians the paired eyes and parietal foramen are far forward on the head; there is a long skull table and cheek region and a short "face." In early land vertebrates the facial region is much more developed, and the posterior part of the head relatively short. This suggests that the early ancestors of the bony fishes were very short-faced and that the facial region is in process of expansion in the crossopterygians. This idea appears to be borne out if we examine the dermal roof pattern. In the back part of the head most of the bony elements are directly comparable to those of tetrapods. Anteriorly, however, the small elements present are variable, and difficult in many cases to homologize with those of land vertebrates; the face, it would seem, was a new, growing development, in which stability of the bone pattern had not yet been attained.

The dipnoans are regarded as an aberrant offshoot of the primitive stock of the Sarcopterygii. The skull roof is certainly aberrant. In modern lungfishes the skull roof is incomplete and includes but a few large dermal elements not readily comparable to those of crossopterygians or amphibians (Fig. 155). In the oldest fossil lungfishes the roof shield consisted of numerous small polygonal bones

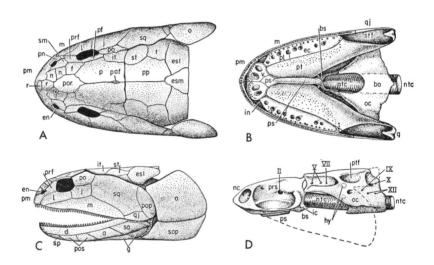

Fig. 154. The skull of a Paleozoic crossopterygian (composite), for comparison with that of a primitive land vertebrate (cf. Fig. 151). *A,* Dorsal view; *B,* palatal view; *C,* lateral view; *D,* lateral view of braincase. From the crossopterygian dermal covering that of a labyrinthodont differs primarily in loss of opercular elements and posterior row of bones on roof; relative reduction of length of posterior part of skull and elongation of "face" region; reduction of small elements in rostral and nasal region. The palate is similar in the two. The labyrinthodont braincase is less completely ossified, formed in one piece instead of the two present in crossopterygians, and lacks the greatly expanded notochord of the latter. *a,* Angular; *bo,* basioccipital; *bs,* basisphenoid; *d,* dentary; *ec,* ectopterygoid; *en,* external naris; *esl, esm,* lateral and medial extrascapulars; *f,* frontal; *g,* gulars; *hy,* hyomandibular articulation; *ic,* foramen for internal carotid; *in,* internal naris; *it,* intertemporal; *j,* jugal; *l,* lacrimal; *m,* maxilla; *n,* nasal; *nc,* nasal capsule; *ntc,* notochord (restored); *o,* opercular; *oc,* otic capsule; *p,* parietal; *paf,* parietal foramen; *pf,* postfrontal; *pl,* palatine; *pm,* premaxilla; *pn,* postnasal; *po,* postorbital; *pop,* preopercular; *por,* postrostral; *pos,* postsplenial; *pp,* postparietal; *prf,* prefrontal; *prs,* presphenoid (sphenethmoid); *ps,* parasphenoid; *pt,* pterygoid; *ptf,* posttemporal fenestra; *q,* quadrate; *qj,* quadratojugal; *r,* rostrals; *sa,* surangular; *sm,* septomaxilla; *sop,* subopercular; *sp,* splenial; *sq,* squamosal; *st,* supratemporal; *stf,* subtemporal fossa; *t,* tabular; *v,* vomer. Roman numerals, foramina for cranial nerves. (*A* and *B* based on Eusthenopteron; *C* based on Osteolepis; *D* based on Ectosteorhachis; data from Jarvik, Romer, Säve-Söderberg, Stensiö.)

which varied not merely from form to form, but even from one individual to another. In later genera there was a trend toward reduction in the number of these elements and for the preservation of a relatively few large plates such as those present today.

The presence of a variable pattern of numerous small bony plates over the entire roofing shield in early lungfishes and on the snout region of crossopterygians suggests that in the early bony fish ancestors in general bony centers were numerous, small, and variable in the head shield, and that only later was there a tendency at various times for a reduction in the number of elements present and for the stabilization of the pattern. Since it is improbable that this process of elimination and stabilization would have been the same in all cases, it is perhaps too much to expect that homologies can be firmly established between individual roofing bones in the various groups of bony fishes.

The actinopterygians (except the paddlefishes) have a well developed dermal roof in which many of the elements are quite stable and placed in positions comparable to those of certain of the bones in crossopterygians and tetrapods (Figs. 108, p. 170; 156; 157). In consequence, these elements are customarily given familiar names, such as parietals, frontals, and so on; we have, however, little guarantee of true homology. A notable difference from crossopterygians and tetrapods is that in ray-finned fishes there is seldom, apart from primitive fossil types, much development of a "cheek" region behind the orbit and no development, normally, of a bone there corresponding to the squamosal. Except in a few early forms there is no parietal foramen. In actinopterygians the orbits are gen-

Fig. 155. Skull roof and palate of the Australian lungfish, Epiceratodus. The braincase (stippled) is cartilaginous, but is underlain by a large parasphenoid (*ps*); the dermal roof includes only a small series of large plates which cannot be readily homologized with those of other forms. The upper jaws are fused to the braincase, and the only ossifications in the upper jaw or palate are large pterygoids (*pt*) and vomers (*v*). Large fan-shaped toothplates are borne by the pterygoids, and a small cutting tooth is present on each vomer. (After Goodrich.)

erally large, and the facial region anterior to them persistently short and undeveloped. The jaws were primitively long, and the maxillae well developed. In higher actinopterygians, however, the gape is reduced and the jaw articulation moved forward; the marginal dentition tends to disappear in teleosts, and the maxilla may be eliminated from the borders of the mouth.

The Palate in Bony Fishes. In crossopterygians the palatal structure (Fig. 154, *B*) is quite comparable to that of their tetrapod descendants; the dermal elements are almost identical in every regard.

In lungfishes the marginal teeth of the mouth are lost, and the remaining upper dentition includes only a pair of large, fan-shaped tooth plates (Fig. 155) fused to the pterygoids and a much smaller anterior pair on the vomers. In correlation we find that the dermal pterygoid bone is well developed, and that there is a small vomer; the other palatal bones, however, have been lost. There is no ossification of any sort in the palatoquadrate cartilage, which is firmly fused to the braincase in autostylic fashion.

In actinopterygians the palatal construction appears primitively to have been similar to that of crossopterygians, with two or more replacement bones forming in the palatoquadrate cartilage. In most living actinopterygians the basal articulation of palate and braincase is absent, and in compensation the hyomandibular is large and well ossified (Figs. 108, p. 170; 156, *B*; 157, *A*); an extra bone,

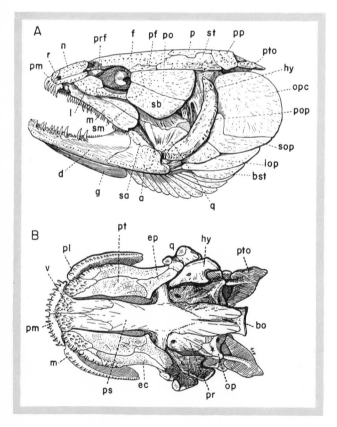

Fig. 156. *A*, Lateral and *B*, palatal views of Amia, least specialized of living actinopterygians. Abbreviations: *a*, angular, *bo*, basioccipital, *bst*, branchiostegal rays; *d*, dentary; *ec*, ectopterygoid; *ep*, epipterygoid; *f*, frontal; *g*, gular, *hy*, hyomandibular; *iop*, interopercular; *l*, lacrimal; *m*, maxilla; *n*, nasal; *op*, opisthotic; *opc*, opercular; *p*, parietal; *pf*, postfrontal; *pl*, palatine; *pm*, premaxilla; *po*, postorbital; *pop*, preopercular; *pp*, postparietal; *pr*, prootic; *prf*, prefrontal; *ps*, parasphenoid; *pt*, pterygoid; *pto*, pterotic; *q*, quadrate; *r*, rostral; *sa*, surangular; *sb*, suborbital; *sm*, supramaxillary; *sop*, subopercular; *st*, supratemporal; *v*, vomer. (The identity of certain of these elements with similarly named bones in crossopterygians and tetrapods is uncertain.) (After Goodrich.)

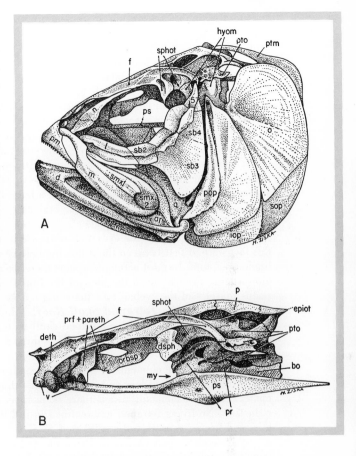

Fig. 157. The teleost Clupea (herring). *A,* Lateral view of skeleton of head and gill cover; *B,* lateral view of braincase. The structure of teleost skulls is highly specialized, but derived from the general pattern seen in Amia. Abbreviations: *ar,* articular; *bo,* basioccipital; *d,* dentary; *deth,* dermethmoid; *dsph,* dermosphenotic; *epiot,* epiotic; *f,* frontal; *hyom,* hyomandibular; *iop,* interopercular; *l,* lacrimal; *m,* maxilla; *my,* opening of myodome (arrow); *n,* nasal; *o,* opercular; *orbsp,* orbitosphenoid; *p,* parietal; *pareth,* parethmoid; *pm,* premaxilla; *pop,* preopercular; *pr,* prootic; *prf,* prefrontal; *ps,* parasphenoid; *ptm,* posttemporal; *pto,* pterotic; *q,* quadrate; *sb 1–5,* suborbitals; *smx 1, 2,* supramaxilla; *sop,* subopercular; *sphot,* sphenotic; *v,* vomer. (After Gregory.)

the *symplectic,* appears in this area to bind further the hyomandibular to the upper jaw complex.

The Braincase in Bony Fishes. In lungfishes the braincase, like other parts of the skeleton, is degenerate, persistently cartilaginous except for a pair of exoccipitals; in the sturgeons and paddlefishes much of the braincase has likewise degenerated to a cartilaginous state. In the ancient crossopterygians and older fossil members of the actinopterygians the whole structure was thoroughly ossified, but most sutures were obliterated during growth, and hence little can be said as to the individual bones present. In modern higher ray-finned forms, including the teleosts, the well-ossified braincase generally shows discrete bones; many appear to be the same as in tetrapods, but the otic region often includes as many as five bones which are not directly comparable to those of land animals (Fig. 157, *B*).

In many regards, even in small details, the crossopterygian braincase structure (Fig. 154, *B, D*) is quite similar to that of typical early tetrapods. There are, however, striking differences. Whereas the braincase of all other known vertebrates is built, in the adult, as a single compact unit, that of the crossopterygians is built in two quite separate pieces. The anterior segment is rather firmly bound to the upper jaw and palatal structures; it includes the nasal, ethmoid, and sphenoid regions, back to the area of the pituitary fossa and the basal articulation. The posterior segment includes the otic and occipital parts of the braincase. Embryologically, the front segment includes the trabeculae and associated structures (cf. p. 177); the back segment is formed from the parachordals, otic capsules, and occipital arches. The two parts are movably articulated with one another, and a further specialization tends to give them a flexible union; the notochord runs forward, without constriction, through a canal in the floor of the posterior moiety to terminate in a socket on the posterior surface of the anterior segment.

This unusual type of braincase construction was long believed to be an insuperable barrier to the derivation of land vertebrates from crossopterygians. Recently, however, there has been discovered in the most ancient of all known amphibians (from the late Devonian) a braincase in which there is at least a partial separation into two moieties and in which a large notochordal canal persists. It thus appears that even in their peculiar braincase construction the crossopterygians are antecedent to the tetrapods.

In actinopterygians the eyes and orbits are usually large, and in relation to this fact we find that between the orbits the braincase may be reduced to a membranous septum. In most actinopterygians there develops behind the pituitary region a large excavation in the floor of the braincase, a *myodome*, in which the rectus muscles of the eyeball take their origin.

History of the Tetrapod Skull Roof.   Rather than discuss seriatim the changes rung on the primitive tetrapod skull pattern as a whole in group after group of higher vertebrates, we shall follow through separately the history of the major components.

As regards the elements of the dermal skull roof, their later history is almost exclusively one of loss and degeneration. Almost never is there any development of a new element; always there is, in time, a greater or lesser degree of reduction. No living tetrapod has retained in full the pattern of its early ancestors, and few have preserved a solid roof covering.

Although a great variety of Paleozoic and early Mesozoic amphibians retained the primitive head shield pattern with little change, the modern amphibians show a greater degeneration of this structure than do many of the amniotes. In the broad, flat skull of a modern frog or salamander (Fig. 158, *B, C*) only a small proportion of the ancient dermal roof elements is preserved. Premaxilla, maxilla, nasal, frontal, parietal, and squamosal form the usual complement of bones; in urodeles a prefrontal is also present, but in anurans the parietal (as seen from embryos) is fused with the frontals, and in some urodeles maxilla and nasal are absent. All other elements have vanished, and much of the upper surface of the head is bare of dermal bone. In the Apoda (Fig. 158, *D*) the skull roof is a solid structure, but there is a similar reduction in the number of bones present; this solidity is probably a secondary condition associated with the burrowing nature of those wormlike forms.

In the stem reptiles (cotylosaurs) (Figs. 159, *A;* 160, *A*) the primitive pattern of the skull roof was retained with practically no change from primitive amphibians; indeed, the only diagnostic difference was the disappearance in some cotylosaurs of the little intertemporal bone. In later reptiles (Figs. 159, *B–D;* 160, *B–F*), however, there are notable losses and structural modifications. The elements which most generally disappear are those in the temporal region and the back margin of the skull—intertemporal, supratemporal, tabular, and postparietal; no one of the four is positively identifiable in any modern reptile. The

parietal foramen became unfashionable, it would seem, in many reptiles; Sphenodon and many lizards retain it, but it has vanished in turtles, snakes, and crocodiles (and it is absent, too, in birds and mammals).

Many major changes in the skull roof of reptiles are associated with the development of *temporal fenestrae* (Fig. 161). In earlier bony vertebrates the temporal muscles closing the lower jaw took origin beneath the solid plate of bone
covering the temple and cheek origin. This was the situation in the stem reptiles,
and the chelonians have apparently retained the primitive, solidly roofed—*anapsid*—condition. In most reptiles, however, one or two openings on each side have
been made in the cheek or temple region to allow freer play for the jaw musculature. Two openings have developed in many extinct and recent reptiles, such as
rhynchocephalians and all the Ruling Reptile stock. This is termed the *diapsid*
condition. One opening is present high up toward the skull roof, a second well
down the side of the cheek; a horizontal arch of bone between the two openings
connects the postorbital and squamosal elements. The Squamata are derived from
early diapsids; the bar closing the lower fossa has, however, been lost in lizards,
leaving but a single arch and single closed opening, and in snakes the upper bar
has been lost as well, leaving the whole cheek clear of dermal bone. By this process of reduction the quadrate has been left as a relatively free element—particularly so in snakes—giving a high degree of motility (useful in swallowing large

Fig. 158. Dorsal views of amphibian skulls. *A*, A primitive labyrinthodont; *B*, a frog; *C*, a salamander; *D*, an apodan. Abbreviations: *en*, external naris; *eo*, exoccipital; *f*, frontal (fused with parietal in
frogs); *it*, intertemporal; *j*, jugal; *l*, lacrimal; *m*, maxilla; *n*, nasal; *p*, parietal; *paf*, parietal foramen; *pf*,
postfrontal; *pm*, premaxilla; *po*, postorbital; *pp*, postparietal; *pr*, prootic; *prf*, prefrontal; *q*, quadrate; *qj*,
quadratojugal; *sm*, septomaxilla; *sq*, squamosal; *st*, supratemporal; *t*, tabular. (*A* after Watson; *D* after
Marcus.)

prey) to the jaw structures. In other (extinct) types (such as the plesiosaurs and ichthyosaurs), the single opening was dorsally situated, the postorbital and squamosal bones meeting below the fenestra in a *parapsid* condition.

The chelonians (Figs. 159, *B;* 160, *B*) are technically anapsids, for there is no true temporal opening. In many turtles, however, the skull roof has been, so to speak, eaten away from behind, and is often strongly scalloped out on either side of the parietals; in other cases emargination takes place at the lower margin of the cheek. In extreme cases the entire temporal region has been excavated, and there is no dermal roof over the cheek region from the orbits to the back edge of the skull. Posterolaterally, the turtle skull is uniquely specialized for the eardrum and middle ear structures.

In Aves (Fig. 162, *A*) the lightly built skull has such a close fusion of elements that sutures are in general obliterated. Birds have evolved from archosaurian reptiles, and the dermal roofing pattern is essentially that found in generalized members of that group. However, the expanding brain and large orbit have, so to speak, crowded the cheek region, originally diapsid in structure; much of the bars behind the orbit and between the two fenestrae has disappeared.

In the evolution of mammals (Figs. 163, 164) a first change, seen in Permian pelycosaurs (Figs. 163, *A;* 164, *A*), was the development of a small temporal opening on the side of the cheek; this is termed the *synapsid* condition (cf. Fig. 160, *B*). In later mammal-like reptiles, the therapsids (Figs. 163, *B, C;* 164, *B, C*), this fenestra enlarged greatly toward the top of the skull; the openings of the two sides almost meet dorsally, leaving only a narrow strip of the original

Fig. 159. Dorsal views of reptilian skulls. *A*, Stem reptile of the Paleozoic; *B*, a sea turtle; *C*, a young alligator; *D*, Sphenodon. Abbreviations: *en*, external naris; *f*, frontal; *j*, jugal; *l*, lacrimal; *m*, maxilla; *n*, nasal; *p*, parietal; *paf*, parietal foramen; *pf*, postfrontal; *pm*, premaxilla; *po*, postorbital; *pp*, postparietal; *pr*, prootic; *prf*, prefrontal; *qj*, quadratojugal; *soc*, supraoccipital; *sq*, squamosal; *st*, supratemporal; *t*, tabular.

parietal surface between them. Ventrally, only a bar, often narrow, formed by the jugal and squamosal, remains below the temporal opening as a *zygomatic arch* (cf. Fig. 171, p. 243). The bar between orbit and temporal opening disappeared in some advanced therapsids and is absent in primitive mammals; its upper end may remain as a process of the frontal. Farther forward, the maxilla (bearing the large canine teeth) expands upward and reduces the size of the lacrimal. The two external nares crowd toward the midline, where they form (as also in turtles) a single bony orifice. Various elements tended toward reduction and were lost by the time the definitive mammalian stage was reached; these include the septomaxilla, prefrontal, postfrontal, postorbital, supratemporal, and quadratojugal. The originally paired postparietals form a small median element in therapsids; this persists in mammals, but is in adults fused with the occipital elements (as apparently are the tabular bones).

The primitive pattern of the mammalian skull roof is preserved, in the main, in such a form as the dog (Figs. 163, *D*; 164, *D*). There are, however, numerous variations in proportions and disposition of skull parts in the different groups of mammals, most of which are apparent in the dermal bone arrangement. The bar behind the orbits was lost in the ancestral mammals, but it has been rebuilt in a number of different groups, and in higher primates a complete, deep, bony wall between orbit and temporal fossa has developed. In some forms (notably among insectivores and edentates) the zygomatic arch may be incomplete. The face is

Fig. 160. Side views of reptilian skulls. *A*, Stem reptile of the Paleozoic; *B*, a sea turtle; *C*, Sphenodon; *D*, a lizard; *E*, a python; *F*, a primitive ruling reptile of a type from which birds, dinosaurs, and crocodilians have descended. Abbreviations: *e*, epipterygoid; *ec*, ectopterygoid; *f*, frontal; *j*, jugal; *l*, lacrimal; *ls*, laterosphenoid; *m*, maxilla; *n*, nasal; *p*, parietal; *pf*, postfrontal; *pm*, premaxilla; *po*, postorbital; *pr*, prootic; *prf*, prefrontal; *pt*, pterygoid; *q*, quadrate; *qj*, quadratojugal; *sm*, septomaxilla; *soc*, supraoccipital; *sq*, squamosal; *st*, supratemporal. (*F* after Broom.)

Fig. 161. Diagrams to show types of temporal openings in reptiles. *A*, Anapsid type (stem reptiles, turtles); *B*, synapsid type (mammal-like reptiles); *C*, parapsid type (extinct plesiosaurs, and so forth); *D*, diapsid type; rhynchocephalians, ruling reptiles, lizards, and snakes derived by loss of one or both temporal arches. Abbreviations: *j*, jugal; *p*, parietal; *po*, postorbital; *sq*, squamosal.

much lengthened in insectivores and is especially elongate in anteaters of several orders; on the other hand, it is shortened in higher primates and withdrawn, so to speak, beneath the expanded brain vault. The external narial opening may move backward over the roof of the face region in forms which develop a flexible snout (as the tapirs) or trunk (elephants), and in the aquatic sirenians and whales. In the cetaceans the nasal opening, the "blowhole," is at the top of the skull; there has been a backward movement of the nasal region and a forward push of the occipital bones as well, so that the original skull roof is practically eliminated from the skull surface. In rodents the masseter muscles of the jaw (cf. p. 285) are highly developed; the side of the face may be deeply excavated for their origin, and a canal leading forward from the orbit on to the snout may be opened out into a large fenestra for their accommodation. In small animals within any group the brain is relatively large, and in consequence the dorsal surface of the skull appears swollen; larger species or races of domestic animals, with relatively small brains but heavy temporal muscles, are more likely to develop a median longitudinal *sagittal crest* for muscular attachment (the dogs show typical

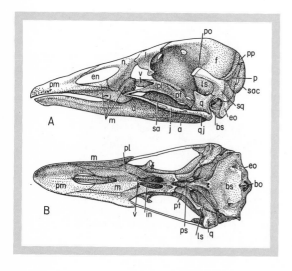

Fig. 162. *A*, Lateral, and *B*, ventral views of the skull of a duck (*Anas*). Abbreviations: *a*, angular; *bo*, basioccipital; *bs*, basisphenoid; *d*, dentary; *en*, external naris; *eo*, exoccipital; *f*, frontal; *in*, internal naris; *j*, jugal; *l*, lacrimal; *ls*, laterosphenoid; *m*, maxilla; *n*, nasal; *p*, parietal; *pl*, palatine; *pm*, premaxilla; *po*, postorbital; *pp*, postparietal; *ps*, parasphenoid; *pt*, pterygoid; *q*, quadrate; *qj*, quadratojugal; *sa*, surangular; *soc*, supraoccipital; *sq*, squamosal; *v*, vomer. (After Heilmann.)

Fig. 163. Dorsal views of skulls to show the evolution of the mammalian skull roof. *A,* Primitive early Permian mammal ancestor (pelycosaur); *B,* a later Permian therapsid; *C,* a progressive Triassic therapsid; *D,* the dog. Abbreviations: *eo,* exoccipital; *f,* frontal; *j,* jugal; *l,* lacrimal; *m,* maxilla; *n,* nasal; *occ,* occipital bone; *p,* parietal; *paf,* parietal foramen; *pf,* postfrontal; *pm,* premaxilla; *po,* postorbital; *pp,* postparietal; *pr,* prootic; *prf,* prefrontal; *prp,* preparietal; *q,* quadrate; *qj,* quadratojugal; *sc,* sagittal crest; *sm,* septomaxilla; *soc,* supraoccipital; *sq,* squamosal; *st,* supratemporal; *t,* tabular; *tl,* temporal lines. (*B* after Watson; *C* after Boonstra.)

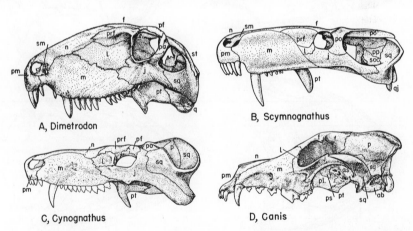

Fig. 164. Lateral views to show the evolution of the mammalian skull. *A,* Primitive early Permian mammal ancestor (pelycosaur); *B,* a late Permian therapsid; *C,* a progressive Triassic therapsid; *D,* the dog. Abbreviations: *ab,* auditory bulla; *as,* alisphenoid; *e,* epipterygoid; *f,* frontal; *j,* jugal; *l,* lacrimal; *m,* maxilla; *n,* nasal; *p,* parietal; *pf,* postfrontal; *pl,* palatine; *pm,* premaxilla; *po,* postorbital; *pp,* postparietal; *prf,* prefrontal; *ps,* presphenoid; *pt,* pterygoid; *q,* quadrate; *qj,* quadratojugal; *sm,* septomaxilla; *soc,* supraoccipital; *sq,* squamosal; *st,* supratemporal. (*B* after Watson; *C* after Broili and Schroeder.)

variations here). A transverse *nuchal crest* may form across the back margin of the roof for muscles and ligaments supporting the head. The tall, domed skull roof of the elephant is not due to brain expansion; largely filled with air sinuses, it provides a broad surface for attachment of the neck muscles and ligaments which support the heavy head and tusks.

The Palatal Complex in Tetrapods. The palatal elements originally present in the earliest tetrapods persist for the most part, but the structural arrangement became considerably modified in the palate of the broadened and flattened skull of the modern urodeles and anurans (Fig. 165). The basal articulation has lost its motility, and palate and braincase are broadly fused here. Anterior to this point of union the gap between the dermal bones of the palate and the base of the braincase is widened out into a pair of broad interpterygoid vacuities. The ectopterygoid is absent, and in urodeles the palatine is also small or absent, so that the palate is poorly developed laterally. Further, ossification is reduced in the embryonic palatal cartilage of modern amphibians. The epipterygoid is never ossified, and in urodeles ossification of the quadrate region is incomplete; here, as elsewhere, the modern amphibian skeleton is definitely degenerate. The apodan palate has a more compact structure, but is essentially comparable to that of other modern amphibians, and the ossifications present are the same as

Fig. 165. The palate of amphibians. *A*, Paleozoic labyrinthodont; *B*, a salamander; *C*, a frog; *D*, an apodous amphibian. Abbreviations: *ec*, ectopterygoid; *eo*, exoccipital; *in*, internal naris; *m*, maxilla; *pl*, palatine; *pm*, premaxilla; *pr*, prootic; *ps*, parasphenoid; *pt*, pterygoid; *q*, quadrate; *qj*, quadratojugal; *se*, sphenethmoid; *sq*, squamosal; *v*, vomer. (*A* after Watson; *D* after Marcus.)

in the frog. In the oldest tetrapods the jaw gape was long, and the quadrate articulation consequently well back of a plane drawn transversely through the occiput. In living amphibians, particularly the urodeles and apodans, the jaws are much shortened and the quadrates level with or in advance of the occiput.

The reptiles (Fig. 166) tended to hold to the primitive type of palate more persistently than did the amphibians; the primitive construction is still seen little changed in Sphenodon and lizards. A prominent lateral flange, often tooth-bearing, developed on the pterygoid in early reptiles, and is still preserved in Sphenodon and lizards. As noted previously, the quadrate has become a relatively free and movable element in lizards. In snakes the palate is still more flexible; indeed, the entire skull structure, except for the compact braincase, is pliable.

In the turtles the palate has become fused to the braincase through the reduction of the originally free basal articulation; the epipterygoid may disappear in the process. In the chelonians the pterygoids have fused with the lateral margins of the braincase floor, closing the interpterygoid vacuities; the quadrate is massive and is broadly in contact with the otic region of the braincase, thus increasing the solidity of the skull structure. The ectopterygoid is lost. The internal nostrils have usually moved some distance back in the roof of the mouth; they are generally situated in a deep dorsal pocket, which may be covered ventrally by bone to a varying degree. We see here the beginning of a *secondary palate*, a structure developed to a much greater degree in crocodiles and in mammals.

In crocodilians palatal mobility is likewise lost. The two pterygoids have gained a firm median union beneath the floor of the sphenoid region and have welded themselves onto the braincase. A further notable change from that of primitive forms is seen in the crocodilian skull in the presence of a highly developed secondary palate. Beneath the original palatal roof the maxillary, pala-

Fig. 166. The palate of reptiles. *A*, Lizard; *B*, a sea turtle; *C*, a young alligator; *D*, Sphenodon. Abbreviations: *bo*, basioccipital; *bs*, basisphenoid; *ec*, ectopterygoid; *in*, internal naris; *j*, jugal; *m*, maxilla; *op*, opisthotic; *pl*, palatine; *pm*, premaxilla; *ps*, parasphenoid; *pt*, pterygoid; *q*, quadrate; *qj*, quadratojugal; *soc*, supraoccipital; *sq*, squamosal; *v*, vomer.

tine, and pterygoid bones have built a secondary shelf of bone; between the braincase floor and this underlying shelf, canals run back from the external nares to open into the mouth far back, above the opening to the windpipe. A flap of skin just in front of this point can close off the pharynx from the mouth so that breathing may be accomplished under water, even with the mouth open, so long as the tip of the nose is above the surface—a useful adaptation in a predaceous water dweller.

In birds (Fig. 162, *B*, p. 234) the palatal structures are lightly built and flexible. The vomers are small bones, centrally placed between the large choanae; the ectopterygoids and epipterygoids are lost. The palatines run lengthwise lateral to the choanae to terminate at a movable articulation with the braincase. The pterygoids are short bars which extend back from this point to the quadrates, which are movably socketed onto the side of the braincase.

In the most primitive of mammal-like reptiles (Figs. 167, *A*, 168, *A*) the palate was still essentially that of their early reptilian and amphibian ancestors. In the therapsids, however, there appear a series of modifications leading to the mammalian type of palate (Figs. 167, *B–D*; 168, *B–D*). Anteriorly, a major change is the gradual development, in mammal-like forms, of a secondary palate

Fig. 167. A series of skulls in ventral view to show the evolution of the mammalian palate. *A*, Primitive early Permian pelycosaur; *B*, a late Permian therapsid; *C*, an advanced Triassic therapsid; *D*, the dog. Principal changes include development of secondary palate in *C* and *D*; loss of movable basal articulation and fusion of braincase and palate in *B-D*; reduction of pterygoid; loss of quadrate from skull structure and development of new jaw joint in *D*; addition of auditory bulla in *D*. Abbreviations: *ab*, auditory bulla; *bart*, basal articulation of palate and braincase; *bo*, basioccipital; *bs*, basisphenoid; *e*, epipterygoid; *ec*, ectopterygoid; *eo*, exoccipital; *gl*, glenoid cavity; *in*, internal nares; *j*, jugal; *m*, maxilla; *op*, opisthotic; *pl*, palatine; *pm*, premaxilla; *po*, postorbital; *popr*, paroccipital process; *pr*, prootic; *prs*, presphenoid; *ps*, parasphenoid; *pt*, pterygoid; *q*, quadrate; *qj*, quadratojugal; *sq*, squamosal; *v*, vomer.

rather comparable to that of the crocodiles. The maxillae and, farther back, the
palatines fold ventrally to produce an elongate shelf lying below the original roof
of the mouth; channels are thus created through which the air passes far back
from the original position of the internal nares before entering the mouth. The
vomers, originally paired, fuse into a single element (they maintain their position
in the original roof of the mouth and hence are almost concealed in ventral view).
They aid in forming a floor beneath the presphenoid and ethmoid and, further, form
a partition between the two nasal cavities. The bony secondary palate does not
extend so far back as that of crocodilians, but is continued by a fold of skin as a
"soft palate." The origin of the secondary palate in mammal-like reptiles and
mammals may be reasonably associated with the development of the constant
body temperature characteristic of mammals. Continuous breathing is practically
a necessity, and the secondary palate is an aid in the maintenance of breathing
while the mouth is functioning in eating.

In the mammalian line, as in many lower tetrapods, movable articulation of
palate and braincase has been abandoned (Fig. 171, p. 243); the pterygoid
bones fuse on either side to the sphenoid region of the skull. In this process the
pterygoids, once large elements, become much reduced in size. The lateral flange
on the palate disappears (and with it the little ectopterygoid bone), and the posterior arm of the pterygoid, once running backward and outward to the quadrate,
gradually dwindles. In a mammal the pterygoids are little more than small wings

Fig. 168. Diagrams to show the evolution of palatal structures and auditory ossicles from primitive
reptiles to mammals. Longitudinal sections of skulls, with bones of skull roof and palate represented as
if cut vertically just to the right of the midline (hatched surfaces). The left half of the skull and the entire braincase removed, so that the palatal structures of the right side are seen in medial view. In addition, the stapes and the articular element of the lower jaw are figured to show the evolution of the auditory ossicles. *A,* A primitive pelycosaur (Dimetrodon); *B,* a primitive therapsid; *C,* an advanced mammal-like reptile; *D,* a mammal. In *A* and *B* incoming air (*arrow*) enters the mouth cavity directly
through anteriorly-placed internal nostrils; in *C* and *D* a secondary palate is developed and there is some
degeneration of the primary palate. In *A* the palate articulates movably with the braincase at a socket
on the epipterygoid; in *B,* the palate becomes fixed to the braincase; the epipterygoid loses its original
function but survives as the alisphenoid bone of mammals. In *B-D* the pterygoid is reduced; the quadrate and articular, forming the articulation between upper and lower jaws are reduced in size and lose
their original function but survive as auditory ossicles. Abbreviations: *a,* articular; *as,* alisphenoid; *e,*
epipterygoid; *ec,* ectopterygoid; *i,* incus; *m,* maxilla; *ma,* malleus; *pl,* palatine; *pm,* premaxilla; *pt,* pterygoid; *q,* quadrate; *s,* stapes; *v,* vomer.

of bone projecting ventrally on either side below the sphenoid region of the brain-case and forming the walls of the posterior end of the air passage.

The original endochondral elements of the palate have changed markedly in mammals and are no longer present as part of the palatal structure. The mammals have acquired a new jaw joint; the skull portion of it, the *glenoid fossa*, is formed by the squamosal, and the quadrate has thus lost its major function. The quadrate was already small, in therapsids, and rather loosely connected with other skull bones. In mammals it has disappeared as a proper skull element; it is, how-ever, present, but as a tiny auditory ossicle. After the fusion of palate with brain-case, the epipterygoid lost much of its original function. The epipterygoid, besides forming a socket for the basal articular process of the braincase, had primi-tively a vertical process extending up to the skull roof lateral to the braincase. In mammals this has fused into the braincase walls as the alisphenoid bone (p. 244).

The Braincase in Lower Tetrapods.   In modern amphibians the brain-case tends to become relatively broad and flat and to become greatly reduced in its degree of ossification. On its under surface it is covered by a parasphenoid, very broad in urodeles and apodans (Fig. 165, p. 236). In the braincase itself little ossification remains. There are paired exoccipitals which may extend into the otic region; often there is a prootic bone, and, anteriorly, a sphenethmoid. Other ossifications have disappeared. In most fossil amphibians and all modern types the condyle, primitively single, is paired. The skull appears to have been short-ened in the occipital region in modern amphibians, and no foramen for a twelfth nerve is present.

In reptiles the braincase tends to remain in a better ossified condition than in amphibians. There is almost never any of the flattening tendency seen in am-phibians; the occipital region remains well developed; there is always a foramen for the twelfth nerve, and the condyle, a convex structure, remains single (except in the line leading to the mammals). The ossifications present are generally those seen in early tetrapods. Fusion of the palatal structures with the braincase in turtles, crocodiles, and various fossil reptiles results in a modification of brain-case form, including a loss of the basal process of the basisphenoid, a union of the otic region with the quadrate, and so forth; but usually the basic structure is readily discernible.

There is, however, one notable difference between the structure of the rep-tilian braincase and that of modern amphibians. In those lower forms the brain-case area between the orbits, in front of the otic region, is relatively thick and has in many cases complete side walls. In primitive reptiles, however, and in many early amphibians, the braincase walls are here incomplete. For much of the height only a membranous septum is present between the orbits; the brain primitively lay entirely back of this point. In certain reptiles, however—the snakes and the crocodilians—there appears to have arisen a functional need for a better enclosure of the brain cavity here. This is accomplished by the development of a new paired braincase ossification, the *laterosphenoid* (Fig. 160, *E*, p. 233).

In birds the brain is much expanded, and the braincase is a swollen struc-ture completely surrounded by bone (Fig. 162, *A*, p. 234). There has occurred here a process somewhat similar to that described below for mammals. Much of the brain expansion is sheathed by new extensions of the old roofing elements —frontals, parietals, and squamosals. In addition, however, a laterosphenoid ele-ment is present.

The Mammalian Braincase.   In the mammal-like reptiles the braincase elements were those seen in early amphibians and reptiles. When the mammalian condition is attained, notable changes have occurred (Figs. 169, 170, 172). The occiput region is basically the same as that of early reptiles, but there is a division of the originally single condyle into a paired structure analogous to that seen in amphibians. In the adult mammal the elements of the occipital region are usually fused into a single *occipital bone*, although ossification centers of all four primitive elements are seen in the embryo. There are usually added to the occipital, dorsally, dermal bone centers which appear to be remnants of the postparietal and (questionably) tabular bones of the ancestral skull roof.

Primitively the otic capsule was, we noted, formed from two centers (prootic and opisthotic). In mammals, however, there is a variable number of centers which in the adult fuse into a compact mass, the *periotic*. In reptiles the otic capsule occupies a relatively large area on the side wall of the braincase; in mammals, in contrast, it is relatively small, and is situated low down at the lateral braincase margins. For the most part the capsule is buried deeply beneath the surface of the skull, but its posterior end may be exposed as the *mastoid process;* this is frequently adjoined, posteriorly and medially, by a *paroccipital process* of the occipital bone.

In the otic region we find in most mammals a new addition to the skull in the shape of the *auditory bulla* (Figs. 167, *D;* 172). Just outside the periotic region lies the middle ear cavity, containing in mammals the three small and delicate auditory ossicles and, at its outer margin, the eardrum (cf. p. 491). In the earliest mammals, as in most marsupials today, this region had no satisfactory protection against injury from without; in most placentals this protection is supplied by the development of the bulla as an ensheathing capsule. Frequently present here is a *tympanic* bone. This, in its most primitive form, is merely a bony ring surrounding the eardrum; but in other cases this bone expands inward to form part or all of the bulla. The tympanic is a dermal element, and embryologic evidence suggests (unlikely as it seems at first) that it is a modification of the angular bone of the reptilian lower jaw, which lies close to the eardrum in rep-

Fig. 169. Median sagittal section of the dog skull. Diagonal lines indicate sectioned bones. It will be seen that most of the bone enclosing the brain cavity is derived from dermal elements (*f, p, sq*), and even part of the occipital is embryologically of dermal origin (cf. Fig. 171). Abbreviations: *as*, alisphenoid; *bs*, basisphenoid; *f*, frontal; *m*, maxilla; *me*, mesethmoid; *n*, nasal; *occ*, occipital; *per*, periotic; *pl*, palatine; *pm*, premaxilla; *prs*, presphenoid; *pt*, pterygoid; *sq*, squamosal; *v*, vomer.

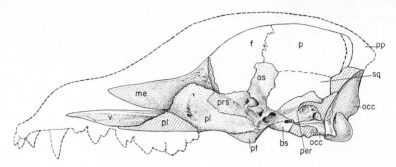

Fig. 170. Diagrammatic dissection of the dog skull in lateral view. All dermal bones of the skull roof are removed (including the dermal component of the occipital), leaving a series of bones comparable to those of the palatal series and braincase of Figure 151, *D*. Dermal palatal elements include vomer, palatine and pterygoid; the alisphenoid (= epipterygoid) is a cartilage bone palatal element. Elements of braincase origin include mesethmoid, presphenoid (plus orbitosphenoid), basisphenoid, periotic and most of the occipital bone. The upper margin of the brain cavity is shown in outline, and the contributions of the dermal roof bones are indicated. Abbreviations: *as,* alisphenoid; *bs,* basisphenoid; *f,* frontal; *me,* mesethmoid; *occ,* occipital; *os,* orbitosphenoid; *p,* parietal; *per,* periotic; *pl,* palatine; *pp,* postparietal; *prs,* presphenoid; *pt,* pterygoid; *sq,* squamosal; *v,* vomer.

tiles (cf. Fig. 246). In addition to the tympanic, there forms in many mammals a second bone, an *entotympanic,* which may surround the middle ear cavity and may fuse in the adult with the tympanic to form a compound bulla. The entotympanic is formed in cartilage. This cartilage, however, is not part of the original tetrapod skull structure; we have here, most exceptionally, the addition of a new element in skull structure. The otic elements—periotic and new bulla—remain discrete in some forms; in others they fuse with one another and with the adjacent squamosal bone of the skull roof to form a compound *temporal* bone.

The basisphenoid forms the braincase floor in the region of the pituitary. In many cases it fuses with neighboring elements—alisphenoid, presphenoid, oribtosphenoid—to form a complex (if small) element termed the *sphenoid.* The parasphenoid, which sheathed the braincase floor in lower forms, has disappeared as a separate ossification in mammals.

The sphenethmoid of lower tetrapods persists in mammals, anterior to the basisphenoid, as the *presphenoid;* its lateral portions, in the orbit, are sometimes distinct and termed the *orbitosphenoid,* but the two form essentially a unit structure. In some mammals, including various primitive types and both major ungulate orders, the presphenoid is the most anterior braincase element; but in other orders, including primates, rodents, and carnivores, a new ossification, the *mesethmoid,* is present still farther anteriorly. When both are present, the presphenoid is restricted to the anterior part of the braincase floor, appearing externally in the roof of the choanae ventrally and (as the orbitosphenoid portion of the bone) in the orbital walls anterior to the alisphenoid. In mammals the nasal pouches have extended backward so that they are separated from the expanded brain cavity only by a transverse plate of bone, the *cribriform plate,* perforated for the passage of bundles of olfactory nerve fibers. The mesethmoid, when present, ossifies in this area, and extends forward as a median septum between the two nasal cavities. In these cavities variable scrolls of cartilage or bone, *turbinals,* which represent the original nasal capsule, are developed in connection with the neighboring bones (maxilla, nasal and mesethmoid). Covered with nasal mucosa, they increase the surface area of the nasal passages.

The bones so far named include the entire roster of elements formed in the braincase proper. But if we examine the actual "braincase" of a typical mammal (Figs. 169, 170), it will be seen that they form little but the floor and the back wall of the brain cavity. The mammalian brain has expanded to such proportions that the braincase proper has been unable, so to speak, to keep up with its growth; most of the walls of bone surrounding the brain in the adult placental mammal have been derived from other skull materials.

The parietals and frontals in early reptiles formed a broad roof over the brain region. With the development of the temporal fenestrae their surface area was much reduced (Fig. 171, *A*). They tended, however, to send flanges downward, deep to the jaw muscles, along the walls of the brain cavity beneath. With the great expansion of the brain in mammals (Fig. 171, *C*), these flanges became much enlarged and spread out laterally over the swollen brain surface to form much of the roof and side walls of the brain box; the squamosal bone from the side of the dermal roof has also been drawn into the work of forming a covering for the brain. These newly expanded areas of the dermal roofing elements give the appearance of being part of the original surface of the skull. They are not, however. They lie beneath the temporal jaw muscles (the original skull roof was external to these muscles). The upper limits of temporal muscle attachment on either side are marked by the *temporal lines*, which may become confluent posteriorly as the sagittal crest (Fig. 163, *D*, p. 235). Only the area of the frontals and parietals which lies between these lines, or forms the sagittal crest, represents the original skull surface; the remainder of the expanse of these bones is a new, deeper, internal growth. One tends, unthinkingly, to regard the zygomatic arches as superficial "handles" external to the skull proper much as the handle or handles of a jug project outward from the vessel itself. This is, as we have

Fig. 171. Diagrammatic cross sections of the skull and jaws of *A*, a primitive mammal-like reptile; *B*, an advanced mammal-like form; and *C*, a mammal; to show features in the development of the skull roof and braincase. (1) Part of the lateral walls enclosing the expanding brain were originally membranous. This lateral area comes to be ensheathed by ventral extensions of the roofing bones and by the incorporation of the epipterygoid of the palatal structure as the alisphenoid. (2) This extension of the roofing bones downward around the brain gives the appearance in mammals of being the original skull surface; the original surface, however, lay external to the temporal muscles, as indicated by the broken lines. (3) The upper jaw elements (*e*, epipterygoid; *pt*, pterygoid) originally articulated movably with the braincase (*bs*, basisphenoid); the two structures are fused in *B* and *C*.

seen, the reverse of the case. The arches are a last remnant of the former skull sidewalls; the solid "brain box" is mainly a new formation deep to the old skull surface.

Still another addition has been made to fill out the walls of the expanding braincase: the incorporation of the epipterygoid bone of lower vertebrates as the *alisphenoid* (Figs. 168, 169, 170, 171, *C*). We have noted the lack of ossification in the reptilian braincase wall between the orbits. The epipterygoid in reptiles is mainly a vertical rod which, as part of the upper jaw structure, lies external to this unossified interorbital region. In therapsids this bar was expanded to a plate, but still lay external to the braincase. In mammals, however, it has been incorporated into the braincase wall, filling the gap above the basisphenoid and so firmly fused with this last bone that (as its new, mammalian name implies) it appears to form a wing of the combined sphenoid element.

In sum, the brain capsule of mammals is a composite affair. The original braincase is able to do little more than form its floor; dermal elements plus the alisphenoid are called into play to form the walls and roof of this expanded structure.

Mammalian Braincase Foramina (Fig. 172). We have mentioned the various openings for nerves and vessels found in the braincase of lower tetrapods. The situation may be reviewed for the mammals, for although many of the openings are the same, the nomenclature (unfortunately) differs; further, the incorporation of the alisphenoid and auditory bulla into the braincase has modified the nature of the openings.

The olfactory nerves in mammals take the form of numerous small filaments which pierce the ethmoid bone in the sievelike cribriform plate. The optic nerve usually enters the brain cavity through an *optic foramen* in the orbitosphenoid.

In early reptiles the area posterior to the ethmoid region, on the side of the braincase as far back as the ear capsule, was open for the exit of nerves III to VI. The filling in of the braincase wall by the alisphenoid has changed this situation. We find a large opening in front of the alisphenoid, the *anterior lacerate foramen* (sphenoidal or orbital fissure); two openings—*foramen rotundum* and

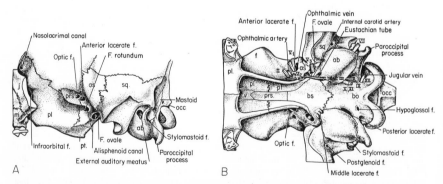

Fig. 172. Braincase region of a dog in *A*, lateral view, *B*, ventral view, to show foramina. In *B* are indicated the main nerves, the course of the internal carotid artery and its palatine branch and the jugular vein. Abbreviations: *ab*, auditory bulla; *as*, alisphenoid; *bo*, basioccipital; *bs*, basisphenoid; *f*, frontal; *j*, jugal; *m*, maxilla; *occ*, occipital bone; *pl*, palatine; *prs*, presphenoid; *pt*, pterygoid; *sq*, squamosal; *v*, vomer.

foramen ovale—usually piercing the alisphenoid; and a *middle lacerate foramen,* lying at the back edge of the alisphenoid (with which the ovale may fuse). Typically, the eye muscle nerves and the most anterior division of the trigeminal nerve pass through the anterior lacerate foramen; maxillary and mandibular branches of the trigeminal use the round and oval foramina; the middle lacerate foramen is of little functional importance except that the internal carotid artery enters the braincase here or close by.

Nerves VII and VIII enter the ear capsule from the brain cavity in an *internal auditory meatus.* The former nerve primitively emerged at the surface toward the front end of the ear capsule; in mammals, however, in relation to the complicated middle ear structure, it remains buried in the otic bones until it emerges back of the bulla region at the *stylomastoid foramen.* At the back end of the bulla, in a gap between the otic and occipital regions, is a *posterior lacerate foramen* (jugular foramen) through which nerves IX, X, and XI and the internal jugular vein draining the skull make their exit. Nerve XII usually occupies a separate *hypoglossal foramen,* sometimes multiple, in the floor of the occiput.

The auditory bulla has, of course, an external opening, the *external auditory meatus,* and at its front end an opening for the eustachian tube from the throat. The internal carotid artery originally ran forward on the under surface of the skull past the middle ear region. This area is covered in mammals by the bulla, beneath which the artery runs forward in a *carotid canal* to a point near that at which it enters the braincase. Near this latter point there is sometimes present an *alisphenoid canal* through which a branch of the artery continues forward toward the palate.

Among other skull openings and ducts not connected with the braincase we may mention the *incisive foramen* near the front of the palate, connecting the mouth with the vomeronasal organ (cf. p. 465); the *infraorbital foramen,* sometimes enlarged to a canal, carrying blood vessels and nerves forward from the orbit to the surface of the snout; the *nasolacrimal canal* from orbit to nasal cavity, for the tear duct; variable canals in the palate for the forward passage of nerves and small blood vessels.

Lower Jaw (Figs. 173, 174). The lower jaw, or *mandible,* although not part of the skull as we have used the term, may be described here. It is in most vertebrates a complex of both dermal and endoskeletal structures. Presumably, dermal elements were present in the jaw of the ancestral jawed vertebrates; in the living Chondrichthyes, however, they have been lost, and the lower jaw of sharklike fishes is, like the upper, simply a tooth-bearing bar of cartilage derived from a gill arch element (Figs. 147, *C,* p. 214; 149; 150, p. 217). This *mandibular cartilage,* also termed *Meckel's cartilage* after its discoverer, is present in the jaw of the embryo in bony fishes and all tetrapods (Fig. 147, *D–F*). In all these types except the mammals the cartilage, or a bone derived from it, persists as part of the adult jaw structure but as a minor part only. Its anterior part may disappear in the adult or remain as a cartilage buried deep within the jaw structure; rarely (as in common frogs), an anterior part of the cartilage may ossify. The posterior portion, which articulates by a socket with the upper jaw, is a cartilage in degenerate forms, but usually ossifies as the appropriately named *articular* bone. Anterior to it is a *prearticular fossa* opening downward into the jaw from above, which affords an area of insertion for muscles closing the jaw and offers a place of entrance into the interior for nerves and blood vessels.

Except in the sharklike fishes the lower jaw consists in great measure of der-

Fig. 173. Left lower jaws, outer views at left, inner views at right, of *A*, a ray-finned fish, the bow fin; *B*, a primitive crossopterygian; *C*, a primitive labyrinthodont; *D*, a primitive reptile; *E*, an alligator. The jaws of modern teleosts, amphibians, and reptiles, in which the number of elements is reduced, have been derived from the types shown in *A, C,* and *D,* respectively.

mal bones. Early fossil amphibians and bony fishes had a complex series of such bones; their descendents have simplified the pattern in various ways. The primitive pattern will be described first.

On the outer surface the major element is the *dentary*, which bears the marginal teeth and corresponds to the maxilla of the upper jaw. Below and to the back of the dentary there is primitively a row of dermal bones which includes anteriorly two small *splenials*, followed by a larger *angular*, and a *surangular*. The symphysis between the jaw rami is mainly formed by interlocking rugosities on the inner surface of the dentaries, but the splenials may enter into the symphysis as well. All these external elements may curve inward ventrally to appear also on the lower part of the inner surface of the jaw.

The internal sheathing elements of the primitive jaw were four in number. A major dermal bone is the elongate *prearticular*, which runs forward from the articular. Toward the upper margin there is a series of three slender bones, the *coronoids*. They bear, in early types, teeth of variable size, and teeth may be present on the prearticular as well. It is of interest that the inner aspect of the lower jaw is primitively very much a mirror image of the upper jaw and palate (cf. Figs. 165, *A;* 173, *C*). The prearticular, running forward from the articular, internal to the prearticular fossa, is comparable to the pterygoid, running forward from the quadrate internal to the subtemporal fossa; the three coronoids are comparable to the three lateral palatal elements.

The structure described above is that found in both early crossopterygians (Fig. 173, *B*) and early amphibians (Fig. 173, *C*). In other groups of vertebrates the changes from this primitive condition are almost entirely a matter of fusion or, more frequently, loss of elements.

In ray-finned fishes various losses and fusions occur, leading to a condition in which, in teleosts, but three bones are recognized, termed dentary, articular, and angular. In sturgeons, paddlefishes, and in lungfishes, skeletal degeneration leads to the retention in the adult of a large unossified Meckel's cartilage and a strong reduction in dermal ossification.

In modern amphibians, too, ossification is much reduced. Typical urodeles have three dermal bones, the dentary and two bones on the inner surface which are probably the prearticular and a coronoid. In frogs there is, apart from the dentary, but a single other element, presumably the prearticular. In reptiles (Fig. 173, *D*) there is never more than one splenial, and almost never more than a single coronoid, but a general retention of other elements—articular, dentary, angular, surangular, and prearticular. In crocodilians (Fig. 173, *E*) and other archosaurs a large lateral jaw fenestra is usually developed in the angular region. In birds the characteristic reptilian elements (except, apparently, the coronoids) are retained in a fused condition, and the archosaurian lateral fenestra is present.

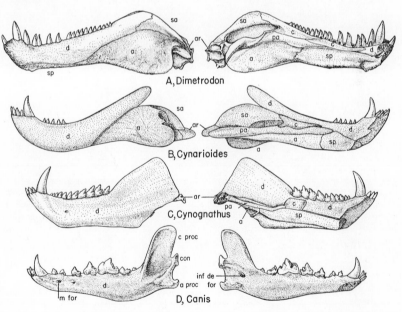

Fig. 174. Left lower jaws of mammal-like reptiles and mammals, illustrating the reduction of jaw elements. Outer views (*left*) and inner views (*right*). *A,* Primitive mammal-like reptile (pelycosaur); *B,* a primitive therapsid; *C,* an advanced therapsid; *D,* a typical mammal (dog). Abbreviations: *a,* angular; *a proc,* angular process; *ar,* articular; *c,* coronoid; *con,* condyle; *c proc,* coronoid process; *d,* dentary; *inf de for,* inferior dental foramen; *m for,* mental foramen; *pa,* prearticular; *sa,* surangular; *sp,* splenial.

In mammal-like reptiles (Fig. 174, *A–C*) can be seen stages in a notable transformation of the jaw structure which is completed in mammals (Fig. 174, *D*). The dentary increases steadily in importance; posteriorly, it extends to a position beneath the squamosal close to the old jaw articulation, and more anteriorly an ascending process grows upward beneath the temporal region for the attachment of temporal muscles. Concomitantly the other jaw ossifications are reduced in size. In mammals we find that these other structures have been lost from the jaw and, in so far as they are still present, are to be looked for in the auditory apparatus. The jaw consists of the dentary bone alone. This includes a *ramus,* the original tooth-bearing part of the bone; an ascending *coronoid process* to which temporal muscles attach; a new backward projection which may bear ventrally an *angular process* (often prominent); posteriorly, a transversely elongate rounded *condyle* which fits into the glenoid fossa of the squamosal bone of the skull and has thus functionally replaced the articular.

9

MUSCULAR
SYSTEM

The muscular system, judged quantitatively, at least, should loom large in any animal study of the present sort, for muscle tissue constitutes from a third to a half of the bulk of the average vertebrate. Functionally, too, the musculature is of highest importance. The activity of the nervous system —even the highest functioning of a human brain—has little mode of expression other than the contraction of muscle fibers. From locomotion to the circulation of the blood, the major functions of the body are caused by or associated with muscular activity. Although movement—of the trunk, limbs, or jaws, or of an organ or organ part—is the main product of muscular activity, subsidiary functions should be kept in mind as well. Often muscle work is expended in negative fashion in maintaining stability of the body or its parts, and muscular activity is of primary importance in the production of body heat.

Smooth Muscle. Histologically, two major types of muscular tissue are distinguished—smooth and striated fibers. Smooth muscle fibers are the simpler and smaller of the two. These fibers are derived from the embryonic mesenchyme, primarily mesodermal in origin and hence developed in association with the connective tissue cells. The main seat of smooth muscle is in the lining of the digestive tract. Certain other sites, such as the ducts of the glands associated with the gut, the bladder, and the trachea and bronchi of the lungs, are outgrowths of this tract. Still other loci for smooth muscle fibers, however, are independent of the gut system, these including circulatory vessels, genital organs, and the connective tissue of the skin and other areas.

A typical smooth muscle fiber (Fig. 175) is a slender, spindle-shaped body averaging a few tenths of a millimeter in length. There is a single, centrally situated nucleus; the cytoplasm appears homogeneous, but with special chemical treatment tiny fibrils can be seen running the length of the cell. In smooth muscle, as the name implies, the fibrils appear to be simple; there is no cross banding of the fiber such as is seen in striated muscle cells. Smooth muscle fibers are sometimes scattered. More generally, however, they are arranged in bands or bundles, with interspersed connective tissue fibers uniting them into an effective common mass (cf., for example, Figs. 241, 249) and in some cases at least, with

249

Fig. 175.   Major types of muscle fibers. (From Hunter and Hunter, College Zoology.)

protoplasmic processes affording direct contact between neighboring cells. In great measure smooth muscle cells are stimulated by autonomic nerve fibers; but they may apparently be stimulated by the contraction of their neighbors as well, and, particularly in the digestive tract, one may find a wave of contraction passing along a band of smooth muscle tissue.

Cardiac Muscle.   In the heart is found a special type of musculature not present elsewhere (Fig. 175). This tissue shows a cross banding similar to that seen in striated fibers, but in other regards cardiac muscle differs markedly from striated muscle. The whole heart musculature is a continuous network of dividing and recombining strands. Prominent cross bands, termed *intercalated discs*, more or less separate this network into short units. It has been generally thought that the heart musculature is a synctium, without boundaries between individual cells; recent work, however, indicates that the intercalated discs are actual boundaries between cellular units, each of which has a centrally situated nucleus. Embryologically, heart muscle, like smooth muscle, is derived from mesenchyme as is smooth musculature; its histologic characteristics are presumably associated with the important functions of this constantly active tissue. The heart beat may be influenced by autonomic nerves, but, as discussed in a later chapter, the heart musculature is essentially autonomous.

Striated Muscle. Fibers of this type form the "flesh" of the body—the voluntary muscles, derived in great measure from the myotomes of the embryo; they are in general arrayed as formed muscles which attach to and move skeletal structures. Striated muscle fibers (Figs. 175, 176) are large cells, elongate and cylindric, with lengths which vary from about a millimeter up to a number of centimeters (lengths of over a foot have been reported). The fibers are arranged in parallel fashion to form muscles. Connective tissues run between the fibers and bind them together, forming sheaths for fiber bundles—fascicles—and, further, form an external sheath, the *epimysium*, for the muscle as a whole.

Striated muscle cells are multinucleate, with numerous nuclei scattered along the entire length. In most vertebrate groups the nuclei are situated in the interior of the fiber; in mammals, and to some degree in birds, the nuclei are, on the contrary, superficial in position. The fiber surface is covered by a thin membrane, the *sarcolemma* (not developed in smooth muscle). As in smooth and cardiac muscle cells, the striated muscle fiber contains a large number of closely packed longitudinal fibrils; these, in turn, contain numerous still tinier filaments, so that it has been estimated that a single fiber may have in section as many as a million of these exceedingly small structures. The striated appearance of the fiber is due to the fact that each fibril consists of alternating light and dark portions; these occur at the same point on each fibril and hence appear as cross striations on the fiber as a whole. (Cardiac muscle shows similar banding, but in less clear-cut fashion.) The banding has long been intensively studied by histologists, by whom a series of letters have been used for fractions of the bands. Under ordinary light there is readily seen in the uncontracted state an alternation of light (I) and dark (A) segments. Within each band further cross markings may be distinguished, such as a light area (H) within the dark (A) band and, especially, a very distinct dark cross band (Z) within the light (I) segment. Changes in the banding occur when contraction of the fiber takes place.

At some point along the outer surface of the striated fiber there is an area devoid of fibrils, a *muscle end plate* into which penetrate the coiled ends of motor nerve fibrils. Each motor nerve fiber usually divides terminally to supply a number of adjacent muscle fibers. In a resting condition, the sarcolemma is electrically polarized. A nerve impulse results in the giving off from the nerve fibril tips a minute quantity of the chemical acetylcholine. This appears to cause a momentary depolarization of the sarcolemma and thereby sets up contraction.

Fig. 176. Banding of striated muscle fibers, as discussed in text. (From Guyton, Textbook of Medical Physiology.)

Muscle Fiber Function. The force of a muscle is exerted through a shortening of its fibers and hence a pull on the bones or other structures to which the two ends of the muscle are attached. There is, of course, no reduction in total bulk; in consequence, the shortened fibers, and the muscle as a whole, become thicker with contraction. In smooth musculature the contraction is relatively slow, and the amount of contraction less than in a striated muscle, but contraction may be long sustained; in contrast, striated muscle may be more rapidly stimulated and contract more vigorously, but is more readily fatigued.

A striated muscle as a whole may contract slightly or strongly, briefly or for a considerable period of time; the result varies according to the number of fibers stimulated and the number and rapidity of the nerve stimuli. Individual muscle fibers, however, work on an "all or none" basis; each fiber either contracts as fully as possible or fails to contract at all. A single sharp contraction of a striated fiber and the more gradual relaxation which follows occupy altogether but a tenth of a second or so. Normally, however, muscle contraction is not caused by a single stimulation, but by a continuous rapid tattoo of nerve impulses. A second impulse given before the effect of the first has worn off will increase the contraction, a third will further increase it, and a long series may bring the muscle fibers to a state of maximum contraction or tension (tetanus).

Speedy release of large amounts of energy is required for muscular activity. In the long run the energy is obtained by consumption of glycogen, abundantly present in the fibers, and the red color of many muscles may be due not only to the presence of abundant blood vessels which supply needed oxygen to the fibers, but also to the presence in muscle fibers of a hemoglobin, similar to that of the blood, which stores up oxygen for use in sustained contraction.

But, even so, it appears impossible to oxidize glycogen with sufficient rapidity for any degree of muscular activity, and muscle cells are notable for the presence in them of considerable amounts of adenosine triphosphate (ATP) which, as discussed in Chapter 4, is notable for its ability, through loss of part of its phosphate, to release energy rapidly and in quantity. Breakdown of ATP thus releases immediate energy for contraction. But before continued contraction can take place, the ATP must be rebuilt, and energy must be supplied for the rebuilding process. Here the "normal" method of carbohydrate oxidation as an energy source comes into the picture. Glycogen stored in the muscle cell is burnt, and the obtained energy used not so much directly for fiber contraction as for rebuilding ATP, using phosphate present in combination with creatine. If, however, activity of the fiber is too great and too continuous, efficient utilization of the glycogen does not take place; "fatigued" fibers contain considerable amounts of lactic acid, a product resulting from incomplete oxidation of the glycogen.

We have, thus, accounted for the energy needed for fiber contraction; but in what fashion does the contraction take place? This is currently a moot question. The major materials of the fibrils and enclosed filaments are spiral elongate molecules of the proteins myosin and actin. It is usually assumed that shortening is accomplished by a folding or increased coiling of these molecules. A recently advanced alternative is that in the arrangement of the filament there are alternating series of long actin and myosin molecules, neither type extending the full length of a fibril "segment," and that contraction consists of the sliding of one series on the other so that the total length is reduced.

Classification of Muscle Tissues. Attempts to range the muscular tissues of the body in major categories have been based on a variety of criteria;

some contradictions are encountered, no matter what criterion is considered fundamental. One obvious suggestion is a classification according to histologic structure, with two main divisions consisting, on the one hand, of smooth muscles (including cardiac muscles) and on the other of the striated muscles. This seems at first sight reasonable. The striated muscles are for the most part under voluntary control, whereas the smooth muscles are under the influence of the involuntary or autonomic nervous system; the striated muscles are in general large, well formed structures, whereas the smooth muscles are often diffuse and may be incorporated in the substance of other organs; most of the striated muscles are formed in the "outer tube" of the body, while the smooth musculature is in great measure associated with the gut tube; much of the striated muscle is derived from the mesodermal somites, while the smooth musculature arises from mesenchyme.

One prominent group of muscles, however, is in many ways anomalous and ruins the seeming simplicity of such a classification. This is the *branchiomeric system* of striated muscles which in primitive vertebrates is associated with the gill bars (the visceral skeletal system) and which remains prominent in the head and "neck" region in all vertebrates. The branchial muscles and their derivatives are striated, but exhibit strong contrasts with all other striated muscles and, curiously, show affinities in diagnostic characters with the smooth musculature. Muscles of this group are not derived from somites as are most other striated muscles, but arise from mesenchyme of the splanchnopleure like smooth muscle fibers (Fig. 179, p. 257). Other striated muscles are innervated from brain or spinal cord by fibers of a specific type—those of the somatic motor system (p. 507). In contrast, the gill arch muscles are innervated, through special cranial nerves, by a different category of neurons, which belong to the visceral motor system; the smooth muscles are likewise innervated by visceral nerves. Finally, while "ordinary" striated muscles lie in the "outer tube" of the body, the gill arch muscles, although often superficial in higher vertebrates, are, like the smooth muscles, primarily associated with the digestive tube—that is, its anterior, pharyngeal region.

All this suggests the picture of the primitive vertebrate as having had two discrete sets of musculature. The first, which we may term the *somatic musculature*, is that forming the muscles of the "outer tube" of the body, the "somatic animal"; this musculature is derived, directly or indirectly, from myotomes, is universally striated, is innervated by somatic motor neurons and is associated with the adjustment of the organism to its external environment. The second is the *visceral musculature*, connected mainly with the gut tube of the "visceral animal"; muscles of this group are all derived from the mesenchyme of the splanchnopleure (never from myotomes), are innervated by visceral motor fibers and are mainly associated with digestion, nutrition, secretion, and circulation—the internal economy, that is, of the animal. In this second group of muscles those of the more posterior segments of the gut retained a simple structure as smooth muscle; but, in the pharyngeal region, important in early vertebrates for food gathering and breathing, the striated condition is assumed, and in some instances striated musculature rather than smooth continues farther back along the gut to the esophagus or (in teleosts) even the upper end of the stomach.

It appears, then, that despite the seeming impropriety of associating in one major group all smooth and some striated elements, the most natural classification of muscles is as follows:

Somatic. . . . . $\begin{cases} \text{Axial} \\ \text{Appendicular} \end{cases}$ $\begin{cases} \text{Trunk and tail} \\ \text{Eyeball} \end{cases}$

Visceral. . . . . $\begin{cases} \text{Branchiomeric} \\ \text{Smooth (gut, and the like)} \end{cases}$

(As will be seen later, the muscles of the eyeball are a special category of the axial musculature. The limb muscles are, historically, derivatives of the axial system, but have assumed such special importance as to merit separate treatment.)

The smooth muscles are, in general, component parts of various organs and need no separate consideration here. We shall in this chapter discuss only the formed muscles of striated type—the various somatic muscle groups and the branchial muscles of the visceral system.

Muscle Terminology. As with other organ systems, muscles are given, as far as possible, names used in human anatomy. Unfortunately the comparative study of musculature is still in its infancy, and we are in doubt in many cases as to the homologues of human muscles in lower vertebrates. Elementary students in zoology, for example, frequently dissect the thigh of a frog and find applied to its muscles the names of those found in the human thigh; but it is doubtful that many of the muscles given like names are really homologous. Another, and better, procedure, often followed, is to give muscles of lower vertebrates of which the homologies are, or have been, in doubt, names which are simply descriptive of their general position or attachments. Thus we have in reptiles an iliofemoralis muscle running from ilium to femur; it may be more or less homologous with some of the gluteal muscles lying in this region in man and other mammals (cf. p. 271), but since exact homologies are doubtful, it is safer to give the reptile muscle a name that avoids a definite commitment.

There are several terms frequently used to describe muscles, particularly limb muscles, according to the type of action they perform. An *extensor* muscle is one which acts to open out a joint; a *flexor* closes it. An *adductor* draws a segment inward; an *abductor* does the reverse. A *levator* raises a structure, in contrast to a *depressor*. A *rotator* twists a limb segment; a *pronator* or *supinator* rotates the distal part of a limb toward a prone or supine position of the foot (i.e., with palm or sole down, or vice versa). *Constrictor* or *sphincter* muscles are those which surround orifices (as gills, anus) and tend to close them when contracted.

Muscles most often attach to skeletal elements at either end. One attachment is usually the more stable, and is considered the area of *origin,* the other the *insertion;* in limb muscles the proximal end is always considered to be the point of origin. The fleshy mass of a muscle is its *belly.* Muscles with two bellies in sequence, with an intervening tendon (as in one of the mammalian jaw muscles), are, reasonably, termed *digastric.* A muscle with multiple heads may be termed bicipital, tricipital and so forth. Muscle fibers never attach of themselves to a bone or cartilage; the attachment is always mediated by connective tissue fibers. In many cases the muscle fibers approach the bone closely, and hence we speak of a "fleshy" attachment; in others, the muscle terminates in a *tendon,* or a flat sheet of connective tissue—an *aponeurosis* or *fascia.* More than one muscle may attach by a common tendon.

Muscle Homologies. The comparative study of musculature is a difficult procedure because of the variability of muscles and the apparent ease with which their functions may alter. A mass of muscle tissue which is a unit in one animal may be split into two or more distinct muscles in another animal, and there appear to be other cases in which originally separate muscles have fused. The general pattern of their arrangement may be of aid in an attempt to sort out individual muscles, but the pattern may be obscured by the fact that a muscle's origin or insertion may shift in relation to differing functional needs.

Embryologic origin is here, as ever, an important criterion for identification of homologies. We find that, in many cases at least, groups of individual muscles in the adult can be traced back to larger aggregations of muscular or premuscular tissue in the embryo (cf. Fig. 183, *B*, p. 267) and that the mode of breaking up these mother masses gives valuable evidence of homologies. Unfortunately, only a limited amount of work has been done on muscle embryology.

The motor innervation of muscles provides valuable clues. Limb muscles, for example, are generally innervated by a series of trunks and branches arising out of a nerve plexus associated with the limb (Fig. 366, p. 505). The pattern of the plexus and the nerves extending into and from it tend to remain rather uniform, and muscles known to be homologous usually receive their nerve supply from like branches of the plexus. In consequence there arose in the minds of many workers a belief that there is an unalterable phylogenetic relation between a given nerve and muscle. Embryology, however, gives no indication that there is any mysterious affinity between specific nerve fibers and the specific muscle fibers which form a given muscle, and in some cases it seems quite certain that the innervation of a muscle is different in different animals. Nevertheless, actual practice indicates that, as the embryologic picture suggests, the nerve supply to a particular mass of muscle does tend to remain constant, and that innervation affords an important clue to the identity of the muscles.

AXIAL MUSCLES

Trunk Musculature in Fishes. The major part of the somatic muscle division in fishes is the axial musculature, which forms much of the bulk of the body (Figs. 177, 178, *A*, *B*). Arranged for the most part in segmental masses along either flank, it forms a major locomotor organ of a fish. By rhythmic, alternate contractions of the muscles of the two sides the fish's body is thrown into waves which, traveling posteriorly and gaining a cumulative effect at the tail, thrust backward against the resistance of the water and propel the fish forward (cf. Fig. 120, p. 181).

Fig. 177. Dissection of a salmon to show axial musculature. In four places a series of myomeres has been removed to show the complicated internal folding of these segmental structures. Within the body each V projects farther anteriorly or posteriorly than it does at the surface. The lateral septum is visible, cutting the main, anterior-pointing V. (After Greene.)

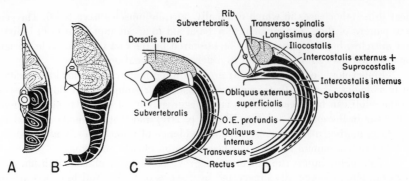

Fig. 178. Diagrammatic sections to show the divisions of the trunk musculature in *A*, a shark tail; *B*, the shark trunk; *C*, a urodele; *D*, a lizard. The epaxial muscles are stippled, hypaxial muscles in black. In *D* a rib is assumed to be present dorsally, and the adjacent parts of the hypaxial muscles are labeled as in the rib-bearing region; more ventrally the names are those of the corresponding abdominal muscles. (Mainly after Nishi.)

Dorsally, the axial muscles form a thick mass extending outward and upward on either side the full distance from the region of the vertebrae to the skin. In the tail there is a corresponding ventral development of the musculature; in the trunk, of course, the body cavity occupies much of the ventral region of the body, and the ventral trunk musculature takes the form of an enveloping sheath.

This axial musculature is in fishes of direct myotomic origin. In the embryo of a shark, for example, one can observe parallel strips of musculature growing down the body on either side as extensions of the dorsally placed myotomes (Fig. 179). The segmental arrangement is for the most part preserved in the adult fish, so that the major part of the trunk musculature consists of successive segments —the *myomeres*—running along each flank, corresponding in number to the vertebrae. The muscle fibers are oriented in an anteroposterior position in each myomere. Few reach skeletal parts directly; between successive myomeres are stout sheets of connective tissue, the *myocommata*, into which the muscle tissue is bound. The myocommata reach inward to tie into the vertebral column, and it is in these segmentally arranged septa that ribs, and the extra intermuscular bones of many teleosts, develop to give further support (Fig. 114, p. 173).

The myomeres develop initially as simple vertical bands; they do not retain this pattern, however, but fold in a zigzag fashion which appears to promote muscular efficiency. In Amphioxus the folds form relatively simple V's, with the point turned forward along the flank. In true fishes the folding is more complicated; it is especially prominent in sharks, and in fishes in general the folding is greater dorsally than toward the belly (Fig. 177). Seen on the surface, each myomere is generally in the form of a W with the upper edge turned forward. There is thus a forwardly projecting V half-way down the flank, and backwardly projecting V's above and below. (There may also be one or two small extra jogs above.) Deep to the surface, the angles of the zigzag become increasingly sharp, so that each V of a myomere has the shape of a plow or engine cowcatcher. Each myomere folds forward or backward beneath its neighbors, so that any vertical cross section through trunk or tail cuts a considerable number of myomeres; their tissues are often seen in section to be grouped in a number of complex folded masses, each of which corresponds to one of the V's seen on the surface (Fig. 178, *A, B*).

In fishes above the cyclostome level there develops on either flank, usually just below the tip of the anterior-pointing V, a *horizontal septum* of connective tissue dividing every myomere into dorsal and ventral portions. It is in this septum, at the point where it intersects successive myocommata, that dorsal ribs are developed (Figs. 2, *D*, p. 6; 114, p. 173). As a result of the formation of the septum, the axial muscles of gnathostomes may be divided into two major groups: the dorsal or *epaxial musculature*, lying above the septum and external to the dorsal ribs (when developed), and the *hypaxial musculature* of the flanks and belly, lying below the septum and in the main internal to the dorsal ribs (Fig. 178).

Although most of the fish trunk musculature is involved in the major structural organization of myomeres, there may nevertheless be minor units separated from the embryonic myotomes as bud or cell masses which form discrete muscles. Most important of these are the median fin muscles. These fins—dorsals, anal, and caudal—have small, symmetric muscle slips placed on either side of the radials supporting them. Paired fin muscles have a similar phylogenetic origin, we believe, but because of the importance of the limb musculature in tetrapods, the muscles of the paired appendages will receive consideration in a special section.

The general description of fish axial musculature just given applies primarily to that found in the main part of the trunk region. Anteriorly and posteriorly, specialized regions may be found. The shoulder girdle may partially interrupt the course of these muscles; farther forward, the gill slits block the lateral part of the trunk muscles, but special dorsal and ventral axial masses pass forward to the head region. Posteriorly in fishes there is little interruption of the

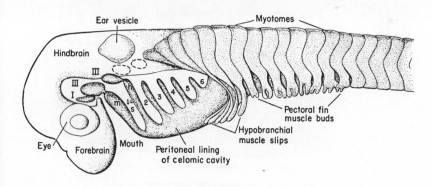

Fig. 179. A diagrammatic view of a shark embryo to show the development of the muscles. Skin and gut tube removed; the brain and eye and ear vesicles are included as landmarks. Posteriorly, the myotomes have extended downward to form myomeres; in the region of the pectoral fin, paired buds are forming from neighboring myotomes as potential fin muscles. Anterior to this, buds from anterior myotomes extend ventrally to form hypobranchial muscles. In the ear region, myotomes (broken lines) are rudimentary or absent, but farther forward three myotomes (I to III) persist to form eye muscles. The position of the spiracular slit (*s*) and normal gill slits (2 to 6) is indicated. These interrupt the continuity of the celom and its peritoneal epithelium. Buds of this project upward between the gill slits; from the splanchnopleure there arise the visceral muscles of the mandibular arch (*m*), the hyoid arch (*h*), and the more posterior gill arches. (In part after Braus.)

axial musculature as it passes backward from the trunk past the pelvic fins and cloaca to the tail, but in land vertebrates the tail muscles may show a different condition from those of the trunk.

In the further treatment of axial muscles here, we shall first follow the history of the two major trunk muscle groups—epaxial and hypaxial—from fishes upward through the tetrapods, and then return to pick up the story of more specialized anterior and posterior regions.

Epaxial Trunk Muscles.   The dorsal musculature has led a relatively uneventful phylogenetic career. In fishes (Figs. 177, 178, *A, B*) generally it is a massive column of segmented muscle, lying lateral to the vertebrae and the medial septum, which runs along the back of the body, from the skull or braincase to the end of the fleshy tail, without, in most instances, any great degree of regional differentiation. We may simply consider the whole mass as a single dorsolateral trunk muscle, the *dorsalis trunci.*

In land vertebrates (Figs. 178, *C, D;* 180; 181) this dorsal musculature—indeed, the trunk musculature as a whole—is much reduced in relative volume. This reduction is, of course, associated with the fact that in land vertebrates the limbs have taken over the propulsive duties of the axial muscles. The axial muscles still function, however, in such lateral movements as continue. In addition, they are responsible for dorsoventral bending of the column, a type of movement practically unknown in fishes.

In most land vertebrates there is little height to the back above the level of the neural arches, and the dorsal muscles are restricted to a channel, of limited

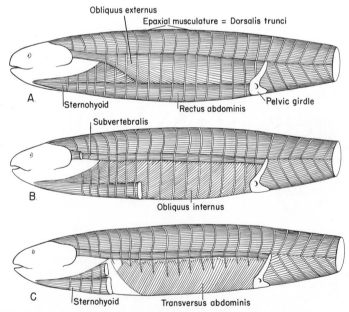

Fig. 180.   Lateral views of the axial musculature of a urodele. *A*, Surface view (a thin superficial sheet of the external oblique, however, has been removed). *B*, The external oblique and rectus have been cut to show the internal oblique and subvertebral muscles. *C*, The internal oblique has been removed to show the transversus. (Modified after Maurer.)

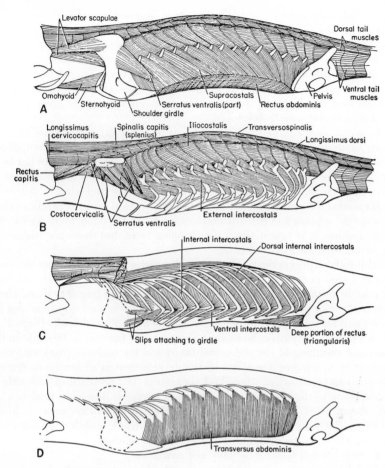

Fig. 181. A series of diagrammatic dissections of Sphenodon to show the anatomy of the axial muscles. In *A* a thin superficial sheet of the external oblique has been removed. In *B* the supracostals, rectus, throat muscles, and more superficial muscles to the scapula have been removed. In *C* the epaxial muscles are cut posteriorly, and the internal intercostals and triangularis (not shown in the last figure) are indicated. In *D* the ribs are cut, and all other muscles removed to show the transversus. (After Maurer and Fürbringer.)

dimensions, running the length of the body between the neural spines medially and the transverse processes laterally and ventrally. In amphibians the dorsal musculature may still be considered a single muscle, the dorsalis trunci, which is persistently segmental and shows little in the way of distinct subdivision.

In reptiles the dorsal trunk muscles remain in part segmental in composition, but tend to have a complex build. Laterally, a thin sheet of dorsal musculature, the *iliocostalis*, extends downward on to the flank, external to the ventral muscles, and attaches laterally to the ribs. A *longissimus dorsi*, the main member of the dorsal series, lies above the transverse processes of the vertebrae. Most medially, between the longissimus and the vertebral spines, we find a complicated crisscross of little muscles which tie together successive vertebral spines and transverse processes. Although they pass under a variety of names, they may be termed collectively the *transversospinalis system*. In snakes, where the axial muscles have resumed the major propulsive function, the dorsal muscles are highly developed and extremely complicated. In turtles, with the development of a solid shell, the dorsal trunk muscles (and the ventral ones, as well) are, of course, much reduced, and in birds, in which the trunk vertebrae are in great measure fused, they are also weakly developed.

In mammals the three reptilian divisions of the dorsal musculature are still present, although little of the original metameric arrangement is preserved. Much of it consists of series of small muscle slips to which a plethora of names has been given. Along the lumbar region the two more lateral divisions may unite into a strong *sacrospinalis*, which helps preserve the arch of the backbone.

Hypaxial Trunk Muscles.   In fishes the hypaxial musculature lies below the horizontal septum and extends downward around the outer body wall to the ventral midline. It is essentially a unit in most cases, but there are frequently signs of dorsoventral subdivision.

Although phylogenetically the hypaxial muscles are derived from the myotomes, they tend in at least some land vertebrates to arise in the embryo not from these muscle blocks but from mesenchyme in the body wall lateral to them. These muscles, like their epaxial colleagues, are considerably reduced in volume and for the most part form but thin muscle sheets around the belly and flanks (Figs. 178, *C, D;* 180; 181). They have, however, taken on a new function in land life in the support and sheathing of the abdominal cavity and the enclosed trunk viscera— a function in which they are aided by the development in all tetrapods (except the modern amphibians) of a powerful rib system. The presence of ribs adds to the complexity of the hypaxial musculature of tetrapods through a tendency for the development of individual slips for each rib from various muscle sheets. Somewhat arbitrarily we may divide the hypaxial trunk muscles of land vertebrates into three groups arranged dorsoventrally as follows:

1. Subvertebral muscles dorsally and medially;
2. A lateral series of superimposed muscle sheets along the flanks;
3. A rectus group ventrally.

Subvertebral musculature is little developed in fishes. In land vertebrates a deep longitudinal band of hypaxial muscle tissue forms at the sides of the vertebrae below the rib articulations, acting as an opponent of the dorsal musculature in dorsoventral movements of the spinal column. The subvertebral musculature is often continuous with the deepest layer of the flank muscles.

Complicated and varied are the *flank muscles*, which follow the curve of the trunk over the general area extending from the transverse processes of the vertebrae to the ventral territory held by the rectus system. Three superimposed major sheets of segmentally arranged muscle may be generally found; each of these, however, may be subdivided in various regions and areas.

In urodeles the reduction of ribs gives us a relatively simple picture of these muscles (that the reduction of ribs and the resulting simplicity is a degenerate condition need not cause us undue concern). The most external sheet is the *external oblique* muscle, the fibers of which run in general anteroposteriorly, but tend to slant upward anteriorly in each segment (a thin, external subcutaneous sheet is generally present in addition to the main muscle). A middle layer is that of the *internal oblique*; the fibers are again essentially longitudinal in orientation, but slant upward posteriorly. The third, deepest layer is that of the *transverse muscle*, whose fibers are oriented, in contrast to the obliques, in a transverse, dorsoventral direction. None of the three layers is of any great thickness, but the diverse orientation of the three muscle sheets makes for a body sheath of considerable strength.

In amniotes the presence of ribs on part or all of the trunk vertebrae creates·a more complicated situation, except in the lumbar region, where, in the absence or reduction of ribs, abdominal sections of the muscle sheets may be present in relatively primitive fashion. In the abdomen the external oblique is split into two layers, superficial and deep (in addition to a subcutaneous sheet in reptiles), and the transversus may be split into two layers as well. In the major rib-bearing region of the trunk the outer layer of the external oblique lies in general superficial to the ribs and produces *supracostal* muscles, and the transversus is for the most part transformed into a *subcostal* series. The intermediate muscle layers, however, form *intercostal* muscles—external intercostals arising from the deep part of the external oblique, internal intercostals from the internal oblique. In most amniotes the transversus tends to persist internally as a continuous if thin sheet; the outer muscle layers, however, tend to become discontinuous, covering only restricted parts of the trunk. From form to form and from one region of the body to another, portions of the various layers of the lateral trunk muscles are given a bewildering series of different names; to follow them through would be as tiring to the author as to the student.

Ventrally, the *rectus abdominis* runs anteroposteriorly from the shoulder region to the pelvis; the portions from each side of the trunk are frequently separated by an intervening tendinous area, the *linea alba*. A superficial portion may be more or less continuous with the external oblique; for the most part, however, the rectus appears to be more closely associated with the internal oblique group. With the growth of the sternum, the rectus is restricted in length, and in mammals is a purely abdominal muscle. Thin transverse bands of connective tissue, termed *inscriptions*, are sometimes present in the rectus and may represent to some degree the original segmental condition of the muscle.

The components of the axial musculature of the tetrapod trunk, as described above, may be classified, in somewhat simplified fashion, as follows:

Epaxial . . . .
- Transversospinalis system
- Longissimus system
- Iliocostalis system

Hypaxial . . . . . .
- Dorsomedial . . . Subvertebralis
- Lateral
  - Obliquus abdominis externus
    - (Subcutaneous)
    - Superficialis = supracostals
    - Profundus = external intercostals
  - Obliquus abdominis internus = Internal intercostals
  - Transversus abdominis = Subcostals
- Ventral . . . Rectus abdominis

Trunk Muscles of the Shoulder Region (Figs. 180, 181).   In many urodeles the ventral trunk musculature extends forward past the pectoral region almost without break to continue on beneath the throat. This continuity, however, is probably not primitive, but due, rather, to a secondary loss of the dermal shoulder girdle. Even in sharks there is a partial interruption of the ventral muscles here, and in bony fishes and tetrapods other than urodeles there is a complete break at the shoulder; the rectus system and the lower margins of the flank muscles typically terminate anteriorly in muscle slips attaching to sternum and coracoid, and more anterior ventral trunk muscles reappear in front of the girdle as the hypobranchial muscles, described below.

Whereas the pelvic limb bears body weights by a solid sacral connection with the backbone, there is no such connection in the shoulder region. In tetrapods, in contrast with fishes, the pectoral girdle and limb have no skeletal connection with the backbone other than that gained indirectly via the sternum. The body is, instead, suspended between the two scapular blades in slings formed by muscles which on either side run from the top of the scapular blade downward to insert mainly on the ribs. The utilization of muscles for this supporting system furnishes an elasticity which makes up in the shoulder region for the lack of the bony strength present in the pelvis; body and limb movements can be pliably adjusted to one another, and (analogous to the use of springs in automobile construction) the body is eased of much of the jolts and jars of locomotion.

The muscles which form those slings are derivatives of the external oblique muscle which have been pressed into service for this special purpose. Seen in side view (Fig. 181, *A, B*), the major elements of this system spread out fanwise fore and aft, mainly from the under surface of the scapula, to attach posteriorly to the chest ribs, anteriorly to cervical ribs or transverse processes. Because of their jagged appearance, elements of this group are known as the *serratus* muscles (serratus ventralis or anterior); the most anterior part is termed the *levator scapulae*. In addition, we find in mammals a more dorsally placed sheet, the *rhomboideus*, which tends to keep the upper end of the scapular blade in place by a pull toward the midline.

Neck Muscles (Figs. 180, 181, *B*). In fishes the gill region interrupts anteriorly the course of the axial muscles; they continue forward, however, above and below the gills, as *epibranchial* and *hypobranchial* groups. In tetrapods the same situation persists (the effect is somewhat masked by the presence, superficially, of visceral striated muscles of the trapezius group; cf. p. 282; Fig. 191, *B*, p. 277). Dorsally the axial muscles run forward as neck muscles which serve for the support and movement of the head. The epaxial series extends forward here in unbroken fashion, although with a special arrangement of small muscle slips connecting head and cervical region. A minor dorsal contribution to the neck musculature is made by the hypaxial muscles; small muscles of the subvertebral series continue forward beneath the column to the skull base.

Throat Muscles (Figs. 180, 181, *A*). The anterior ventral part of the fish axial muscles, the *hypobranchial musculature*, runs forward along the "throat" beneath the gills. The main elements of this musculature are known collectively as the *coracoarcuales*, since they originate posteriorly from the coracoid region of the shoulder girdle and in their forward course to the jaw area send off slips which attach to the lower segments of the adjacent gill arches. (Note that these muscles are *not* part of the special group of branchial muscles situated in the gill region.) In land animals this musculature persists in its original location, in reduced form, as a series of ventral slips running from sternum and shoulder girdle to the thyroid cartilage of the larynx and to the hyoid, and from these elements to the region of the jaw symphysis (*sternohyoid, omohyoid* muscles, and so forth).

We find one remarkable development of the hypobranchial musculature in tetrapods. The tongue develops in the floor of the mouth from the region of the base of the hyoid arch, As it develops, it carries with it a mass of the hypobranchial muscle fibers present in this region; these constitute the flesh of the tongue.

The embryology and nerve supply of the hypobranchial muscles are not without interest. As axial muscles, they are of myotomic derivation; however, the development of the gill slits separates the throat region from direct connection dorsally with the myotomes of the occipital and neck regions from which we would expect them to come. In some embryos, slips from these myotomes are seen in process of migrating circuitously backward above the gills, down behind the gill chamber, and then forward in the throat to form the hypobranchial (and tongue) muscles (Fig. 179, p. 257). We have noted earlier that there tends to be a constant nerve supply to a given mass of muscle, even if it has migrated far from its original position. In correlation with this fact we find that the hypobranchial muscles in fishes are innervated by nerves, from the occipital region of the skull and the anterior part of the cervical region, which follow the same path of migration as did the muscle tissue, around the back of the gill chamber and forward along the throat. In amniotes comparable nerves form the hypoglossal nerve and cervical plexus; in the embryo these nerves follow the ancestral route back and down behind the embryonic gill pouches, and even in the adult they pursue a roundabout course to the throat and tongue (cf. p. 522).

Diaphragm Muscles.   Mammals are notable for the development of the *diaphragm*, a partition separating thoracic and abdominal cavities and of functional importance in the expansion (and contraction) of the lung cavities (cf. pp. 295–296). The movement of the diaphragm is performed by a series of striated muscles which converge from all sides toward its center—from the sternum ventrally, the ribs laterally, and the lumbar vertebrae dorsally. These muscles appear to be derivatives of the rectus abdominis system of axial muscles. They are innervated by a special (phrenic) nerve which arises in the cervical region. This strongly suggests that the muscles of the diaphragm originated from an anterior part of the rectus musculature, perhaps in the shoulder region, and migrated posteriorly in an early stage of pre-mammalian history in conformity with a backward expansion of the lungs.

Caudal Muscles.   In fishes the axial musculature continues into the tail without interruption, except for the cloacal or anal opening. The epaxial musculature of the tail is simply a continuation of that of the trunk. Ventrally, however, in the absence in the tail of the body cavity and its contained viscera, the hypaxial muscles change from a series of sheetlike structures to a compact pair of ventral bundles similar to the epaxial muscles above (Fig. 178, *A*, p. 256).

In tetrapods the great development of the pelvic girdles and the limb muscles arising from them has tended to break the continuity of the axial muscles between trunk and tail. The epaxial muscles are relatively little affected; in many amphibians and reptiles they extend backward on to the tail with little or no interruption. The hypaxial muscles, however, are completely, or nearly completely, interrupted at the pelvis. In the more distal regions of the tail they form a relatively uniform cylindric muscle bundle occupying a position on either side below the transverse processes of the tail vertebrae similar to that of the dorsal muscle above. Anteriorly, approaching the pelvic region, the hypaxial tail muscle mass becomes constricted and sends terminal fibers downward and forward to insert on to the ischium, or upward and forward to the ilium. In urodeles and in reptiles the basal region of the tail is expanded to contain, ventrally, beside the tail muscles proper, large muscles which run forward and outward to the femur; these, however, are parts of the limb musculature, not axial muscles (cf. p. 273). Needless to say, there is a reduction or loss of caudal musculature in forms in which the tail is reduced. Remnants of tail musculature may still be found attached to the bony tail stump of birds, frogs, and the like. In mammals generally the tail is still moderately elongate, but slender, and the caudal muscles are correspondingly reduced in volume. From the ventral muscles just behind the pelvic girdle there usually develops in land vertebrates a sphincter muscle which can close the cloaca; in mammals there is a corresponding anal sphincter.

Eye Muscles.   The muscles which move the eyeball form a far-flung anterior outpost of the axial musculature. In embryonic cyclostomes there is present, as in Amphioxus, a series of mesodermal somites continuous from the front part of the head back to the trunk. In most vertebrates the series is interrupted, for with the expansion of the braincase in the ear region the somites there tend to be vestigial or absent. More anteriorly, however, in the region of the developing eye socket, small somites persist in every vertebrate class (Fig. 179, p. 257). When well developed three pairs are to be found. They are in great measure separated at an early stage from the lateral mesoderm by the development of the gill slits, and play little if any part in the formation of skeletal or connective tissues; they appear in the embryo as small *head cavities* from the walls of which arise the muscles of the eyeball. Associated with these three somites, and innervating the muscles which they form, are three small cranial nerves—III, IV, and VI of the numbered series (pp. 515, 521).

In the vast majority of vertebrates we find six typical straplike muscles developed from these somites (Fig. 182). They take origin from the surface of the braincase and fan outward to attach to the eyeball somewhat internal to its "equator"; in varied combinations, their pull will rotate the eye in any desired direction. Four of them, the *rectus muscles*, arise posteriorly, often close to the eye stalk or optic nerve; the other two, the *oblique muscles*, spring from the anterior part of the eye socket. Typically, the superior rectus and the superior oblique attach to the upper margin of the eyeball, a pair of inferior muscles to its lower edge; the two remaining rectus muscles insert on the anterior (or internal) and posterior (or external) margins.

Four of the six muscles are innervated by nerve III, the superior oblique by nerve IV, the posterior rectus by nerve VI. As this would lead us to suspect, we find that in the embryo four of these muscles arise from the first of the three somites concerned, and one each from the other two.

Fig. 182.   Eye muscles. A lateral view, with the eyeball (in outline) removed; the ovals are the muscle attachments. The three eye muscle nerves are shown (III, IV, VI). (After Goodrich.)

Variations are, of course, found on this basal pattern of six eye muscles. In hagfishes and other vertebrates with degenerate eyes the muscles are correspondingly degenerate or absent, and the homology of certain lamprey muscles is uncertain. Accessory muscles are frequently present, particularly in land vertebrates. In a majority of tetrapods (birds and primates are exceptions) there is a *retractor bulbi* muscle which tends to pull the eyeball deeper in its socket; in most amniotes we find a *levator palpebrae superioris* derived from the eyeball muscles, but raising the upper lid, and rather variable slips which move the nictitating membrane of the eye.

LIMB MUSCLES

The musculature of the paired appendages is derived, historically, from the general myotomic musculature of the trunk and hence is part of the somatic system. The limb muscles, however, are so distinct in position and nature and so important in higher vertebrates that they deserve special treatment.

We have noted previously the decline of axial musculature in tetrapods; limb muscles, modest in size and simple in composition in fishes, grow, on the other hand, to relatively enormous bulk and to great complexity in land vertebrates, as they take over the major duties of body progression. As a homely example to emphasize this contrast we may compare our utilization as food, of a fish and of a domestic mammal. Fish as food is axial muscle, and the paired fins are discarded as not worth bothering with. In a steer, lamb, or hog, however, there is little axial muscle except small morsels which cling to the ribs or backbone. Our meat is almost entirely limb muscle. A chop with bone attached seems to testify to its being of axial origin. However, the main part of the chop is a limb muscle which takes origin from the trunk, and only the scrapings off the bone itself are really axial.

As derivatives of the somatic system, the limb muscles should, in theory at least, originate in the embryo from the myotomes. In some lower vertebrates— specifically, sharks—this origin appears to be demonstrable. Paired finger-like processes extend out from the ventral ends of a considerable number of myotomes developing near the base of the paired fins; these form masses of premuscular tissue above and below the fin skeleton (Fig. 179, p. 257). In tetrapods, however, the myotomic origin of appendicular muscles has not been demonstrated, and the muscle masses of the tetrapod limb appear to develop as condensations in the mesenchyme of the region of the budding limb. It is, of course, possible that this mesenchyme is derived from the myotome, but proof is lacking.

Paired Fins. In the fins of fishes the limb musculature is simple in construction. Two opposed little masses of muscle are usually readily discernible, running outward from the girdle to the base of the fin (Fig. 183, *B*). A dorsal muscle mass serves primarily to elevate or extend the fin, a ventral muscle mass to depress or adduct it. There may be, in addition, small slips developed from either group which serve to give rotary or other special fin movements.

Tetrapod Limbs. In land vertebrates we meet with a different situation. Not only is the limb musculature much more bulky, but it is also much more complex. The mode of development affords, however, a clue to a natural classification of the muscles present.

Early in the ontogeny of a land limb, while the arm or leg is still a relatively short bud from the body, a mass of premuscular tissue (Fig. 183, *A*) is formed on both the upper and lower surfaces of the developing skeleton. It is clear that these two masses are equivalent to the opposed dorsal and ventral muscle masses which in fishes raise and lower the paired fins. From them arise, by growth and cleavage, all the complicated muscles of the mature limb. From the dorsal mass develop the muscles on the extensor surface of the limb and related muscles of the girdle region; from the ventral mass arise the flexor muscles of the opposite limb surface.

A distinction is frequently made between "extrinsic" and "intrinsic" limb muscles, the former name being given to muscles that arise from the body and run either to girdle or limb, the latter to muscles which do not leave the confines of the limb. This distinction is misleading. Embryologic study shows that on the one hand muscles which arise from the trunk and run only to the limb girdle are not limb muscles at all, but axial muscles, which arise directly from somites. On the other hand, various true limb muscles may take origin from the trunk and run outward onto the limb. Their real nature is shown by the fact that they arise in the embryo as part of the limb muscle mass and only during the course of development spread inward on to the trunk. Where a muscle inserts, not where it arises, is the test as to whether it is a true limb muscle or not.

How to treat such a complex series of structures as limb muscles in a brief work of this sort is a problem, for there is an immense amount of variation from group to group in the arrangement of the musculature (and also, sad to say, in the nomenclature). On the one hand, one might describe, seriatim, the limb muscles of the various groups, in a fashion which would be not merely exhaustive, but exhausting. On the other hand, one might (as is sometimes done) make a few hasty generalizations about extensors, flexors, and so on, and pass hurriedly on. We shall here take a middle course (which probably includes the disadvantages of both extremes). The various muscle groups of the limbs will be considered and compared in fair detail in two types: (1) lizards, as representing a rather primitive and generalized tetrapod condition,* and (2) a primitive mammal, the opossum (Didelphis), as representing a mammalian type of specialization. A few remarks will follow on the musculature of other forms, and a table of homologies presented.

Embryology, as we have seen, shows that the musculature of each limb can be naturally divided into dorsal and ventral groups, proximally none too readily distinguishable in the adult, but distally clearly forming extensor and flexor series of the limb. We shall follow this logical order in considering successively the muscles of pectoral and then of pelvic limbs. Little will be said of the functions of individual muscles. It must be emphasized that rarely is a movement performed by the contraction of a single muscular element. In general, several muscles cooperate; the movement is a resultant of forces. The function of a given muscle varies according to the company it keeps.

PECTORAL LIMB.   *Dorsal Muscles* (Figs. 184, 185).   A number of dorsal muscles are present which attach to the humerus near its head and are responsible for much of the movement of that bone on the shoulder girdle. Superficially there are seen in both reptile and mammal prominent fan-shaped dorsal muscles of this sort, the *latissimus dorsi* and the *deltoideus*, the former arising from the surface of the back and flank, the latter from the scapula and the clavicle, often

* Other reptiles (except Sphenodon) and the frog are more specialized, and the urodeles are degenerate in their musculature.

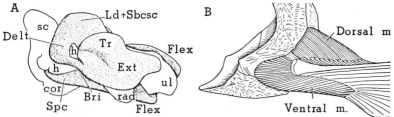

Fig. 183. *A,* External view of the left pectoral girdle and limb and its musculature in a lizard embryo (the skeleton unshaded, the muscle tissue stippled); *B,* the pectoral girdle and fin in a fish (sturgeon). In the fish fin the musculature consists simply of opposed dorsal and ventral muscle masses. In the adult land vertebrate the limb has a large number of discrete muscles, but in the embryo these are arranged in two opposed masses comparable to those of the fish fin. At the stage figured the two masses are barely beginning their differentiation into the muscles of the adult (cf. Fig. 184, *A*). The dorsal mass is well shown; the ventral mass is mostly concealed beneath the limb (in which the foot is not yet developed). *Bri,* brachialis inferior; *cor,* coracoid region; *Delt,* deltoid; *Ext,* extensor muscles; *Flex,* flexor muscles; *h,* humerus; *Ld,* latissimus dorsi; *rad,* radius; *Sbcsc,* subcoracoscapularis; *sc,* scapula; *Spc,* supracoracoideus; *Tr,* triceps; *ul,* ulna.

Fig. 184. Shoulder and upper arm muscles in the lizard (*A, B*) and opossum (*C, D*), lateral views; the right hand figures in each case are comparable deep dissections with latissimus, deltoid, pectoralis, and long muscles (triceps, biceps, brachialis) removed. Notable is the upward migration of the supracoracoideus to become the two "spinatus" muscles.

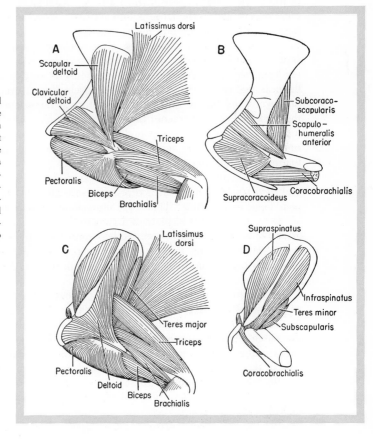

in two parts. In mammals a slip of the latissimus has gained contact with the scapula and separated as the *teres major*. A deep muscle associated with the latissimus at its insertion—the *subcoracoscapularis* of reptiles, *subscapularis* in mammals—arises from the inner surface of the girdle.

In reptiles a small deep muscle arises from the outer surface of the scapula as the *scapulohumeralis anterior;* in mammals this has been pushed to the back margin of the scapular blade as the *teres minor*. In mammals, too, it will be noted that the scapular part of the deltoid, which in reptiles took origin from the front edge of the scapula, now arises from the centrally situated spine of that bone. What has caused these shifts? As will be seen shortly, they are due to the "invasion" of the scapula by the "spinatus" muscles.

The dorsal surface of the humerus is covered by a stout muscle, the *triceps*, which arises from the humerus and by one or more heads from adjacent parts of the girdle; the muscle attaches distally to the olecranon of the ulna—this attachment is in fact the reason for existence of that process—and serves to extend the forearm.

The dorsal arm musculature is continued beyond the elbow by muscles of the extensor series. Most prominent is a sheet of long muscles running down the upper surface of the forearm from the elbow region and fanning out to the forearm bones and on to the hand; a series of short muscles are present in the region of the "wrist" and fingers. Lizard and opossum show much the same arrangement except that in the latter a long extensor from the elbow has tendons, lacking in reptiles, running into individual fingers.

Ventral Muscles (Figs. 184, 185). On the under side of the shoulder a superficial and important muscle is the *pectoralis*, the chest muscle, which spreads far back over the sternum and ribs and inserts on a powerful process beneath the proximal end of the humerus. The muscle gives a strong pull on the humerus downward and backward, and thus is of great importance in locomotion. From the back end of the coracoid the *coracobrachialis* runs out on the under side of the humerus. Two muscles extend out to flex the radius and ulna: the *brachialis*, running down the outer and anterior margin of the humerus, and the *biceps*, originating from the coracoid.

These four muscles are present in similar fashion in both lower tetrapods and in mammals. But a fifth reptile muscle appears, at first sight, to have no homologue in a mammal. This is the *supracoracoideus*, a large fleshy muscle which arises from the coracoid plate and runs to the underside of the humerus. In the primitive tetrapod posture, with the legs sprawled at the sides, this muscle is very important in keeping the body from sagging downward between the limbs. In mammals there is no muscle in this position; indeed, there is no coracoid plate from which it could arise.

The muscle is, however, actually present in the form of the *infraspinatus* and *supraspinatus* muscles on the scapula (Fig. 186); this major muscular migration is presumably responsible for the reduction of the coracoid region of the girdle which afforded it origin in reptiles and for the development of the spine and supraspinous fossa of the mammalian scapula. The reptilian muscle (as can be seen in the mammal embryo) has pushed its way upward beneath the deltoid and has (*a*) taken over the old scapular blade as the infraspinatus (and restricted the scapular deltoid muscle to the old front margin, now the spine of the scapula), and (*b*) occupied a new shelf, the supraspinous fossa, built for its reception in front of the old anterior margin of the scapula. With the changed limb posture of

Fig. 185. Muscles of the forearm and hand in the lizard (*A* to *C*) and opossum (*D* to *F*), somewhat diagrammatic and simplified. *A* and *D* are views of the extensor surface; *B* and *E* superficial, *C* and *F* deeper dissections of the flexor aspect. On the extensor surface the most prominent change from reptile to mammal is the reduction of short muscles on the manus and the development from the common extensor of tendons to the toes. Long special muscles have developed for movement of the "thumb" and fifth digit. On the flexor aspect a prominent feature in reptiles is the presence of a stout and complex aponeurosis on the "palm" with which connect the long flexors proximally and a variety of tendons and short muscles to the toes. In mammals this is broken up; the palmaris longus inserts into a superficial aponeurosis over the wrist, which is cut away in the figure, and the two deeper flexors present here have each developed a broad palmar tendon. Deeply placed in the hand are various short muscles of the digits, which are not shown.

mammals the supracoracoid muscle ceased to function in its old position. It has, however, retained its supporting function by the insertion of the two homologous mammalian muscles at the very tip of the humerus anterior to the glenoid; the resulting lever motion tends to swing the limb downward and forward or, conversely, to pull the body up and back on the arm.

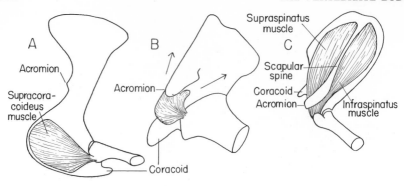

Fig. 186. Diagrams of the shoulder region of *A*, a lizard, *B*, an embryonic opossum and *C*, an adult opossum, to show a major shift in shoulder musculature between reptiles and mammals and the consequent modification of shoulder girdle structure. In the lizard the supracoracoideus is a large ventral muscle running from coracoid plate to humerus. In the embryo opossum a comparable muscle is found, but this is, at the stage figured, tending to split and grow upward (*arrows*) on either side of the acromion. In the adult mammal this muscle mass has become the dorsally situated supraspinatus and infraspinatus muscles; a new portion of the scapula has developed for the reception of the supraspinatus muscle, while the coracoid has been reduced to a nubbin. (*B* after Cheng.)

In the distal part of the limb the main propulsive effort is a backward push of the forearm and digits, accomplished by the muscles of the ventral, flexor surface. These muscles are in consequence more powerful than the extensors. A series of long flexors arises from the entepicondyle of the humerus and, somewhat as on the extensor side, fans out to the lower end of the forearm and to the hand. Flexion of the digits by a muscle from the elbow is rendered difficult by the fact that it must pass round the curve on the under side of the wrist. This difficulty is avoided in reptiles by the development of an *aponeurosis,* a pad of connective tissue beneath the carpus to which long flexors attach proximally and certain of the short toe muscles distally. In mammals this pad of tissue is subdivided into several superimposed tendon sheets in an effective but complex fashion.

PELVIC LIMB.   *Dorsal Muscles* (Figs. 187, 188).   As in the pectoral appendage, the muscles of the distal part of the limb are readily separable into dorsal and ventral (flexor and extensor) series, and the proximal muscles are equally divisible on an embryologic basis.

Certain of the muscles or muscle groups in the hip and thigh region are readily comparable in lower tetrapods and mammals. Of short muscles, reptiles have a powerful fleshy *puboischiofemoralis internus* (what names these muscles have!) which arises from the lumbar region and the inner surface of the girdle and runs back to insert onto the femur near its head. In mammals this is split into *psoas* from the lumbar region and *iliacus* from the ilium (with a small group of fibers from the pubis termed the *pectineus*). Frequently grouped as the *quadriceps femoris* is a series of extensor muscles running from girdle and femur to the head of the tibia; the insertion is by a stout tendon in which the patella is placed in mammals. Separate heads, in mammals, are termed the *rectus femoris* (from the ilium) and the *vasti* (from the femur); the *sartorius,* the "tailor's muscle," is sometimes grouped with the quadriceps. In reptiles, *iliotibialis* and *femorotibialis* are clearly homologous with the first two; the homology of the *ambiens* of reptiles with the sartorius is less certain.

Two other muscles arising from the reptilian ilium are not, at first, readily compared with mammalian muscles arising in this region. We have noted that in mammals there has been a major shift in posture of the thigh, and in consequence shifts in its musculature are to be expected. In reptiles the *iliofemoralis* runs from the iliac blade directly laterally to insert on the upper surface of the femur. In mammals we find the powerful *gluteal muscles* running from ilium to femur, and it is believed that the iliofemoralis corresponds to at least part of these muscles. They have, however, quite a different position and function; they run backward and downward (not outward) from the ilium to the femur and attach to its outer (back) margin—particularly strongly to the proximal end of the bone, where they exert a powerful leverage in pulling the knee back, or conversely, pushing the body upward and forward on the leg. In reptiles there is, further, from the ilium a long *iliofibularis* muscle running to the fibula. There is no such muscle in mammals; possibly it is represented by a long member of the gluteal series.

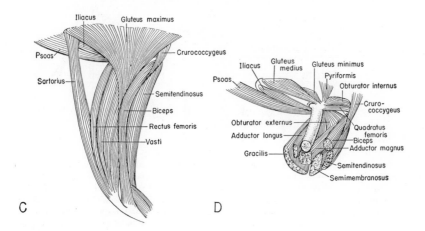

Fig. 187.   Limb muscles of the pelvis and thigh in a lizard (*A, B*), and opossum (*C, D*), lateral views. *A, C,* Superficial views; *B, D,* dissections to show deeper layers of musculature.

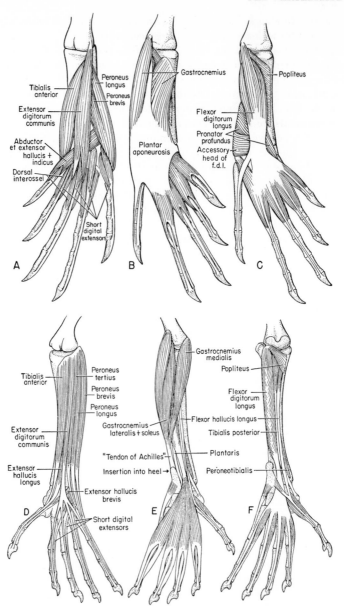

Fig. 188.   Muscles of the lower leg and foot in a lizard (*A* to *C*) and opossum (*D* to *F*), somewhat diagrammatic and simplified. *A* and *D* are views of the extensor surface; *B* and *E* superficial, *C* and *F* deeper dissections of the flexor aspect. The extensor surface of the lizard hind leg is comparable to that of the forearm and manus except for a lesser development of individual muscles on the inner (tibial = radial) side. In the change to mammals the modifications are similar to those seen in the front leg, including the development of toe tendons from the common extensor and the development of long muscles working on the first and fifth toes. The flexor aspect of the lizard hind leg resembles that of the front in many regards, including the development in reptiles of a stout plantar (sole) aponeurosis, into which much of the musculature attaches both proximally and distally. It differs, however, in the absence of the

Beyond the knee the extensor muscles of the pelvic limb in lizards show a pattern essentially comparable to that of the pectoral appendage, with a series of long extensors fanning out distally from the knee region and numerous shorter distal muscles. As in the front leg the mammal has long tendons to the toes, not present in reptile ancestors.

PELVIC LIMB. *Ventral Muscles* (Figs. 187, 188). The muscles of the hip and thigh region mainly adduct the femur and flex the knee joint; in locomotion, that is, they raise the body off the ground and push it forward. They are hence large, important, and complex. They are disposed in three main groups:

1. The muscles running from pelvis to femur are for the most part deeply buried. They include three major elements. (a) A large muscle arises fleshily from much of the outer surface of the pubis and ischium (the fenestration of these elements is related to this muscle attachment) and inserts on the under side of the femur near its head; it acts powerfully in a down pull of the femur. In reptiles this is termed the *puboischiofemoralis externus;* in mammals the *obturator externus* is essentially homologous (but the *quadratus femoris* is a separate fraction of this same muscle group). (b) A smaller muscle emerging from the inner side of the ischium and running to the head of the femur is called in lower tetrapods the *ischiotrochantericus,* in mammals the *obturator internus.* (c) In reptiles an *adductor femoris,* arising from the puboischium, runs far down the under side of the femur; part, if not all, of the variable femoral adductors of mammals are homologous.

2. Covering the under surface of the thigh is a large and complicated group of long muscles which flex the tibia. A superficial sheet is the *gracilis* (generally called the *puboischiotibialis* in reptiles); variable deeper bellies termed the *flexor tibialis externus* and *flexor tibialis internus* in reptiles appear to be homologous in mammals with the *semimembranosus* and *semitendinosus* and possibly the *biceps* as well. (A separate deep reptile slip, the *pubotibialis,* is of doubtful homology.)

3. Powerful ventral limb muscles, the two *caudifemorales* (long and short) arise in typical reptiles from the under side of the tail vertebrae. Running forward, these two muscles narrow to tendons which insert midway along the femur; they act powerfully in a backward pull of the femur and hence contribute greatly to forward locomotion in a reptile. In mammals, however, with the reduction of the tail and changed limb posture, this group of muscles has been reduced to small and variable slips such as the *pyriformis.*

The long ventral muscles of the lower leg are in all tetrapods a powerful series; most of their bulk is centered in the *gastrocnemius* whose muscle bellies constitute the "calf" of the leg. As in the case of the front leg, the problem of "rounding the turn" of the carpus to the under side of the foot is a major structural problem. Reptiles generally have solved this by placing a pad of tissue— an aponeurosis—beneath the ankle, with muscles and tendons attaching at its

(Fig. 188 continued)

flexors running down either side and the development of a powerful two-headed "calf" muscle, the gastrocnemius. In mammals the calf musculature has (except for the plantaris) changed to a new attachment on the "heel bone." The long flexor of the digits, however, runs on to the reduced plantar aponeurosis. From this extend, as in reptiles, distal tendons and toe muscles (in *F* the superficial muscles of this set have been removed to show the deeper tendons and muscles). In both reptile and mammal there are, on the flexor surface, deep, short toe muscles not shown in the figures.

proximal and distal ends. In mammals, however, a new type of foot-raising device has been evolved by the leverage action of calf muscles inserting in the heel tuber of the calcaneum. The major gastrocnemius heads no longer extend to the sole of the foot, but insert by the "tendon of Achilles" on to this tubercle (Fig. 189).

LIMB MUSCLES IN OTHER TETRAPOD GROUPS. We shall not attempt to note in detail all the variations from the rather generalized lizard pattern which are found in other nonmammalian tetrapods. Among reptiles, Sphenodon is similar in almost every regard to lizards. In chelonians the presence of the shell has tended to make locomotion a specialized affair. Limb muscles as well as limb skeleton have been modified accordingly, but the basic pattern is comparable to that of lizards; the most notable differences are those caused by the peculiar orientation of the shoulder girdle noted in discussing the skeleton (p. 188). In crocodiles most of the muscles are comparable to those of lizards, but certain modifications are suggestive of the avian relatives of that group. The modified pelvic structure is associated with marked changes in the arrangement of the ventral muscles of the thigh and these changes are, in turn, due to a modified position of the hind leg, which moves fore-and-aft rather than assuming the sprawled position of typical reptiles.

In birds the pattern of limb muscles is similar to that of reptiles, but there are numerous differences. In the wing the pectoral muscles which give the main down and back pull to the wing in flight are enormous; they constitute most of the "white meat" of the fowl. The dorsal wing muscles are relatively slender. Most of the short musculature of the reptilian "fingers" has disappeared; on the other hand, there are developed special dorsal slips to the thick dermis of the wing membrane. Even more than in the crocodilians the pelvic muscles are specialized in relation to the forward rotation of the hind limbs and the associated modifications of pelvic girdle structure.

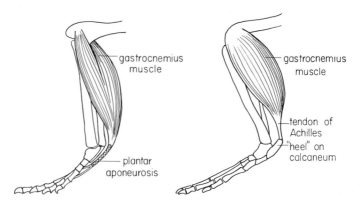

Fig. 189. Side views of the hind leg of a lizard (*left*) and a typical mammal (*right*) to show the contrast in action of the main calf muscle, the gastrocnemius, in extending the foot. In lower tetrapods it rounds the ankle region to act on the under surface of the foot by attaching to a sheet of connective tissue, the plantar aponeurosis, which in turn makes connections with the toes (cf. Fig. 188, *B*). In mammals its action is simplified by the development of a heel on the calcaneum (cf. Fig. 188, *E*); attachment of the muscle tendon here raises the foot as a whole.

The urodeles show a simply built type of limb musculature, but there is considerable evidence that this is more a degenerate than a truly primitive condition. In the urodele shoulder girdle the loss of the primitive dermal structures has resulted in specialization of the shoulder muscles. The clavicular deltoid arises from a long anterior process of the coracoid as a *procoracohumeralis* muscle. The short dorsal toe extensors are not developed. There is no biceps in the arm in amphibians. Probably this amniote muscle has arisen by a fusion of fibers of the supracoracoideus with those of the adjacent brachialis; in some urodeles and in frogs part of the former muscle separates as a *coracoradialis*, which sends out a long tendon to the radius and thus serves somewhat the functions of a biceps in flexing the elbow.

There are numerous differences from reptiles in the urodele hind leg. In the quadriceps femoris equivalent there is no development of the strong femoral heads present in all amniotes. On the ventral surface of the thigh, the long tibial flexors are much simplified, and the caudifemoralis longus does not reach the femur, but simply ties into the side of the gracilis. There is no development of a gastrocnemius of reptile or mammal type.

In the frog the musculature is highly developed, but highly modified in relation to the jumping habits of the animal and the peculiar structure of the girdle and limb skeleton. In Table 2 (pp. 278–281) we have given the usual names accorded the muscles; the nomenclature is patterned on that of mammals, but, as may be seen, many of the muscles are not homologous to those whose names are applied to them.

As might be expected from the wide variety of limb skeletal structures, there are many variations in the different mammalian groups from the generalized muscle pattern; no attempt will be made to discuss them. The loss of the clavicle in some mammals tends to bring about confusion in the deltoid and pectoral regions; the great modifications in the feet have, of course, resulted in wide differences in the build of the distal musculature of the limbs.

BRANCHIOMERIC MUSCULATURE

Markedly different from the striated musculature so far considered is the musculature of the gill region, highly developed in fishes and persistently prominent, although in much modified form, in even the highest groups. We have noted earlier the distinctive nature of the skeleton of the pharyngeal region of primitive vertebrates and shall note later the equally distinctive nature of the nerves innervating the pharynx. Its musculature—musculature of the "visceral animal"—is also noteworthy. In contrast to other, somatic, striated musculature, it arises, not from the myotomes, but from mesenchyme derived from peritoneum of the lateral plate (Figs. 67, *C*, p. 117; 179, p. 257). The smooth musculature of the gut proper, posterior to the pharynx, arises in similar fashion, and branchial and gut muscles, striated or smooth, are but anterior and posterior parts of a single great visceral system of muscles whose primary locus is in the walls of the digestive tract.

The contrast between the striated condition of the anterior, branchial, part of the digestive tract and the presence of smooth muscle posteriorly may be associated with the contrast in functions between anterior and posterior regions. For food gathering and gill breathing—the primitive functions of mouth and pharyngeal regions—the vigorous movement characteristic of striated muscles is appropriate; for the slower movement fitting for digestive processes, smooth musculature suffices.

In higher vertebrates much of the striated visceral musculature has abandoned the gut lining and assumed a variety of natures as facial and jaw muscles and even a part of the shoulder musculature. Primitively, however, the pharyngeal walls appear to have been its proper, truly visceral locale. In many instances the branchial muscles are associated with skeletal structures, primarily the gill bars, whereas the more posterior smooth visceral muscles lie exclusively in soft gut tissues. But in cyclostomes the skeletal connections are of little importance. And of great theoretic interest is the fact that the striated muscles of the gut are not confined to the pharyngeal region of the digestive tube, where these skeletal structures lie. In fishes generally the striated muscles may extend backward into the esophagus, and the same condition is repeated in mammals (although here their presence is perhaps secondary). There is thus no sharp, definite line of demarcation between branchial and smooth muscle regions, a fact which emphasizes their relationship.

In the gnathostome fishes and all higher types the most anterior set of branchial muscles have been much modified in function to serve the jaws, and in land vertebrates the surviving branchial elements serve a further series of aberrant functions, as facial, neck, and shoulder muscles, and even as tiny elements accessory to the auditory apparatus.

Branchial musculature is well developed in the cyclostomes, both as sheets of muscles constricting the gill pouches and as specialized muscles operating the peculiar "tongue." The construction of the lamprey musculature is, however, quite unlike that of other vertebrate groups and will not be considered further here.

In the sharks (Fig. 191, *A*) we find the branchial muscles well developed, with a pattern which in many regards may be considered basal to that in all other gnathostomes. In the jawless ancestors of the gnathostomes the musculature of the "mandibular" and hyoid arches may have been originally generalized; it is, however, already specialized to a considerable degree in sharks. We shall therefore use an indirect method of attack, and consider first the simple and presumably more primitive arrangement seen in the typical gills farther back in the shark pharynx. We shall follow the fate of the muscles of these arches upward through the higher vertebrates, then return to consider the muscles farther forward in the region of the fish hyoid and mandibular arches.

The branchial musculature is, of course, primarily a pumping device to force water through the gills (pp. 318, 322). We may note, incidentally, that although the branchial muscles are those most intimately connected with the visceral skeletal elements, somatic trunk muscles may also become associated with the gill bars. We have already mentioned (p. 262) that the hypobranchial muscles of the floor of the throat may attach to them below; and in sharks the epibranchial muscles of the neck may also gain contact with the upper margins of the gill arches.

Behind the hyoid arch there are typically, in fishes, five gill slits with four intervening arches, each arch with its own proper musculature as well as its own skeletal bars. Even when, in land vertebrates, the gills themselves have disappeared as landmarks, muscles derived from various parts of the branchial system can be readily traced because of their innervation. The gill muscles are supplied by a special series of cranial nerves, numbers V, VII, IX, and X (cf. pp. 519–521, and Fig. 375). The jaw arch is supplied by nerve V; the hyoid by nerve VII; the first typical gill bar is the territory of nerve IX; and the further gill bars are innervated by special branches of nerve X (which continues onward far down the gut).

Muscles of the Typical Gill Bars and Their Derivatives (Figs. 190, 191, *A*). Although there is frequent fusion of muscle tissues above and below

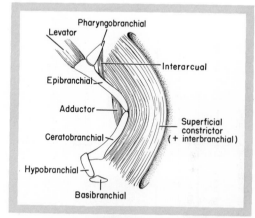

Fig. 190. A single gill arch of a shark and its musculature.

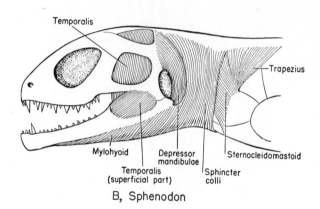

Fig. 191. Lateral views of the branchial arch musculature and its derivatives in a shark and the reptile, Sphenodon. (*A* after Allis; *B* after Adams and Fürbinger.)

A, Chlamydoselache

B, Sphenodon

Table 2. Muscle Homologies in Various Tetrapod Groups.

No attempt has been made to include all the variants present in different members of the groups tabulated, and many details are omitted. For each group only one common name is given for each muscle; often there are synonyms. In many instances homologies are doubtful.

Pectoral Limb, Dorsal Musculature

MAMMAL	REPTILE	URODELE	FROG	BIRD
Latissimus dorsi Teres major	Latissimus dorsi	Latissimus dorsi	Latissimus dorsi	Latissimus dorsi Coracobrachialis posterior
Subscapularis	Subcoracoscapularis Scapulohumeralis posterior	Subcoracoscapularis		Subcoracoscapularis Scapulohumeralis anterior
Deltoideus	Dorsalis scapulae Deltoides claviculares	Deltoides scapularis Procoracohumeralis longus	Dorsalis scapulae Deltoideus	Deltoideus + propatagialis
Teres minor	Scapulohumeralis anterior	Procoracohumeralis brevis	Scapulohumeralis brevis	Deltoideus (part)
Triceps	Triceps	Triceps	Anconeus	Triceps
Supinator	Supinator	Supinator longus	Extensor antibrachii radialis	Extensor antibrachii radialis
Brachioradialis Extensores carpi radiales	Extensores carpi radiales	Extensores carpi radiales	Extensor carpi radialis	Extensor carpi radialis
Extensor digitorum communis Extensor digiti quinti	Extensor digitorum communis	Extensor digitorum communis	Extensor digitorum communis	Extensor digitorum communis
Extensor carpi ulnaris Anconeus	Extensor carpi ulnaris Anconeus	Extensor carpi ulnaris	Extensor carpi ulnaris Epicondylocubitalis	Extensor carpi ulnaris Extensor antibrachii ulnaris
Abductores pollicis Extensores digitorum 1–3	Abductor pollicis longus Extensores digitorum breves	Supinator manus Extensor digitorum brevis	Abductor indicis longus Extensores digitorum breves	Abductor pollicis Extensores digitorum breves

278

Pectoral Limb, Ventral Musculature

MAMMAL	REPTILE	URODELE	FROG	BIRD
Pectoralis Supraspinatus ⎫ Infraspinatus ⎬ Biceps brachii Coracobrachiales Brachialis	Pectoralis Supracoracoideus Biceps brachii Coracobrachiales Brachialis inferior	Pectoralis Supracoracoideus Coracoradialis (Not formed) Coracobrachiales Brachialis	Pectoralis Coracohumeralis Coracoradialis (Not formed) Coracobrachiales ——	Pectoralis ⎧ Coracobrachialis anterior ⎨ Supracoracoideus Biceps brachii Coracobrachialis Brachialis inferior
Pronator teres Flexor carpi radialis ⎫ Flexor digitorum sublimis ⎬ Palmaris longus Epitrochleoanconeus	Pronator teres ⎫ Flexor carpi radialis ⎬ Flexor palmaris superficialis Epitrochleoanconeus	Flexor carpi radialis Flexor palmaris superficialis Flexor antibrachii ulnaris	⎧ Flexor antibrachii medialis ⎨ Flexores carpi radiales Palmaris longus ⎧ Flexor antibrachii laterales ⎨ Flexor carpi ulnaris ⎩ Epitrochleocubitalis	Epicondyloradialis Flexor digitorum sublimis
Flexor carpi ulnaris	Flexor carpi ulnaris	Flexor carpi ulnaris		Flexor carpi ulnaris
Flexor digitorum profundus —— Pronator quadratus	Flexor digitorum profundus Pronator profundus	Ulnocarpalis Flexor palmaris profundus Pronator profundus	Ulnocarpalis Flexor palmaris profundus Pronator profundus	Flexor accessorius —— Pronator profundus

Superficial short digital flexors: palmaris brevis, contrahentes, lumbricales, etc.

Deep short digital flexors, digital interossei, etc.

Table 2 (*Continued*)

Hind Leg, Dorsal Musculature

MAMMAL	REPTILE	URODELE	FROG	BIRD
Sartorius.....	?Ambiens	?Iliotibialis	?Tensor fascia latae	?Ambiens
Rectus femoris.....	Iliotibialis	Ilioextensorius	Crureus glutaeus	Iliotibialis / Sartorius
Vasti.....	Femorotibialis			Femorotibialis
Gluteus maximus.....	?Iliofibularis	?Iliofibularis	?Iliofibularis	?Iliofibularis
Iliacus }			Iliacus	
Psoas }	Puboischiofemoralis internus	Puboischiofemoralis internus	Pectineus	Iliofemoralis internus
Pectineus }			Adductor longus	
Gluteus { medius / minimus }	Iliofemoralis	Iliofemoralis	Iliofemoralis	Iliofemoralis externus / Iliotrochantericus
Tibialis anterior.....	Tibialis anterior	Tibialis anterior	Extensor cruris brevis	Tibialis anterior
Extensor digitorum longus }	Extensor digitorum communis	Extensor digitorum communis	Tibialis anticus longus	Extensor digitorum communis
Extensor hallucis longus..... }				
Peroneus tertius				
Peroneus longus.....	Peroneus longus	Peroneus longus }	Peroneus	Peroneus longus
Peroneous brevis.....	Peroneus brevis	Peroneus brevis }		Peroneus brevis
Extensores digitorum breves.....	Extensores digitorum breves	Extensores digitorum breves	Tibialis anticus brevis	Extensores digitorum breves
—	Dorsal interossei	Dorsal interossei	—	—

Hind Leg, Ventral Musculature

MAMMAL	REPTILE	URODELE	FROG	BIRD
Obturator externus } Quadratus femoris } Obturator internus } Gemelli }	Puboischiofemoralis externus	Puboischiofemoralis externus	Adductor magnus (pt.) Gemelli } Obturator internus }	Obturator externus
	Ischiotrochantericus	Ischiofemoralis		Ischiofemoralis
Adductores femoris brevis et longus	Adductor femoris	Adductor femoris	Obturator externus } Quadratus femoris } ?Adductor magnus (pt.) }	Puboischiofemoralis
Adductor magnus	?Pubotibialis	?Pubotibialis		
Crurococcygeus	Caudifemoralis longus	Caudifemoralis longus	Caudalipuboischio-tibialis	Coccygeofemorales
Pyriformis	Caudifemoralis brevis	Caudifemoralis brevis	Pyriformis } Semitendinosus } Sartorius }	
	Puboischiotibialis	Puboischiotibialis		
Gracilis } Semimembranosus }				
Semitendinosus	Flexor tibialis internus	Ischioflexorius	Semimembranosus } Gracilis }	Ischioflexorius
Biceps	?Flexor tibialis externus			Caudilioflexorius
Gastrocnemius medialis } Flexor hallucis longus } Flexor digitorum longus }	Gastrocnemius internus	Flexor digitorum sublimis } Flexor digitorum longus } Pronator profundus }	Plantaris longus	Gastrocnemius internus } Flexor hallucis longus } Flexor profundus }
Tibialis posterior Popliteus	Flexor digitorum longus Pronator profundus Popliteus	Popliteus		Tibialis posticus } Popliteus }
Gastrocnemius lateralis } Soleus } Plantaris }	Gastrocnemius externus	Fibulotarsalis (?)	Tibialis posticus	Gastrocnemius externus }
Interosseus	Interosseus	Interosseus	—	—

Superficial short digital flexors: flexor digitorum brevis, contrahentes, lumbricales, etc.

Deep short digital flexors: digital interossei, etc.

the gill openings, each typical gill arch of a shark has a characteristic series of muscle slips proper to it, which are distinguishable by innervation from those belonging to neighbors in the series. The most prominent element in a shark gill is the *superficial constrictor;* this is a broad, if usually thin, sheet of muscle whose fibers generally run dorsoventrally in the flap of skin extending outward in the gill septum. Dorsally and ventrally most of the constrictor fibers terminate in sheets of fascia on the back and throat. The deeper fibers, however, may attach to the outer surface of the gill bar elements and may form separate *interbranchial* muscles.

In addition, there develop deeper muscles. The *adductors* of the visceral arches run from epibranchial to ceratobranchial and tend to bend the two together; dorsal *interarcual* muscles connect the epibranchials with the pharyngobranchials of the same or neighboring arches. Dorsal to the constrictor, muscle fibers run diagonally downward and backward from the dorsal fascia and may insert on the dorsal region of successive gill bars as arch *levators.* In many sharks, however, most or all of these fibers slant back to attach to the shoulder girdle; this is characteristic of the tetrapod muscle derived from this muscle series, the trapezius, and this name is frequently applied to the shark muscle.

In bony fishes the development of the gill musculature is more restricted. Since the gill septa are reduced (in the presence of an operculum), the superficial constrictors are absent, but, ventrally, slips of this system persist as varied *subarcual muscles;* in teleosts the levators are lost, and the adductors and interbranchial muscles are reduced or absent.

Among tetrapods, gill-breathing larval amphibians retain a series of gill muscles which resemble those of bony fishes; but in true land forms the muscles moving the typical gill bars have disappeared, except for small slips associated with the hyoid apparatus and larynx. There is, however, one conspicuous if aberrant group of muscles of this series which survives in land vertebrates—the *trapezius* musculature (Fig. 191, *B*), derived, as mentioned, from the arch levators of fishes. The trapezius is always present and frequently greatly expanded in land vertebrates, and its origin may extend far down the back. The thin trapezius sheet converges downward from the occiput and back fascia to insert along the anterior margin of the shoulder girdle. Primitively, the attachment was to the dermal elements—cleithrum and clavicle; but with their reduction or loss the insertion lies along the primitive front margin of the scapula (the scapular spine in mammals) and may reach the sternum ventrally. More anterior and ventral slips of the trapezius group may separate as individual muscles—*sternomastoid, cleidomastoid,* and so on—and with reduction of the clavicle may (in many mammals) fuse with slips from the deltoid to form long, slender compound muscles extending directly from head to front limb.

Muscles of the Hyoid Arch.   Presumably in the ancestral jawless fishes the muscles of the hyoid arch were comparable to those of the typical gill arches. But in all living jawed vertebrates the hyoid arch (and its gill slit) has become highly modified, and the musculature is correspondingly modified. The muscles of this arch are always identifiable through their innervation by nerve VII, the facial nerve.

Related, presumably, to the loss of independence of the hyoid arch (which is modified for jaw support), all the deeper hyoid muscles are absent in sharks, and only the superficial constrictor remains (Fig. 191, *A*). This muscle, however, may be variously subdivided in many fishes. Some deep slips may separate to

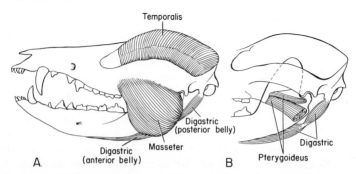

Fig. 192. Jaw musculature of the opossum. *A*, Superficial view; *B*, deeper dissection. The jaw is represented as transparent to show the pterygoid muscles, which attach to its inner surface.

connect hyoid arch elements with one another and with the jaw joint. Certain of these slips may persist in tetrapods in the hyoid and ear region; some are insignificant, but two of them, as noted later, achieve importance in land animals in connection with mouth opening. A ventral part of the constrictor may form, in fishes, part of the muscle (intermandibular) connecting the jaws ventrally, but in land vertebrates the hyoid contribution to this muscle sheet vanishes.

The most important part of the hyoid musculature is the dorsal part of the constrictor sheet developed in the gill septum of the hyoid arch. In bony fishes this septum is greatly expanded to form the bony operculum covering the gill chamber; the hyoid constrictor is highly developed to control the movements of this gill cover.

In land vertebrates the operculum disappears; the constrictor of the hyoid, in the absence of the more posterior constrictors (they had disappeared in bony fishes), is the only superficial muscle remaining in the developing neck region. It expands over this territory as a thin sheet, the *sphincter colli*, circling the neck ventrally and laterally (Fig. 191, *B*). This muscle tends to adhere to the skin. In mammals it expands in spectacular fashion over the surface of the head to form the muscles of expression, discussed later (p. 286).

Mechanisms for mouth opening have apparently not been taken seriously (so to speak) by vertebrates (mouths tend, rather, to open by themselves), and various makeshift devices for this purpose are seen in different groups. Ventrally, the primitive series of hypobranchial axial muscles run forward, as we have noted earlier, from shoulder to jaw, and a backward pull of these muscles is sometimes utilized for jaw opening in fishes. In most tetrapods except mammals there is substituted a *depressor mandibulae* (Fig. 191, *B*), an anterior slip of the hyoid constrictor which arises laterally from the posterior part of the skull, and passes down behind the one-time spiracle (now the eardrum region) to attach to the back end of the lower jaw (there is frequently a retroarticular process of the jaw which gives the muscle good leverage).

In mammals we have seen that the jaw is refashioned; the elements about the former region of attachment of the depressor are either lost or taken into the ear. The depressor muscle, its function lost, vanishes.

Another slip of hyoid musculature, however, emerges to take the place of the depressor and contributes to the formation of the *digastric* (Fig. 192, *B*). This mammalian jaw-opener is, as its name implies, a compound muscle with two bellies. An anterior belly is formed by fibers of jaw-arch origin running back beneath the jaw ramus. Posteriorly, this connects with a slip of hyoid muscle which runs upward behind the jaw to attach to the skull in the ear region. The two bellies lie at an angle to one another, but between them they successfully perform the none too arduous task of depressing the jaw.

Jaw Muscles (Figs. 191, 192). With the modification in gnathostomes of the elements of an anterior gill arch to form basic jaw structures, the muscles of this arch have become highly modified to serve special jaw functions. Since no typical gill opening adjoins the jaw, there is, of course, no development here of an expanded gill flap; in consequence there is no development of a typical constrictor sheet. The jaw musculature, as seen in sharks, consists of three parts:

1. The upper jaw is in sharks but loosely attached to the skull. A dorsal segment of the jaw musculature runs out and down from the braincase in front of the spiracle to attach to the upper jaw cartilage as an elevator of the upper jaw, a *levator palatoquadrati* rather comparable serially to one of the trapezius components which attach to the ordinary gill arches.

2. The major muscle mass of the jaw segment is the *adductor mandibulae*, which performs the most important function of any single branchial muscle in gnathostomes—the pressing together of the jaws in the biting or grinding motions essential for the ingestion of food. In sharks the main mass of the adductor muscle is arranged in a simple fashion, running from the palatoquadrate cartilage, which here forms the upper jaw, down to the mandibular cartilage. (A specialized portion, a *preorbital* muscle, runs forward from the main adductor to the front of the orbit, and, pulling the upper jaw forward, aids in anchoring it to the braincase.) The adductor of the mandible is comparable in position to the adductors of the normal branchial arches, but probably includes in its composition the material that farther back forms the main bulk of the constrictor, absent here.

3. Unimportant is a ventral element: fibers representing the most ventral part of the constrictor, form in fishes (together with a hyoid derivative) an *intermandibular* muscle, a thin sheet of fibers between the two lower jaw rami.

In higher vertebrates the more ventral and dorsal parts of the jaw arch musculature are unimportant. In tetrapods the ventral fibers continue to form a thin sheet between the lower jaws as the *mylohyoid* muscle; a slip from this forms (as noted earlier) one belly of the digastric muscle which lowers the jaw in mammals. The upper jaw and palate continue to be movably articulated with the braincase in most bony fishes and a number of tetrapod groups. In such types the levator of the palatoquadrate persists, but in varied form. In bony fishes it may expand to connect the hyomandibular and even the operculum with the braincase. In land vertebrates it is represented by small muscles connecting the braincase with the quadrate (as in birds) or pterygoid (as in lizards and snakes). In vertebrate groups where the upper jaw is fused to the braincase—such as chimaeras, lungfishes, living amphibians, turtles, crocodiles, mammals—this type of musculature is useless. It has usually disappeared; in many reptiles and amphibians, however, a relic portion is found in the inner part of the orbit where its swelling or contraction tends to push the eyeball outward.

The adductor mandibulae is prominent throughout the gnathostomes. In bony fishes it is bulky. The "cheek" region in which it lies is covered over by dermal bone, and the attachments of the jaw muscles are in part on the under side of this dermal roof and may extend inward to the braincase as well. In lower tetrapods the adductor musculature is divided into two main groups: (1) temporalis and (2) pterygoideus. The *temporalis* muscle in tetrapods primitively arose from the under surface of the cheek region of the skull roof and from adjacent parts of the palatal complex and braincase, to insert in and about the fossa in the lower jaw. As discussed in connection with the reptilian skull, fenestration or emargination of the originally solid skull roof in all amniotes except some turtles and the extinct cotylosaurs allows greater freedom of action for the temporal musculature. Associated with modification of the jaw structure and articulation in mammals, we find that the primitive temporal musculature has been divided into two parts. One, the temporalis in a narrow sense, has much the original position of the muscle and inserts into the coronoid process of the mandible. A second muscle, the *masseter*, is more superficial in position. Its fibers run at a considerable angle to those of the temporalis, and pull the jaw forward and upward; in rodents, particularly, it may be highly developed and is often stronger than the temporalis. The little *pterygoideus* muscles form a deep division of the adductor mass. They typically originate from the pterygoid region of the palate (but may extend on to the braincase) and insert on the inner or back surface of the jaw.

SKIN MUSCULATURE

In fishes the surface of the skeletal muscles is tied in closely to the dermis. In tetrapods, particularly the amniotes, this is no longer the case, and the skin lies relatively loosely over the underlying musculature. However, we find in many instances thin sheets or ribbons of muscle partly or completely embedded in the skin, and functioning in skin movements; these muscles are derived during development from the body muscles beneath them. In some cases the distinction between the major skeletal muscle system and its superficial dermal derivatives is clear; in other cases, however, this is not so, and the student dissector is all too often troubled to decide whether a given muscle sheet is a proper part of the trunk or limb segment which he is dissecting or a skin muscle which he may, for his immediate purpose, disregard.

In amphibians and reptiles the dermal musculature is in general little developed, except for the occasional presence of a dermal slip of the pectoral musculature—a condition repeated in many mammals. A notable exception lies in the Ophidia. The large scales of snakes each have attached to them a stout dermal muscle which can erect the scale so that it acts as a holdfast on the ground and prevents a backward slip of the body in undulatory motion; the scales thus have much of the functions of the absent feet. In birds, dermal elements, developed from a number of the shoulder and wing muscles, insert distally into the thick skin of the wing and aid in flight.

We find the greatest development of dermal musculature in mammals. In most mammals (higher primates are exceptional) almost the entire trunk and neck are wrapped about by a continuous sheath of skin muscle termed the *panniculus carnosus* (Fig. 193); the twitch of a horse's skin where a fly has settled is evidence of the presence and functioning of this dermal muscle sheet. The panniculus carnosus is, so to speak, indifferent as to the underlying source of its muscle fibers, for we find that while the trunk sheath is derived from the underlying axial muscles, the ring of superficial fibers about the neck, the sphincter colli, is, as we have noted, a part of the visceral musculature of that region and innervated by the facial nerve (VII). In mammals this dermal musculature undergoes a striking development (to which, indeed, the facial nerve innervating it

Fig. 193. Dermal muscles sheathing the body of a mole. (After Nishi.)

Fig. 194. Facial musculature; the head and neck of a dog. (After Huber.)

owes its name). Slips grow forward from the neck over the skull and on to the cheeks to form the *facial muscles*, or muscles of expression (Fig. 194). Although widely distributed over the scalp and face, these muscle bands tend to be especially concentrated about the orbits, the outer ear, and lips (which last, hence, acquire a mobility and usefulness unknown in lower vertebrates). Lacking facial muscles, nonmammalian vertebrates generally can neither smile nor frown; lacking a mouth sphincter, they can neither kiss nor suck; lacking ear muscles, movement of the ear pinna (as seen in most mammals, including especially gifted human beings) would be impossible.

ELECTRIC ORGANS

In three types of fishes—rays of the genus Torpedo, the electric "eel" (Gymnotus), and the electric catfish (Malapterurus)—there is a development of special organs capable of producing a heavy electric shock to any animal in contact with them, and in several other types of rays and teleosts similar if weaker phenomena are produced. The present chapter is the most appropriate place for their consideration, for these electric organs (Fig. 195) appear to be, in most cases, modified muscular tissues. Muscle fibers are structures chemically adapted, as we have seen, for the rapid utilization and release of energy; in the present in-

Fig. 195. Electric organs. *A*, The torpedo, a ray in which musculature of the expanded pectoral fins has been transformed into *electric cells* (*e*). The skin is dissected away to show the electric organs. *B*, Section of the tail of the electric "eel" of South America (Gymnotus). Typical axial musculature (*m*) is present above and below, but much of the tail muscle has been transformed into electricity-producing tissue (*e*). (*A* after Garten; *B* after du Bois-Reymond.)

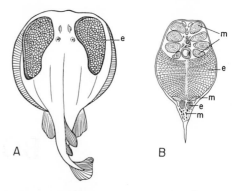

stance the energy is utilized, however, for the production of electricity rather than for muscular contraction.

The elements of which these electric organs are composed are generally flattened plates of multinucleated protoplasm, termed *electroplaxes*, each innervated by a nerve fiber. In certain instances where their development is known they are seen to arise from embryonic striated muscle cells, but become much altered in shape and internal structure. In other cases it is apparently the motor end plate rather than the muscle fiber itself which develops as the electroplax. These electric plates are arranged, one above another, in series of piles. This arrangement is immediately comparable to the old-fashioned voltaic pile, famous in the history of electrical discovery; these piles of electric cells form essentially an organic battery, made effective by plus and minus differences between the two surfaces of each plate. In the torpedo strengths of more than 200 volts and 2000 watts have been recorded.

In forms with a powerful electric organ, it is obvious that this structure can be of considerable value to a fish either in warding off enemies or paralyzing its prey. The utility of the electric organ in forms in which it is of a weaker nature was long a puzzle. It has, however, been recently discovered that certain fishes have long been utilizing the principles of radar, only discovered by man in recent years. Waves emitted by electric organs and reflected by nearby objects are of aid in navigation, particularly in turbid waters. In one instance, at least, sensory organs of the lateral line system (cf. p. 281) are known to act as receptors.

Despite the basic similarity of their construction, the electric organs vary greatly in position and appearance in the different types which have them; it seems probable that such organs developed independently a number of times. In the torpedo they are present as two large groups of piled-up plates, one on either side of the head in the expanded pectoral fin of this flattened elasmobranch. There are hundreds of piles and some hundreds of plates in each pile; in one species of torpedo it has been calculated that over 200,000 plates are present. In the electric "eel" Gymnotus of South America, in which the tail makes up four fifths of the body length, the massive electric organ is formed from the modified ventral half of the tail musculature. In the catfish Malapterurus from the Nile the electric tissue forms a sheath encircling the whole body just beneath the skin from the back of the head to the base of the tail. In this case the plates, although numerous, are not arranged in neat piles, and since the electric tissue is superficial to the body musculature, its origin from musculature is not so certain (perhaps modified glands form the source).

10

BODY CAVITIES

In the vertebrates, as in all the more highly organized invertebrate types, most of the body organs are not bedded in solid tissues or mesenchyme, but are situated within the bounds of body cavities, more properly *celomic cavities*. These are fluid-filled spaces in which the viscera are placed in a situation relatively free from ties, and more or less at liberty to move freely during their functional activity and to change the more readily in size or shape during growth processes. We may here give a brief résumé of their arrangement before proceeding to the description of organs which are enclosed in these cavities and which border them.

Development of the Celom. The body cavities are developed in the mesodermal tissues, and their linings are formed by a serous mesodermal epithelium, the *peritoneum*. We have noted that in Amphioxus, as in echinoderms, the celomic cavities arise in part, at least, from segmental pouches pinched off from the primitive gut as mesodermal somites (Figs. 65, 66, p. 116). In true vertebrates, however, this presumably primitive method of celom formation is abandoned, and the body cavities are formed by a splitting of mesodermal sheets after that tissue has separated from other germ layers. Although small celomic cavities may appear in the somites or the kidney-forming tissue, these are ephemeral, and the term "celom," in all late embryonic and adult stages, is confined to the cavities in the more lateral and ventral parts of the mesoderm, the lateral plate.

In forms developing from a mesolecithal type of egg, the lateral plate of mesoderm at an early stage extends down the flanks of the body on either side so that the two sheets presently meet, or come close to meeting, in the ventral midline (Fig. 67, p. 117). In large-yolked types the lateral plates are at first directed outward laterally over the yolk, and are continuous with the mesoderm of the extra-embryonic regions (Fig. 62, p. 112); only later, with the assumption of body form, do these sheets meet ventrally. Each of the two lateral sheets is a continuum, to begin with, from the head to the hinder end of the trunk region, and above the lamprey level never shows any indication of segmentation. At first each plate is solid, but presently it splits in two to form a liquid-filled embryonic celomic cavity between outer and inner walls. These walls, apart from giving rise to connective tissues and other materials, are destined to form, re-

288

spectively, the somatic and splanchnic layers of the peritoneum (Fig. 196). The *somatic peritoneum* (or parietal peritoneum) forms the inner surface of the great external "tube" of the body, termed in the embryo the somatopleure, in which the somatic skeleton, somatic musculature, kidneys, and gonads presently develop. The *splanchnic peritoneum* forms the outer covering of the digestive tract and its outgrowths, which constitute the splanchnopleure.

In this fashion there is formed a pair of celomic cavities, one on either side, with a large gut cavity between them. The diameter of the gut, behind the pharyngeal region, becomes relatively small as development proceeds, and the two celomic cavities come to lie adjacent to one another both above and below the gut tube (Figs. 2, *B, D*, p. 6; 200, *B*). At this stage the right and left celoms are separated by longitudinal thin sheets of tissue, bounded on either side by peritoneum; these are the dorsal and ventral mesenteries. The *dorsal mesentery* is a persistent structure, containing nerves and blood vessels supplying the gut. The *ventral mesentery*, however, is of little functional importance in the adult and usually disappears for most of its length. With this disappearance the two celomic cavities are merged.

In the early embryo the sheet of lateral plate mesoderm containing the celomic cavity is continuous along the length of the gut (Fig. 67, *C*). The anal or cloacal region is the definitive posterior boundary of the trunk, and neither the celom nor the viscera associated with it extend into the tail. Anteriorly, the situation is complicated by the development of the gill system of the pharynx. The developing gill slits disrupt the lateral plate in the side walls of the pharyngeal region, so that in this part of the embryo the celom is confined to the ventral part of the throat, below the pharynx (cf. Fig. 179, p. 257).

The celomic structure of an early embryo is simple and readily understood; that of the adult is not. It is complicated, owing to three factors: (1) a pushing into the celomic space of other organs than those of the digestive tract—heart, gonads, kidneys and lungs; (2) longitudinal subdivision into compartments—in most cases into a heart cavity and general body cavity, but with further subdivision in mammals and birds; (3) elaboration and twisting of the gut segments and

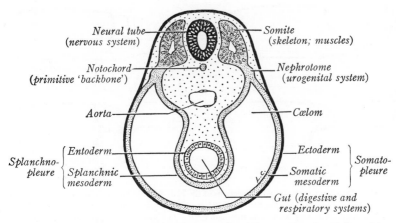

Fig. 196. Diagrammatic transverse section of a mammalian embryo to show the relations of the mesoderm. (From Arey.)

outgrowth of gut appendages—liver, pancreas—with a consequent complicated folding of mesenteries.

Pericardial Cavity.   The most anterior and ventral region of the embryonic celom becomes the pericardial cavity, in which the heart develops. This area, as noted above, lies primitively in the floor of the "throat," below and somewhat posterior to the fish pharynx. In the early embryo of all vertebrates the pericardial cavity opens widely at the back into the general abdominal cavity. Soon, however, there forms a *transverse septum* at the level of the most posterior chamber of the heart, the sinus venosus, and of the cardinal veins which enter it (Figs. 197, *A;* 198; 199).

The septum as thus formed blocks off the lower part of the passage between pericardium and general celom, but leaves a gap above. In most vertebrates this gap is closed in the adult; but in hagfishes, elasmobranchs, and a few lower ray-finned fishes a small dorsal opening between heart cavity and general celom persists into the adult stage. In the early embryo the liver bud, growing forward below the gut, enters the transverse septum and expands within its substance, so that in lower vertebrates the main liver attachment is to the posterior surface of the septum. This lower vertebrate condition is essentially repeated in the stage of a mammalian embryo seen in Figure 198. In many higher forms the liver tends in the adult to pull away again from the transverse septum, but remains attached to it by a relatively narrow *coronary ligament.*

In most groups of land vertebrates the disappearance of a functional gill system and the development of a neck are correlated with a marked change in the relative position of the pericardial cavity. It has been pushed back into the floor of the thorax, where it lies, protected by the coracoids or sternum, diagonally below the anterior end of the main body cavity. Above it in paired recesses of the celom lie the lungs. Separating heart and lung cavities, a *pleuropericardial membrane,* bounded on either surface by celomic epithelium, extends forward from the top of the transverse septum, of which it is an extension (Figs. 197, *C;* 199).

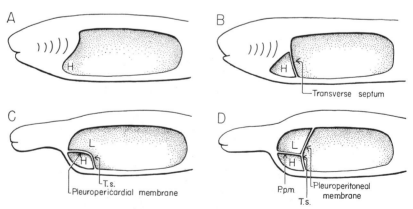

Fig. 197.   Diagrammatic longitudinal sections of the body to show the evolution of the celomic cavity. *A,* A primitive condition, with the entire celom forming a single cavity. *B,* Typical fish condition; the pericardial chamber is separated from the main cavity. *C,* Typical amphibian and reptilian condition; the lungs are developed but the spaces in which they lie are in continuity with the main celom. *D,* Mammalian condition, with a formed diaphragm. *H,* Heart, *L,* lungs.

Fig. 198. Lateral view of a dissection of the trunk of a human embryo 3 mm. in length, showing pericardial cavity (heart removed), pleural, and peritoneal cavities; anterior end of the body to the left. The transverse septum, with the developing liver, has formed behind the heart, but all body cavities are in open communication (cf. Fig. 197 *A, B*). (After Arey.)

Fig. 199. A lateral view similar to that of Figure 198, but a later stage (16 mm.); anterior end of body to the left. In addition to the transverse septum, pleuropericardial and pleuroperitoneal membranes are present. The last, together with the septum, are the primary elements forming the diaphragm. (Cf. Fig. 197 *B, C*.) (After Arey.)

General Body Cavity. With the separation of the pericardial cavity, there remains in the majority of vertebrates a single great celomic cavity occupying, with its enclosed organs, most of the trunk region. This is partially subdivided into right and left halves by the mesentery system.

The ventral mesentery, we have noted, usually disappears for most of its length. (It is persistent in a few types of fishes and present for most of its length in salamanders.) A short posterior segment may remain as a ligament tying in the bladder with the rectum. Anteriorly, however, the mesentery persists in connection with the liver, which arises in the midst of the primitive ventral mesentery. The part of the ventral mesentery connecting stomach and liver forms the gastrohepatic ligament or *lesser omentum;* that part below the liver is the *falciform ligament* (Fig. 200).

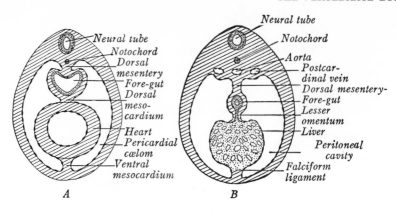

Fig. 200. Diagrammatic sections through the heart and liver regions of an amniote embryo to show the relations of the mesenteries. (From Arey, after Prentiss.)

The dorsal mesentery is a simple, continuous longitudinal sheet of tissue in the early embryo. But in later stages the development of the gut tube and its outgrowths into a series of distinctive organs results in a parallel development of distinct mesenteric areas. The term "mesentery" is sometimes used in a narrow sense to apply merely to that part of the sheet supporting the small intestine (where such a gut subdivision is developed), and special terms such as mesocolon, mesorectum, and so forth, may be used for other parts. Of special importance is the mesogaster, or *greater omentum*, supporting the stomach. The dorsal mesentery system is present in all vertebrates, since it is along the mesenteries that arteries, lymphatics, and nerves descend to the gut. In reptiles and mammals the dorsal mesentery remains unbroken; in birds and amphibians, however, there may be gaps along its length, and in some fish groups it is broken up into discontinuous segments. In teleosts and land vertebrates in which a coiled small intestine is developed, the mesentery is, of course, folded in a complicated fashion, and parts of the mesentery may fuse with one another in a confusing way (Figs. 201, 204).

The stomach, as developed in most groups of jawed vertebrates, swings to the left side of the body, and that part of the dorsal mesentery forming the greater omentum swings with it. In consequence, the right part of the celomic cavity adjoining the stomach encroaches on the left side of the body. This encroachment is exaggerated by the fact that generally the greater omentum (in which the spleen is embedded) does not descend directly from the dorsal body wall to the stomach, but tends to sag downward to the left of the stomach (Fig. 201). Ventrally, this folded area is, of course, closed off by the expanse of the liver, tied to the stomach by the lesser omentum. As a result this area of the right celom becomes essentially a pouch, the *omental bursa*, opening out to the right above the liver. In many lower vertebrates it is not especially developed and may open broadly to the right side.

Dorsally, various structures not part of the digestive system may project into the body cavity, as is noted elsewhere (cf. Figs. 2, *D*, p. 6; 279, p. 387). The testes or ovaries, formed from the genital ridges of the embryo, usually expand into the body cavity, surrounded by its peritoneum, and may be supported

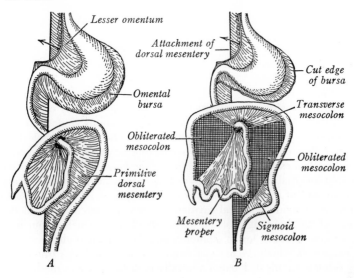

Fig. 201. Diagrammatic ventral views of the gut and mesenteries of a mammal in *A*, an embryo, and *B*, essentially adult conditions. *A* shows the general type of folding which the mesenteries must undergo because of the asymmetrical position of the stomach and twisting of the intestine. As shown in *B*, this folding may result in obliteration or fusion of parts of the mesentery. In *A* the bursa is a structure of minor dimensions; in many mammals the enlarged bursa would extend down, covering over much of the intestine, but has been cut off short in Figure *B*. The opening from the bursa to the celom of the right side (epiploic foramen) is shown by an arrow; the double line "above" the arrow (i.e., ventral to it) is the cut attachment of the lesser omentum to the liver. For lateral views of the same structures, see Figure 204. (From Arey.)

by special mesenteries—*mesorchium* or *mesovarium*. Farther laterally the developing kidneys of the embryo also expand into the body cavity as longitudinal swollen ridges, and in the adult the kidney bulges to a varied degree into the celom from the dorsal side. The oviducts arise in the kidney ridges and may persist there, but are often suspended by a special paired mesenteric structure, the *mesosalpinx*.

Lung Pockets. The lungs, as developed in certain bony fishes and in land animals, push backward from the pharynx along either side of the esophagus and extend posteriorly into the body cavity. Here they lie above the pericardium on either side of a forward extension of the gut mesentery, termed the *mediastinum*, in which the esophagus is embedded. In lower tetrapods the lungs are usually supported by separate paired mesenteries, *pulmonary folds*, extending down to them from the dorsal wall of the body cavity and continuing downward to tie into the upper surface of the liver on either side (Fig. 202). The left fold—and consequently the left pouch—is usually little developed. The right fold, however, is conspicuous in the embryo of every tetrapod and frequently remains so in the adult. Its persistence is definitely associated with the fact that the posterior vena cava utilizes it to make its short circuit down into the liver and thence to the heart (cf. p. 440).

In amphibians and a majority of reptiles the dorsal and anterior recesses which contain the lungs are still parts of the general body cavity. In some reptiles the lungs may be more or less buried in the body wall dorsally, with little or no projection into the celom. In still others, however, there may be a partial or even—in crocodilians and some lizards and snakes—complete closure of the lung pockets from the remainder of the celom, making *pleural cavities*, much as in mammals.

The Celom in Birds. The great development of air sacs in birds (p. 335) is associated with a complicated subdivision of the body cavity which appears to promote the efficiency of the breathing apparatus (Fig. 203). The pericardium forms, of course, a separate anterior chamber, and posteriorly a transverse septum divides off a large cavity containing intestine, kidneys, and gonads. Between these two extremities lies the area of the lungs, liver, and stomach; here three paired longitudinal septa, more or less horizontal in position, bring about the development of four pairs of cavities. The uppermost septum shuts off the two lungs into individual pleural cavities; this septum somewhat parallels the development of the diaphragm of the mammals, described below, but is of independent origin. Another, lower septum causes the formation above it of a lateral pair of cavities in which are air sacs connected with the lungs (these are hence not true celomic cavities). Farther ventrally is the area where the liver expands on either side of the gut; here a horizontal septum running lengthwise along either side of the liver separates celomic cavities dorsal and ventral to that organ.

Mammalian Celomic Cavities; Diaphragm. Quite another type of celomic development has occurred in mammals. There are, of course, no air sacs of avian type and none of the fantastic subdivision of the main body cavity which accompanies that development. The major features are (1) a high degree of de-

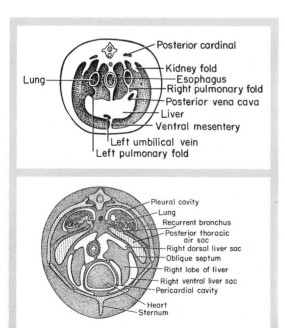

Fig. 202. Diagrammatic cross section, looking forward, through the body of a lizard in the region of the lungs, to show the pulmonary folds, between which and the esophagus lie pulmonary recesses. The left pulmonary fold is little developed; it is down the right fold that the posterior vena cava makes its way from the region of the posterior cardinal vein to the liver (cf. p. 440). (After Goodrich.)

Fig. 203. Diagram of transverse section through the thorax of a bird to show especially the subdivision of the celomic cavity. In addition to the pericardial cavity, the pleural cavities and the sacs dorsal and ventral to the liver are shown; the main intestinal celom is too far posterior to be included in this section. The thoracic air sacs (hatched) are also present in section. (After Goodrich.)

velopment of the omental bursa and, especially, (2) the presence of pleural cavities closed off by the diaphragm.

We have noted the presence to a variable degree in other vertebrates of a pouch, the omental bursa, of the right celomic cavity between stomach and liver and the development of the greater omentum associated with this condition. In mammals this recess is much developed; the greater omentum becomes a huge fold extending down as an apron over much of the ventral surface of the abdominal cavity (Fig. 204). The opening to the bursa (on the right side) is closed except for the small *epiploic foramen* (foramen of Winslow, Fig. 201).

In mammals the lungs, as will be noted in discussing those organs, are enclosed in paired *pleural cavities*, recesses in the thorax which are shut off from the major abdominal (or peritoneal) cavity. The partition between thoracic and abdominal parts of the celom is the *diaphragm;* movements of this partly muscular structure, together with rib movements, are responsible for the typical breathing action of mammals.

In the adult mammal the diaphragm has the appearance of a relatively simple partition, tendinous in its central part, but with a sheet of muscle all about its periphery; it extends across the body below the base of the rib basket and above the liver and stomach to divide the thoracic region from the abdomen. Despite its apparent simplicity, the diaphragm is complicated in its mode of development and in its structure; we shall here give the barest outline of this story.

We have noted in connection with the formation of the pericardium the transverse septum, developed at the back of the heart and in front of the liver, which closes off the pericardial cavity from the main celom. This is the principal

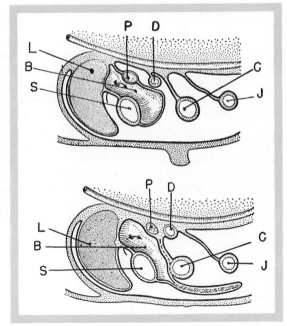

Fig. 204. Diagrams of embryonic and adult conditions of the omentum and bursa in a mammal; longitudinal sections, seen from the left side, with head end at left. In the embryo (upper figure) the bursa is small; the entrance (epiploic foramen) is indicated by an arrow. In the adult of many mammals (lower figure) the dorsal mesentery, as the greater omentum, has become a long fold. The diagrams further show how the mesenteries of the gut may be fused together (as is here that of the transverse colon to the greater omentum), or obliterated (as is that of the duodenum, in the diagram): *B,* omental bursa; *C,* transverse colon; *D,* duodenum; *J,* jejunum; *L,* liver; *P,* pancreas; *S,* stomach. For comparable ventral views, see Figure 201. (After Arey.)

Fig. 205.   Anterior view of the diaphragm region of an embryonic mammal, to show the various elements which make up the diaphragm. Heart and lungs have been removed to show the posterior walls of the pleural and pericardial chambers. At this stage (as in the comparable Figure 241, p. 337) the pericardial cavity still extended to the ventral wall of the chest, whereas in the later stage of Figure 242, *B*, (p. 337) the pleural cavities extend below it. (After Broman, Goodrich.)

ventral component of the diaphragm. In reptiles the lungs are dorsal to the heart, above the top of the septum. In mammals, in contrast, the large lung pockets expand downward on either side of the heart. As a result the lung cavities may approach one another ventrally below the heart, leaving only a median strand of tissue, a *ventral mediastinum*, connecting the pericardial sac with the ventral body wall (Fig. 242, p. 337). To close off these enlarged lung pockets from the abdominal celom as pleural cavities, adjuncts to the transverse septum are demanded (Fig. 205). The more medial parts of the opening are closed by mesodermal folds growing dorsally from the top of the transverse septum. Laterally, *pleuroperitoneal membranes* (Fig. 199, p. 291) fold inward from the body wall to close much of the opening, and, as the lungs continue to expand, the body wall itself takes part in forming the lateral areas of the diaphragm beyond the base of the original pleuroperitoneal membranes. A small opening persists for a time far dorsally on either side; here a final closing fold develops from the dorsal mesentery or the mesentery supporting the lung itself. When in such reptiles as the crocodilians the lung cavities are separated from the general celom, the partition consists simply of peritoneal membranes and connective tissue. In contrast the mammalian diaphragm is supplied with a sheet of muscle, striated and subject to voluntary control, which is obviously a derivative of the axial musculature (p. 263), although its embryologic origin is not well known.

 Abdominal Pores.   In the ancestral fishes there appear to have been present a pair of small abdominal pores connecting the celom with the exterior in the cloacal region (Fig. 293, p. 405). Such openings are present in cyclostomes and most elasmobranchs, and occur in some bony fishes, although most teleosts have lost them. In land vertebrates the pores have been lost in most cases, but may be found in turtles and crocodilians. In cyclostomes these pores serve as exits for the sperm and eggs. In all gnathostomes, however, special ducts have taken over the transportation of the sex cells, and the only function which we can assume the abdominal pores to have is that of getting rid of surplus liquid from the celomic cavity.

MOUTH, PHARYNX, RESPIRATORY ORGANS

The digestive tract, with its various outgrowths and accessory structures, looms large in both bulk and importance in body organization. The major digestive organs, including stomach and intestine, form the more posterior segments of the tract. In the present chapter we shall consider the mouth and pharyngeal regions, "introductory" sections of the digestive tube. These play little role in alimentation beyond the reception of food, but are highly important in other regards—notably as the place of origin of respiratory organs and of important glandular structures.

THE MOUTH

From the mammalian or human point of view the mouth appears to be a well defined structural unit, with fixed, uniform features such as the lips, tooth row, tongue, and salivary glands. But a broad survey of the vertebrates shows that mouth structures vary widely; every one of the familiar landmarks may be absent in one group or another. Except that it is an inturned area, a *buccal cavity*, leading to the pharynx, we can make few statements about the mouth that will hold true for all vertebrates.

Development. In the embryologic story the opening from mouth to pharynx is late in appearance, suggesting that a mouth opening into the digestive tube may have been a relatively late phylogenetic development in vertebrate ancestry. In types of vertebrates with a mesolecithal egg, the early embryonic gut may open posteriorly at the blastopore, roughly homologous with the anus of the adult, but invariably the archenteron ends blindly at its anterior end. This blind end (Figs. 206, *A*; 248, p. 345) is the region of the future pharynx. Above and in front

297

Fig. 206. *A,* Diagram of a larval amphibian (at about the stage of Fig. 70, *E*), in longitudinal section, to show the extent of the endoderm (stippled) and its relation to structures of the mouth region. *B,* Diagram to show the comparative position of the mouth margins in various types of vertebrates (cf. text).

of the pharyngeal region there early appears an expanded brain and a consequently expanded head region. The head turns downward over the surface of the yolk-swollen body or yolk sac, producing beneath it an inturned fold or pocket of ectoderm, the *stomodeum*. This forms the primitive mouth cavity. At its inner end this fold lies close to the anterior, pharyngeal end of the gut tube. A membrane long persists at this point, separating the two structures. Eventually this membrane breaks down; mouth and pharynx are placed in continuity, and the digestive tube has acquired an anterior opening. The epithelia of the two regions concerned blend with each other and are difficult or impossible to distinguish at later stages. In a broad way, however, it is clear that the pharynx is mainly if not entirely lined with endoderm, but the mouth epithelium is ectoderm, essentially a continuation of the skin epidermis.

The embryonic gut cavity of vertebrates, the archenteron, was long ago recognized as comparable to the adult digestive cavity of coelenterates and a number of other simple invertebrate animal types. In these forms the adult gut has but a single opening, to which the vertebrate embryonic blastopore and adult anus are frequently compared. But in the more highly organized invertebrate phyla—annelids, molluscs, arthropods, echinoderms—a second opening, a mouth, has developed as a progressive feature; vertebrates presumably followed a similar evolutionary course, as suggested by the ontogenetic history.

Mouth Boundaries.   The extent of the mouth cavity in the various vertebrate groups is highly variable (Fig. 206, *B*). One would, *a priori,* expect that the mouth of the adult would correspond roughly in extent with the embryonic stomodeum formed from inturned ectoderm. It is probable that in general the posterior boundary of the mouth in the adult is indeed approximately the boundary between the stomodeum and the embryonic gut. Are, however, the anterior and outer margins of the mouth fixed in position? Does the mouth always include the same area of infolded stomodeal tissue? Not at all.

Two good landmarks are always present in the roof of the stomodeal region. Near the outer end of this funnel, beneath the swelling forebrain, is the embryonic nasal region, a pair of ectodermal pits or thickenings in most vertebrates, a single pit in cyclostomes. Farther back in the potential mouth roof is a median pit—the *hypophyseal pouch* (Rathke's pouch)—which later closes off, its epithelium forming the major part of the pituitary body lodged beneath the brain. In an adult shark or ray-finned fish the nasal sacs lie external to the mouth, while

Fig. 207. Section of the head of a larval lamprey. At this stage nasal and hypophyseal sacs are still ventral in position (cf. Fig. 231, p. 324).

the area from which developed the embryonic hypophyseal pouch lies well in-side it; the jaw margins bounding the mouth cavity thus lie between these two landmarks. In typical crossopterygians and all land vertebrates the situation is different. The jaw margins form a cross-bridge beneath the nasal pockets, so that both external and internal narial openings are present. Here, then, we have a more fully developed, more extensive, mouth cavity than in most fishes.

The opposite extreme is seen in the cyclostomes. A lamprey or hagfish has a well defined mouth; but the embryonic development shows that this mouth cor-responds only with the inner recesses of the mouth cavity of other vertebrates. In the larval cyclostome (Fig. 207) a nasal pit and a hypophyseal pouch are found in the stomodeal depression, somewhat as in other vertebrates. But as the embryo increases in size, forces of differential growth cause a rotation of both nostril and pit (the two are closely connected) forward and upward on to the outer surface of the head (as in the hagfish, Fig. 17, p. 37) and, in the lamprey, to a position high on the dorsal surface, far removed from the adult mouth (Fig. 231, p. 324). Most of the outer surface of the lamprey head is thus covered by ectoderm which in gnathostomes lies within the mouth.

In a majority of vertebrates the mouth margins are formed by *lips*, soft pli-able structures of epidermis and connective tissue. In cyclostomes the mouth opening is rounded (a feature to which the group owes its name); in hagfishes it bears marginal sensory tentacles and in the lampreys the circular margins con-stitute an effective sucker by which the animal attaches itself to its prey (Fig. 231). In jawed fishes, amphibians, and reptiles, the lips are in general small and unimportant skin folds, external to teeth and jaws. Deposits of keratin in the epi-thelium may transform the lips into a horny bill or beak—as in turtles, birds, and a few mammals. In typical mammals, lips are highly developed, separated by deep clefts from the jaw margins and rendered mobile by the presence of the facial musculature peculiar to this class. The mouth opening between upper and lower lips generally terminates posteriorly in mammals (in contrast to many lower vertebrates) well forward of the jaw articulation, and there is thus created a skin-covered *cheek* region. In rodents and Old World monkeys the potential storage spaces in the cheeks have been expanded into *cheek pouches*, useful in the car-riage of food. (The pocket gophers—Geomys, and the like—have enormous pouches developed in this region, which, however, are hair-lined external pouches, opening to the surface, not into the mouth.)

Palate. In typical fishes the roof of the mouth is a rather flattened vault, unbroken by any opening (once the embryonic hypophyseal pouch has closed). In typical crossopterygians and in amphibians, however, we find that paired open-ings, the *choanae* or internal nares, are present near the anterolateral margins. In amphibians (Fig. 208, *A*) the mouth roof is nearly flat; in reptiles (Fig. 208,

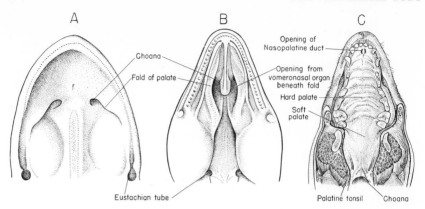

Fig. 208. The roof of the mouth in *A*, a urodele; *B*, a lizard; and *C*, a mammal (dog); to show particularly the position of the choanae.

B) and birds, however, the roof is well vaulted, and a pair of longitudinal *palatal folds* aid in forming a channel from the choanae back through the mouth above the tongue to the pharynx for the freer passage of air. In crocodilians and mammals (Figs. 166, *C*, p. 237; 167, p. 238; 208 *C*, 209) this air channel has been completely shut off from the mouth cavity by the development of a bony secondary palate, noted in our discussion of the skull; this "hard palate" is extended backward in mammals by a thick membrane, the *soft palate* (Figs. 208, *C*; 209). The vomeronasal organs (p. 466) gain openings to the mouth roof independent of the choanae in some reptiles; these organs persist in the majority of mammals and in some open through the secondary palate into the mouth cavity, through anterior palatine foramina.

The epithelium of the palate, and of the mouth cavity in general, is usually of a stratified squamous type. In living amphibians a rich capillary network underlies it, and it functions as an important breathing organ. In bony fishes, amphibians, and reptiles, teeth are frequently present on the palate. In mammals transverse ridges of cornified epithelium, which aid in the manipulation of food, are often present on the palate; they are highly developed in most ungulates and carnivores. In the toothless whalebone whales (Mysticeti) these ridges have developed into long parallel plates of horny "whalebone" hanging down into the mouth cavity; fringes on their margins pick up small marine organisms which are licked off by the tongue and form the food supply of these giant mammals.

Tongue. In fishes the lower ends of the gill bars, with accompanying musculature, slant forward below and between the jaws into the floor of the mouth. In many teleosts these bars bear teeth, which work against those of the palate; in other fishes, however, the mouth floor is relatively smooth. Movements of the gill system may raise or depress it, but there is seldom any structure comparable to a tongue. In cyclostomes this name is given to an extrusible mouth structure bearing horny "teeth" wherewith to rasp the flesh of the animal's prey (Figs. 231, p. 324), but this apparatus is surely a parallel development rather than one homologous with a true tongue.

In the water the manipulation of food in the mouth is a relatively simple matter; on land, food materials are more difficult to deal with. With the reduction of the gills in tetrapods, the gill bars and their muscles became available for other uses, and the mobile tongue characteristic of most land vertebrates developed. The tongue musculature, we have noted, is derived from the hypobranchial musculature, and the tongue is anchored at its base by a skeletal system—the hyoid apparatus—formed of a series of modified gill bars.

Apart from its normal use in handling food, the tongue serves various minor functions: in mammals it is the major bearer of taste buds; in man it is an aid to speech; cornified tongue papillae aid in the manipulation of food, and so forth. In a number of groups the tongue may elongate and take on an active role in the gathering of food, particularly insect food. Thus, while some anurans are tongueless, common frog and toad types are able to flip out an elongate tongue (attached anteriorly, free at the back) to pick up an insect with its sticky tip. The chameleon's tongue can be protruded and retracted with lightning rapidity for the same purpose. The tongue is well developed in snakes and some lizards, and may be used (as noted later) as an accessory olfactory organ; on the other hand, it is poorly developed in turtles and crocodilians. In the woodpeckers the tongue is extremely elongate, and in mammals several types of termite eaters and anteaters have similar adaptations. In some cases a modest expansion or protrusion of the tongue may be caused by filling of blood sinuses or lymph sac, but rapid tongue expansion can be caused only by muscular action. In the woodpeckers extension is brought about through the protrusion by hyoid muscles of an extremely elongate but slender and flexible basihyal element; there is a special bony tube curving around the occiput and forward on the upper skull surface for reception of this rod when withdrawn.

Mouth Glands. In fishes there are numerous mucus-secreting cells in the mouth epithelium. Seldom, however, is there any marked development of formed mouth glands. One of the few exceptions is a special gland in the lamprey, the secretion of which tends to prevent coagulation of the blood of its prey.

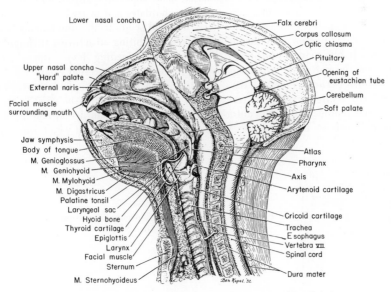

Fig. 209. Median section of the head and neck of a rhesus monkey. (After Geist.)

In water dwellers the water itself is a major aid in the moistening and swallowing of food. In land vertebrates, in the absence of a water medium, *salivary glands* make their appearance (they tend, however, to be secondarily reduced in groups which have returned to an aquatic existence). Such glands in general secrete mucin and a more watery material to produce the saliva.

In amphibians such glands are relatively poorly developed, but mucous glands are usually to be found on the tongue, and there is normally a large median *intermaxillary gland* in the anterior part of the palate. Reptiles have a series of small mucous glands along the lips, on the palate, and on and beneath the tongue. Modified salivary glands form the poison glands of the snakes and the Gila monster (the one poisonous lizard); the gland opening lies at the base of the poison fang, whence the venom passes into the wound via a duct or groove in the substance of the tooth. Many birds, particularly water-feeders, are almost devoid of mouth glands, but in others an abundant series of mucous glands may be present. Highly developed salivary glands are present in mammals; most prominent are the *parotid* and *submaxillary glands*, and the *sublingual*, lying in the cheek region and opening into the mouth above and below by long ducts. For the most part, salivary glands lack chemically active materials; but in some frogs, many birds, and a number of mammals (man included) there is present in the saliva an enzyme—*ptyalin*—which initiates starch digestion. True digestion appears to have been confined exclusively to more posterior regions of the digestive tube in the lower vertebrates; in the salivary enzyme we find an advance guard of the enzyme army present at the portals of the alimentary canal.

DENTITION

Although the *teeth* are in reality modified parts of the dermal skeletal materials, they may be appropriately discussed here, since they are "inhabitants" of the oral cavity. Teeth are unknown in lower chordates and in jawless vertebrates, living or fossil. With the advent of jaws, it would seem, teeth simultaneously appeared. Their presence made the jaws useful as biting structures; through the changed habits made possible by this new type of feeding device the way was paved for the rise of the gnathostome vertebrates to their present estate.

Tooth Structure (Fig. 210). In their simplest and presumably most primitive form, teeth are conical structures of a type such as may be seen in many fishes and reptiles and in the anterior part of the mammalian dental battery. Frequently, however, more complex forms appear, notably teeth in which the upper

Fig. 210. Sections through a mammalian incisor, *A*, and molar, *B*. (After Weber.)

surface is more or less flattened to form a *crown* for crushing or chewing food materials. In the interior of a tooth is a *pulp cavity*, with soft materials including small blood vessels and nerves. At the base there may be present one or more *roots*, processes by which the tooth may be firmly implanted in the jaw.

The major tooth materials are enamel (or an enamel-like substance) and dentine. *Enamel*, as found in mammal teeth, is exceptionally hard and shiny in appearance and generally forms a thin layer over the tooth surface. It is almost entirely devoid of organic matter. Two thirds of its substance consists, as seen in mammals, of long prisms of calcium phosphate, arranged with their axes at right angles to the surface; most of the remainder is a filling of similar material between the prisms. *Dentine* forms the main bulk of the tooth. It is almost identical with bone in chemical composition; about two thirds of its substance is a deposit of a form of calcium phosphate, laid down in a fibrous matrix. Structurally, however, dentine differs notably from bone. There are no cell bodies within its substance; the cells, *odontoblasts*, are, instead, arranged in a layer in the pulp cavity at the base of the dentine. From them a series of long slender parallel tubules pass outward through the dentine. In mammals the teeth are implanted in deep sockets and attached firmly to the bony jaw by a spongy, bonelike material, *cement*.

There are numerous variations from this typical mammalian tooth structure. In many mammals the enamel, instead of forming a continuous surface layer, is penetrated by tubules reaching the tooth surface, and in reptiles the prismatic structure is absent. Further, although the teeth of lower vertebrates is almost always covered by a hard shiny material, this material is probably not, in most cases, to be considered as truly homologous with enamel. True enamel (as described later in this section) is formed by ectodermal cells. But in such fishes as have been studied with regard to tooth development and in some amphibians, the outer shiny layer is formed by the mesoderm, as is the dentine, and is thus merely a hard outer layer of that material—*vitrodentine*. In some forms the dentine is nourished directly by capillaries rather than by tubules from the odontoblasts. In some lower vertebrates the teeth may be, as in mammals, implanted in deep sockets (although almost never with the multiple roots found in the cheek teeth of mammals). This is the *thecodont* condition (Fig. 211). Usually, however, the socket is a shallow one; but there is generally a cement-like material binding tooth and jaw bone. In some forms the tooth may be fused (as in Sphenodon and most teleosts) to the outer surface of the bone or the summit of the jaws—the *acrodont* type. A further variation is the *pleurodont* condition, common in lizards; where the tooth is attached by one side on to the inner surface of the jaw elements. In sharks, in the absence of bone, the teeth are attached to the jaw cartilages by fibrous ligaments, and ligamentous attachment is present in some teleosts and lizards, and in snakes.

Tooth Position. At the top and bottom of the series of tooth-bearing vertebrates—in mammals on the one hand and sharks on the other—we find the functioning teeth limited to a single marginal series along each upper and lower

Fig. 211. Diagrammatic sections through reptilian lower jaws to show the distinction between thecodont, *A*, pleurodont, *B*, and acrodont, *C*, tooth attachments.

jaw. Such marginal teeth are to be found in representatives of every class of gnathostomes, and are the most important element in the vertebrate dental equipment.

It must be noted, however, that in many groups teeth are by no means confined to the jaw margins. Wherever ectoderm is present, teeth or toothlike dermal structures may be found,* the mouth is lined with epidermis derived from the skin ectoderm; and in a wide variety of bony fishes, amphibians, and reptiles teeth are found in the mouth cavity internal to the marginal series. Teeth are present on the palatal elements of the mouth roof in many members of these groups, on the parasphenoid bone underlying the braincase, and on the inner surface of the lower jaw. In many fishes and amphibians certain of the teeth on the palate are large and may form a row paralleling the marginal teeth (cf. Figs. 151, *B*, p. 220; 152, *D*, p. 221). We have noted (p. 223) that the shark jaws are not identical with the jaw margins of bony fishes and tetrapods, but instead appear to correspond to palatal structures. This suggests that the marginal teeth of sharks are not really identical with the marginal row of higher vertebrates, but are homologous with the palatal tooth rows of other groups.

We assumed above that the ectodermal lining of the digestive tube gives way to endoderm, in the adult as in the embryo, at about the boundary between mouth and pharynx. Conditions in actinopterygians, however, more than suggest that there the ectoderm, with its tooth-forming potentialities, grows back into the pharyngeal region. In teleosts the maxilla is toothless, and in some the entire marginal dentition disappears. In compensation, there is a high degree of development of teeth in the inner parts of the mouth cavity, and also of *pharyngeal teeth* situated on the bony elements of the visceral arch system.

Tooth Development and Replacement. Except for the true enamel of higher vertebrates, the entire tooth structure is mesodermal in origin. It is, nonetheless, the ectoderm which appears to be the active agent in tooth development. The first embryologic indication of the appearance of teeth is an infolding of the ectoderm. In marginal tooth rows (on which most developmental studies have been made) this is a continuous furrow the length of the jaw, a *dentinal lamina*, from which individual *tooth germs* develop (Fig. 212). In later stages of development the dental lamina is reduced and does not reach the surface of the mouth. Usually, however, there persists a strand of tissue deep within the jaw connecting successive tooth germs. As will be seen presently this longitudinal connection of tooth germs is important as regards tooth replacement. If, as is the case in most lower vertebrates, there is to be a continuous succession of teeth during life, the germinal material is not used directly in tooth formation. Instead, the tooth germs remain protected, well below the jaw surface, while successive teeth take their origin from bits of tissue which bud off from them and gradually move upward toward the surface. These tooth buds typically form as cones or cups, hollow below, which outline the crown form of the future tooth. On the lower surfaces lies a special series of cells—*ameloblasts*—which in higher vertebrates secrete the enamel; from this fact the tooth bud is frequently termed the *enamel organ*. (This is a rather unfortunate term, for enamel formation is at best a minor function of the ectodermal tooth bud.) Within the hollow of the bud there gathers a mass of mesenchymal cells—the *odontoblasts*. These form an embryonic tooth pulp, a

---

* Teeth are found outside the mouth in the sawfish (Pristis) and saw shark (Pristiophorus), elasmobranchs with a long, slender, forward-projecting rostrum which bears a long row of teeth on each margin.

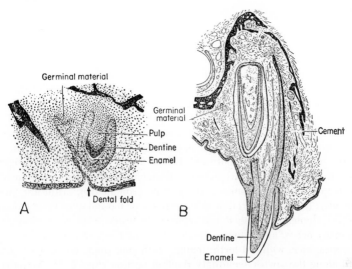

Fig. 212. Two sections of a crocodilian upper jaw to show tooth development in lower tetrapods. *A*, Embryo with a first tooth developing and germinal material in reserve at the base of the dental fold. *B*, Mature animal; a tooth is functioning, but is being resorbed at the inner side of the root, where the next successional tooth is already in process of formation. Germinal material for successional teeth persists. (After Röse.)

dental papilla with which small blood vessels and nerves become associated. Stimulated by the presence of the enamel organ, the odontoblasts proceed with the task of dentine deposition, and in lower vertebrates form a superficial enamel-like material as well. They become, at the end of growth, cells of the pulp cavity. As the tooth takes shape, it works toward the surface and erupts into functional position. In forms with continuous tooth succession each tooth eventually becomes subject to resorption at its base and is shed from the jaw. Meanwhile, one or more successional buds have already formed from the germinal material and push outward as replacements.

The prominence of the ectoderm in tooth development is in agreement with our general ideas of the phylogenetic origin of teeth. It has long been recognized that teeth and the dermal denticles of the shark skin (cf. Fig. 97, p. 157) are essentially similar in nature and hence presumably homologous. Mouth lining and body skin are comparable in origin, both being formed from ectoderm and connective tissues gathered beneath it. They hence may be expected to develop homologous structures.

It was once thought that teeth originated directly from dermal denticles which lay in the margins of the mouth overlying the forming jaws. Our current conceptions of the nature of the primitive fish as having a bony external skeleton demands a modification of this idea. We have noted that the surfaces of the plates shielding the body of primitive fishes (Fig. 96, *A*, p. 156) are frequently ornamented with tubercles resembling both shark denticles and primitive teeth. Shark denticles, we have said, appear to represent the last surviving parts of these plates in the skin of modern sharks; the deeper layers have, so to speak, melted away in the course of evolutionary history. When jaws evolved in ancient fishes, dermal plates were present along the jaw margins. The denticles present on these jaw plates became the teeth. Teeth and dermal denticles are thus, in modern concepts, still regarded as homologous. Teeth are not, however, derived from denticles; instead, both are modified derivations of tubercles found in the dermal bony plates of armored ancestral vertebrates.

In mammals (as we are well aware) there is no tooth replacement apart from the succession of "permanent" teeth for a "milk dentition" in the front of the mouth. Far different is the situation in most other vertebrates. Little is known of the replacement of teeth found on the palate and inside of the jaw in many bony fishes, amphibians and reptiles, and certain of the large tooth plates present in various fishes and reptiles appear to undergo little if any replacement. But as regards the major, marginal dentition of most fishes, amphibians, and reptiles, it is clear that tooth replacement continues through life. Teeth are constantly being formed deep within the tissues of the germs, grow in size, erupt and function, and presently, through resorption at their bases or loosening of their connections with the jaw elements, are shed and replaced by a new tooth generation.

In many fishes, amphibians, and reptiles the tooth row has a seemingly irregular appearance, with old teeth, mature teeth, and young teeth, newly erupted, scattered along the jaw in seemingly random fashion (Fig. 213). Actually there is method in this seeming madness. Replacement is taking place in an interesting way which guarantees a continuous function of the dentition despite frequent renewal of individual teeth. The teeth and tooth germs give the impression of be-

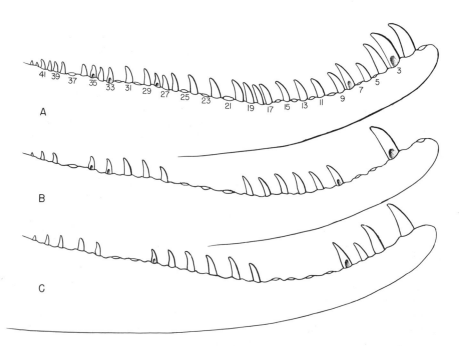

Fig. 213.   Inner surface of the lower jaw of a primitive fossil reptile (Ophiacodon) to show the alternation in tooth replacement between odd and even tooth series. The gaps in the tooth row seem haphazard at first sight; however, if the two series be considered separately, as in *B* and *C*, it will be seen that each includes several waves of replacement arranged in a regular alternating manner. (Certain teeth —3, 8, 28, 33, 35—show resorption at the root and are at the point of being lost.)

ing arranged in two series, the "odds" and "evens" in each tooth row. One may find a condition in which, for example, in a given area of the jaw, the odd-numbered teeth are functional; between them, in place of the even-numbered ones, are sockets beneath which new teeth are in process of formation. Later this region may show a condition in which both sets of teeth are in place at the same time, but the odd set shows evidence of age and wear. Still a bit later, the odd-numbered teeth will drop out, leaving the even series the functional set, and so on. This neat device guarantees that at least half the teeth in any region will be functioning at any given time.

The situation is complicated by the fact that replacement appears to take place in waves which travel along the jaw rami; at a given time the "even" set may be functioning in some areas of the jaw ramus, the "odd" set in others. Still further complicating and puzzling is the fact that in series of "odd" and "even" teeth over a segment of the jaw, the oldest teeth of a series are frequently at the back, the youngest at the front. This suggests that tooth formation travels from back to front. But one is loathe to believe that this is true; in general, development of structures of any sort in a vertebrate proceeds from front to back, and this is certainly true of the teeth of mammals. How can we solve this puzzle? What is the real principle governing this rhythmic replacement?

Recent study of reptile and amphibian dentition has resulted in a hypothesis which gives a reasonable solution—to the effect that tooth replacement results from waves of stimulation which proceed (properly) from the front of the tooth row to the back and that the alternating appearance of "odds" and "evens" is simply due to the spacing between successive waves.

The probable situation is that shown in Figure 214. In *a* and *b*, the horizontal lines represent the persistent strand of tissue connecting successive tooth germs in many vertebrates, the vertical lines the distance from the level of the tooth germs up to the surface of the jaw. In *a1* it is assumed that an impulse for tooth formation has begun at the most anterior germ position, and a tooth rudiment (or anlage, represented diagrammatically by a black dot) has formed. In *a2* the impulse has travelled to the next position and started a second rudiment; meanwhile the first embryonic tooth in position one (represented by a small cir-

Fig. 214. Diagrams (discussed in the text) to show the mode of tooth replacement in typical lower vertebrates. (After Edmund.)

cle) has grown somewhat and moved up a bit toward the mouth surface. The stimulus continues to travel backward, initiating tooth development at successive positions until, in the diagram at *a8*, this first stimulus has produced a row of teeth of which the first (represented by a large circle) has reached maturity. But meanwhile a second stimulus, spaced somewhat more than two tooth germs behind the first, has followed, and a third has just made its appearance.

If this sequence be continued, the mature jaw will obviously come to have the structure diagrammatically shown in *b*, and as seen in side view, in Figure *c*. Here there is, at first sight, a seemingly irregular arrangement of old, mature, and young teeth and tooth germs of various sizes; but, as we have just seen, the underlying principle is a simple and orderly one. In the example just cited, the *apparent* sequence in "odd" and "even" series (as in one shown in black in *c*) is back to front—the reverse of the true situation. This appearance is due to the (seemingly inconsequential) fact that the spacing between impulses is assumed to be somewhat greater than two tooth germ intervals. If the spacing were exactly two intervals, there would be an exact alternation of odd and even series the length of the jaw. And if (heaven forbid!) the reader wishes to make the necessary diagrams, he will see that making the interval between impulses somewhat less than two units will result in seeming front to back waves in both series.

Teeth in Fishes.   No teeth are present in lower chordates or in jawless vertebrates. The early fossil ostracoderms presumably gained their food by straining particles from the water current passing through their gill systems; teeth were unnecessary and could not function in the absence of jaws. The larval lamprey is likewise a food strainer. The adult cyclostomes prey on fishes and have, in the rasping "tongue," a jaw substitute. This is armed (as is the mouth cavity as well in the lamprey) with conical pointed toothlike structures. These, however, are not true teeth, but consist of cornified epithelium. In the extinct placoderms teeth as well as jaws made their appearance. In some acanthodians simple sharklike teeth were present; in the arthrodires teeth are sometimes found fused to the jaw plates, but in general these ancient fishes relied for biting purposes on sharp cutting edges on the jawbones themselves.

The most generalized type of tooth is that of a simple cone. In sharks the tooth is sometimes of this type, although usually with accessory cusps fore and

Fig. 215.   The lower jaws of a primitive living shark, Heterodontus (Cestracion), the Port Jackson shark of the Pacific. The teeth differ greatly between front and back parts of the jaw. Rows of successional teeth are formed down within the inner surface of the jaws. (From Dean.)

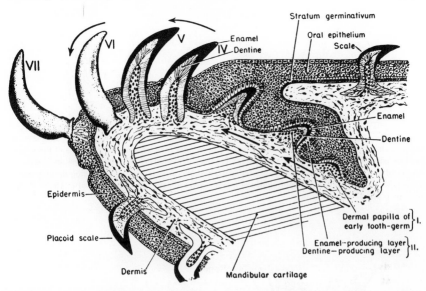

Fig. 216. Section through the jaw of a shark, to show stages (I–VII) in the development of a tooth to its functional stage and to the point where it is about to be shed (VII). For comparison, placoid scales (denticles) in the adjacent epithelium are shown as well. (From Rand, The Chordates, The Blakiston Company.)

aft. Frequently, however, the tooth is lengthened from front to back at the base, giving a triangular shape; anterior and posterior margins may be sharp and serrate. Flattened teeth have developed for crushing "shellfish" in such forms as the Port Jackson shark (Fig. 215), and many skates and rays develop a crushing battery of such teeth. In a shark (Fig. 216) the teeth develop in the soft tissues on the inner surface of the jaws, and in a dried specimen a whole series of successional teeth can usually be seen (Fig. 215); each tooth generation (usually with the familiar odd-and-even alternation) gradually swings up into position on the jaw margins and is eventually shed. In many rays advantage is taken of the early development of successional teeth to incorporate them in an expanded crushing battery for mollusk feeding. In chimaeras, likewise primarily shellfish eaters, the dentition is, in contrast, reduced to a pair of large crushing plates in both upper and lower jaws and an accessory pair of small upper plates (Fig. 217, *A*). An analogous development is present in lungfishes (Fig. 217, *B*); the marginal teeth are lost, and the dentition typically consists of four fan-shaped compound dental plates (plus an accessory upper pair). In the living Epiceratodus of Australia the tooth plates exhibit a series of smooth radiating ridges; the embryonic and phylogenetic stories agree in showing that each ridge is composed of a fused row of originally discrete conical teeth. Among actinopterygians the conical tooth shape is primary. In teleosts the cement-like material joining the tooth and jaw bone may form a massive base for the tooth as essentially a separate bone of attachment (Fig. 218). In many instances large "fangs" are attached to the jaw by an elastic hinge, bending inward to allow the prey to enter the mouth but opposing its escape. In higher actinopterygians the maxilla becomes toothless, and in some teleosts the marginal dentition disappears entirely; reliance is placed on

A   B   C   D

Fig. 217. *A*, Dorsal view of the lower jaws of a chimaera, to show the pair of large tooth plates, of complex shape, which cover most of their surface. *B*, Similar view of the bony elements of the jaws of the lungfish Epiceratodus, to show the pair of fan-shaped toothplates. *C*, External view of a grooved labyrinthine tooth characteristic of crossopterygians and ancestral tetrapods. *D*, Section through such a tooth to show the complicated folding of the enamel layer (heavy black line). (*A* after Dean; *B* after Watson; *C* and *D* after Bystrow.)

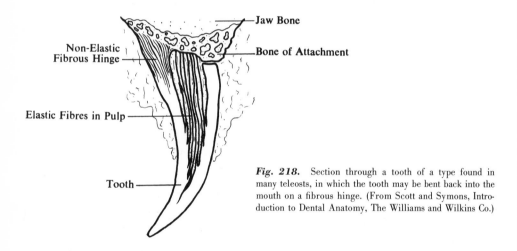

Fig. 218. Section through a tooth of a type found in many teleosts, in which the tooth may be bent back into the mouth on a fibrous hinge. (From Scott and Symons, Introduction to Dental Anatomy, The Williams and Wilkins Co.)

palatal and pharyngeal teeth. Such teeth may become flattened and numerous, forming an efficient grinding mill; in one catfish genus there are said to be 9000 of such teeth. Many ancient crossopterygians were notable for the presence of longitudinal grooves on the teeth; these represent infoldings of the enamel, often of complicated pattern, giving the tooth in cross section a labyrinthine appearance (Fig. 207, *C, D*).

Teeth in Tetrapods. This crossopterygian tooth type is repeated in many of the oldest amphibians; it is so prominent a feature that it gives the name Labyrinthodontia to the ancestral amphibian group. The marginal teeth were generally highly developed, and in addition there were powerful palatal fangs. In modern amphibians, living on small and soft materials the teeth are small and simple in structure, and are entirely absent in some toads. A curious feature of the teeth in most modern forms is the presence of a zone of weak calcification near the tooth bases, so that frequently in prepared skeletal specimens only the stumps of the teeth are preserved.

In a majority of reptiles the teeth are essentially of the simple conical type, although somewhat flattened teeth are found in some lizards and crocodilians, and flat tooth plates were present in some fossil forms. Palatal teeth were present in ancestral reptiles and are preserved in Sphenodon, snakes, and lizards; such teeth are absent in crocodilians. Turtles have lost their teeth, relying instead on a horny bill. Ancestral reptiles generally had teeth inserted in shallow sockets, and typical thecodont teeth are seen in crocodiles. Most lizards, however, have a pleurodont type of tooth attachment, and some lizards (including chameleons) are acrodont, as is Sphenodon. Snake tooth attachments are ligamentous. The primitive bird Archaeopteryx was toothed, but the bill (plus gizzard stones) has replaced the dentition functionally in later birds.

In the fossil mammal-like reptiles are seen stages in the initiation of the mammalian type of dentition. The most ancient members of this series, the pelycosaurs, show the development of large upper stabbing teeth comparable to mammalian canines, separating incisors anteriorly from a series of cheek teeth (Fig. 164, *A*, p. 235); various therapsids (Fig. 164, *B, C*) show further stages in the evolution of a mammal-like dentition.

Tooth Differentiation in Mammals. In mammals the teeth are reduced to a short marginal series in each jaw half, above and below. In the more generalized members of the class, four tooth types can be distinguished in the adult in anteroposterior order (Fig. 219, *A*). Most anteriorly are the *incisors*, nipping teeth with a simple conical or chisel-like build. Next in each series is a single *canine*, primitively a long, stout, deep-rooted tooth with a conical shape and sharp point, useful in attacking a carnivore's prey. Following the canine is a series of *premolars* (the "bicuspids" of the dentist), which frequently show a degree of grinding surface on the crown, and finally, a *molar* series, the members of which generally assume a chewing function and develop a complex crown pattern.

In early fossil mammals the number of teeth in these various categories appears to have been rather variable and the total number rather higher than in living forms. The primitive placentals, however, had settled down to a count in which there were present in each half of both upper and lower jaws three incisors, one canine, four premolars, and three molars. Few animals today retain precisely this number. But while there is often a reduction of teeth in one or several categories, there is seldom any increase over the primitive placental number (some whales and porpoises are conspicuous exceptions). There has been devised a simple "shorthand" for the nomenclature of placental teeth, and a for-

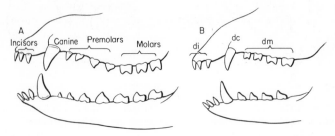

Fig. 219. Left side view of the dentition of a generalized placental mammal, showing permanent dentition in *A*; *B*, deciduous teeth. *dc*, Deciduous canine; *di*, deciduous incisors; *dm*, "milk molars" (= deciduous premolars).

mula to express the number of teeth present in any mammal. The letters *I, C, P,* and *M,* followed by a number in an upper or lower position will define any tooth in terms of the original placental formula: I^1, for example, refers to the most anterior upper incisor; M_3, the last lower molar. The number of teeth of each type present, above and below, in the dental equipment of any mammal can be formulated in succinct fashion. The *dental formula* $\frac{3.1.4.3}{3.1.4.3}$ indicates that in either side of both upper and lower jaws the primitive placental number of teeth is present (the four successive figures represent the number of incisors, canines, premolars, and molars present). The total number of teeth present in the mouth of such an animal is forty-four. The human formula is $\frac{2.1.2.3}{2.1.2.3}$; i.e., we have lost an incisor and two premolars of the primitive placental series from each half of each jaw and reduced our teeth to a total count of thirty-two.

Incisor teeth, useful in nearly any mode of life, are retained in most mammalian groups. Various herbivores, however, have evolved specialized cropping devices in which the incisors are modified or lost. Ruminants, such as cows, sheep, and deer, have, for example, lost the upper incisors, but retained the lower ones (Fig. 220, *B*); the elephant's tusks are greatly elongated upper incisors. Rodents have developed a pair of upper and of lower incisors as gnawing chisels which grow persistently throughout life at their roots as their tips are worn away.

Canines are primitively prominent biting and piercing weapons and as such are emphasized in carnivores; they reached their peak in the now-extinct sabertooth "tigers" (Fig. 220, *A*). In nonpredaceous mammals the canines are sometimes prominent, and are used in defense or, in males, in mating battles. More often, however, they are reduced (as in man) and are insignificant or absent in most herbivores.

The cheek teeth—the premolars and molars—whose patterns are discussed below, have a varied history. In herbivorous forms, such as the ungulate groups, these teeth are generally retained (except for frequent loss of the first premolar).

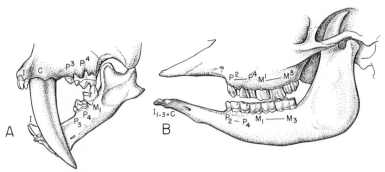

Fig. 220. Two specialized mammalian dental types. *A*, Felid; *B*, the cow. (For the felid, the extinct saber-tooth, with extreme specialization, is shown.) In the felids the dentition is much reduced; there are modest incisors and lower canine (concealed in the figure) and stabbing upper canine. In the cheek little remains except the carnassials $\frac{(P^4)}{(M_1)}$. In the ruminants the cheek teeth are expanded into a grinding battery; they are separated by a diastema from the cropping teeth—here consisting only of lower incisors and canine, working against a horny pad on the upper jaw.

Fig. 221. Diagrams of molar tooth patterns of placental mammals. In all cases, outer edge of tooth above, front edge to right. *A*, Right upper molar of a primitive form. *B*, The same of a type in which the tooth has been "squared up" by addition of a hypocone at the back inner corner. *C*, Left lower molar of a primitive form with five cusps. *D*, The same of a type in which the tooth has been "squared up" by the loss of the paraconid.

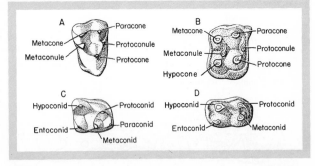

They are usually elaborated to form an efficient grinding battery, which (as may be seen in a horse or cow jaw) becomes separated, spatially as well as functionally, from the cropping teeth by a gap in the tooth row—a *diastema* (Fig. 220, *B*). In carnivores in which there is little or no chewing of food the cheek teeth are generally reduced in number—strongly so in the cat family.

Mammalian Molar Patterns. In mammals the cheek teeth, particularly the molars, generally develop an expanded crown with a varied and complicated pattern of projecting cusps—a structural arrangement which appears to be of major functional value in chewing and grinding food. The variations in this pattern are of diagnostic importance and are of great interest to systematists, paleontologists, and anthropologists, for a single molar tooth will often furnish precise generic or even specific identification of the animal to which it pertains. Such patterns have been much studied, but only the general features will be noted here (Figs. 221, 222).

The nomenclature used is basically simple. Each cusp is termed a *cone*. The names of specific cones are formed by adding the prefixes *proto-, para-, meta-, hypo-,* and *ento-;* and, where necessary, by suffixes: *-ul(e)* indicates a minor cusp, and *-id* a lower jaw element. The term *cingulum* is applied to accessory ridges of enamel around the margins of cheek teeth, the term *style* to vertical marginal ridges.

Neglecting some variations in pattern among early fossil mammals and among marsupials, we find that the earliest and most primitive of placentals have upper molar crowns in the general shape of a right-angled triangle, with two cusps along the outer edge of the tooth row and the right angle at the antero-external margin. There are three major cusps, the *protocone* at the apex, the *paracone* and *metacone* along the external border. Between the protocone and the external cusps is usually found a pair of conules (with which we shall not here concern ourselves further).

The primitive lower molar has as its major portion a high, well-developed triangular area—the *trigonid*—which has a pattern similar to that of the upper molar, but reversed; there is an external apex, the *protoconid,* and an internal base, where *paraconid* and *metaconid* are present. If upper and lower teeth are fitted properly together—that is, placed in *occlusion* (Fig. 222, *B*)—it will be seen that each lower tooth (which lies somewhat internal and to the front of its upper mate) would bite past its neighbors above without meeting them effectively, if it consisted only of a trigonid. This situation is prevented through the fact that

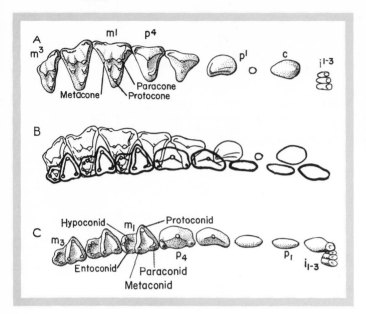

Fig. 222. Diagrams of the dentition of a primitive placental mammal (based on the Eocene insectivore Didelphodus). *A,* Crown view of right upper teeth; *C,* crown view of left lower teeth; between, in *B,* the teeth are placed in occlusion, the outlines of the lower teeth (heavy lines) superposed on those of the uppers. (After Gregory.)

each lower tooth has, posteriorly, a second crown portion, a *talonid,* primitively lower and less developed than the anterior part of the tooth, and bearing two additional cusps, *hypoconid* (externally) and *entoconid* (internally). The protocone of the upper tooth bites into the basin of the talonid, and proper occlusion is effected. We thus have a generalized primitive tooth pattern of cheek teeth with three main upper cusps and five lower ones. The full pattern is present in the molars. Passing forward in the premolar series, the pattern tends to become more simplified and approaches the essentially conical shape of the canine and incisors.

In primitive placental mammals the cusps were sharp-pointed structures, well adapted to deal with insects and similar food materials, and some living insectivores still have teeth of this sort. Most modern mammals, however, have departed widely from this primitive pattern and have evolved a variety of tooth types which can be discussed only in summary fashion here. Carnivores which tend to reduce the number of cheek teeth generally preserve a simple and primitive pattern in those which remain. Notable, however, is the development in the carnivore cheek of a pair of sharp-crested, shearing teeth which deal with tendons and bones—the *carnassial teeth,* the last premolar in either upper jaw shearing against the first lower molar (Fig. 220, *A*).

The premolars generally remain simpler than the molars in cusp pattern. In certain herbivores, however, they are "molarized"—that is, assume a molar-like cusp pattern; this is exemplified in the horse. Generally there has been a "squaring up" of the molars in herbivores by alterations in the cusps present (Fig. 221, *B, D*). In the originally triangular upper molars there is often added a fourth cusp, a *hypocone,* at the back inner corner, to turn the triangular tooth into a rectangular one. Below, a four-square condition is attained, not by adding a cusp, but by dropping one—the paraconid at the anterior edge of the trigonid.

In mammals with a mixed diet (such as men and swine) the cheek tooth cusps tend to become low and rounded, forming small hillocks on the crown—

A   B   C

Fig. 223. Crown views of molar teeth of *A*, rhinoceros; *B*, horse; *C*, ox; to show types of molar patterns. The white areas are worn surfaces showing dentine; the black line surrounding the white is the worn edge of the enamel; stippled areas, cement covering or unworn surface. *A* is a simple lophodont type, with an external ridge (above) and two cross ridges; the development of this pattern by connecting up the cusps seen in Figure 221, *B* can be readily followed. The horse (*B*) shows a development of the same pattern into a more complex form in which the primitive lophodont pattern is obscured. *C* shows a selenodont pattern characteristic of the ruminants; each of four main cusps takes on a crescentic shape.

the *bunodont* type. In many ungulates which have taken up a herbivorous mode of life the cusp pattern has become complicated; individual cusps may, for example, assume a crescentic outline, a *selenodont* pattern; or cusps may connect to form ridges, the *lophodont* condition (Fig. 223).

Grazing habits present a serious "problem" to an ungulate, for grass is a hard, gritty material which rapidly wears down the surface of a grinding tooth. If the low-crowned tooth of a primitive mammal were retained in a large grazing mammal, it would be worn to the roots in a short time. In relation to this we find in such hoofed mammals as the horses and cattle the development of a high-crowned and prism-shaped tooth—the *hypsodont* condition (Fig. 224). One could, in imagination, develop a high-crowned tooth by elongation of the dentine-filled bulk of the tooth body, with the cusps in their original shape on the grinding surface. This type of high-crowned tooth did form in some early fossil mammals, but has generally proved unsuccessful. Once the enamel surface is worn away, most of the wear comes on the relatively soft and easily abraded dentine; the resistant enamel remains only as a thin rim. Successful hypsodont forms have teeth built on quite another plan. The height is attained by a skyscraper-like growth of each cusp or ridge on the tooth; these slender peaks are fused together by a growth of cement over the entire tooth surface before eruption. As wear takes place, it grinds down through a resistant complex of layers of all the tooth materials—enamel, dentine, and cement.

In mammals tooth renewal (to the regret of all except dentists) is a much reduced process; there is only one replacing set, and that is incomplete, for the most posterior—molar—teeth have no successors. We usually think of the mam-

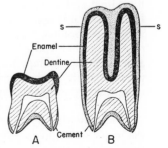

Fig. 224. Diagrams to show the development of a hypsodont tooth. *A*, Normal low-crowned tooth (cf. Fig. 210). *B*, Hypsodont tooth, with cusps elevated and the whole covered by cement. As a tooth of this sort wears down to any level, such as that indicated at *s-s*, it will be seen that no less than nine successive layers of contrasting materials are present across the crown surface.

Fig. 225. Diagram to show the composition of the "permanent" dentition of a mammal; left upper teeth of a generalized placental mammal. One complete set of teeth (I) develops from incisors back to molars. All of these except the molars, however, are shed (as indicated by stipple). A second set of teeth develops (II), but never produces molars. Hence the "permanent" dentition includes portions of two tooth series (cf. Fig. 219).

malian dentition as comprised of a set of "milk" teeth—a *deciduous* or lacteal dentition—which has no molars included, and a complete permanent set (Fig. 219, p. 311). If, however, we consider the development of the teeth we gain a different concept (Fig. 225). The "milk" teeth, in a typical mammal (man is representative), usually develop successively in anteroposterior order from incisors to deciduous premolars or "milk molars" (the canines, with long roots, may lag in eruption). After the appearance of the last "milk molar" there begins the successive eruption of the three molar teeth. Meanwhile, without waiting for the completion of this first wave, the anterior teeth are replaced in order back to the premolars. But the succession proceeds no further, and the molars are not replaced. Obviously, we have one complete set of teeth and a partial second set; the molars, although permanent, belong in series to the set which, farther forward, is deciduous in nature. An adult mammal thus has in its mouth parts of two dental series; the molars are part of the first set, the more anterior teeth belong to the second set. This concept explains various peculiarities such as the fact (well known to paleontologists and anthropologists) that the molars in many cases resemble much more closely the short-lived "milk molars" than they do the permanent premolars which they adjoin for most of the span of life.

GILLS

The *pharynx* is a short and unimportant segment of the digestive tract in the higher vertebrate classes—a minor connecting piece between mouth and esophagus where ventrally the *glottis* opens to the lung apparatus, and dorsally the paired *eustachian tubes* lead to the middle ear cavities (Fig. 209, p. 301). In mammals it is merely the place where air and food channels cross one another in awkward fashion, and where there accumulate masses of lymphoid tissues, the *tonsils*. But from both phylogenetic and ontogenetic viewpoints the pharynx is an area of the utmost importance; it is the region from which are developed the gill pouches, basic in the construction of respiratory devices in lower vertebrate classes, and persistently important in the developmental story in higher groups.

The body cells constantly demand oxygen for their metabolic activities and as constantly must be rid of the carbon dioxide, which (with metabolic water) is the major waste product resulting from oxygen utilization. Internal carriage of these gases to and from the cells is by means of the circulatory system. The oxygen source and the carbon dioxide destination is the surrounding medium—water or, in higher groups, air. Exchange of gases—the process of respiration—occurs by diffusion through moist vascularized membranes.

In many small aquatic invertebrates the exchange takes place through the general body surface and this seems to be true in great measure even in Amphi-oxus, where the gill slits appear to have little respiratory function. Such surface exchange may persist among vertebrates, and skin respiration is found here and there in types as far removed from one another as eels and salamanders. In general, however, vertebrates and most multicellular invertebrates have developed special respiratory organs. Skins are often too thick or hard, and too little vascularized to function effectively in respiration; and surface-volume relations generally come into play in animals of any considerable size even when the body surface is competent as an exchange medium. In water dwellers of various phyla, *gills* of one sort or another are developed—structures with a moist, thin surface membrane, richly supplied with blood vessels, and folded in complicated fashion to give a maximum amount of surface for gas exchange.

Among invertebrate groups such gills are usually situated outside the main mass of the body as external gills. In a limited number of cases analogous developments are seen among vertebrates—the external gills of larval fishes and amphibians (described later), projecting gill filaments of other larval fishes, hairlike respiratory growths on the slender pelvic fins of the South American lungfish and on the pelvic limbs of the male "hairy" frog of Africa (Astylosternus), for example. But the characteristic structures of the lower vertebrates—indeed, a most fundamental trademark of almost every chordate—are *internal gills:* respiratory structures located in a series of slits or pockets leading from the pharyngeal region to the outer surface of the body. As the locus of origin of these slits the pharynx is a highly developed and highly important part of the digestive tube in the lower classes of vertebrates.

The Gill System in Sharks.

The characteristic development of the vertebrate gill system is that seen in the sharklike fishes, the Chondrichthyes, on the one hand, and the higher bony fishes on the other. Gill construction in the two groups differs in certain important respects, but the basic pattern is the same.

In the sharks (Fig. 226, *C*) the pharynx is a long, broad duct, continuing backward from the mouth region without break and terminating posteriorly at the constriction whence the short and narrow esophagus leads on to the stomach and intestine. On either side a series of openings runs outward to the surface of the body. Anteriorly, there is generally present a small and specialized paired opening, the spiracle, described later. Back of this point, on either side, are found the typical *gill slits*, five in most sharks, but six or seven in a few special cases. In these slits are found the respiratory organs, the gills. Water is typically brought into the pharynx through the mouth and flows outward through the gill slits; in its passage past the gill surfaces, the respiratory exchange takes place. The term *gill arch** is applied to the tissues lying between successive openings. The region between mouth and spiracle is the *mandibular arch;* that between the spiracle and the first normal gill slit, the *hyoid arch;* more posterior gill arches are generally referred to by number.

---

* There is a source of confusion here, for the term "arch" is often used in three different senses in connection with the gill region. As noted in Chapter 7, it may refer to the series of bars which form the skeleton of each gill segment. The word is also used to describe the arterial blood vessels—aortic arches—which traverse each gill (cf. Chap. 14). In the present chapter it is used in a broader, inclusive sense, to describe the total gill structure lying between two successive gill slits.

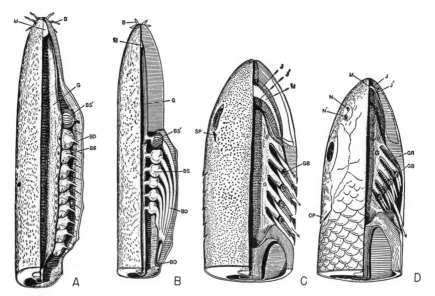

Fig. 226. Heads of various fishes to show gill arrangement. *A*, The slime-hag Bdellostoma; *B*, the hagfish Myxine; *C*, a shark; *D*, a teleost. The right half of each is sectioned horizontally through the pharynx. Abbreviations: *B*, barbels around the mouth; *BD*, ducts from gill pouches; *BO*, common outer openings of gill pouches; *BS*, gill sacs; *BS'*, sacs sectioned to show internal folds of gill; *G*, gut (pharynx); *GB*, cut gill arch; *GR*, gill rakers; *J*, *J'*, upper and lower jaws; *M*, mouth; *N*, *N'*, anterior and posterior openings of nasal chamber; *OP*, operculum; *SP*, spiracle. (From Dean.)

Typical shark respiratory movements are a combination of suction and force pump effects, produced by the action of the branchial muscles described in the preceding chapter. With the mouth open and the external gill openings closed, the pharynx is expanded and water drawn in via the mouth; the pharynx is constricted, and the water forced out through the slits.

Each of the series of gill arches includes a number of characteristic structures (Fig. 227, *A*). Running dorsoventrally, close to the pharyngeal wall, are the skeletal supports, the gill bar elements of the arch; skeletal *gill rakers* may extend inward from them into the cavity of the pharynx, screening food particles from the gills and diverting them backward toward the esophagus; *gill rays* run outward toward the surface, stiffening the gill structure. In each gill arch there is in the embryo a finger-like upward extension of the celomic cavity (Fig. 179, p. 257); this disappears in the adult, but from its mesodermal walls is derived the branchial musculature of the arch (Fig. 190, p. 277). Each gill arch has a set of aortic arch blood vessels which bring blood from heart to gill and carry it thence, after aeration, to the dorsal aorta; (pp. 425–431). Down each gill arch passes a special cranial nerve trunk or branch (cf. Fig. 375, p. 517). Extending outward in the center of each arch is a *gill septum*, a vertical sheet of connective tissue.

The gill passages of elasmobranchs are slits which are narrow anteroposteriorly, deep in a vertical plane; primitively they appear to have opened widely both to the pharynx and to the exterior, but in most forms these entrances and exits are narrowed down to relatively short slits. In sharks the external openings are lateral in position; in skates and rays, with flattened bodies, the gill openings

Fig. 227. Horizontal sections of a gill arch of *A*, a shark; *B*, a teleost. External surface above, pharynx margin below; cartilage or bone in black. In the shark there is a projecting septum, reduced in the teleost.

are on the ventral surface, below the expanded pectoral fins. In elasmobranchs the gill septum and its epithelial covering extend out to the surface of the body as a fold of skin which overlaps and protects the gill next posterior to it.

The gill itself is an elaborately folded and richly vascularized structure, covered with a thin epithelium. The gill surface takes the form of numerous parallel *gill lamellae* which greatly increase the effective surface for exchange. Through them course capillaries, connected at one end with the afferent vessels from the heart and at the other with the efferent vessels leading to the dorsal aorta and thence to head and body. For the most part the gill is, in elasmobranchs, closely attached to the gill septum; at its outer tip, however, it may extend freely for a short distance.

Such a gill may develop as a dorsoventral sheet on either anterior or posterior side of any gill slit, or, stated in another fashion, it may develop on either surface of a gill arch (Fig. 229, *A*). In most cases the gill arch carries a gill on both surfaces of the septum, and such a gill arch is considered to be a "complete" gill, a *holobranch*. Less commonly in fishes, a gill may be developed on only one surface of a gill arch; in this case the term *hemibranch* is applied. No vascular aortic arch is present behind the last gill slit; and, in consequence, there is almost never any gill development on the posterior surface of the last slit. All other typical slits in sharks, however, bear gills on both sides; in terms of gills rather than slits, there are four holobranchs. There is no gill development on the posterior side of the spiracle; hence the hyoid arch behind it is a hemibranch.

The *spiracle* is a gill opening lying between mandibular and hyoid arches which appears to have gained its specialized nature early in the history of jawed vertebrates. We have noted that in typical jawed fishes the hyomandibular element of the hyoid arch has become tied into the jaw joint as an effective prop for the jaws. Presumably the ancestral vertebrates had a fully developed gill slit

Fig. 228. Horizontal sections through the head and pharynx regions in embryos of *A*, a frog (Rana); and *B*, an elasmobranch; to show development of gill pouches. In *A* the pouches are developing as narrow slits, which have not as yet opened to the surface. (The mouth is also closed.) In *B* all the slits except the last one are open. *e*, Esophagus; *eg*, external gill developing; *h*, hyoid arch; *M*, mouth; *m*, mandibular arch; *Ph*, pharynx; *s*, spiracular gill slit; *1* to *5*, postspiracular slits.

between jaws and hyoid arch. When, however, the hyomandibular extended across this area, the slit was necessarily interrupted, and has become restricted to a dorsal opening from throat to surface (Fig. 149, C, p. 217).

But though we may account for the special nature of the spiracle as due to skeletal developments, this opening has a positive functional history. If we survey the sharklike fishes, we find that among the sharks themselves the spiracle is small in many forms and is absent in certain of the more active, fast-swimming genera. On the other hand, some of the more sluggish sharks, which spend much time on the bottom, show a considerable enlargement of the spiracle, and in the depressed, bottom-dwelling skates and rays it is an enormous opening on the dorsal surface behind the eye (Fig. 23, p. 43). This correlation of spiracular development with habits is indicative of the use to which the spiracle is put. In bottom-dwelling elasmobranchs the mouth, the usual point of entrance of the water current, may be more or less buried in mud or sand; the spiracle, dorsally placed, then affords a channel for the inflow of clear water to the gills.

Presumably the spiracular slit, when fully developed, originally carried a typical pair of gills. Even in its reduced state a small gill structure is generally to be found on the anterior side of the spiracle—that is, on the posterior surface of the jaw arch. This gill, however, is of a peculiar nature. Every proper gill receives blood for aeration directly from the heart by way of one of the aortic arches. But though such an aortic vessel runs to the mandibular gill arch in the shark embryo, it disappears before the adult stage is reached, and this little spiracular gill is supplied by blood that has already been purified by passage through the gills behind it (Fig. 309, B, p. 427). It is, thus, a deceptive "imitation" gill— a *pseudobranch*. It may, however, serve some useful purpose, for the blood from this gill passes, in the shark, to eye and brain, where a supply of "superpure," doubly oxygenated blood is presumably of especial importance.

The chimaeras, although related to the sharks and skates, show certain notable differences (Fig. 22, C, p. 42; 24, p. 44; 229, B). The spiracle has been lost, and the last gill slit is closed. A major contrast lies in the system of gill protection. In sharks, it was noted, a skin fold is developed from each gill arch. In chimaeras, in contrast, there is but a single large skin flap, which grows backward from the hyoid arch and covers the entire gill series; skin folds and supporting rays have been reduced on the more posterior arches. This protective device is an *operculum;* with its development we find but a single outer gill opening on either side of the body at the back end of the gill region. Comparable developments are found in both higher and lower fish types.

Gill Development (Fig. 228).   The gill slits of elasmobranchs arise embryologically in a fashion characteristic of vertebrates generally. Early in development paired pouches push out from the endodermal lining of the anterior end of the embryonic gut. Extending toward the surface, they interrupt the continuity of the mesodermal plates of this region and come in contact with infoldings of the surface ectoderm. Presently the intervening membranes break down, and ectoderm and endoderm join to form a continuous lining for the gill slits. After this occurs the development of gill structures along the lining of the slits.

In both Chondrichthyes and bony fishes the gills appear to be formed from the ectodermal part of the epithelium of the slits. In cyclostomes, exceptionally, the evidence suggests that gill formation is endodermal (but the evidence for this has been questioned). Some have argued that if cyclostome gills are of endodermal derivation, they cannot be truly homologous with those of other fishes. How-

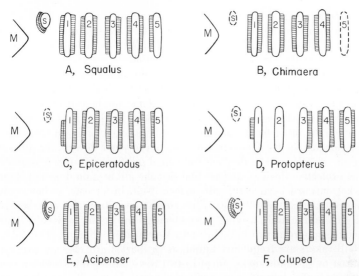

Fig. 229. Diagrams to show the gill arrangement. *A*, Shark; *B*, a chimaera; *C*, the Australian lungfish; *D*, the African lungfish; *E*, sturgeon; *F*, a teleost (herring). Broken line indicates a closed slit. Hatched area adjoining slit indicates gill surface; vertical line through hatching indicates pseudobranch. The presence in Protopterus of a gill surface on the posterior side of the last slit is unique. *M*, mouth; *s*, spiracle; postspiracular slits numbered.

ever, this point of view, which regards the germ layers as sacrosanct, should not be taken too seriously. The lining of the gill passages in any fish includes derivatives of both ectoderm and endoderm, indistinguishably fused and apparently similar in nature. The development of a gill is presumably due to the action of morphogenetic forces upon this epithelium. Apparently either ectoderm or endoderm, if lying in the area of potential gill development, might respond.

Gill pouches are formed in paired longitudinal series, and it is only natural that many workers have tried to correlate the gill arches with the segmental arrangement seen in the myotomes and the segmentation of skeletal structures and nerves associated with this somite musculature. There is, however, no conclusive evidence of any real relation between these two systems (cf. Fig. 179, p. 257). The gill "segmentation" is based on pouches of endoderm; that of the trunk muscles and associated structures is based on somites of mesodermal origin; the two seem to be quite independent developments.

Gills in Bony Fishes. The gills of the Osteichthyes (Fig. 226, *D*, p. 318) are built on the same basic plan as those of sharklike forms; there are, however, important differences due to the universal presence of an operculum. Developing as a fold from the hyoid arch, it is basically comparable to that just mentioned for the chimaeras. The operculum of Osteichthyes, however, is a bony structure, forming a plate of armor between head and shoulder on either side (Figs. 108, p. 170; 154, p. 226; 156, p. 228). A considerable *branchial chamber* may be present between the opercular cover and the gills. The opercular opening is primitively a great crescentic slit, convex in contour posteriorly, lying just in front of the dermal shoulder girdle. In some specialized teleosts, however, the opening may be reduced to a small hole.

Breathing methods in most bony fishes are comparable to those of sharks, except that opercular movements in great measure replace the opening and closing of individual gill openings seen in the shark. Water enters through the mouth, with a closing of the external gill opening behind the operculum and an expansion of the branchial chamber. Valvular skin folds about the mouth help to close that orifice during the reverse movement of constricting the pharynx and expelling water through the external gill aperture. Some stiff-bodied bony fishes utilize the water current through the gills as a locomotor device, after the fashion of a jet plane; on the other hand, such forms as the mackerel rely on their fast-swimming movements for the production of a stream of water through the gills, simply holding the mouth open as they go. Individual gill flaps are unnecessary in bony fishes as protective devices, and we find that the gill septum does not extend (as in sharks) outward beyond the gill surface itself. In teleosts, in fact, reduction has gone so far that the gill septum has shrunk away from the area between the pair of gills on the arch, leaving these elements projecting outward without any extraneous support as two branches of a V-shaped holobranch (Fig. 227, *B*, p. 319). Gill rakers are frequently found, as in sharks; gill rays are present, but, in contrast to elasmobranchs, form in two rows, rather than one, on each gill arch, stiffening the delicate pair of gill structures.

Normal gill slits are, almost universally, five in number in bony fishes as in typical elasmobranchs (Fig. 229, *C–F*, p. 321). Polypterus, however, has (like the chimaeras) lost the last pair of gill slits, and aberrant conditions are found in some teleosts. The pattern of distribution of gills along the slits is subject to reduction in various types. In actinopterygians the hemibranch on the anterior surface of the first slit is lost except in a few primitive types (sturgeons, paddle-fish, gar pikes); this is understandable, since the first slit, covered closely by the operculum, is in an unfavorable position to gain a good flow of water. The lung-fish Epiceratodus of Australia has a full complement of gills; but that on the anterior side of the first slit is without a direct blood supply and hence is a pseudobranch. The other lungfishes exhibit further gill reduction; these forms tend to rely in considerable measure on lungs rather than gills for respiration. In Lepidosiren the first gill slit is closed, but three holobranchs remain. In Protopterus gills are reduced in both size and number. All the normal gill slits are open, and there is a true if small gill on the anterior surface of the first slit, but two branchial arches behind this slit have no gills at all.

That the spiracle was primitively present in bony fishes is attested by its retention in the one surviving crossopterygian and in the three living types of chondrosteans. In all other living bony fishes it is lost, although a few additional actinopterygians show a blind internal pouch in its former position. Curiously, however, we find that a majority of actinopterygians have, despite loss of the spiracle, retained the pseudobranch which was associated with it. Tucked beneath the edge of the operculum, or, near by, beneath the base of the skull, it sometimes retains its gill-like structure, sometimes forms a small mass of tissue sunken beneath the surface. Probably this former gill serves a sensory function, but its nature is unknown.

An important function in addition to respiration is served by the gills in marine teleosts. As discussed later (pp. 368–370), such animals are living in an external environment containing a greater concentration of salt than is present in their own proper "internal environment." Osmotic processes constantly tend to increase the body salt concentration to a lethal condition, and the kidneys are unable to counteract this entirely. It is found that in at least some marine teleosts the gill epithelium has the ability to take excess salt from the blood and excrete it into the water current flowing through the gills. Still further, the gills of teleosts have an additional functional resemblance to the kidneys in that they have glandular elements able to excrete nitrogenous wastes such as ammonia (Fig. 230).

Although ancestral bony fishes presumably had lungs as accessory breathing organs, these structures were later transformed by almost all actinopterygians into a hydrostatic air sac, described later, of little or no value in respiration. A variety of modern teleosts, however, live today under conditions in which air breathing may become a necessity. Some are more or less amphibious, spending part of their lives on land; others live in a muddy environment, where the water often forms too thick a gruel for satisfactory gill respiration. For a number of teleosts, air gulped into the digestive tract has some respiratory value, with the air bladder lining or the gut epithelium functioning in gas exchange, and in the nearly scaleless eels the skin may function in water "breathing." More frequently, however, we find lung substitutes in the form of structures developed in or from the branchial chambers, kept moist beneath the operculum. In various catfishes, for example, and the "tree-climbing perch" (Anabas) of the East Indies, familiar in popular lore, rosettes or branching filaments of vascularized epithelium are developed behind or above the gills in the branchial chambers. In several cases these chambers themselves are expanded into lunglike shapes, extending backward into the trunk as a pair of elongated sacs lined with a respiratory epithelium.

Gills in Jawless Fishes.   Descending the scale from the gnathostomes, we find that in the lampreys and hagfishes (Fig. 226, *A, B,* p. 318) gills are equally well developed, but in a rather different fashion. The gill passages are

Fig. 230.   Two lamellae from the gill of an eel; the large cells at the base of the lamella are salt-secreting. (After Keys and Willmer.)

not in the form of slits, but of spherical pouches, connected by narrow openings with the pharynx on one hand and the exterior on the other. In the lamprey larva the gills are arranged as hemibranchs on anterior and posterior surfaces of each pouch; in the adult cyclostome, however, the gill lamellae have come to form a ring around the margins of the gill sac. The branchial skeleton forms a continuous but flexible lattice-work about the pouches (Figs. 106, p. 169; 147, *A*, p. 214). There is a well developed musculature which, working upon these structures, constricts and expands the sacs. In this fashion a pumping effect can be obtained; water can be pulled in through the external openings and forced out again through them, thus permitting respiration to continue even when feeding operations block anterior entrance of water to the pharynx.

Such anterior entrances vary within the group. In the larval lamprey, as in the hagfish, the mouth leads to a pharynx of normal construction which in turn connects posteriorly with the esophagus. In the metamorphosis to the adult, however, a radical change takes place in the pharynx. This splits into two separate tubes (Fig. 231). A dorsal duct leads back without interruption from mouth to esophagus. Below is a large tube with which the gills connect; this ends blindly at its posterior end, and is a purely respiratory part of the pharynx. In the hagfishes no such subdivision of the gut is found, but an equally peculiar device is present. The combined nostril and hypophyseal sac breaks through posteriorly into the pharynx roof (Fig. 17, p. 37).

In contrast to the usual gnathostome condition of five normal slits plus a spiracle, we find in most cyclostomes a higher count of gill pouches. In the lamprey Petromyzon seven pairs of pouches are present; in the hagfishes the number varies from six to fourteen. In addition, all members of the hagfish group have an extra unpaired gill-less duct on the left side, usually at the back of the pouch series, leading from pharynx to exterior. The pouch count in cyclostomes suggests that in primitive vertebrates the number of gills was somewhat higher than in modern jawed fishes.

Variations are seen in the arrangement of the porelike external openings of the gills of cyclostomes. In lampreys and the slime hag Bdellostoma each gill

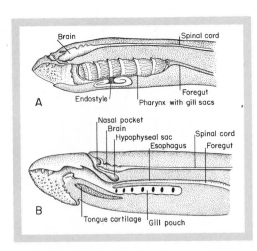

A Endostyle   Pharynx with gill sacs

Fig. 231. Sagittal sections of *A*, the ammocoete larva of a lamprey; *B*, adult lamprey; to show especially the division of the adult pharynx into two parts. The endostyle of the larva becomes the thyroid gland of the adult (not shown). (After Goodrich.)

pouch opens by a separate orifice. But in another hagfish (Paramyxine) the tubes of each side, although separate, are crowded close together at the surface, and in the common hag, Myxine, the whole series of tubes on either side fuses externally to form a single outer opening. There is thus developed here a condition somewhat similar to that of operculate jawed fishes. Whereas in most vertebrates, and even in lampreys, the gills are situated close up to the head structures, they are removed some distance back in the hagfish group. This appears to be an adaptation to the semiparasitic life of these forms; the gill openings may remain free even if the head region of the hagfish is completely buried in the flesh of its prey.

The Ammocoetes larva of Petromyzon spends its existence half-buried in the bottoms of streams and ponds. Lacking the "tongue" device which develops in the adult for a carnivorous mode of life, it subsists on microscopic food particles. The gill system forms the food-collecting mechanism. The particles contained in the water current entering the mouth are strained in passage through the pharynx and are carried on down the digestive tract by a series of ciliated channels similar to those described for Amphioxus and the tunicates in an earlier chapter (pp. 15–16, 18).

It is apparent that this food-collecting function of the gill system in the Ammocoetes is not merely an accessory one, but a function even more important here than that of respiration—which could be largely carried on by the skin of these small, soft-bodied animals. This situation leads one to the concept that in the vertebrate ancestors, food collecting was the primary *raison d'être* of the internal gill system, and that originally respiration may have been an accessory function only—the development of actual gill structures along the gill tubes may have been an afterthought. The fact that, as we have seen, all typical lower chordates likewise make their living by straining water through a highly developed system of pharyngeal gill slits adds emphasis to this concept.

Further evidence can be adduced from study of the most ancient of jawless vertebrates, the fossil ostracoderms (Figs. 18, 19, p. 38). A considerable amount of data is available regarding the gill system of these Paleozoic forms. The mouth was generally small; the gill region and pharynx, on the other hand, are highly developed. In some the gills opened to the exterior, rather as in a hagfish, by a common opening on either side; in others a series of round holes is present on the lateral or under body surface, showing a condition similar to that of lampreys. The number of gills is somewhat variable, but no ostracoderm yet investigated shows more than a dozen pairs—a number above that of jawed fishes, but within the general range of modern cyclostomes. The internal structure is often unknown, or poorly known, but in some cases is so well preserved that a fairly accurate reconstruction of the gill region can be made (Fig. 232). The gills here were certainly in part respiratory—the hard armor would render the skin of little value in this regard—but the relatively enormous size of the gill apparatus in such a form as that figured strongly suggests that food straining was a major function in many ostracoderms.

The ostracoderm story, added to that described earlier for the lower chordates, leads with certainty to the conclusion that the history of the pharynx and gill slits began with their development as a feeding apparatus—a function proper to the inclusion (otherwise incongruous) of these structures in an introductory part of the digestive tract. The passage through this food-screening system of a constant current of water from which oxygen could be readily obtained presumably facilitated the development here of gill structures; in ancestral vertebrates

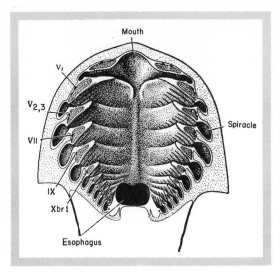

Mouth

V_1

$V_{2,3}$

VII

Spiracle

IX

Xbr 1

Esophagus

Fig. 232. Restored view of the pharyngeal region of a late Silurian ostracoderm of the cephalaspid type; the "head" viewed from below after the removal of the bones of the "throat" (cf. Fig. 19, *B*, p. 38). The mouth is tiny, the pharynx an expanded food-straining device. V_1, V_2, V_3, *VII*, *IX*, *Xbr1*, Sections of branchial nerves associated with successive gills (cf. Fig. 374, p. 517). Two gill pouches are present anterior to that which appears to represent the spiracle. (After Stensiö.)

this pharyngeal system served a double function, as it does today in the larval lamprey. With the development of jaws (or cyclostome substitutes for them), the feeding functions of the gill system were, for the most part, lost; but in typical fishes the pharynx and gill apparatus are structures which, though somewhat reduced in relative size, are still highly developed and generally indispensable for respiratory purposes.

Pharynx and Gills in Tetrapods. With the appearance of lungs and the subsequent shift of tetrapods to a terrestrial life, there came about a further decrease in the size and importance of the pharynx and gill system. In amphibians we see a transitional stage. In water-dwelling larvae of this group pharyngeal gill slits are still present. They are, however, much reduced even here. The bony operculum of the fish ancestors is absent; the anurans develop a saclike opercular structure, but this is probably a new, larval adaptation. The erstwhile spiracle seldom opens and is generally incorporated into the auditory apparatus. Four of the five typical gill slits open up in the larvae of most amphibians. But never are typical internal gills developed in the walls of these slits (although the peculiar gills of the tadpole, noted later, may be in part derived from internal gill structures). Further, the gill openings disappear with the end of the larval period; only in such urodeles as fail to metamorphose completely do certain of the slits (from one to three of them) persist. The function of the slits in amphibians seems to be simply the insurance that a water current is set up near the external gills (described below), upon which larval amphibians mainly depend for blood aeration.

In amniotes, gill pouches always push outward from the pharynx in every embryo, and surface furrows push inward to meet them; but gill slits open only in a transitory manner in the embryo of reptiles and birds, and open seldom if at all in mammals. In no case is there, in amniotes, the slightest development of respiratory functions in the gills. The amniote embryo, in conservative fashion, repeats the embryological processes of countless ancestral generations; but never is there any true ontogenetic repetition of the development of the full-grown gill system found in the fish ancestor.

In the adult amniote, as was said in the introduction to this section, the pharynx retains hardly a vestige of its former importance. It has greatly shortened, permitting the development behind it of the constricted neck region, traversed by an elongated esophagus. The lungs developed from the pharyngeal region in fishes, and the lung entrance is still to be found in the pharyngeal floor. Of the gill pouches, the spiracle persists in modified form in connection with the ear; in the adult the others have disappeared completely.

External Gills.   In the larvae of a few bony fishes and of amphibians, accessory respiratory structures are present in the form of external gills. Among fishes they are found only in Polypterus and in the African and South American lungfishes. As seen in the lungfishes, they consist of four feathery processes growing out on either side of the "neck" region above the gill openings. In life they have a reddish color, due to the presence of an abundant supply of blood—the blood coming from the vascular aortic arches. Polypterus (Fig. 233) shows similar outgrowths, but they are limited to a single pair. Fish external gills appear at an early embryonic stage, before the operculum is formed, and arise from the dorsal ends of successive gill bars. Possibly they are ancient specializations from the internal gill system.

The climatic conditions which (we have noted elsewhere) tend to favor the presence of lungs in these same animals obviously are significant in relation to the presence of external gills. Drought and a consequent paucity of oxygen in stagnating waters give a situation especially unfavorable for young and growing fishes, which have a high rate of metabolism. External gills increase respiratory surfaces considerably and enable the larva to make better use of such poor oxygen supplies as are available. As is the case with lungs, external gills are of little importance in the ray-finned fishes. Since, however, we find them present in some members of both major groups of Osteichthyes, we can reasonably assume that (like lungs) they were present in the ancestral bony fishes, to be lost later among the more advanced actinopterygians.

To be distinguished from true external gills are filaments protruding from the internal gills in various fish types. Such external filaments are found in the early stages of all elasmobranchs. They float in the albuminous fluid lying in the egg case and appear to serve for the absorption of food material as well as for respiration; they disappear at the time of hatching. Somewhat similar, but purely respiratory, filaments are found in sturgeons and paddlefishes and, as noted earlier, in a limited number of teleosts.

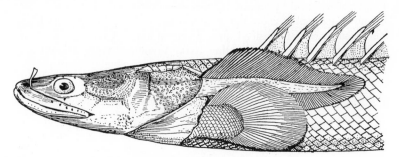

Fig. 233.   Larval form of the primitive African ray-finned fish, Polypterus; the large external gill extends back above the pectoral fin. (From Dean.)

Presumably, external gills were present in the crossopterygian ancestors of the tetrapods, and we find them present in the urodele amphibians in a form similar to that seen in their lungfish cousins—feathery, coral-colored outgrowths, usually three pairs of them, above the gill slit region of larvae (Fig. 70, *E, F,* p. 118). Throughout life certain urodeles tend to remain water-dwelling larvae; retention of external gills is a diagnostic feature of these "perennibranchiate" forms. In the Apoda there is a development of external gills similar to that of fishes and urodeles. In the Anura there is a specialized larval gill system. Four gill slits break through in the early tadpole stage of typical frogs and toads. Their external openings, however, are sheathed by the peculiar "opercular" fold, not exactly homologous to the fish operculum. This is so extensive that it envelops the under surface of the throat region and even the developing forelimbs; in most anurans it has but a single opening to the exterior, usually on the left side. There is enclosed a considerable chamber filled by a mass of vascularized filaments. Part, at least, of this gill tissue is derived from external gills which bud out above the gill slits at an early stage, before the operculum develops. There are, however, additional filaments, formed later, which arise more ventrally in the gill slit region and are sometimes thought to be modified internal gill structures.

Many amphibians, including representatives of all three orders, develop away from streams and ponds in a variety of situations, such that they must breathe air from an early developmental stage. A number of different types of respiratory devices have been evolved in these cases; frequently, elaborate external gills function as embryonic or larval lungs.

Like the internal gills, external gills have disappeared, without trace, in amniotes.

THE SWIM BLADDER

Characteristic of most actinopterygian fishes is the presence of a swim bladder, an elongate sac arising as a dorsal outgrowth from the anterior part of the digestive tube (Figs. 234, 235, *A–C,* 237 *C*). The swim bladder is distensible and is filled with air or other gases; its major function is that of a hydrostatic organ. The specific gravity of a fish (or any vertebrate) is slightly greater than that of sea water. Filling or emptying the swim bladder will change the specific gravity of the fish as a whole, and facilitate its keeping to a depth, high or low in the water, proper to its habits. It is thus obvious that this structure is of greatest use to a form living in the ocean or other deep-water bodies.

Among actinopterygians the most primitive form, Polypterus, has no air bladder as such, but has, instead, paired ventral lungs. A typical dorsal air bladder is, however, present in the other living ray-finned types below the teleost

Fig. 234. Diagrammatic longitudinal sections of the air bladder in various teleosts. *A*, Primitive type, open to the gut; *B, C*, closed types, with gas-producing red body and other areas for gas resorption.

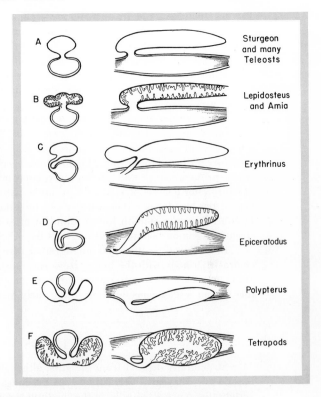

Fig. 235. Diagrammatic cross sections and longitudinal sections of the air bladder or lung in various fishes and in tetrapods. *A*, Typical dorsal air bladder of actinopterygians; *B*, a bladder type found in holosteans with a folded inner surface capable of some breathing function; *C*, an unusual teleost type with a lateral opening suggestive of a transition from lung to air bladder; *D*, the Australian lungfish, with the bilobed lung rotated dorsally, although the opening remains ventral in position; *E*, the archaic actinopterygian, Polypterus, with a ventral lung, probably primitive and antecedent to all other lung or air bladder types; *F*, the type of lung developed in land vertebrates, with complex internal structure. (After Dean.)

Sturgeon and many Teleosts

Lepidosteus and Amia

Erythrinus

Epiceratodus

Polypterus

Tetrapods

level, and is retained in most teleosts. It is absent, for example, in the bottom-dwelling flounders, in which a hydrostatic organ would be functionally useless, but even there it is present in the embryo. It seems certain that the dorsal swim bladder was developed by the actinopterygians early in their history; it is not found in any other fish group whatsoever.

A *pneumatic duct*, leading from the digestive tract upward along the dorsal mesentery to the bladder, is present in all the more primitive teleosts and in lower ray-finned forms. Primitively, the duct is short and broad and may open from the back end of the pharynx in lower actinopterygians. In teleosts, however, it becomes a narrow and often elongate tube, opening frequently from the esophagus, but in some cases from a point farther back in the gut. Finally, in a large series of advanced teleosts the connection with the digestive tract is entirely lost.

The swim bladder is typically an elongate oval sac, lying above the celomic lining of the abdominal cavity, below the dorsal aorta and vertebral column. Its shape is variable; frequently it is constricted into anterior and posterior subdivisions. An elastic connective tissue surrounding it allows for expansion, and both smooth and striated muscle fibers function in contraction.

In some primitive surface-dwelling fishes air is taken into the sac through the pneumatic duct. But even in many forms in which the duct is present this appears to serve merely as a release valve, and in most cases the swim bladder depends upon its own internal mechanisms for supply and absorption of its gaseous content. In the anterior part of the bladder of most teleosts is found the *red body*, which owes its name to the marvelous network of capillaries—a rete mirabile—contained in it. This is the gas-producing organ; how it operates, often against considerable pressure, appears to puzzle the physicists but not the fish.

The gas includes, as in air, nitrogen, oxygen, and carbon dioxide, but in varying proportions. In most cases oxygen is the main constituent; in some forms, however, the gas is almost pure nitrogen. A gas-absorbing tissue is present in the posterior part of the bladder—in the posterior chamber when two are present. Primitively, this is a broad area of thin epithelium lying in the general surface of the bladder. In advanced forms, however, absorption is restricted to the *oval*, a sunken pocket which can be closed off by a sphincter.

Although the major use of the teleost air bladder is as a hydrostatic organ, other attributes can be ascribed in some cases. As noted in a later chapter, it is a hearing aid in some teleost groups (p. 487). Still further, it is sometimes an accessory air-breathing organ. This function is well developed in the gar pike and Amia, primitive fresh-water actinopterygians and is found, as well, in a number of fresh-water teleosts of relatively primitive nature. In these fishes the inner surface of the bladder is rather cellular and lunglike in texture (Fig. 235, *B*), quite in contrast to the smooth lining found in most teleosts. This condition gives a strong suggestion that air breathing was the original bladder function.

In its dorsal position and single rather than paired nature the swim bladder contrasts strongly with the lungs. However, most anatomists believe that the two are in some fashion and to some degree homologous structures. We shall discuss this further after a consideration of the early history of the lungs.

LUNGS

Structurally distinct from the gills, although similar in basic function, and, like them, pharyngeal derivatives, are the lungs, which in typical air-breathing vertebrates replace the gills as the medium through which oxygen is brought to the blood and tissues. In most tetrapods the air-breathing apparatus has a characteristic pattern which may be briefly sketched at this point (Fig. 236). Entrance to the air duct is gained by a median ventral opening in the pharynx, the *glottis*. Immediately beyond the glottis the duct enlarges to a chamber, the *larynx*; beyond this a ventral median tube, the *trachea*, extends backward to divide into primary *bronchi*, one leading to each lung. The paired *lungs*, primitively ventral, may expand to occupy a lateral or even dorsal position in the anterior part of the celomic cavities.

Embryologically, the lung structures first appear in the form of a ventral outpocketing of the floor of the throat, median in position, but in many cases distinctly bilobed at an early stage. Growing backward, this endodermal pouch structure divides into paired outgrowths from which the lungs develop; associated with it are tissues of mesenchymal origin which strengthen its walls and produce skeletal elements related to larynx, trachea, and bronchi.

Lung Structure.   The inner surface of the lung and its compartments is lined by an epithelium of endodermal origin;* the external surface, facing the celom or a subdivision of it, is covered by the epithelium of that cavity. Within the substance of the lung are variable amounts of connective tissue, smooth muscle fibers, and an abundance of blood vessels. In many reptiles and in mammals a lung is a spongy structure with air passages—bronchi, *bronchioles* radiating

---

* It is believed by some that in the very thin lining of the air spaces of the complex mammalian lung the endodermal layer is incomplete.

Fig. 236. Ventral view of the respiratory system of man. The lungs dissected to show the bronchi. (After Toldt.)

from the bronchi, and small terminal pouches, the *alveoli*, through the walls of which there is an exchange of oxygen for carbon dioxide (Figs. 236, 238, p. 334). The lung is richly supplied with blood capillaries, which branch from a special pulmonary artery coming from the aortic arch of the last gill or, in higher tetrapods, from the heart itself (cf. p. 430). From the lung the blood returns by a pulmonary vein to the heart. Between blood and lung alveoli there lie but thin membranes, through which diffusion of gases can readily take place.

In fishes which have lungs, and in amphibians, the lung sacs have a relatively simple internal construction. The efficiency of a lung depends, of course, in the main upon the amount of internal membrane surface present for gas exchange. Advanced tetrapods, with greater activity and greater needs for oxygen, increase the exchange area, not so much by increasing lung size, as by increasing the complexity of internal subdivision. Here, as usual, we must keep in mind the problem of surface-volume relationships; in large animals the lungs must be disproportionately increased in size, or attain greater complexity of subdivision, so that the exchange surface may keep pace with the volumetric growth of tissue demanding oxygen.

Although lungs are the structures normally present in tetrapods for breathing functions, they are not universally present in amphibians, and in many air-breathing members of that class much of the oxygen intake is gained by other means. Exchange of oxygen and carbon dioxide with the air can take place at the surface of any moist mucous membrane properly supplied with blood vessels. Even though lungs are present in frogs and toads, they are of relatively little importance. If a frog is observed it will be noticed that the floor of the mouth is periodically lowered and raised. This movement expands and contracts the mouth cavity, drawing in and expelling air through the nostrils; the moist mouth epithelium acts as a substitute lung. Only relatively rarely is there a convulsive movement of the throat indicating inspiration into the lungs. Even more important than the mouth as a breathing organ is the moist skin of modern amphibians. This is richly vascular and appears to be so effective that in some salamanders "breathing" is accomplished by the skin in satisfactory fashion despite a total absence of lungs.

Lungs in Fishes.   Although lungs are most characteristically developed in tetrapods, they are phylogenetically older structures. Lungs are present in the dipnoans, who gain their popular name of lungfishes because of this fact, and surely were present in their close relatives, the ancient crossopterygians, from which land animals are descended. Still further, lungs are present in Polypterus, the most primitive of all members of the ray-finned group of bony fishes.

Fish lungs are simple in construction. In Polypterus (Fig. 235, *E*, 237, *A*) an opening (with a sphincter) in the floor of the pharynx leads to a bilobed sac; the lobes pass back on either side of the esophagus, and the right lobe, much the longer, continues backward and upward into the mesentery above the gut. The lung sacs are of simple construction, with but a few internal furrows. Except for the elongation of the right lobe, this would appear to be a primitive lung type, resembling the simple lung of amphibians (Fig. 235, *F*).

In the Dipnoi this generalized pattern has been modified (Fig. 235, *D*, 237, *B*). The entrance, as always, lies in the floor of the pharynx. Instead, however, of a symmetrical development, we find that the duct to the lungs, long and un-branched, curves upward around the esophagus to a lung or lungs dorsal in posi-tion. The lung structure is more efficient than that of Polypterus, for there is some degree of internal subdivision into pockets and alveoli. In the Australian lungfish the lung is a single structure, but in the African and South American genera the lungs are definitely paired. The course of the duct suggests that the dorsal position of the dipnoan lungs is a secondary condition, the entire structure having twisted upward around the right side of the body. Strong proof of this as-sumption is afforded by the blood supply (Fig. 237, *B*). If the dorsal position were the original one, we would expect the arterial blood supply to come from

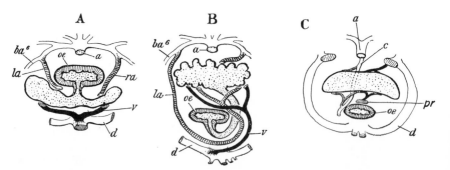

Fig. 237.   Diagrammatic cross sections of bony fishes (seen from behind) to show the position of the lung or swim bladder and the blood vessels connected with it. *A*, Polypterus, a primitive actinoptery-gian, with a ventral paired lung; *B*, Epiceratodus, a lungfish, with a single lung dorsal in position, but with a ventral opening from the gut; *C*, a teleost with air bladder (duct lost). In the lung, the arterial supply is from the last aortic arch; in *B* the curve of the vessel from the left arch below the gut indi-cates the path of dorsal migration of the lung. In the teleost the arterial supply to the air bladder is from the dorsal aorta (by way of the celiac artery). In the lung the venous return is directly to the heart region. The Epiceratodus veins show an asymmetrical condition comparable to that of the arteries. In the air bladder the blood returns to the heart via the normal venous system. *a*, Dorsal aorta; *ba*[6], sixth aortic arch; *c*, celiac artery, whence branches run to teleost air bladder; *d*, common cardinal vein (duct of Cuvier); *la*, left pulmonary artery; *oe*, esophagus; *pr*, portal vein, draining part of teleost air bladder; *ra*, right pulmonary artery; *v*, pulmonary veins. (After Goodrich, 1909).

adjacent vessels in some simple fashion. We find, however, that an artery from the left side of the body reaches the lungs by looping ventrally around the esophagus and then up on the right side, showing by its course the route of phylogenetic migration of the lung system.

Origin of Lungs. Although gills are present in lung-bearing fishes, the lungs are important breathing structures; indeed, the African lungfish will suffocate and drown if kept from air. We have earlier commented (p. 45) on the climatic conditions of seasonal drought which appear to give lungs a considerable survival value in those few modern tropical fishes that have them, and on the fact that such conditions were presumably widespread in the Devonian period when the bony fishes arose. That lungs were probably present as adjunct breathing organs in early bony fishes of all types is indicated by the fact that they are a feature, not only of the Sarcopterygii, but also of the most primitive of living actinopterygians. Lungs may perhaps be still more ancient in vertebrate history. There is no trace of them in the modern Chondrichthyes. But fossil evidence indicates the presence of a pair of ventral pharyngeal pouches which seem surely to be primitive lungs in a Devonian member of the Placodermi—a group at the very bottom of the scale of jawed vertebrates.

The mode of origin of lungs, phylogenetically, is none too certain. However, as we have noted, air breathing can be carried on through any moist and permeable membrane, and it may be that in some ancient fishes, much as in amphibians today, the lining of the mouth and pharynx functioned in this fashion. Any pocket-like outgrowth of the pharynx increasing the respiratory surface would, of course, be advantageous. In amphibians the lungs sometimes appear in early embryonic stages as pockets which have the appearance of an extra pair of gill pouches. Perhaps the oldest lungs were a modified pair of posterior pharyngeal pouch structures.

Lung Versus Swim Bladder. If we assume, as most students of the subject have done, that lungs and swim bladder are homologous structures, which is the ancestral type? Early writers took it for granted that, since the swim bladder is a fish structure and the lung a characteristic tetrapod feature, the swim bladder was the progenitor of the lung. But consideration of the evidence now available strongly indicates that, despite the seeming reasonableness of the older theory, the reverse is the case: the lung is the more primitive of the two. The swim bladder is found only in one subdivision of the bony fishes, the actinopterygians, whereas the most primitive member of that group, and members of the Sarcopterygii as well, have a lung. The air bladder, thus, would appear to have evolved from a more ancient and widespread lung structure during the course of actinopterygian history.

The shift from lung to swim bladder in actinopterygians can be correlated with known facts in their history. The lung was an adaptation for survival of the individual among the early Devonian bony fishes during seasons of drought. Lungs are still of advantage to the few fishes which have them, living as they do in tropical areas in which such conditions are present today. For actinopterygians generally the lung became of little advantage. Most members of this group lay thousands or even millions of eggs; individual survival is of little importance, for a few survivors can soon remake a population. Further, as a ventral structure, a lung makes a fish top-heavy; if a dorsal shift of the air sacs to the swim bladder position could be accomplished, greater stability would be gained. A final point to be noted is that later ray-finned fishes migrated in great numbers to the seas.

In the oceans there is no drought and no need, and generally no opportunity, for air breathing. And on the other hand an air bladder, if present, would prove highly useful to dwellers in the deep as a hydrostatic organ.

We have no satisfactory structural intermediates in living actinopterygians between the lung of Polypterus and the swim bladder of more progressive forms. However, the lungfishes, although of course not belonging to this series, suggest the method of transition. The dipnoan lungs open by a ventral duct, but are actually in the dorsal position of a swim bladder, and in Epiceratodus only a single symmetric dorsal lung is present. The further changes needed to parallel the presumed development of a swim bladder are shifts in the duct opening and in the blood supply, and one existing teleost shows a transition in the first regard (Fig. 235, *C*, p. 329).

Lungs in Lower Tetrapods.   In amphibians the lungs show little advance over the fish condition, and are relatively inefficient structures. In some urodeles the inner walls remain smooth; generally, however, there is, in amphibians, a development of septa—ridges containing connective tissue which somewhat increase the respiratory surface and give the internal surface of the lung a honeycombed appearance (Fig. 238, *A*).

Among reptiles, the lungs of Sphenodon, snakes, and many lizards are not much further advanced (Fig. 238, *B*). They are still saclike structures, with a modest internal subdivision of the walls into alveolar pockets. (Parenthetically we may note that in a variety of limbless lizards, snakes, and in apodous amphibians as well, only a single lung—usually the right—attains any degree of development in the slender body.) In some lizards and in turtles and crocodiles the lungs are built in more complicated fashion. The septa, originally confined to the outer walls of the sac, have grown inward and subdivided in complicated fashion to give the lung as a whole a rather spongelike texture. A main central tube runs down the length of the lung as a continuation of the bronchus leading to it from the trachea. From this, branches lead outward between the major septa to subdivide and finally reach the alveoli.

In amphibians, owing to reduction of ribs, the lungs are filled by "swallowing" air, a force pump mechanism; in reptiles the action is that of a suction pump. In most reptiles the elongate lungs lie in the general body cavity. The action of trunk muscles raises the ribs and expands the capacity of the trunk as a whole; air is sucked into the lungs, which expand to fill the additional space. In some reptiles there is a modest development of air sacs of the type highly developed in birds and described below. In crocodilians there develops a structure

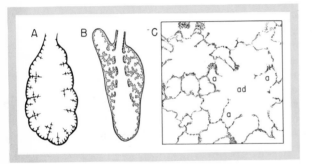

Fig. 238.   Diagrammatic sections through the lung of *A*, a frog, and *B*, a lizard. *C*, Section of a small area of a human lung, × about 50, showing its complex construction. *ad*, An alveolar duct, smallest component of the duct system; *a*, one of the alveoli to which it leads. (*A* after Vialleton; *B* after Goodrich.)

somewhat comparable to the mammalian diaphragm. Turtles, of course, cannot move their ribs, and mostly rely on specialized abdominal muscles which act to expand and contract the lungs.

The Lung in Birds. In birds, with their high metabolic rate and consequent demand for great amounts of oxygen, the lung apparatus has developed into a complex series of structures. The lungs themselves are relatively small and compact. Out from them, however, grow numerous extensions as paired *air sacs* which invade every major part of the body (Figs. 239, *A*, 240). A pair of cervical sacs grow upward along the neck; clavicular sacs (usually fused) are found beneath the "wishbone"; two pairs of lateral sacs are present in the thoracic region; a pair of abdominal sacs extends far back among the viscera. With sac development is associated a complicated subdivision of the body cavity (cf. p. 294; Fig. 203, p. 294). From the sacs further air spaces invade certain of the bones of the skeleton in most birds and partially replace the bone marrow. The lining of the air sacs is in general smooth; they are thus of little value as respiratory surfaces (they may aid, as cooling devices, in the regulation of body temperature). They nevertheless play a major role in respiration. In the birds, as in other

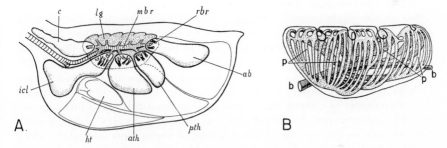

Fig. 239. *A,* Diagram of the trunk of a bird, left side view, to show the position of the respiratory sacs. *ab,* Abdominal air sac; *ath,* anterior thoracic sac; *c,* cervical air sac; *ht,* heart; *icl,* interclavicular air sac; *lg,* left lung; *mbr,* bronchus running through the lung and leading from trachea to various air sacs; *pth,* posterior thoracic air sac; *rbr,* recurrent bronchi which return air from sacs to respiratory areas of lung. *B,* Lateral view of the left lung of a bird. The primary bronchus, *b,* traverses the length of the lung to the abdominal sac. Branches are given off, leading to other air sacs and to parabronchi (*p*). These connect at both ends with the bronchus. Notches in the dorsal outline of the lung are rib impressions. (*A* after Goodrich; *B* after Locy and Larsell.)

Fig. 240. Ventral view of the lungs of a bird to show the connections with the various air sacs.

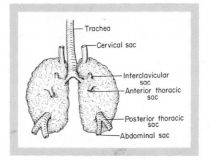

amniotes, the breathing mechanism is that of a suction pump, but the lung itself does little in the way of expansion or contraction. When the bird is at rest, air is drawn in by a forward and upward movement of the ribs which expands the trunk capacity; during flight, the action of the wing muscles causes a similar movement. Most of the inspired air passes through the lungs, by channels continuous with the bronchi, directly to the air sacs without much respiratory exchange taking place on the way. The sacs, however, are connected with the lung proper by smaller tubes in addition to the continuations of the bronchi through which the air enters them; when, on expiration, the air is forced out of the sacs, it passes through these openings to the lung tubes and respiratory surfaces.

The structure of the bird lung itself is unique among vertebrates. In other amniotes the respiratory membranes are in "dead-end" alveoli. Nothing of the sort is found in bird lungs; every passage, large and small, is open at both ends so that there is a true circulation of air (Fig. 239, *B*). Within the lung a series of tubes, the *parabronchi,* loop from the bronchi through the lung tissue and back to the bronchi; the respiratory exchange takes place in the walls of countless tiny *air capillaries* which loop outward from the walls of the parabronchi and return to them again.

The Mammalian Lung. In mammals the lungs are large but with a rather simpler pattern than that found in birds. They are relatively short, anteroposteriorly, but expanded, frequently with a varied subdivision into lobes; together with the heart, lying between them, they occupy most of the thorax. The lungs are finely subdivided into tiny but exceedingly numerous alveoli (Fig. 238, *C*), to which the air passes by means of a branching series of larger and smaller bronchi and, finally *bronchioles;* the alveoli cluster about the terminal alveolar ducts like grapes on a stem. Phylogenetically, as indicated by conditions in amphibians and more primitive reptilian types, increasing complexity of lung structure was attained by increasing development of septa, large and small, which brought about finer subdivisions of the cavities of the sac. By the time the mammalian condition is reached, however, it is, so to speak, the alveolar "hole" rather than the septal "doughnut" which is prominent. The tubes and terminal alveoli form the lung pattern; the mesodermal tissues about them appear to play a relatively passive part in lung ontogeny. In the embryo the primary lung bud invades a compact mass of mesenchyme (Fig. 241), within which, by repeated budding and subdivision of cavities, the adult lung structure finally emerges.

Breathing is accomplished by a highly efficient suction mechanism. In contrast with the condition in primitive amniotes, the lungs are not in the general celomic cavity; instead, a tendinous and muscular partition, the diaphragm (cf. p. 295), separates the thorax from the abdominal region, and each lung lies anterior to the diaphragm within an individual *pleural cavity,* a subdivision of the embryonic celom (Fig. 242). Expansion of the thorax is accomplished in part by upward and outward movement of the ribs, as in reptiles and birds. More important, however, is a posterior or downward movement of the diaphragm. Each lung lies free within its pleural cavity, attached only at the anterior end, where the bronchus and blood vessels enter. Rib and diaphragm movements expand the chest and consequently the pleural cavities; air is pulled into the lungs as they expand to fill the vacuum which would otherwise exist.

Larynx. (Figs. 209, p. 301; 243). With the increased importance of the lungs in land life, there develops in tetrapods a differentiation of the entrance section of the lung passage, in the form of the larynx, an enlarged vestibule ante-

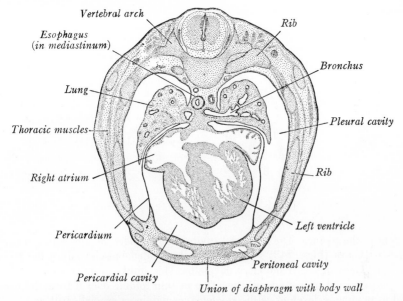

Fig. 241. Cross section of a human embryo (at eight weeks) to show the development of the lungs and of pleural and pericardial cavities and heart. (From Arey.)

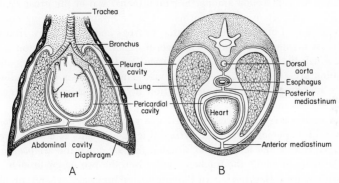

Fig. 242. Diagrammatic longitudinal, *A*, and cross sections, *B*, of the thorax in mammals to show the position of heart and lungs and of pleural and pericardial cavities.

Fig. 243. The larynx of the rhesus monkey, in side view. The hyoid apparatus, with its greater and lesser horns, is seated above and anterior to the larynx. The rhesus monkey has a resonating chamber in the laryngeal sac. Shown are the thyroid and cricoid cartilages, tracheal cartilages, and a membrane connecting the hyoid and the thyroid cartilages. A muscle runs from thyroid to cricoid and covers most of the latter; there are several other small muscles proper to the larynx more deeply situated and not shown. (After Hartman and Straus: Anatomy of the Rhesus Monkey. Williams and Wilkins Co.)

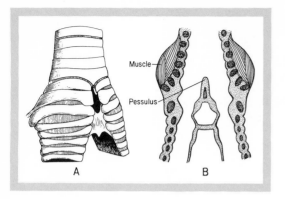

Fig. 244. The syrinx of a songbird (magpie). *A*, External view; *B*, in section. Vibratory membranes on the inner aspect of the two bronchi meet at the base of the trachea to form the median pessulus; further membranes may develop between the expanded rings at the tracheal forks. The syrinx is controlled by musculature of the hypobranchial group. (After Haecker.)

cedent to the trachea. The laryngeal cavity is surrounded by a complex of cartilages or bones (Figs. 243; 148, p. 215). Associated muscles adjust the laryngeal cartilages and open and close the glottis. This slitlike opening from the pharynx is protected in many forms by a flap of skin folding over it from the front, and in mammals develops as the *epiglottis*, containing a special cartilage.

Many tetrapods are voiceless in any true sense. This is particularly true of the salamanders and Apoda among the amphibians, and of the great majority of reptiles, although certain of these forms can make hissing or roaring noises by a violent expulsion of air through the glottis. In frogs and toads, a few lizards, and, notably, most mammals, the larynx is a vocal organ. Voice production is accomplished through the presence of a pair of *vocal cords*, ridges containing an elastic tissue, which are stretched across the larynx. The two cords can be closely appressed to one another, and set in vibration by the passage of a current of expired air between them.*

In birds the larynx is present, but lacks vocal cords, and voice production takes place in a special organ, the *syrinx* (Fig. 244). This is a structure somewhat comparable to the larynx, but situated farther down the air passage, typically at the point at which the trachea divides into the two major bronchi,

Trachea and Bronchi. In Polypterus the lung sacs expand directly from the pharyngeal opening, but in other lung bearers there is usually, for a greater or lesser distance, a median air passage, the trachea; this usually has a ciliated epithelium, with in addition mucous cells and glands. It leads in tetrapods from the larynx to the point where the two lung tubes diverge (Fig. 236, p. 331). In anurans and typical salamanders, in the absence of a developed neck region, the trachea is of negligible length; a formed tracheal tube is, however, present in some long-bodied salamanders and in the Apoda. In amniotes, where head and trunk are separated by a distinct neck region, a trachea is always present, its length, naturally, varying with the degree of elongation of the neck. Some birds (the swan, for example) have an extra length of tracheal tube coiled, for some purpose unknown, beneath the sternum. In almost every case the trachea is stiffened by cartilaginous structures within its walls. In amphibians these are rather

---

* In frogs the "voice" is aided by resonating sacs, commonly paired, in the throat region, opening into the floor of the mouth. Resonating chambers may develop in the larynx itself, as in the case of the gibbon or the South American howler monkeys.

irregular nodules; in amniotes they are rings, generally incomplete except in some birds (Figs. 148, 209, pp. 215, 301; 242–244).

In amphibians and some reptiles the lungs spring almost directly from the end of the trachea; in most amniotes, however, the air duct itself bifurcates before reaching the lungs, giving rise to a pair of primary bronchi which may also be stiffened by cartilaginous rings. When the internal structure of the lung attains the complicated pattern found in some reptiles and in all birds and mammals, the primary bronchi run on into the lung substance before dividing into smaller bronchi which in turn divide into bronchioles and subsidiary ducts.

PHARYNGEAL DERIVATIVES

Despite its reduction in the higher vertebrate classes, the pharynx is important in every group as the embryonic source of glandular structures. In fishes glands arise from the endodermal pharyngeal epithelium, and such structures are even more important in tetrapods. Nature is a tidy housewife, seldom wasteful, and the pharyngeal pouches appear to be areas of epithelium which are easily adaptable to glandular development. We have noted that the gill epithelium in teleosts may take on glandular activity in the excretion of salts. Other glands are derived from the endodermal epithelium of the gill pouches in all gnathostome classes. These glands are formed by thickenings of gill pouch epithelium at either dorsal or ventral borders of the pouches—thickenings which later separate from the epithelium to become varied masses of tissue buried in the throat region of the adult (Figs. 245, 246). Certain of these pouch-derived glands, notably the parathyroids, and the thyroid, formed in the pharyngeal floor, are glands of internal secretion; their description will be deferred for a later chapter.

Thymus Gland. Almost universally present, often prominent and seemingly important, but of uncertain function, is the thymus gland. This consists of clusters of soft glandlike material found in variable arrangement in the gill or throat region. When well developed, the thymus tissue is arranged in lobules, each containing a cortex and medulla (Fig. 247). Characteristic are *reticular cells* which form a network throughout the gland and constitute most of the bulk of

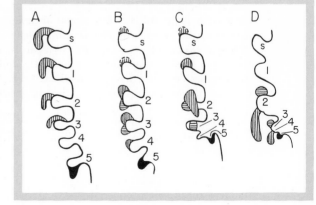

Fig. 245. Diagrams of the gill pouches of the left side of the pharynx in *A,* a shark; *B,* a urodele; *C,* a lizard; *D,* typical mammals; to show the derivation of thymus, parathyroid, and ultimobranchial bodies. The dorsal part of each gill pouch is, for purposes of the diagram, at the upper side. Broken outline, variable thymus derivatives; vertical hatching, thymus; horizontal hatching, parathyroid; solid black, ultimobranchial body. *s,* Spiracular pouch. (Mainly after Maurer.)

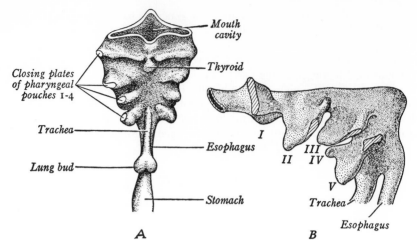

Fig. 246. *A*, Ventral view of a model of the anterior part of the gut tube and its outgrowths in an embryo mammal (Homo). *B*, Lateral view of the pharynx in a slightly later embryo. Closing plates separating tips of gill pouches from the surface are hatched; pouches, including the spiracular pouch (middle ear), indicated by Roman numerals. (From Arey.)

the medulla. The cortex mainly consists of cells identical in all regards with lymphocytes (a common type of white blood corpuscle). In addition, there may be other histologic features—elongate muscle-like cells, spherical corpuscles which perhaps are masses of degenerating cells in the medulla, and so on. A thymus has not been identified in hagfishes, and there is some doubt as to its presence in lampreys; it is, however, found in all higher fishes, usually as a paired series of soft, irregular masses of tissue situated deep to the surface above most or all of the gill slits. In amphibians the thymus is found deep within the lateral surface of the neck region, behind the pharynx. In frogs it consists of a single pair of compact oval bodies; in addition, a pair of *jugular bodies* are thymus-like lymphoid structures which are gill pouch derivatives. In the other two amphibian orders the thymus is generally a rather diffuse, lobulated mass of tissue. In young reptiles it is frequently in the form of a strand of tissue running the length of the neck on either side. It retains this form in adult crocodilians, but usually in reptiles forms more compact bodies—two pairs of them in Sphenodon, lizards, and snakes, a single pair in most turtles. In birds, as in their crocodilian relatives, the thymus is generally a long strand of tissue extending the length of the neck; it is somewhat irregularly and variably lobate. Among mammals the most common condition of the thymus is that of a pair of glands which have migrated from the throat back to a position in the anterior ventral part of the thorax, deep to the sternum and near the point at which the major vessels leave the heart. However, the thymus is sometimes cervical in position, and in some mammals both cervical and thoracic bodies may be present.

The thymus is, in part at least, derived from the endodermal lining of the embryonic gill pouches, generally from epithelial thickenings formed at the dorsal side of such pouches. There is, however, much variation in the specific pouches concerned (Fig. 245). In fishes every typical gill pouch may produce a thymus bud, and even the spiracle is implicated in many sharks. Among the amphibians the Apoda produce thymic material from every embryonic pouch; but

Fig. 247. A small part of a mammalian thymus, showing the numerous white blood corpuscles, the cells forming the reticulum and one of the peculiar corpuscles characteristic of the gland. (After Dahlgren and Kepner.)

in salamanders the number concerned is usually reduced, and in frogs and toads only the first posthyoid cleft contributes. Reptiles also show a variable condition, but usually only two pairs of pouches contribute to the adult thymus. In birds the thymus usually comes from the second and third posthyoid pouches. In mammals the second postspiracular gill cleft is the usual seat of thymus origin. The mammalian thymus buds are, in contrast to the usual situation, derived from the ventral rather than the dorsal parts of the gill pouches. Another odd feature in mammals is that the cervical part of the thymus, which we have mentioned as present in various forms, does not come from the gill endoderm at all, but from an inpouching of skin in the neck of the embryo; it is, seemingly, a new development, comparable in structure to a true thymus, but not homologous with it. The reticular cells of the thymus appear definitely to be derived from epithelium. The lymphoid cells, however, do not appear to have this origin, but develop directly (as do other blood cells) from mesenchyme.

The thymus grows rapidly during embryonic life and is frequently a massive structure of the throat region of young or larval vertebrates (the calf thymus forms a good proportion of commercial sweetbreads). By the time the adult stage is reached, however, the thymus has ceased to grow and often shrinks; it thus becomes relatively, and often absolutely, smaller than in earlier stages. Its tissues tend to degenerate, and in many adult mammals the thymus has disappeared entirely.

Despite much work and study, little is known of the functions of the thymus. One is tempted to believe, nevertheless, that it has some important relation to the growth and welfare of the young vertebrate. The wealth of lymph cells associated with it strongly indicates that it may be a seat of origin of white blood cells in the young.

12

DIGESTIVE
SYSTEM

The mouth and pharynx, described in the last chapter, are part of the digestive tube. They constitute, however, only its forward outposts, with gathering of food materials as their original major duty. The business of digestion is the function of the remainder of the digestive tract, to which the ancient and simple Anglo-Saxon term "gut" may be properly applied. The gut, so limited, together with its outgrowths—liver and pancreas—will be considered in the present chapter.

Gut Functions. The functions of the gut may be considered under four heads: (1) *Transportation.* Once food materials are gathered, they must be carried along the "dis-assembly line" of the successive gut sectors, and wastes must be ultimately disposed of posteriorly as feces. (2) *Physical treatment.* Although food may be taken in as small particles or brought down to small size in the mouth by chewing, food materials frequently pass back into the gut in large masses, the size of which must be reduced before an efficient chemical attack on them can be made. Further, fluid materials must be added to bring the food to a pasty condition and thus facilitate digestive activity. (3) *Chemical treatment.* This is digestion in the technical sense, the breakdown of potentially useful "raw materials" in the food to relatively simple substances which can be utilized by the body cells. (4) *Absorption.* When this chemical breakdown has been accomplished, the products are absorbed by the intestinal wall for circulation to body cells and storage areas.

Although cilia may be present in certain instances in initial sections of the digestive tract, transportation is mainly the function of the visceral musculature which surrounds the digestive tube for its entire length. At the anterior end of the gut proper (the region of the esophagus), striated musculature, an extension of that of the pharynx, may be present to a variable degree. Along the remainder of the tube the musculature consists of sheets of smooth muscle cells, most typically including layers of both longitudinally and circularly arranged fibers which pass in a somewhat spiral fashion about or along the gut (Fig. 250, p. 346). These gut muscles are innervated by nerves of the autonomic (involuntary) nervous system which may either stimulate or inhibit their movement, and may also be affected by hormones. To a considerable extent, however, they operate quite

342

independently of any central control, being stimulated by the contraction of neighboring fibers or through a local nerve net. The major muscular activity causing movement of food materials is *peristalsis*—successive waves of muscular contraction causing constrictions of the gut which travel backward and push the food before them.

Food taken into the digestive tract must be reduced to a soft pulp, the *chyme*, before effective chemical attack can be made. This reduction is mainly accomplished by muscular action. Most effective here are (in contrast to peristalsis) rhythmic contractions of the gut musculature in food-containing areas. The gut epithelium includes throughout its length mucous cells or mucus-producing glands; the slime they produce facilitates the passage of food and, further, gives an appropriate consistency.

In Chapter 4 we reviewed the chemical requirements of the cells of the body. Needed are oxygen, water, a variety of inorganic salts, glucose, fats, amino acids, and small amounts of other organic compounds—the vitamins—which the cells themselves cannot manufacture. Oxygen is mainly obtained via the gills or lungs; for all other items reliance is had on the food materials brought to the digestive tract and, after absorption, carried on to the cells (or to the liver for storage or reworking) by the circulatory system. Certain of the requirements—water, simple salts—can be obtained from nonliving sources: sea water, for example. The organic materials, however, can be obtained only from other living organisms—from the plants by which alone most needed substances are manufactured, or from animals which have already obtained these substances from plants.

Water, necessary salts, and vitamins as well, are readily absorbed into the circulation by the lining of the intestine. But the situation is different as regards the glucose, fat materials, and amino acids needed in the body. The body cells utilize these in general as building stones to form more complex materials, and in the animal food eaten they are present, naturally, in similar complex form. As such they would not, of course, be immediately useful to the body cells if they were taken into the circulation; but more than that, they are incapable of being absorbed into the gut lining while in this state. A chemical breakdown is requisite; this is accomplished by the action of the digestive enzymes, together with accessory substances which activate these catalytic agents or facilitate their work.

Varied enzymes are present in every cell to bring about the internal chemical changes associated with life processes. In the gut we have a special situation, for in the digestive tube and its glands there are formed enzymes which act outside the confines of the individual cell. Such enzymes are discharged into the gut cavity and attack the organic compounds in the food materials, reducing the complex carbohydrates to simple sugars, most fats to glycerol and fatty acids, the proteins to amino acids. When the work of the enzymes has been accomplished, the organic materials are reduced to molecules of a size and nature which enable them to pass through the cells lining the intestine, and to enter the circulation through the blood vessels and lymphatics surrounding that organ. Sugars and amino acids pass via veins to the liver and thence to the heart and body; part of the fats, reconstituted once the intestinal lining is passed, reaches the general circulation by way of lymphatic vessels.

Development. In Chapter 5 we described the earliest stage in the development of the digestive tract: the formation, in one fashion or another, of an archenteron, or primitive gut.

In Amphioxus (Fig. 65, p. 116) this is a simple cylindric pouch, lined by a single layer of endodermal cells which contain a modest amount of yolk. In mesolecithal egg types, such as amphibians, the early gut is similarly constructed, except that the floor of the gut is not a simple epithelium, but a thick mass of endodermal cells rich in yolk. The embryo's belly is in consequence a paunchy, distended structure (Fig. 70, p. 118) until, at a later stage, this yolk material has been absorbed into the animal's circulation and has contributed to its growth.

In telolecithal eggs the great amount of yolk material has, we have seen, caused a radical change in the nature of the embryonic gut. Instead of forming a mass of yolky endodermal cells, the yolk fails to cleave at all, and the gut lining is at first simply a flat plate lying over the inert yolk. As the embryo develops, the endoderm grows down around the yolk, to enclose it eventually in a yolk sac which is an extension of the gut cavity (Figs. 63, p. 113; 71, *D, E,* p. 119; 74, p. 120). The yolk is gradually digested, the sac being gradually reduced in size as absorption proceeds. Above the yolk sac the embryo proper has meanwhile begun to take form; the endoderm underlying its other structures gradually separates from its yolk sac extension, although the two regions remain connected by a yolk stalk. The gut proper eventually becomes tubular, comparable at last to that of mesolecithal types. Mammals, despite the secondary absence of yolk, follow the telolecithal pattern of gut development and produce a yolk sac, although an empty one (Figs. 63, *D,* p. 113; 74, p. 120; 248). In amniotes we noted (Fig. 63, *B, D*) the presence of a second diverticulum from the embryonic gut, the allantois.

For part of its development the embryonic gut, whether in mesolecithal or telolecithal types, usually has the essential form of a tube closed at both ends. We noted in the last chapter the development anteriorly of a stomodeal depression of the ectoderm which forms the mouth cavity and eventually breaks through to connect with the pharyngeal region of the gut (Fig. 206, p. 298). Posteriorly, mesolecithal types have in the gastrula stage a posterior opening, the blastopore, in approximately the region of the anal or cloacal aperture of the adult. But even in most mesolecithal types the blastopore closes over in an early postgastrula stage; in telolecithal eggs the blastopore is at the best transitory and atypical in its appearance, and, posteriorly as anteriorly, the gut tube ends blindly for much of embryonic life. Analogous to the development of the stomodeum anteriorly is the appearance posteriorly of the *proctodeum* (Fig. 206), an indipping pit of ectoderm beneath the tail, which comes to be closely apposed to the distal terminus of the embryonic gut, separated from it by a membrane which eventually disappears.

Within the gut tube, postgastrular phenomena consist primarily of a lengthening of the tube, a serial differentiation of successive regions into adult organs, and the building up of the complex gut wall structure (Figs. 248, 249). The most anterior gut compartment, the pharynx, has been described previously. The most posterior subdivision is the cloaca; this becomes associated with urinary and genital as well as digestive systems, and its consideration is best postponed until these other systems have been described. Subtracting these specialized terminal areas, there remain for consideration here the major segments of the endodermal tube to which the term gut is for present purposes restricted.

Gut Regions.   A study of the higher vertebrates gives one the impression that the succession of structures along the gut tube is consistent and uniform: esophagus, stomach, small intestine, large intestine, and on to rectum and anus.

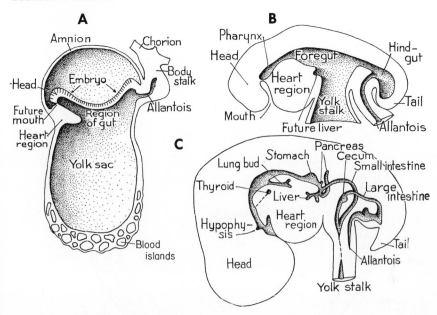

Fig. 248. Diagrams to show the development of the digestive tract in a mammal (Homo). *A*, Stage somewhat later than that of Figure 63, *C*; *B*, stage slightly later than that of Figure 63, *D*; *C*, an embryo of about the age of that in Figure 74. (After Arey.)

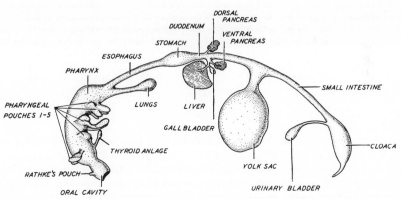

Fig. 249. A diagram of the digestive tract and its outgrowths in an amniote embryo similar to that of Figure 248, *C*, but with the structures concerned shown as solid objects rather than in section. (After Turner.)

But when we extend our view to the lower groups, the picture becomes confused (Fig. 251). As inspection of a shark or cyclostome gut makes evident, the distinction between large and small intestine breaks down completely in primitive vertebrates; the esophagus may be absent as a distinct region; and in some fishes the stomach does not exist. In Amphioxus and cyclostomes the postpharyngeal gut is essentially a single tubular unit; most familiar landmarks are absent.

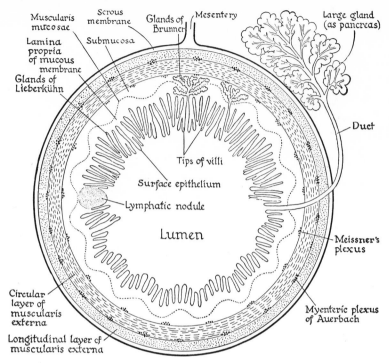

Fig. 250. A diagram of a generalized cross section of the gut. In the upper half of the drawing the mucous membrane is provided with glands and villi; in the lower half it contains only villi. Meissner's plexus (submucous plexus) and the myenteric plexus are part of the autonomic nervous system. The tunica mucosa extends outward as far as the muscularis mucosae; it is followed outward in the section by the submucous tissue, the muscular tunic, in two layers, and finally, the serous tunic. The glands of Brunner and of Lieberkühn are two types of glands characteristic of the mammalian small intestine. (From Maximow and Bloom.)

It is, however, possible to establish in most vertebrates one constant and definite point of division along the length of the gut. Between stomach and intestine there is generally found a distinct *pylorus*, a constriction in the gut tube which guards the gateway into the intestine and is usually furnished with an efficient band of sphincter muscle fibers. In some fish types the pylorus may be poorly marked or absent, but the fact that the bile duct from the liver always enters the intestine a short distance beyond the pylorus enables us, even so, to establish a line of demarcation.

We shall here term the region anterior to the pylorus the *foregut;* the intestinal area beyond, the *hindgut.* In most vertebrates there is some overlapping of function between the two areas, but primitively, it would seem, the two served different purposes: the foregut was merely a short and unimportant connecting link with the pharynx; the intestine, forming the hindgut, was alone responsible for chemical treatment of food as well as its absorption. In the course of vertebrate evolution, however, the foregut has assumed a greater importance; stomach

Fig. 251. Digestive tracts of *A*, a lamprey; *B*, a shark; *C*, a chimaera; *D*, a lungfish; *E*, a sturgeon; *F*, a teleost (perch). The "stomach" of the lungfish is nonglandular and is simply a somewhat enlarged section of the esophagus. (From Dean.)

and, in land forms, esophagus have grown to be gut segments of prominence, and the former has assumed a true digestive role.

Gut Tube Structure.   Although highly variable from region to region and from form to form, the gut tube is generally formed, from the inside outward, of four successive layers, or "tunics" (Fig. 250). (1) The *tunica mucosa* includes the internal epithelium and a connective tissue layer beneath it; this latter often contains smooth muscle fibers. The epithelium is the sole part of the tube formed from the endoderm. Anterior and posterior boundary zones (esophagus, rectum) may develop a stratified epithelium; over the greater length of the gut, however, the lining is a mucous membrane of a simple columnar type. The cells of this epithelium may have varied functions, as secretory cells or (posteriorly) absorptive areas. The epithelium may produce a variety of glandular structures, some the seat of formation of enzymes or other chemically active materials, others producing (as do some, at least, of the superficial cells in every gut region) a mucous material useful in softening and transporting food. (2) The *submucous tissue* is usually a thick layer, mainly connective tissue, but containing numerous small blood vessels and nerve cells and fibers. (3) The *muscular tunic* generally includes two prominent layers of smooth muscle: internally a circular layer capable of constricting the gut, externally a longitudinal layer capable of locally shortening its length. Between and adjacent to the two layers there may be diffuse plexuses of cells and fibers of the autonomic nervous system (cf. p. 509). (4) For most of its length the gut, lying in the abdominal cavity, is surrounded externally by a *serous tunic* consisting of celomic epithelium underlain by connective tissue.

Esophagus.   Not only in Amphioxus and cyclostomes, but in a fair number of jawed fishes as well—chimaeras, lungfishes, certain teleosts—the entire foregut consists merely of a simply constructed piece of tube interjected between pharynx and intestine (Fig. 251, *A, C, D*). Its epithelium is abundantly supplied with mucous cells and often ciliated. No stomach is present in the forms listed; the term "esophagus" may perhaps be applied to this simple gut segment. In all other living fishes—elasmobranchs and most ray-finned forms—a stomach is present in the foregut, leaving a short and ill defined area anterior to it to be considered an esophagus. In many fishes a sphincter may be found between esophagus and stomach.

It is not until we reach land vertebrates that the esophagus assumes prominence. Here, with the loss of gill breathing, the pharynx becomes restricted in length to a short area within the confines of the head and a distinct neck region is developed in amniotes. With pharyngeal reduction, the esophagus elongates proportionately, as the neck region develops, to form a tubular connection between the pharynx and the remaining gut segments, concentrated posteriorly in the abdominal region of the trunk back of the lung region.

Only exceptionally has the esophagus any function beyond that of transportation of food from mouth and pharynx to the important gut structures of the abdomen. The epithelium is in general of a tough stratified squamous type, able to withstand rough food particles; there are generally longitudinal internal folds which render the esophagus distensible. Glands are in general little developed except for mucous cells, but in a few cases there is greater gland development and even some enzyme formation. In a number of elasmobranchs, amphibians, and reptiles (except for turtles), the epithelium may be ciliated; but, in general, food transport is due to peristaltic movements, and there is a stout muscular coat. This is, of course, visceral musculature (cf. p. 275), but the esophagus lies at the boundary zone between striated and smooth muscle regions of the gut, and the nature of the muscle fibers varies. In a majority of vertebrate groups smooth muscle fibers are present; in many fishes, however, and again in mammals there is a notable development of striated musculature (in some fishes this extends to the stomach). Most of the digestive tract lies more or less free within the abdominal cavity; the esophagus, however, lies for most of its length within the compact structures of the neck and "chest."

Two unusual developments may be noted. In the adult lamprey (Figs. 231, *B*, p. 324; 251, *A*) the pharynx is split into two parts. As we have seen, the lower segment is a blindly ending pouch, the upper part a tube leading directly from mouth to gut and hence giving the appearance of an elongate esophagus. In birds there develops part way down the esophagus a distensible sac, the *crop* (Fig. 252, *C*), which serves as a place for the temporary storage of grain or other food; in doves the crop lining exudes, in both sexes, a milky material with which the young are fed.

Stomach. The stomach, found in most (but not all) vertebrates, is a muscular, pouchlike expansion of the foregut, lying in the anterior part of the abdominal cavity. Its epithelial walls are generally highly folded and studded with mucous cells; in specific areas, deep-seated glands produce digestive secretions as well. Accustomed as we are to thinking of the stomach as a normal and useful part of the gut, its absence in a variety of types seems at first an anomalous situation. It is absent in Amphioxus; in true vertebrates it is absent not only in the cyclostomes, but also in chimaeras, lungfishes, and a fair number of teleosts. All other vertebrates have a stomach which, despite great variations in form, has much the same functions in all cases.

The stomach serves as a place for storage of food awaiting reception into the intestine, for the physical treatment of this food, and for initial chemical treatment of protein food materials. These functions give some suggestion of the history of the stomach. In "food strainers" such as Amphioxus (and, we believe, the ancient jawless ostracoderms) food particles were small and collected more or less continuously; they could be passed on directly to the intestine without the necessity of storage or preliminary treatment. Quite in contrast are the food habits of such a predaceous jawed fish as a shark. The food intake is irregular; a large quantity may be taken in at one time and must be stored until the intestine can take care of it. Further, food may be bolted in large chunks upon which the intestinal juices cannot act effectively without proper preparation. We may reasonably conclude that the primary functions of the stomach, when developed in the course of early jawed fish history, were, first, food storage and, secondly, physical treatment of the stored materials. The introduction of digestive enzymes was presumably a phylogenetic "afterthought." Quite possibly the absence of a stomach in cyclostomes is primitive. Chimaeras and lungfishes do not bolt their prey, but cut it into bits before swallowing and hence have less need of a stomach as a storage area. Its absence in these groups and in some teleosts may well be secondary.

As regards external shape (Figs. 252, 253), the central type of stomach structure is that seen in forms as far apart phylogenetically as sharks and men. At the end of the esophagus the digestive tube curves to the left, "descends" and expands into a major sac, and then "ascends" at the right to end at the pylorus. Topographically, the proximal end of the stomach, closest to esophagus and heart, is termed the *cardiac region;* the expanded middle part, the *fundus;* the distal limb, the *pyloric region.* Stomach shapes may vary greatly from group to group. It should be noted that, as found from studies on man, the shape of the stomach in a dead, dissected animal may be quite different from that in life, and that violent motions with marked changes of shape may occur from moment to moment in an active stomach (Fig. 254).

Highly important is the nature of the internal epithelium lining the various regions of the stomach. Beyond the presence throughout of mucus-secreting cells, four epithelial types may be distinguished. (*a*) *Esophageal.* The proximal end of the stomach in many mammals has walls similar to the nonglandular, stratified epithelium of the esophagus; such a stomach region is essentially an expanded

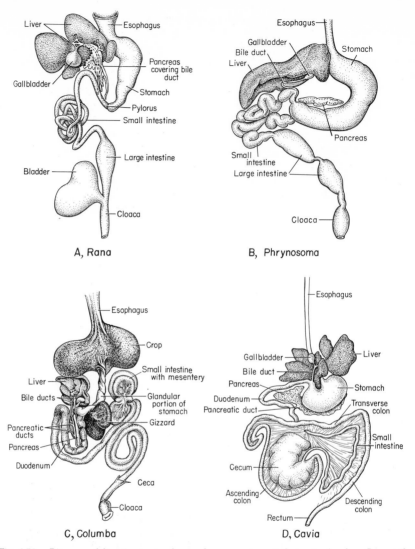

A, Rana

B, Phrynosoma

C, Columba

D, Cavia

Fig. 252.   Diagrams of digestive tract and appendages, seen in ventral view in *A*, a frog; *B*, a reptile; *C*, a bird (pigeon); *D*, a mammal (guinea pig). (*A* after Gaupp; *B* after Potter; *C* after Schimkewitsch.)

part of the esophagus. (*b*) *Cardiac.* In mammals alone there is usually distinguished a transitional region at the proximal end of the stomach in which the epithelium contains compound tubular glands with a mucous product. In this and the following stomach regions the endodermal gut lining is a simple columnar epithelium, although often folded in complicated fashion. (*c*) *Fundus* (Fig. 255). Although the intestine is entirely competent to deal by itself with chemical digestion, the fundus region of the stomach is characterized by the presence of numerous tubular glands in which (in addition to mucous secretion at the gland "neck") there are produced digestive enzymes, prominently *pepsin*, which aids in

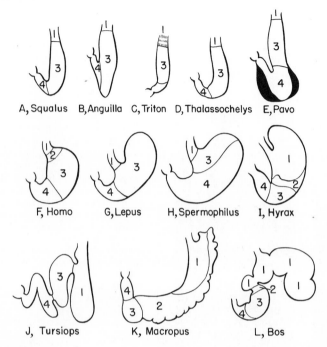

Fig. 253. Diagrams to show stomach form and nature of internal lining in *A*, a shark; *B*, a teleost (eel); *C*, a salamander; *D*, a turtle; *E*, a bird (peacock—the thickened wall of the gizzard is indicated); *F*, man; *G*, a hare; *H*, a ground squirrel; *I*, the coney of Africa; *J*, a whale; *K*, a kangaroo; *L*, a cow. *1*, Epithelium of esophageal type (ciliated in *C*) which may penetrate into stomach, particularly in mammals; *2*, cardiac epithelium (found only in some mammals); *3*, fundus epithelium; *4*, pyloric epithelium. (After Pernkopf.)

Fig. 254. Skiagrams of a human stomach taken at intervals after food, showing its variable shape when active. (After Cole, from Fulton.)

the breakdown of proteins preliminary to intestinal digestion, and a fat-splitting lipase. Hydrochloric acid, which gives the gastric juice an acid condition favorable for the action of pepsin, is produced here as well. In most vertebrate groups both enzymes and acid appear to be produced by cells of a single type. But in mammals there are distinguishable two sorts of cells, both often contained in the same tubule—*chief cells* producing enzymes, and *parietal cells* yielding hydrochloric acid. (*d*) *Pyloric.* This epithelial type, occurring in the distal part of the

Fig. 255. *Left,* a section of a portion of the fundus region of a mammalian stomach, showing the gastric pits (*p*) and the glands deep to the pits and opening into them. Mucous cells (*n*) are present in the neck region of the glands; below, two cell types can be distinguished: parietal cells (*a*), secreting hydrochloric acid, and smaller and more lightly staining chief cells, producing pepsin; *m,* smooth muscle cells. *Right,* a section through the pyloric epithelium, showing pits and glands of essentially mucous type. (From Windle, Textbook of Histology, The McGraw-Hill Company.)

stomach, contains branched tubular glands, comparable to those of the cardiac region.

Although three of the four epithelial types just described are given names used in stomach topography, their distribution is not necessarily correlated with the regions so named. External appearance may be misleading as regards histologic conditions. Thus, for example, the stomach of a mouse is shaped much like that of a man, but, in contrast to human conditions, the greater part of the stomach lining is of esophageal type.

There are numerous variants among vertebrates in stomach form and epithelial linings (Fig. 253). As regards general proportions, shape may vary greatly even in forms with a simple type of stomach. Teleosts, for example, often develop a deep V-shaped fundus, sometimes with a blind sac extending back from the apex of the V; on the other hand, a variety of fishes, long-bodied amphibians, lizards, and snakes have a perfectly straight, cigar-shaped stomach. The stomach has stout muscular walls which through repeated regional contraction may squeeze and soften the food and aid in preparing it for intestinal treatment. Usually this muscular tissue is more or less evenly distributed; in crocodilians and birds, however, it is concentrated in a distal muscular compartment, the *gizzard,* in contrast to a proximal stomach region, the *proventriculus* (Figs. 252, *C*, 253, *E*). The bird proventriculus is notable for the arrangement of the fundus glands in a series of pockets, giving the appearance of compound glands. In grain-eating birds, small stones are swallowed to lodge in the gizzard, and aid this rough-walled chamber in its function as a grinding mill which replaces the lost teeth.

Among many specialized mammalian stomach types, that seen in the cud-chewing artiodactyl ungulates—the ruminants, such as cow, sheep and deer—is notable (Fig. 256). In these forms four stomach chambers are present. Food when eaten descends to engage the attention of the first two of these chambers, the *rumen* and the *reticulum*. The former is a large pouch, the latter a smaller accessory chamber, whose interior surface consists of a criss-cross series of ridges with deep intervening pits (honeycomb tripe!). In these chambers the food is reduced to a more workable pulp by the addition of liquid, is kneaded through the action of the muscular walls, and is subjected to fermentation through the action of bacteria and protozoans, for the breakdown of complex plant materials, particularly cellulose. These microorganisms further aid the ruminants' metabolism by manufacturing useful organic compounds, including amino acids and proteins; still further, they manufacture, from ingested carbohydrates, fatty acids which can be directly absorbed in the rumen.

The rumen having done its best, the animal regurgitates the "cud" for further chewing—or rumination, if you will. On its second descent the food bypasses both the rumen and reticulum, by way of a deep fold in the anterior wall of the latter chamber, and enters the *omasum* (or psalterium) whose parallel internal ridges reminded early workers of the leaves of a hymn book. After further physical reworking here the food at long last enters a final compartment, the *abomasum*. Here are present all three types of epithelium proper to the mammalian stomach—cardiac, fundus, pyloric (Fig. 253, *L*). It becomes obvious that this compartment alone is the "proper" stomach, the other three in advance of it are essentially elaborations of its proximal part.

The Intestine (Figs. 251, p. 347; 252, p. 350; 257, 258).   The major stages in the true digestive process normally occur in the hindgut—the variably built intestine. More anterior segments of the digestive tract receive, transport, store, and prepare food materials. In the intestine, however, occur most—and primitively, all—of the chemical processes which constitute digestion in a narrow sense. And here alone occurs, in most cases, the final crucial step, the absorption of food materials for body use.

Although the production of digestive enzymes may well have been in the vertebrate ancestors an exclusive function of the intestinal epithelium itself, that

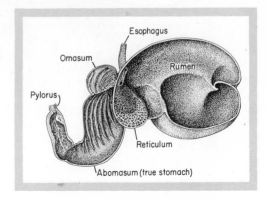

Fig. 256.   The stomach of a sheep, sectioned to show the four compartments characteristic of higher ruminants. (After Pernkopf.)

Esophagus

Omasum

Rumen

Pylorus

Reticulum

Abomasum (true stomach)

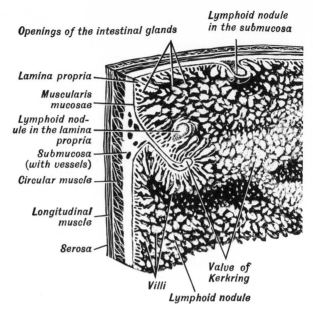

Fig. 257.   Part of the wall of the mammalian small intestine. (After Maximow and Bloom.)

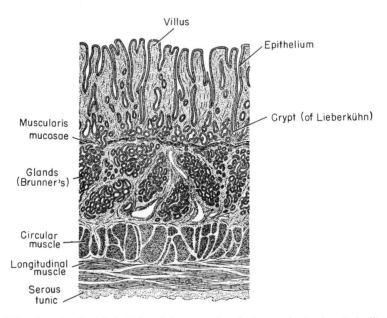

Fig. 258.   A section through the lining of the mammalian duodenum, showing intestinal villi, the crypts between them, a thin muscle layer (the muscularis mucosae) at the base of the mucosa, glands, muscular tunic, and the serous tunic, facing the celomic cavity. (After Young, The Life of Mammals, Oxford University Press.)

is no longer the case in living vertebrates. A special glandular outgrowth of the intestine, the pancreas, has evolved to become the place of origin of a considerable part of these enzymes, poured from it into the anterior end of the intestine; the enzyme pepsin has come to be formed in the stomach; as we have seen, an enzyme may even be produced by the salivary glands of the mouth region. Despite all this, the intestine itself is still important as a seat of enzyme production. It secretes a series of these substances, forming an "intestinal juice" instrumental in the final breakdown of all types of organic materials. Several enzymes aid in preparing sugars for absorption; others split starches and fats, activate trypsin, break down peptides into amino acids, and split phosphoric acid from nucleotides.

Most intestinal enzyme production takes place in a series of small glandular outgrowths in the intestinal walls. The intestinal epithelium proper (Fig. 258) is of a simple columnar type. Occasional goblet cells supply mucus to lubricate food passage, and, despite the development of glands, a certain amount of enzyme formation may occur in the surface cells; these cells, further, produce hormones which, via the blood stream, stimulate to activity and "assistance" the pancreas, gallbladder and intestinal glands (cf. p. 567). In general, however, the intestinal epithelium has as its dominant function the absorption of digested food. Into the substance of its cells pass the water, salts, simple sugars, fats as glycerol and fatty acids (or in part as neutral fats), amino acids, and vitamins needed by the cells of the body; these are discharged from the inner surface of the epithelium into the capillaries and lymphatics with which the intestine is richly supplied.

To afford efficient absorption, a large area of intestinal epithelium is necessary; a short, straight, smoothly lined tube in general will not suffice. Methods of increasing this internal surface are demanded by every vertebrate. This is particularly so in large animals; for here (as in so many cases) surface-volume relations enter the picture, and the area capable of absorption must be roughly proportional to the bulk of the tissues to be nourished. Increases in area may be brought about on three levels of magnitude. (1) Countless small foldings of the gut lining, essentially of microscopic size, which involve only the innermost, mucous tunic of the gut, are found in all vertebrates. Primitively these mucous layer folds appear to have been in the form of a network of tiny ridges with pockets between them; a more specialized condition, prominent in mammals, is the presence of countless *villi*, small finger-like projections from the gut wall (Fig. 257). (2) In numerous instances somewhat larger folds may be present, often as a series of rings, in which the submucous layer is involved (as in the mammalian folds of Kerkring; Fig. 257). (3) Major structural developments occur which greatly increase the area of the intestinal surface. Two are most notable: the spiral valve intestine, short, but of complicated internal structure, characteristic of primitive vertebrates; and the slender tubular intestine, developed by teleosts and by tetrapods, in which length—and hence surface area—is increased by coiling.

THE SPIRAL INTESTINE (Figs. 21, p. 41; 24, p. 44; 26, p. 46; 251, *A–E*, p. 347). In members of every major group of fishes we meet with a type of intestine seemingly primitive for vertebrates—the spiral intestine. This is characteristically developed in elasmobranchs, in which it is typically a large cigar-shaped body, extending nearly straight anteroposteriorly and occupying most of the length of the abdomen. Internally, it is seen to have a complex structure. In addition to minor epithelial folds, the surface area is greatly increased by the presence of a *spiral valve*. This is a fold of epithelium and connective tissue extending from one end of the intestine to the other, which in typical forms twists numerous times in spiral fashion along the walls of the gut. A somewhat similar structure would be formed if we took a carpenter's auger, or bit, and enclosed it in a tube. In some sharks the spiral valve may become exceedingly complex, with dozens of turns along its course. The development of the spiral fold greatly increases the surface area inside the gut, and also its functional length, for the food material must follow a long course down around the twists of the spiral staircase to reach the end of the seemingly short intestine. In a minority of sharks the spiral valve has a different form. The base of the valve twists but little and hence is relatively short; the valve fold, however, is highly developed and rolled up into a great scroll running lengthwise of the intestine.

The primitive nature of the spiral structure is demonstrated by its widespread presence in other fish groups, although the number of turns is never as high as in typical sharklike fishes. The spiral intestine is present in chimaeras and to some degree in cyclostomes, and fossils even demonstrate its presence in the ancient class of placoderms. Further, it was present in the early bony fishes, for living lungfishes and all lower actinopterygians retain a spiral valve, and even a few teleosts have a vestige of this structure.

Many workers on the digestive tract consider the intestinal region, here termed as a whole the hindgut, to be basically composed of two parts, which in mammals form the small and large intestines. Conditions in fishes show that this belief, based on human conditions, is unsound. In sharks the spiral intestine alone includes almost the entire length of the digestive tube between stomach and cloaca. Anteriorly, there is merely a short connecting piece, at the most, between stomach and spiral valve region. Posteriorly, there is only a short terminal segment, somewhat comparable to the rectum of higher types, leading to the cloaca. Sharks have in the "rectal" region a finger-shaped *rectal gland*, which has much the appearance of the cecum of land vertebrates. It is, however, not homologous with that structure, but secretes a fluid which is a thick solution of sodium chloride and is thus important in ridding the shark blood of excess salts (a problem discussed in the following chapter).

THE INTESTINE IN HIGHER VERTEBRATES. The teleosts, and land vertebrates as well, have abandoned the old-fashioned spiral intestine for a new type of hindgut structure. In these forms (Figs. 251, *F*, p. 347, 252, p. 350) the intestine is a slender tube, without major internal folds. In compensation, however, it is generally much elongated; in teleosts its length is, on the average, half again that of the whole body. A long, coiled part of the teleosts' hindgut is a highly active digestive region, functionally comparable to the spiral intestine of their ancestors, on the one hand, and on the other roughly comparable to the small intestine of their tetrapod cousins. Distal to this we find a relatively short and straight end gut segment, somewhat similar to the colon of land vertebrates, leading to the anus. Apart from gut coiling, most teleosts and their lower actinopterygian relatives add to their intestinal surface by the development of distinctive *pyloric ceca* —pouches, sometimes very numerous, in the proximal end of the intestine, into which food materials may enter and be absorbed.

In the vertebrate embryo the intestine is supported dorsally by a straight and simple dorsal mesentery. When, in teleost or tetrapod, intestinal coiling occurs, this mesentery becomes a complex, tangled structure, fanning out here, crumpled there; frequently the sheet supporting one intestinal coil may fuse with an adjacent one, or an intestinal loop may fuse with the dorsal celomic wall (cf. Figs. 201, 204, pp. 293, 295).

In both teleosts and land vertebrates there are enormous differences from form to form in the degree of convolution of the intestine and consequently in the amount of absorptive surface as well as in the length of the food channel. Two factors may be correlated with intestinal length: absolute size, which we have already discussed, and food habits. Plant food, often in the shape of compact masses of complex carbohydrates, particularly cellulose, is difficult to digest, and in general the intestine is longer in herbivores than in flesh eaters. From teleosts to mammals (although with many variants), small flesh eaters tend to have the shortest intestines, large feeders on plant materials the longest.

Although a spiral intestine was surely present in the crossopterygian ancestors of the land vertebrates, no living tetrapod has the slightest trace of this organ. Instead, land forms have paralleled the teleosts in the development of a rather simple tubular intestine, coiled to a variable degree. A seemingly primitive and generalized tetrapod type is that found in a variety of amphibians and reptiles (Fig. 252, *A, B*, p. 350). The hindgut is usually divided into two distinct segments. The proximal, and longer, part is a *small intestine,* of narrow calibre, usually considerably coiled and often much longer than the entire body of the animal. At the end of the small intestine in lower tetrapods there is frequently a valvular constriction beyond which may lie a well defined end gut broadly homologous with the *colon,* or large intestine, of mammals; this is a relatively short, straight segment, expanded proximally and well furnished with mucous lubrication. There is usually a small out-pocketing, a *cecum,* at the proximal end of the colon (present also in lungfishes). Materials which have failed to be absorbed in the small intestine pass into the colon to be collected into the feces. Digestive juices carried down from the small intestine may continue their work while food materials are in the colon. This region is, further, populated with bacteria which putrefy the food residues, break down proteins into a variety of substances which are of dubious value to the organism or are actually toxic, and may effect the difficult task of digesting the complex plant carbohydrate, cellulose. Through the walls of the colon is absorbed much of the water remaining in the prospective feces as well as some further food substance and part of the products resulting from putrefaction.

In birds (Fig. 252, *C*) the small intestine is similar to that of lower tetrapods in build, but more highly convoluted; on the average, the length of its coils is more than eight times that of the whole body. This great elongation is presumably correlated not merely with the herbivorous habits of a large percentage of birds, but even more with their great activity and high metabolic rate, which results in an increased food demand and the consequent requirement of additional absorptive surface in the intestine. The end gut is relatively short and not expanded proximally. Distally, it is expanded and not sharply marked off from the cloaca, so that, since birds have no functional urinary bladder, urine and feces tend to be mixed, to be discharged as a "slushy" material. Paired ceca are generally present.

In mammals (Fig. 252, *D*) the small intestine has undergone a development comparable to that of birds. In relation, again, to metabolic needs the intestine is complexly coiled, with a length which averages seven to eight times that of the body, and is several times greater than this figure in some large herbivores. In man it is customary to distinguish three successive regions of the small intestine (duodenum, jejunum, ileum) but the differences between them are not marked, and in many mammals these terms can be applied only in a rather arbitrary manner.

In some small mammals the large intestine, or colon, usually (but not always) separated by a valve from the small intestine, may be a short, straight structure; in most mammals, however, this gut segment is highly developed—much more so than is usual in other tetrapod classes. It is a tube of considerable diameter, but of irregular shape, usually with a series of outpocketings and longitudinal muscle bands (absent, however, in carnivores and ruminants). Its characteristic shape, as seen from the ventral surface, is that of an inverted U, or of a question mark. The morphologically proximal segment is the "ascending" colon, running anteriorly along the right side of the body; the small intestine enters this segment at a sharp angle. After a flexure, the "descending" colon runs posteriorly along the left wall of the body cavity. In primates a transverse segment is present between ascending and descending portions, and in most herbivores further coiling occurs.

Almost every mammal has a cecum, furnishing an additional area for colonic functions and a reservoir of intestinal bacteria. As its development shows, the cecum is a ventral side pocket of the gut tube; but in most mammals the adult condition gives it the appearance of being a part of the ascending limb of the colon, with the small intestine opening into its side. Frequently its diameter is as great as that of the colon itself, or greater. Its length is variable; it may be long and even much coiled in herbivorous animals. In man it terminates in the narrow *vermiform appendix.* This is frequently cited as a vestigial organ supposedly proving something or other about evolution. This is not the case; a terminal appendix is a fairly common feature in the cecum of mammals, and is present in a host of primates and a number of rodents. Its major importance would appear to be in the financial support of the surgical profession.

The mammalian *rectum,* endowed with muscular sphincters of both smooth and striated types, is an end piece of the digestive tract, leading to the anus. As will be seen (p. 406), it is a part of the embryonic cloaca and hence not strictly comparable to the terminal gut segment to which this name is sometimes given in groups in which a cloaca is retained in the adult.

The Liver.   In concluding this chapter we treat of two organs, liver and pancreas (derived embryologically from the gut endoderm), which are important both for secretions which they furnish to the intestine and for their functions in the metabolism of food already digested.

Amphioxus has a large saclike structure branching off the gut in a position comparable to that of the liver (Fig. 4) and having a venous portal system corresponding to the hepatic portal. But this sac, with a ciliated glandular epithelium, seems to be a seat of enzyme production and lacks the characteristic metabolic functions of the liver. If this sac is truly antecedent to the liver, there was certainly a major evolutionary change above the Amphioxus stage. All vertebrates possess a definitive liver which, as the most massive of the viscera, always occupies a considerable area in the more ventral and anterior part of the abdomen. As shown by its embryonic history, the liver develops as an outpocketing of the gut in the ventral mesentery below the anterior part of the intestine (Fig. 2, *D,* p. 6) and is, hence, covered by celomic epithelium. It remains connected to the stomach by a part of the ventral mesentery, termed in mammals the *lesser omentum.* Below the liver a persistent part of the ventral mesentery, the *falciform ligament,* ties it to the ventral body wall. Its major attachment, however, is an anterior one. In lower vertebrates, as we have seen, a transverse septum develops, separating the pericardial cavity from the remainder of the celom (cf. p. 290);

in mammals this septum is incorporated in the diaphragm. The liver is attached to septum or diaphragm—broadly, or by a narrowed *coronary ligament*—and from this point extends backward to expand into the abdominal cavity.

From the point of view of gross morphology the liver is of little interest. It has no constant form, and needs none; sufficient bulk and an appropriate internal arrangement, on a microscopic level, of its cells and vessels are all that are necessary for its proper functioning. In various types more or less distinct right and left lobes are developed; but details of arrangement and lobation vary greatly from form to form and even between individuals. Ancient priests divined the future from the liver patterns of animal sacrifices; there was plenty of scope for interpretive imagination. Essentially one may say that the liver accommodates its form to that of the other viscera and expands into any part of the abdominal area not needed by other structures.

In general, as we have noted, the endoderm forms only the thin lining of the gut tube and gut glands. Only in the liver (and to a lesser extent in the pancreas) does endodermal material bulk large in body composition. Except for a framework of connective tissue and the varied vessels which weave through its substance, the liver is composed entirely of the countless *liver cells*, of endodermal derivation. These are polyhedral structures, morphologically similar in all parts of the liver. Despite a deceptive simplicity in microscopic appearance, these cells play a complex series of varied roles in the life of the body.

One function of the liver is that of a gland tributary to the intestine. In the adult vertebrate this function is a minor one, but historically the liver presumably arose as a glandular structure (whether or not homologous with the Amphioxus pouch) and embryologically arises as a glandlike outgrowth from the gut tube (Figs. 198, p. 291; 206, *A*, p. 298; 248, *C*; 249, p. 345). The liver appears at an early stage in the development of the primitive gut as thickened masses of tissue which push out ventrally and anteriorly from the gut wall, surrounding a median tubular outgrowth. The main mass of liver tissue extends forward in the developing ventral mesentery to the region of the transverse septum, leaving behind a side pocket of the tube which forms the gallbladder. From its anterior base in the septum or diaphragm the liver tissue rapidly expands posteriorly into the celom.

In the adult the primary glandular structure of the liver is for the most part lost. Throughout the liver there remains, however, a network of tiny *bile tubules* with which every cell is in contact. These tubules gather cell secretions, the *bile*, into a *hepatic duct* draining the liver (Fig. 259). Part way toward the intestine this main duct is joined by the *cystic duct*, connected with the *gallbladder*, in which bile may be stored. Beyond this junction a *common bile duct* (ductus choled-

Fig. 259. Diagram of an early stage of liver development to show the relationship of the ducts.

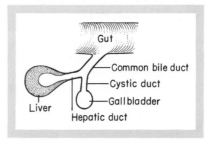

ochus) typically empties into the small intestine, sometimes in association with a duct from the pancreas. This normal arrangement is subject to great variation. The gallbladder may be absent (as, for example, in lampreys and many birds and mammals); several separate bile ducts may open into the intestine; more rarely duct as well as bladder may be missing. Of the bile contents, most are purely excretory, including products of decomposition of protein materials and bile pigments derived from the hemoglobin of worn-out red blood cells. The only actively useful materials are the bile salts, which, discharged into the intestine, aid a pancreatic enzyme in the splitting and absorbing of fats.

The major duties of the liver cells, however, are not those directly connected with digestion, but with the treatment, within the confines of the liver, of food materials after their digestion and absorption into the body. In part this activity is that of a storage depot. All classes of food materials may be stored in the liver, but particularly notable from a quantitative point of view is carbohydrate storage. Large quantities of the simple sugars received into the body are stored in the liver as glycogen, and released again into the blood stream when needed. Every cell of the body is capable of producing, for its own needs, various changes in the food materials it receives; the liver cells do more, acting as chemical retorts whose complex activities benefit the body as a whole. Proteins may be synthesized, fats altered in composition, proteins and fats made into carbohydrates, blood cells done away with, nitrogenous cell wastes such as ammonia transformed into uric acid or urea to be eventually excreted by the kidneys.

For its major functions as storage depot and manufacturing plant the liver is strategically situated along a "main line" of the transportation system formed by the blood vessels. The liver receives by way of an arterial blood supply the oxygen necessary for its activities. Bulking much larger is the venous blood flow through the liver. As will be described later (pp. 436–438), all the venous vessels from the intestine carrying absorbed food collect as a hepatic portal system of veins which carry blood to the liver; after passing through a series of sinusoids in that organ, this venous blood finally reaches a hepatic vein which runs on toward the heart. From the vessels which they border, the liver cells thus have the first opportunity to select, for storage or chemical modification, food materials newly arrived in the body.

In relation to the overwhelming importance of its metabolic rather than its secretory functions, the liver has tended to abandon its original glandular structure in favor of one in which a pattern of proper arrangement of cells in relation to the circulatory vessels is dominant. The pattern varies from group to group and, owing to its complexity, is not too well understood in many cases. In mammals much of the liver appears to consist of *lobules* of microscopic size (Figs. 260, 262). These are, crudely, polyhedral blocks of cells arranged in what one may term a three-dimensional honeycomb. Surrounding each lobule are connective tissue sheets in which are located a "trinity" of vessels: branches of the bile duct and of both the portal vein and the hepatic artery bringing blood inward. Bile tubules and capillaries from the artery penetrate into the lobule from outside, as do sinusoids from the portal system. Inside each lobule a central cavity contains a *central vein* which carries the blood from the sinusoids onward to the hepatic vein. The liver tissue between the sinusoids has the appearance of strands or cords of cells. Actually, however, these apparent cords are cut sections of plates of cells (Fig. 262) lying in a tangled network about the sinusoids. These plates are generally not more than two cells thick, so that every cell faces a sinusoid on one side or the other; in birds and mammals they are but one cell thick.

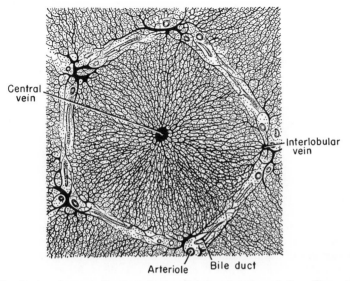

Fig. 260. Section of a mammalian liver, showing a lobule and portions of others. The portal system of veins has been injected (black), showing the course of the blood from interlobular veins *via* a multitude of sinusoids through the sheets of liver cells to central veins of the lobules; branches of the bile duct and of the hepatic artery are seen in the interlobular septa. (After Young, The Life of Mammals, Oxford University Press.)

Fig. 261. Diagrams to show the development of liver lobules. Masses of liver tissue (parenchyma) become clustered about branches of the excurrent hepatic vein; the portal vein branches (and those of the hepatic artery and bile duct, not shown) ramify external to the developing lobules. (From Arey, after Mall.)

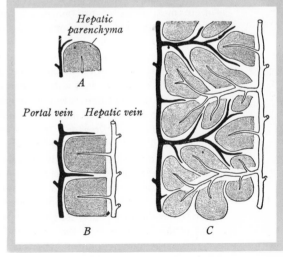

The Pancreas. Common to all vertebrates, this organ is generally found as a mass of soft tissue lying in the mesentery not far distal to the stomach and morphologically dorsal to the intestine; it opens by one or more ducts into the proximal part of the intestine near the point of entrance of the bile duct. It is a major item among the glandular materials which appear on the table as "sweetbreads." In most vertebrates it is a moderately compact if somewhat amorphous

Fig. 262. Diagrammatic enlargements of a small portion of a liver lobule (such as is shown in Fig. 260) to show the structure of the plates of liver cells. The plates are separated and perforated by channels which in life are occupied by sinusoids. *Left,* typical structure in a lower vertebrate; the plates are in general two cells thick. *Right,* mammalian structure; the plates are in general one cell in thickness. (After Elias.)

body, but in various cases, notably teleost fishes, it may be diffuse, spreading out thinly along the mesenteries and even invading the substance of the adjacent liver or spleen. In many instances there is but a single pancreatic duct. The opening of this duct is variable in position; it may enter either morphologically dorsal or ventral surfaces of the intestine, and, if ventral, may be combined with that of the common bile duct. Multiple ducts may occur; three, for example, are usual in birds.

Histologically, the greater part of the pancreas is a typically exocrine glandular structure, with fine branching ducts collecting secretions produced by the cells of terminal acini and passing them on to the duct system (Fig. 263). In nearly all forms studied, however, areas of tissue of another type can be seen distributed through the gland as isolated pancreatic islands; these form an endocrine organ, discussed in Chapter 17.

The exocrine functions of the pancreas are well known. It secretes a number of enzymes (or, rather pro-enzymes) which are discharged into the proximal end of the intestine and are responsible for a great part of the digestive activities of the gut. The pancreatic enzymes are important for the digestion of all three major types of organic food materials. It was once thought that the pancreas produced a single enzyme for each of the three. Modern work has, however, shown the presence of more than half a dozen enzymes in the pancreas. Only one is known for fat digestion, but there are two or more for both carbohydrates and proteins, and it is not unlikely that still others may be discovered.

The functional "reason" for the evolution of the pancreas is readily deduced. Originally, we may well believe, the intestine itself was the place of production of all the enzymes which it utilizes. Some, as we have seen, are still produced in the gut; but the segregation of much of this type of activity in a distinct organ would appear to have been an advantageous development. Conditions in Amphioxus and the cyclostomes render such a story reasonable. In the former there is no separate pancreas, but groups of cells lying in the wall of the anterior part of the intestine show the characteristics of pancreas cells. The cyclostomes show a transitional condition. There is no formed pancreas, but these cells have formed a series of tiny separate glands around the gut near the opening of the bile duct. Lungfishes likewise show a primitive condition, with the pancreas tissue embedded in the wall of the intestine.

The embryologic picture also agrees with this interpretation of pancreas evolution and, further, throws light on the varied nature of pancreatic ducts (Fig. 264). The pancreas is not a single structure, but a compound one. In the early

INTERLOBULAR SEPTUM   PANCREATIC ACINUS

INTERLOBULAR DUCT   BLOOD VESSEL   ISLET OF LANGERHANS

Fig. 263. A section through the pancreas of a rat, to show both exocrine tissue (pancreatic acini) and a pancreatic island. A duct of the exocrine part of the gland and a connective tissue septum between lobes are also shown. (From Turner.)

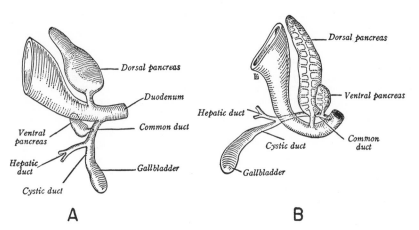

Fig. 264. Diagrams showing two stages in the development of the human pancreas. *A*, An early stage, with both dorsal and (smaller) ventral pancreas developing. *B*, Later stage in which dorsal and ventral portions are beginning to fuse. (After Arey.)

stages of representatives of a number of vertebrate groups clusters of pancreatic cells are found in the gut wall near the area in which the liver diverticulum is developing. A major outpocketing of pancreas tissue takes place at the dorsal edge of the gut tube. Part, however, of the pancreatic tissue may become involved in the mouth of the future bile duct, and one or a pair of pancreatic outgrowths forms in the walls of that tube. These tend to grow upward and fuse with the dorsal pancreas. Not always do all three structures persist in the adult, but usually the dorsal outgrowth and one, at least, of the ventral pair contribute to the adult pancreas. Each part may retain a separate duct; on the other hand, the duct systems may fuse, and a single outlet, dorsal or ventral, may serve the entire gland. As still another variant, the dorsal pancreas may fail to separate as distinctly as is usual from the gut wall, and its various parts may all drain separately into the intestine.

13

EXCRETORY AND REPRODUCTIVE SYSTEMS

From a functional point of view, a joint consideration of urinary and genital systems seems absurd, for excretion and reproduction have nothing in common. Morphologically, however, the two systems are closely associated in their mode of development and their use of common ducts, and it is impossible to describe one without numerous cross references to the other. This association appears to be due mainly to embryonic propinquity; in the embryo the major organs of the two systems arise in areas of the mesoderm which lie close to one another in the walls of the trunk near the upper rim of the celomic cavity (Fig. 279, p. 387).

URINARY ORGANS

Kidney Tubule Structure and Function. Paired kidneys (Greek *nephros*, Latin *ren*), developed in varied form in all vertebrates, are the major organs of the urinary system. The basic kidney structure is the minute *kidney tubule*, or *nephron;* the numerous tubules connect with a duct system which eventually leads, posteriorly, to the body surface.

Among vertebrates as a whole the most generalized type of tubule is that shown diagrammatically in Figure 265, *A;* tubules of this type are present in such diverse forms as sharks, fresh-water and many marine teleosts, and amphibians. The proximal part of the unit is the spherical *renal corpuscle* (malpighian corpuscle). If sectioned, this is seen to consist of two parts, a *glomerulus* and a *capsule* (Bowman's capsule). The glomerulus is formed by the circulatory system; it is a compact little cluster of small blood vessels the size of capillaries, which coil through the mass in intricate loops (Fig. 266). The capsule is a proximal part of the tubule; its shape is that of a double-layered hemisphere. The inner layer is closely adherent to the lining of the vessels of the glomerulus, so that

365

only thin membranes separate the blood stream from the cavity between the two layers of the capsule. This cavity is continuous with that of the *convoluted tubule.** The tubule may attain considerable (relative) length; usually distinct proximal and distal segments can be distinguished. Along its course it is closely bordered by a network of capillary vessels. Distally, each tubule connects, in a fashion which varies in different groups, to ducts leading to the exterior of the body.

The result of the activity of the tubule and its corpuscle is the production of urine, destined for excretion and derived, obviously, from the associated circulatory vessels. Urine is composed mainly of water, but contains to a variable degree other substances in solution. These include salt ions, particularly sodium, potassium, chloride, and sulfate; bulking much larger, however, are waste materials, mainly simple nitrogen compounds, which are generally in the form of urea or uric acid. The major functions of the kidney tubules are twofold: (1) regulation of the internal environment and (2) elimination of waste.

In Chapter 4 we pointed out that for the health of the body cells it is necessary that they live in a proper environment, and that a most important feature of this is the continued presence, in solution in the interstitial fluids which surround them, of appropriate amounts and proportions of specific simple salts. These salt ions are present in the same proportions in the blood stream and in the interstitial fluid with which it readily interchanges through capillary walls. The maintenance of proper salt content in the body liquids as a whole demands a proper balance between body intake, mainly via the intestine, and output. Deficiencies in salt intake are the concern of the digestive apparatus; excesses in intake, which bring the salt concentration above the proper level, require excretory devices for their removal. Such structures as the salt-excreting glands of the lamprey and teleost gills, the shark rectal gland, the nasal glands of marine birds, or the sweat glands of the mammalian skin are of use here. The kidney tubules, however, furnish the main means for the elimination of excess salts on the one hand and, on the other, for the removal of excess amounts of liquid which tend to dilute too greatly the body fluid.

Apart from regulation of salt and liquid content, however, there is a further important kidney tubule function: the elimination of wastes and harmful materials from the body. Digestion may bring into the body fluid compounds which are, for cellular utilization, inert, or may be actually destructive or poisonous; the kidneys are in most cases effective in removing them. Most important of materials needing removal are the broken-down products of metabolism, particularly of proteins. From carbohydrates and fats the main end products put out by the body cells are, as we have seen (p. 89), carbon dioxide and excess water, both of which are readily eliminated. Protein metabolism, however, produces other substances, primarily simple compounds containing nitrogen. The greater bulk of the nitrogenous waste as it leaves the cell consists of ammonia, which is highly toxic. In some vertebrates—teleosts, crocodiles—it remains in this form until excreted. In most, however, nearly all the ammonia is transformed in the liver, almost as fast as it appears in the blood, into harmless ammonia compounds— urea and uric acid. Urea includes the greater part of the excreted nitrogenous waste in sharks, amphibians, aquatic turtles and mammals; uric acid (an almost

---

* Note that the term "tubule" is generally used in two ways: (1) as a synonym of nephron, i.e., a name for the entire nephric unit of renal corpuscle and convoluted tubule; and (2), more properly, for the latter structure only.

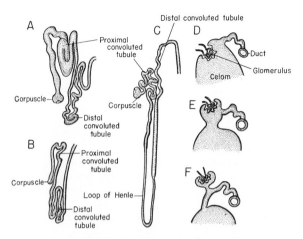

Fig. 265. Tubule types. *A* to *C*, The three major types common in adult vertebrates. *A*, Presumably the most primitive, with corpuscle of good size, found in elasmobranchs, fresh-water bony fishes, amphibians. *B*, Corpuscle reduced or absent, characteristic of salt-water teleosts, reptiles. *C*, Corpuscle large; a loop of Henle inserted; found in mammals, birds. *D* to *F*, Primitive tubule types found in lower vertebrates, principally in the embryo, and perhaps illustrating the early evolution of kidney tubules. *D*, Tubule runs from celom to kidney duct; glomerulus, if present in celom, not associated with tubule. *E*, Special small celomic chamber formed for glomerulus. *F*, This chamber has become the capsule of a renal corpuscle; tubule still connects with celom; closing the celomic opening leads to more progressive tubule type.

insoluble material) is the bulk of the material in lizards, some chelonians, and birds, excreted as chalky sludge (with useful conservation of water as compared with urea in solution). Nitrogenous materials may be eliminated by the gills in teleosts, and a minor amount by the sweat glands in mammals. For the most part, however, the kidneys bear the responsibility for the excretion of nitrogen wastes.

The way in which a kidney functions is today fairly clear. Two distinct operations are present, one having to do with the renal corpuscle, the other with the tubule proper. The structure of the corpuscle suggests that we are dealing with a relatively simple filtering device; that through the membranes separating the glomerulus from the cavity of the capsule there passes a filtrate of the blood plasma. Studies on amphibians show that this is indeed the case. Liquid drawn from the capsule by micropipette proves on analysis to have in it many of the materials found in the blood, and in the same proportions. Blood corpuscles, of course, do not pass through this filter, nor large molecules, such as the proteins specific to the blood stream. All other materials, however, including not only wastes, but also valuable food materials, particularly glucose, pass through readily. Still further, the amount of liquid filtered is excessive. It has been calculated that if all the liquid passed through the glomeruli of a frog were to be eliminated from the body, nearly a pint of urine would be produced daily by this small animal, and that a man would produce about 50 gallons!

Obviously, nothing of the sort happens. If the only kidney action were simple filtration from the glomerulus, the body would be dehydrated in short order. Further, glomerular filtration would do little to alter the proportions of materials found in the body fluid; wastes and harmful or excess materials would still be present in the remaining fluids in the same relative amounts, and in addition valuable food elements would be sacrificed.

The corrective to this situation lies in the work of the convoluted tubule. From the nephric corpuscles the filtrate traverses the length of these tubules to kidney ducts and, in many groups, to a storage reservoir, the bladder. Analysis of the resulting urine after this passage tells a different story: we are dealing with a different substance. For one thing, the volume is greatly reduced. In a frog, not more than 5 per cent of the liquid filtered from the glomeruli reaches the bladder, and in a man hardly 1 per cent. Further, the composition is much changed. Useful food materials such as glucose, although readily filtered into the tubule, do not ordinarily reach the bladder, and of other substances, the relative proportions are radically altered.

It is thus obvious that, in addition to the glomeruli, the kidney tubules themselves play a major role in the process of excretion; they are not morphologic curiosities, but highly important functionally. They are lined with epithelia which change from one part of the tubule to another in patterns which are quite variable in different vertebrate types, and the structure of the kidney is so fine and complex that in many groups the specific function of different tubule segments is uncertain. As a whole the tubule cells have two activities. A major one is that of reabsorption of most of the filtrate. Much of the water is obviously resorbed, and food materials are withdrawn from the fluid as it passes by—principally glucose, it appears, in the proximal part of the tubule, salt distally. On the other hand, there is further active excretion of waste substances through tubule cells into the urine as a supplement to the filtrate.

In a nephron the crude work is, so to speak, done by filtration from the glomerulus; the tubule proper adds the necessary refinement to the process.

Tubule Types and Vertebrate History.   Whether fresh or salt water formed the original vertebrate home has been a problem of interest to students of kidney function as well as students of classification and phylogeny. The paleontologic record strongly suggests that the earliest fishes dwelt in fresh waters

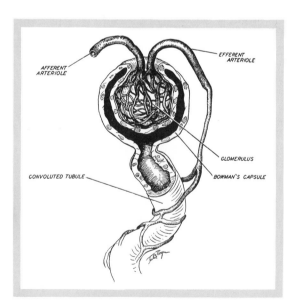

Fig. 266.   A mammalian renal corpuscle. Here the vessels around the tubule come from the arteriole; in animals with a renal portal circulation, capillaries from this system surround the tube instead. (After Turner.)

and only later invaded the seas. A study of kidney tubule structure and function leads to the same conclusion.

Three main types of nephric units may be found in the functional adult kidney of one group or another (Figs. 266, 267). All have a well convoluted tubular region. (*a*) In one type (Fig. 265, *A*), found characteristically developed in such varied forms as amphibians, most bony fishes, and elasmobranchs, there is a renal corpuscle of good size, and the amount of filtrate (and consequently of water output) is high. (*b*) A second type (Fig. 265, *B*) is that found, with variations, in various salt-water teleosts and in reptiles. Here the corpuscle is small or absent (and in marine teleosts the distal convoluted tubule is absent as well); obviously water output is low. (*c*) A third type (Fig. 265, *C*) is that seen in mammals and, in less extreme form, in birds. Here we see the interjection, into the middle of the convoluted tubule, of a long, slim extra loop, the *loop of Henle.* Although, with a large corpuscle, a large amount of fluid is produced, relatively little reaches the bladder through this type of tubule.

From the distribution of these tubule types among the vertebrates a consistent story can be constructed regarding the environmental history of vertebrates. It is assumed that (*a*) is the primitive tubule type, possessed by early fresh-water vertebrates and retained by forms which still inhabit such waters. Such an animal lives in a medium more dilute than its own body fluids; in consequence, water tends to invade the body by osmosis at any membranous surface. To prevent overdilution of the body content and death, large amounts of water must be elim-

Fig. 267. Diagram of kidney tubules of various vertebrates, all reduced on the same scale, to show the relative size of the components in the different groups. The glomeruli are at the upper end in each case, and the tubules are represented as if straightened out. The glomeruli are well developed in most groups and of enormous size in cyclostomes and elasmobranchs, but of reduced dimensions in reptiles, and are done away with in some marine teleosts (5). All have a proximal convoluted segment of the tubule; an intermediate segment, followed by a distal convoluted tubule, appears in some fishes and is present in all land forms. The intermediate segment becomes the loop of Henle in birds (in part) and mammals; this loop may be much elongated in the latter group. 1, Hagfish; 2, skate; 3, sculpin; 4, catfish; 5, toadfish; 6, frog; 7, painted turtle; 8 and 9, chicken; 10 and 11, rabbit. (After Marshall, Kepton, from Prosser.)

inated, and this is afforded by the large corpuscle and its large output of water in the dilute urine.

In a marine fish, on the other hand, the sea water has a higher salt concentration than the body fluids, and the result tends to be loss of water into the surrounding "brine," dehydration, and an overconcentration of salts in the body. In marine teleosts and lampreys salt excretion from the gills (cf. p. 322) partially remedies the situation; in addition, however, reduction or loss of the renal corpuscle from the tubule system conserves a vast amount of water in many marine teleosts, and much nitrogenous waste is excreted from the gills to make up for decreased kidney function.

From this discussion of fish tubules it is reasonable to conclude that the presence of a large glomerulus is a primitive character; that this is a result of its efficiency as a pump for the discharge of quantities of water; and that the desirability of such discharge is due to the fresh-water environment of early vertebrates.

But one could still, as far as we have here carried the argument, advocate a marine environment as primitive and suggest that the development of a large glomerulus came later, when vertebrates moved into fresh water. The thesis that a large glomerulus is associated with fresh-water existence seems to be negated by the sharks, for here we have fishes which have a large glomerulus and a tubule of type (*a*) and yet are marine!

It is the sharks, however, which clinch the argument for fresh water, when the situation is studied. The shark lives in a medium in which the salt concentration is greater than that in his own body fluids; yet he does not lose water to his environment and can pump water out of his system through large glomeruli with as little concern as a fresh-water fish. For although his salt concentration is that of any other animal, and low compared to sea water, his total osmotic pressure (and that is what counts) is comparable to that of the sea, or even slightly higher. To some degree the shark has solved the problem of salt concentration by the development of a rectal gland, mentioned in the last chapter, which can rid him of a considerable amount of sodium chloride. But more especially, the shark has adopted a unique mechanism; it retains without apparent harm much of its nitrogenous waste, in the form of urea, in the blood stream and thus raises its total concentration of materials in solution without increasing its salts. A special section of each shark kidney tubule has the function of resolving urea from the urine flowing through it.

We have thus in sharks and in salt-water teleosts and lampreys two radically different kidney adaptations to salt water. If the sea had been the original home of fishes, we would hardly expect such differences to exist. It is more reasonable to assume that the ancestors of both sharks and marine teleosts lived in inland waters; that (as the fossil record indeed shows) they invaded the seas independently; and that in the two cases quite different methods were evolved for combating the dangers of too great salinity.*

There is still a further quirk to the story. Of all vertebrates whose blood composition is known, one—the hagfish—fails to regulate its salt content, and simply adopts the composition of the sea water surrounding it as that of its own

---

* Oceanic birds and sea turtles, which have only sea water as drink, have similar problems. The marine birds have evolved an efficient salt gland within the nasal cavity; the sea turtles have similar glands in the orbit, presumably a specialized part of the lacrimal gland system.

internal environment. From this it has been argued that the primitive vertebrates, like the living hagfish, lived in the sea, with no regulation of their salt content, and that such regulation—and life in fresh waters—came later. But a little reflection will show the improbability of such a conclusion. It implies that salt regulation, with a variety of different methods of attaining this, was "invented" independently by a number of different fish groups—lampreys, sharks, bony fishes. In consideration of alternative theories in any situation one should apply Occam's razor—never adopt a complicated solution when a simple one is readily available. It is much more probable that early vertebrates generally regulated their salt content, but that the hagfishes, invading the oceans, failed to find an answer to the problem of keeping salt concentration down and, so to speak, gave up in despair.

Land vertebrates have basically much the same problem as a marine fish. They live in a dry environment, where water is continually lost through the body surface, with danger of dehydration and consequent increase in salt concentration in body liquids. Conservation of water is necessary, particularly since there can be no gill excretion of salt or waste. It is probable that the ancestral reptiles had kidney units of type (*a*), with a large corpuscle and normal tubule, and a free flow of watery urine. Some saving of water is effected by urine retention in a cloacal bladder (p. 405) with absorptive walls. In living reptiles further reduction of water output has been attained by reduction of the size of the corpuscles and a consequent reduction of the amount of water filtered through them. Mammals have developed a different method of conserving water. The normal corpuscle is present, and a large quantity of urine is poured into the tubule. The tubule, however, is an "Indian giver." There is a considerable resorption of water in any type of tubule; in these forms there is inserted between proximal and distal convoluted tubules the long, thin loop of Henle, which descends into the medulla of the kidney (cf. Fig. 276, p. 382). Here processes involving sodium exchanges and osmotic relations result in further resorption in the distal convoluted tubule and collecting tubule, and consequently in conservation of body water. Birds have some development of a loop of Henle. In addition, nitrogenous waste is excreted, as in many reptiles, as uric acid; this is almost insoluble and needs little water for its carriage.

Primitive Tubule Structures. The types of nephric units described in the foregoing discussion are those most characteristic of adult vertebrate kidneys. Still other types, however, may be noted; they are more often found in embryos, particularly in the first units developed, than in adults, and more common in lower than in higher vertebrate types; there is hence considerable reason to consider them primitive in nature.

These types (Fig. 265, *D–F*) have in common the fact that they have openings into the celomic cavity which are commonly ciliated funnels. In some cases there is, in addition to the celomic opening, a typical renal corpuscle connected with the tubule. In a few instances we find a glomerulus which protrudes into the celomic cavity near the funnel instead of having a position in the tubule structure. And in still other cases no corpuscle or glomerulus of any sort is present.

One theory of the origin of the vertebrate nephric structures suggests that the last-described condition was the truly ancestral one; that the tubules first functioned in draining waste products and excess liquid from the celomic cavities. A subsequent development of blood vessels, as glomeruli, in the walls of the celom afforded a greater supply of liquid for the tubules to work upon. A third stage, the theory suggests, was the incorporation of the glomerulus in a corpuscle forming an integral part of the nephric unit; the final stage, a loss of the primitive celomic connection, and dependence upon the glomerulus alone for a supply of filtrate.

Most major invertebrate groups have excretory structures of various types, termed *nephridia*. These, however, are not homologous with the vertebrate nephron, which appears to have evolved independently, mainly as a water "pump" for life in fresh water, with elimination of wastes as a secondary function. Amphioxus strikes a seemingly discordant note, for this creature has a segmental series of little nephridial structures which have no structural relationship to the vertebrate kidney but are similar to those of many mollusks, annelids, and flatworms. They never connect with the celomic cavity; they open individually to the body surface; they arise from ectoderm, not mesoderm; instead of glomeruli, the urine-collecting structures are peculiar "flame cells" (solenocytes). These nephridia appear to be primarily for waste disposal, rather than water expulsion. Possibly such structures were present in the marine chordate ancestors of the vertebrates but were abandoned with the "invention" of the water-pumping tubule which enabled early vertebrates to move into fresh water.

Organization of the Kidney System.   So far we have discussed merely the nature of the vital microscopic kidney elements. Now to be considered is the organization of these secretory units and the duct systems leading from them to form the gross structure of the urinary system.

As seen in the higher, amniote classes of vertebrates, the pattern of the kidney system is fairly uniform and apparently simple, with paired, compact kidneys projecting into the abdominal cavity from its dorsal walls, and paired ureters carrying urine from the kidneys and often emptying into a median bladder. Rather comparable structures are seen in various lower types. Study, however, shows that there are great differences from group to group in the construction of the urinary system. The kidneys themselves are varied in structure; the ducts vary; the bladder is variable.

These variations have two major causes: (1) Unlike most body organs, the kidney must begin its operations at a rather early stage of development, to take care of the metabolic wastes of the rapidly growing embryo. In consequence there is no possibility of the peaceful and undisturbed development of a kidney structure suitable for postnatal life alone; there must be rapidly constructed a functioning embryonic kidney which, however, is subject to modification or replacement in later developmental stages and adult existence. (2) The sex glands, testis and ovary, lie adjacent to the kidney structure; these glands—the testis particularly—tend to "invade" the urinary system and take over part of its tubes and tubules as a conducting system for their products. The urinary organs have been markedly modified in most vertebrate groups as a result of this invasion.

Holonephros and Opisthonephros.   We may begin our discussion of types of urinary systems by the description of the structure and embryonic development of an "idealized" primitive kidney which may be termed a *holonephros*.

In our embryologic story we noted that in every trunk segment the mesoderm includes, on either side, a nephric region, often segmentally distinct as a *nephrotome*, a small discrete block of tissue interposed between somite and lateral plate (Figs. 63, *D*, p. 113; 67, *C*, p. 117; 269). In the ancestral vertebrate, we believe, each nephrotome gave rise to a single nephric unit; the small celomic

Fig. 268. Diagrams of kidney types. *A,* Pronephros (embryonic); *B,* theoretical holonephros (each trunk segment with a single tubule), much as in a young hagfish or apodous amphibian; *C,* primitive opisthonephros: pronephros reduced or specialized, tubules segmentally arranged, as in hagfish. *D,* Typical opisthonephros; multiplication of tubules in posterior segments, testis usually taking over anterior part of system, trend for development of additional kidney ducts (most anamniotes). *E,* Metanephros of amniotes: an opisthonephros with a single additional duct, the ureter, draining all tubules. In *A,* both sides of the body are included; in *B* to *E,* one side only (cf. Fig. 288).

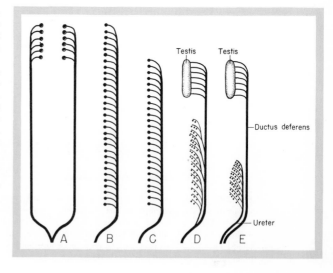

cavity of the nephrotome became the cavity of a renal corpuscle, and out from this grew a kidney tubule. There would thus be established a row of nephric units, segmentally arranged, down either side of the body. As with the somites, the differentiation of nephrotomes takes place in embryos from front to back; in consequence the oldest members of the tubule series in our ideal ancestral type would be those at the anterior end of the series, the last-formed those at the posterior end of the trunk. With the downgrowth of the myotomes, the kidney units would be separated from the surface of the body by the trunk musculature and associated skeletal elements. The nephrotome lay above the celom, and the developing kidney region would in later stages lie dorsal to the celomic region, well to either side of the midline (Fig. 279, p. 387). As noted earlier, conditions in embryos of lower vertebrates suggest that the nephric units in an ancestral vertebrate retained the celomic connection now seen in early embryonic stages and occasionally in adults in various lower groups.

In many invertebrates the kidney elements open directly to the exterior. In the vertebrate embryo, however, a longitudinal duct develops on either side, gathering the urine from the series of segmentally arranged units; the two ducts often unite before emptying to the exterior in the region of the cloaca. The primitive kidney duct has been variously named; it will here be termed the *archinephric duct.** This duct is, like the tubules, of mesodermal origin. Most typically it forms by a fusion of the tips of the tubules of the most anterior and first formed nephric units (Figs. 268, *A,* 269, *A, B*). It grows backward along the lateral surface of the nephrotomes, frequently using further nephrogenic material in its formation. As tubules develop farther back, they grow outward to connect with this

---

* It is often called the *wolffian duct,* after its discoverer. *Pronephric duct* and *mesonephric duct* are terms applied to it on embryologic grounds. When serving as a kidney duct in the adult of lower vertebrates, it is sometimes incorrectly called a ureter. If taken over by the genital system, it becomes the duct of the epididymis and the ductus deferens (pp. 402–404).

374

Fig. 269. Diagrams of the anterior part of the trunk of an embryo (skin removed) to show the development of the archinephric duct. *A*, Most anterior—pronephric— nephrotomes are budding out tubules which tend to fuse posteriorly. *B*, The pronephric tubules have formed the duct; some of the nephrotomes farther posteriorly are forming tubules which are to enter the duct. *C*, The more posterior tubules have joined the duct. *D*, The pronephros lost, but the archinephric duct formed by it persists to drain the more posterior part of the kidney.

previously formed structure. The end result (Figs. 268, *B*, 269, *C*), ideally, is a holonephros: a kidney with a single nephric tubule in each trunk segment on either side of the body, the series draining through a pair of archinephric ducts. Such an ideal is found only in the larvae of hagfishes and the Apoda among the amphibians.

The adult hagfish has a kidney which does not differ greatly from this type, but even here the most anterior and first-formed kidney tubules—those which form the duct—are specialized or degenerate; and the same is true of all higher vertebrates. These anterior tubules are termed the *pronephros* (Figs. 268, *A*, 269, *B*, 270, *A*). The remaining, major part of the kidney system, from which is formed, in one fashion or another, the kidney of adult living vertebrates, may be termed as a whole the *opisthonephros*, the "back kidney" (Fig. 268, *C*, *D*). This opisthonephros generally differs from the theoretic holonephros in three main particulars: (1) The anterior tubules, the pronephros, do not form part of this structure. (2) The simple segmental arrangement is no longer present (above the hagfish level). For most, at least, of the length of the adult vertebrate kidney numerous tubules may develop in each segment; in fact, separate nephrotomes may fail to develop, and, particularly toward the back end of the trunk, there may be a development of a mass of tubules from a longitudinal band of unsegmented nephric tissue. (3) In most vertebrate groups the archinephric duct is utilized by the male for sperm transport, and part or all of the business of urine transmission may be performed by a newer type of duct, a ureter or some equivalent.

Amniote Kidney Development. To show an extreme contrast with the "ideal" holonephros, we may describe the development of the kidney in mammals (Fig. 270); the story is similar in the other amniote groups—reptiles and birds. Our departure here from a logical sequence is due to the fact that study of the mammalian kidney has been influential in the development of concepts of kidney types and their nomenclature.

As the differentiation of mesodermal somites progresses in the mammal embryo, simple, segmental, rounded nephric vessels, or nephrotomes, appear below them in a limited number—not over a dozen—of the anterior body segments, at the back of the head and along the future neck region. These vesicles form the pronephros. In the nephrogenic tissue adjacent to these rudimentary tubules there forms the anterior end of the archinephric duct; this grows rapidly backward toward the cloacal region. In a mammal the tubules constituting the pronephros disappear at an early stage; indeed, the first ones begin to degenerate before the last members of this short series are formed.

Segmental growth of the kidney structure continues backward without interruption beyond the end of the pronephric tubule series. The tubules now formed are considered to belong to a second embryonic nephric structure, the *mesonephros*, which is the functional kidney for a considerable period of embryonic life in mammals and may persist until after birth in reptiles. Still segmental, to begin with, mesonephric tubules continue to form along the trunk as far as the lumbar region. Pronephric units in mammals are at best simple structures, without glomeruli and often rudimentary; the mesonephric elements, on the other hand, have characteristic glomeruli and well-coiled tubules. At first there is but one tubule to a segment in the mesonephric region; later, however, additional tubules develop, and the segmental condition is obscured.

As the back portions of the mesonephros are developed, the more anterior tubules are degenerating. Long before birth in many mammals the entire mesonephric series has lost its original urinary function, as has the original urine tube, the archinephric duct, although, as will be seen, mesonephric tubules and duct

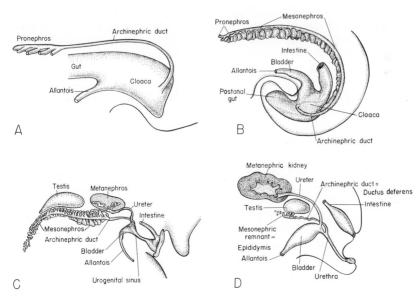

Fig. 270. Diagrams to show formation of the metanephros of an amniote (male) embryo as seen from the left side. *A*, Pronephros and duct formed; *B*, mesonephros partly formed; *C*, pronephros reduced, posterior part of mesonephros functional, ureter formed, and metanephros beginning to differentiate; *D*, definitive stage; mesonephros reduced, and tubules and duct utilized only for sperm transport; metanephros, the functional kidney.

persist in modified form as part of the reproductive system of the adult male (pp. 402–404, Figs. 270, 277, p. 383; 289, p. 400).

The most posterior part of the nephrogenic tissue is not utilized, however, for the mesonephros. It does not become segmented, but instead forms into a spherical mass in the roof of the lumbar region of the body cavity. In this mass of mesoderm there presently appear large numbers of kidney tubules. These tubules are to form the *metanephros,* the functional kidney of the late embryo and the mature mammal. Unlike the mesonephric units, these tubules do not empty into the archinephric duct; there develops a new tube, the *ureter,* to drain them. This is an outgrowth of the archinephric duct. From near the point where each archinephric tube enters the cloaca, this new duct buds off and grows forward and upward to enter the metanephric tissues. Here it forks repeatedly into smaller tubules. At the tips of the smallest branches of the ureter, the *collecting tubules,* clusters of nephric tubules come to open. Further growth and differentiation of this metanephric mass produce, on either side of the body, the adult kidney, which is thus in form, position, and mode of drainage quite distinct from pronephros and mesonephros.

Pronephros, Mesonephros, and Metanephros.   We see in this story the development in the amniote embryo of three successive kidney structures— pronephros, mesonephros, metanephros. It is often stated or implied that these three are distinct kidneys which have succeeded one another phylogenetically as they do embryologically. Upon consideration, however, it will be seen that there is no strong reason to believe this. The differences are readily explainable on functional grounds; the three appear to be regionally specialized parts of the original holonephros which serve different functions.

In many vertebrates the pronephric tubules differ in structural features from those of the mesonephros; but these differences are not constant, and sometimes part or all of the pronephric units are identical in nature with those behind them. The one really distinctive feature of the pronephros is that the archinephric duct is formed here. But there is nothing really significant or mysterious about this; it is a practical matter. An actively growing embryo has wastes to excrete. When kidney tubules are formed anteriorly, they begin the process of urine formation. The formation of a urinary tube for drainage cannot be delayed until the entire kidney is formed; the anterior tubules just cannot wait that long.

In amniotes the metanephros is readily distinguished from the mesonephros. It is a discrete formation; it attains a vastly greater size; its drainage by the ureter rather than by the archinephric duct is definitive. But although the metanephros assumes a distinctive nature, it is, to begin with, simply a greatly enlarged posterior termination of the band of nephrogenic tissue from which mesonephros and pronephros were also formed. Its large size is, of course, due to the presence of large numbers of tubules; the need for large numbers of tubules in the amniotes is correlated in part with the relatively large size of the late embryo and adult, in part with the high metabolic activity of birds and mammals. The efficiency of a kidney depends upon the amount of surface present in its glomerular filters and tubule walls, and the same surface-volume relationship confronts us here as in the case of many other organs. The presence of a special duct system is obviously related to the impossibility of attaching all the countless tubules directly to a single unbranched archinephric duct. Further, the utilization of the archinephric duct for sperm transportation in the mature male makes a separation of a urinary transporting agency desirable.

The adult kidney of fishes and amphibians is frequently termed a mesonephros and assumed to be homologous with the embryonic kidney alone in amniotes. This position appears to be untenable; it implies that there is nothing in the kidney of a shark or frog comparable to the metanephros of amniotes. But the embryologic story shows that the entire length of the band of nephrogenic tissue is used in the development of the kidney of lower vertebrates, and hence the back portion of their kidney is formed from the same materials as the metanephros. Never, it is true, is the adult kidney of a lower vertebrate so completely concentrated in one short region as is the case with the metanephric type, but somewhat similar conditions may be observed. It is often stated flatly that the anamniote kidney is drained by the archinephric duct, as in the case of the embryonic mesonephros; but, as we shall see (Fig. 277, p. 383), various cartilaginous fishes and amphibians have structures comparable to ureters. All in all, it is perhaps best to confine the term mesonephros solely to the kidney of embryonic amniotes. The adult anamniote kidney may be termed the opisthonephros, with the understanding that the amniote metanephros is a special variety of this structure.

Pronephros and Head Kidney. We have described the pronephros as the most anterior and first developed part of the embryonic kidney—essentially that set of tubules associated with formation of the archinephric duct. In amniotes and Chondrichthyes the pronephros is an exceedingly short-lived structure, never survives in the adult and, except for its association with duct formation, hardly deserves the dignity of a separate name. In contrast are conditions in other fishes and amphibians, with small-yolked eggs, and in which the embryo generally becomes an active food-seeking larva at an early stage. The pronephros persists in these larvae to satisfy excretory needs; it is, however, highly specialized and is frequently termed a *head kidney*, in reference to its anterior position. In most cases a fair number of tubules from the more anterior body segments are involved; however, the number is usually reduced during embryonic development, so that the larval head kidney has but from one to three large convoluted tubules, and in frogs and salamanders only two or three units are involved at all.

In the head kidney the tubules generally have ciliated funnels opening from a celomic space containing a single large glomerulus. This nephric part of the celom may be closed off from the remainder of the celomic cavity as a closed pocket—a sort of large renal corpuscle. In the cyclostomes the portion of the celom drained by the head kidney is the pericardial cavity; as a further peculiarity in this group, we find that the liquid filtered from the pericardial cavity does not pass into the kidney duct, but, instead, into an adjacent vein. The larval head kidney disappears as a functional organ in the adult amphibian and in many fishes; it is commonly modified into a mass of lymphoid tissue. It persists, however, throughout life in many teleosts and in hagfishes.

The Opisthonephros of Anamniotes (Figs. 271, 272, 273). We shall here survey the varied form which the opisthonephros assumes as the functional adult kidney in lower vertebrates. In larval hagfishes, as we have seen, the kidney is essentially a holonephros; in adult cyclostomes this is not the case, for the pronephric part has disappeared from the kidney system. The structure is nevertheless simple. In an adult hagfish the opisthonephros consists simply of a long series of tubules arranged in segmental fashion most of the length of the trunk, each tubule draining directly into the archinephric duct. In a lamprey the tubules are rather more numerous, but the structure is otherwise similar.

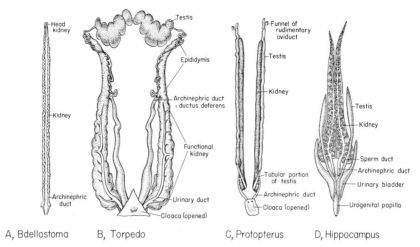

A, Bdellostoma   B, Torpedo   C, Protopterus   D, Hippocampus

Fig. 271.   Urogenital systems in ventral view of males of *A*, the slime hag, Bdellostoma; *B*, the elasmobranch Torpedo; *C*, the lungfish Protopterus; *D*, a teleost, the seahorse Hippocampus. In *A* the testis, not shown, is pendent from a mesentery lying between the two kidneys and has no connection with them. In *B* the testis has appropriated the anterior part of the kidney as an epididymis, much as in most land vertebrates, and utilizes the entire length of the archinephric duct as a sperm duct. In *C* the testis ducts drain, on the contrary, only into the posterior part of the kidney and thence to the archinephric duct. In *D* the sperm duct is entirely independent of the kidney system. (*A* after Conel; *B* after Borcea; *C* after Kerr, Parker; *D* after Edwards.)

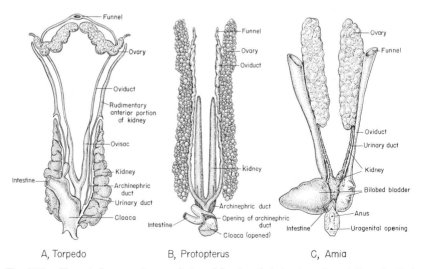

A, Torpedo   B, Protopterus   C, Amia

Fig. 272.   Urogenital systems in ventral view of females of *A*, the elasmobranch Torpedo; *B*, the lungfish Protopterus; and *C*, the primitive actinopterygian Amia. (In Torpedo the shell gland is not developed.) (*A* after Borcea; *B* after Parker, Kerr; *C* after Hyrtl, Goodrich.)

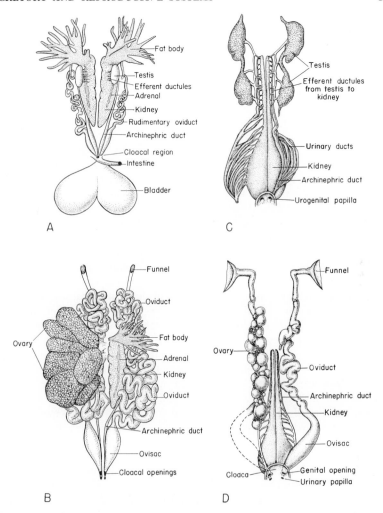

Fig. 273. Urogenital system of amphibians. *A, B*, Male and female organs of a frog (Rana); in *B* the ovary (shown only on the right side of the body) is in a condition close to breeding maturity. The bladder and intestine are not shown in *B. C, D*, Male and female organs of the urodele Salamandra. In *C* the urinary ducts of the right side are detached and spread out to show their connections with the kidney. In *D* the ovary is shown only on the right side; the oviduct of the same side is partly removed to show the more posterior urinary ducts. Ventral views. (*A* and *B* after McEwen.)

In gnathostomes the kidney is universally more complex. Two major developments are seen in the various jawed fishes and amphibians: (1) There is a notable increase in tubule number, with loss of segmental arrangement and growth of kidney bulk, often associated with a concentration of the functional kidney into a small portion of its original anteroposterior extent; (2) part of the opisthonephric kidney system in the male is utilized for the passage of sperm. These two features are correlated, for in many groups the testis tends to take over some one specific region of the kidney—usually at its anterior end—for its special use; this region may lose all or part of its proper renal function, and the remaining portion becomes in compensation greatly hypertrophied.

The anamniote kidney is generally elongate; in its length are included most of the trunk segments behind the pronephric region. Seldom, however, is the entire length of the kidney well developed and functional as a urinary organ. In sharks and chimaeras the anterior part is slender, and the great bulk of the kidney substance is concentrated posteriorly in a dozen body segments or less, a condition obviously antecedent to the development of the metanephric kidney type. The reason for this concentration appears to be the fact that the testis has become associated with the anterior part of the kidney and has come to use its tubules for sperm transport to the archinephric duct (cf. Fig. 277, *C, D*). This portion of the kidney loses part or all of its urinary function; it may become in the male essentially an accessory to the testis (comparable to the mammalian epididymis) and may degenerate in the female. The salamanders and Apoda among the amphibians show a kidney structure comparable to that of the cartilaginous fishes. The anurans, in which only a few segments are present in the entire trunk, have, as one would expect, a short, compact kidney.

The general trend in kidney evolution in anamniotes has been toward posterior concentration of urinary function in the opisthonephros and an approach to the metanephric kidney type of amniotes. The actinopterygians, however, have struck out along a line of their own in kidney evolution as in other regards. In teleosts (and Polypterus as well) the testis has acquired a duct quite independent of any connections with the urinary system, and an elongate opisthonephros often persists (Figs. 271, *D*, 277, *G*, 288, *C*). The lungfish illustrated in Figures 271, *C*, 277, *F*, 288, *B* shows a morphologic stage antecedent to this condition.

The Amniote Kidney.   As indicated by our story of mammalian development, the amniote kidney is a specialized end type in which the trends seen in lower classes toward compact structure and separation from the genital system have attained a peak development. There remains no connection between the formed kidney and the male genital organs, for the old archinephric duct has been completely abandoned to testicular use in the male, and the kidney is drained by the ureter and its branches (cf. Fig. 277, *E*). The anterior part of the opisthonephros is functional in the embryo as the mesonephros, but has disappeared in the adult except for vestiges attached to the testis. The mature kidneys, the metanephroi, are formed by a great expansion of nephric material in the region of the most posterior body segments and are relatively short and stout structures, bulging downward into the abdominal cavity in the lumbar region.

The reptilian kidney (Fig. 274) frequently has a crenulated appearance due to the fact that it is built of numerous small lobules. The lobulation, in turn, is due to the arrangement of the urine-collecting system. The ureter has, typically, numerous long branches into which series of collecting tubules empty; each branch of the ureter is the center of formation of a lobule. Compared to other amniotes, the number of tubules is low; estimates of 3000 to 30,000 are recorded for various lizards. This may perhaps be associated with the generally low rate of metabolic activity in reptiles as compared with birds and mammals.

Embryology indicates that the adult bird kidneys (Fig. 275) arise from nephrogenic tissue belonging to but a single segment at the end of the trunk, but these organs are of relatively enormous size, typically filling large paired cavities in the roof of the abdomen, shielded by the sacrum and ilia. Each of the rather elongate kidneys is usually divided into three or more irregular lobes, and these

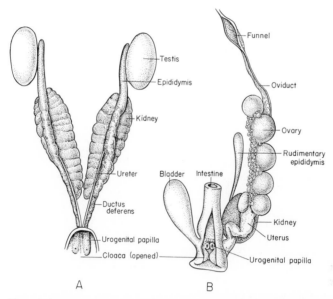

Fig. 274. Urogenital organs in reptiles. *A*, Male organs of the lizard Varanus. *B*, Female organs of Sphenodon. In *A* the bladder is omitted; in *B* it is shown turned to one side. In *B* the organs of the left side only are figured. Ventral views. (*A* after Vandebroek; *B* after Osawa.)

into a large number of small lobules, each containing a branch of the ureter. The glomeruli are small, and tubules are exceedingly numerous; a fowl, for example, has been calculated to have some 200,000 of them, or twice as many as a mammal of comparable size.

The mammalian kidney (Fig. 276) has generally a smooth external surface. Internally, it shows a markedly different build from that of other amniotes. Within the substance of the kidney the ureter instead of sending off branches, as in reptiles and birds, expands into a cavity, the *renal pelvis*, into which the collecting tubules drain. Frequently the pelvis is partially subdivided to form small cup-shaped cavities, *calyces*. The kidney is most commonly a bean-shaped structure, and these cavities lie along its inner curve (the *hilus*). Into each calyx converge collecting tubules in a radiating structure termed a renal *pyramid*.

We have earlier (Fig. 265, *C*, p. 367) noted the structure of the mammalian nephric unit; characteristic are large glomeruli and the presence of the long straight loop of Henle between proximal and distal convoluted regions. In section, the mammalian kidney usually shows distinct "rind" and marrow—*cortical* and *medullary* portions. The former contains principally the renal corpuscles and the convoluted portions of the tubules. The medulla is mainly composed of long, straight collecting tubules and loops of Henle; it is these which give the striated appearance to the pyramids. Although the number of nephrons is not so great as in birds of similar size, it is nevertheless high; even a mouse appears to have about 20,000, and in such large mammals as a man or cow the number may run into the millions.

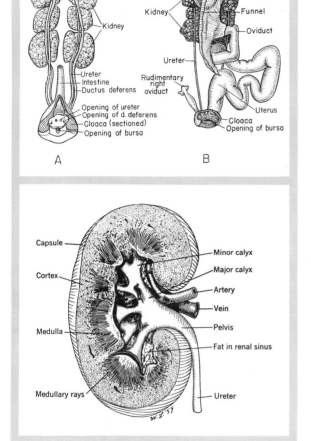

Fig. 275. Urogenital organs of pigeon; *A*, male; *B*, female. The bursa (of Fabricius) is a pouch, of uncertain function, opening dorsally into the cloaca of birds. (*A* after Röseler and Lamprecht; *B* after Parker.)

Fig. 276. Section through a mammalian kidney. (From Windle, Textbook of Histology, The McGraw-Hill Company.)

Blood Supply to the Kidney. The functions of the kidney demand a profuse blood supply for the filtration activities of the glomeruli and for the activity of the tubules. The nature of the kidney circulation will be touched upon in the next chapter, but may be briefly noted here.

In cyclostomes and in mammals the entire blood supply to the kidney is arterial. In all intermediate groups, however, from jawed fishes to reptiles and birds, we find an accessory blood supply in the renal portal system (cf. pp. 440–441). Venous blood from the tail or hind legs, or both, in its course to the heart is forced to pass through a venous capillary system within the kidney.

In vertebrates with only an arterial blood supply the arteries furnish blood both to the glomeruli and to capillaries which cluster about the tubules. In forms with a renal portal system the functions of the two blood supplies are distinct. The glomeruli are always supplied by arterial blood, and there may be some arterial capillaries at the proximal end of the tubules—notably in birds. Venous blood, on the other hand, is never concerned with the glomeruli, but forms a network around the convoluted tubules. No fully satisfactory reasons have been advanced for the development of the renal portal system and its later abandonment in mammals, nor for the curious division of labor between arterial and venous systems when both are present.

Evolution of Urinary Ducts (Figs. 277, 288, p. 398). In the primitive vertebrate kidney, as seen in cyclostomes, a pair of simple archinephric ducts sufficed for the drainage of urine. In gnathostomes, however, a complicating factor enters the situation. Sex rears its head; the archinephric duct is invaded in the male by the genital system.

In cyclostomes the sperm are shed into the celomic cavity and reach the exterior through a posteriorly placed abdominal pore. But in primitive gnathostomes, it appears, there arose connections between the sperm tubules and kidney tubules; the path of sperm discharge came to be via the archinephric duct. As a result, this duct came to serve a dual purpose. Among modern vertebrates it functions fully for both sperm and urine conduction in a few scattered forms—the Australian lungfish, lower actinopterygians such as sturgeons and gar pikes,

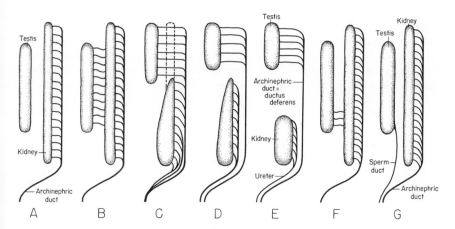

Fig. 277. Diagrams to show the differentiation of urinary and genital ducts in the males of various vertebrates. Ventral views, left side only shown. *A,* Condition seen in cyclostomes; archinephric duct solely for urinary system; gonad not involved. *B,* Condition presumably primitive for gnathostomes, preserved in the sturgeon and gar pike. Testis connects at various points with kidney and thence with archinephric duct. *C,* Stage beyond *B* as seen in many sharks and urodeles. The testis has taken over the anterior part of the original kidney; the functional posterior part of the opisthonephros tends to drain by a series of ureter-like ducts. *D,* Stage more advanced toward the amniote condition, found in some sharks and urodeles; the kidney drainage is by a single ureter-like duct. In females (not shown) of the types represented by males in *C* and *D,* the tendency toward development of new ducts for kidney drainage is generally not so marked as in the males; the condition shown in *D* is reached by few female forms below the amniote level. *E,* Amniote condition; a definite single ureter formed in both sexes. *F* and *G,* Lungfish and a teleost, showing a type of specialization peculiar to modern bony fishes. The testis tends to concentrate its connections toward the back end of the kidney (as in *F*), and in teleosts evolves a separate sperm duct, releasing the archinephric duct for its original urinary functions. Note that the two ducts for sperm and urine in *G* are *not* respectively homologous with ductus deferens and ureter, as might be thought at first sight.

the common frog, and a few apodans and urodeles such as Necturus (the mud puppy).

A condition of this sort is, however, unsatisfactory. It is clear that in the course of gnathostome history there has been a struggle between urinary and genital systems for possession of the archinephric duct.

Among bony fishes the urinary system has been the winner. In African and South American lungfishes and Polypterus (Figs. 277, *F*, 288, *c*, p. 398) sperm enter this kidney duct, but only near its posterior end; for most of its course it is a purely urinary tube. In teleosts development of a discrete sperm tube has been completed; there is a separate route for sperm conduction back from the testis, and the archinephric duct is triumphantly restored to its original function of conduction of urine alone (Figs. 277, *G*, 288, *g*, *h*, p. 398).

In all other gnathostomes—sharks on the one hand, most tetrapods on the other—the fight has gone the other way; in most the archinephric duct has been completely taken over in the male sex as a sperm duct. In both sexes, new tubes have appeared, to care for drainage of urine from the kidney.

Among the amphibians are seen a number of stages in the development of functional replacements for the archinephric duct (Fig. 277, *C*, *D*). In some members of all three orders the archinephric duct still carries both products; a series of short collecting ducts empty into it along the length of the kidney. In other members of both anuran and urodele orders, however, the more posterior collecting ducts make their own way to the cloaca independently of the archinephric duct, and in males of such anurans as Alytes, the "obstetrical toad," and of the common newt Triturus, these tubules have joined to form a single duct draining the entire kidney quite independently of the archinephric duct. Such a duct appears to be essentially the equivalent of the ureter of amniotes. In female amphibians a similar but rather more retarded development of a ureter can be seen, despite the lack of other use of the archinephric duct.

In the Chondrichthyes a parallel development has occurred. In no male shark or skate is the archinephric duct concerned with urine transport. A fan of tubes collects urine from the opisthonephros and unites posteriorly into a common stem—a ureter. In sharks and skates, as in amphibians, ureter development is not so marked in the female, where there is no conflict with sex organs, as in the male. In some female elasmobranchs the archinephric duct still drains the anterior part of the kidney, while more posteriorly the drainage is by a fanwork of ureter-like tubes emptying posteriorly into the end of the original duct. And in advanced elasmobranchs of both sexes, the most anterior part of the kidney is reduced or absent, and the ureter type of drainage is complete.

In all amniotes, as we have seen (p. 376), the end result of a similar evolutionary process has been the same—a definite ureter has been developed; the archinephric duct has been abandoned completely to the use of the genital system as a ductus deferens for sperm (Fig. 277, *E*).

Urinary Bladder in Fishes.   In a majority of vertebrates there is developed a bladder of some sort, a distensible sac in which urine may be stored before being voided. In elasmobranchs and primitive bony fishes such structures are developed from the urinary ducts themselves. In female elasmobranchs the posterior end of each archinephric duct may become enlarged for urine storage; since the two ducts fuse near their external opening, there may be a median portion to this simple type of bladder. In the male elasmobranch these primary ducts are utilized for the passage of sperm, and no bladder develops along their course.

but, as we have just seen, the sharks and rays tend to develop on either side new tubes distinct from the primary duct, for urine passage. Much like the primary ducts in the female, these urinary ducts may expand in bladder-like fashion.

In primitive bony fishes generally—lungfishes and lower actinopterygians— a small urinary bladder develops out of the conjoined ends of the archinephric ducts and hence seems essentially similar to that of female sharks. In teleosts there may be similarly a bladder just inside the urinary opening (Fig. 262, *D*); here, however, a pocket of the cloaca—present in the embryo, but not in the adult—takes part in the formation of the bladder walls. In the lamprey there is a comparable small bladder or sinus formed from a pinched-off portion of the cloaca, into which the urinary duct opened in the embryo (Fig. 293, *A*, p. 405).

The Bladder in Tetrapods. In tetrapods a bladder is useful as a rudimentary sanitary measure; it is, further, useful in water conservation, and in anurans and turtles, for example, resorption of bladder water is important in preventing desiccation under terrestrial conditions. The tetrapod type of bladder appears among the amphibians. It is a new type of structure, not seen in fishes, which appears as a pocket in the floor of the cloaca and often lacks a direct connection with the kidney ducts (Fig. 294, *A*, p. 406). Voiding of urine from the bladder takes place through the common cloacal outlet.

The reptilian bladder is of similar construction and position. It is found in Sphenodon, in turtles, and in most lizards. It is lost, however, in other lizards, in snakes, and in crocodilians; and, further, the bladder has disappeared in birds except in the ostrich. In the absence of a bladder the urine is poured directly into the cloaca and may be mixed in the feces.

We have noted in an earlier chapter (p. 115) that the tetrapod bladder plays an important part in amniote embryology. In all forms with this developmental pattern an important embryonic membrane is the allantois, a pouchlike structure arising from the floor of the most posterior part of the primitive gut. This outgrowth is obviously elaborated from the urinary bladder. At birth the allantois itself disappears, but the adult bladder develops as an expansion of the allantoic stalk.

Fig. 278. Section of a mammalian bladder showing "transitional epithelium." The epithelium is shown as in a relaxed state; when the bladder is distended, this peculiar type of epithelium may be strongly stretched and its thickness reduced to a third or so of that shown here. (From Windle, Textbook of Histology, The McGraw-Hill Company.)

In mammals the tetrapod urinary bladder is definitely incorporated into the urinary system. As noted later (p. 407), the ureters come to enter directly into the wall of the bladder, and no passage of urine through a cloacal cavity is necessary to reach it.

The tetrapod bladder is a highly distensible organ with stout walls. It is endowed, particularly in mammals, with thick coats of smooth musculature. The inner lining is of a peculiar type known (inappropriately) as *transitional epithelium* (Fig. 278). When the bladder is empty it appears to be of thick, stratified nature. When the bladder is filled and the epithelium expanded in area, it becomes thinned down to a layer or two of flat squamous cells. An epithelium of such a readily distensible type is especially necessary in bladder construction, but is often found in other parts of the urinary system as well.

GENITAL ORGANS

Sexual reproduction is universal in vertebrates. Among certain groups of invertebrates the hermaphrodite condition, in which the same individual may function as both male and female, is commonly found; in the vertebrates the sexes are functionally separate in almost every case.

The basic reproductive structures are the *gonads*—ovary or testis. In these organs are produced the *gametes*—eggs (ova) or sperm—by the union of which, in the process of fertilization, the new generation is produced. In all gnathostomes there are associated with the gonads tubes or ducts (with accessory structures) for the transport of gametes and in certain cases for the protection and nourishment of the growing young within the female body. In addition, copulatory organs, which aid in internal fertilization of the eggs, may develop in the region of the external opening of the genital tract. And, finally, secondary sexual characters are frequently found in other bodily structures; sex may affect general body size or proportions, and the development of such features as the plumage in birds, mammary glands in mammals, antlers and horns in ruminants.

Sex Development. Although in gnathostomes the genital systems differ greatly in the two sexes, there are frequently found in the one sex rudiments of the structures characteristic of the other. This is due to the fact that for some time during embryonic life there is an *indifferent stage*, during which gonads and ducts proceed far in their development without any indication of which sex the individual is to become (Figs. 279, *C*, 281, *A*, *B*). The gonads may attain considerable size without showing specific features of either ovary or testis; and both male and female duct systems may differentiate to a considerable degree in potential members of both sexes. Eventually, however, there appears a definite sexual stage; the gonads become specifically testes or ovaries, and only the ducts and other accessory structures appropriate to one sex or the other continue their development. The nonpertinent structures of the opposite sex generally cease to develop and may be resorbed, but are sometimes merely arrested in their growth to persist as rudiments in the adult.

The presence of the indifferent stage in sexual development is correlated with the nature of vertebrate sex determination. As discussed in Chapter 5, the early development of the embryo is mainly due to the organization already present in the unfertilized egg; the influence of the sperm and the hereditary characters which it introduces are not appreciable until a relatively late stage. Whether

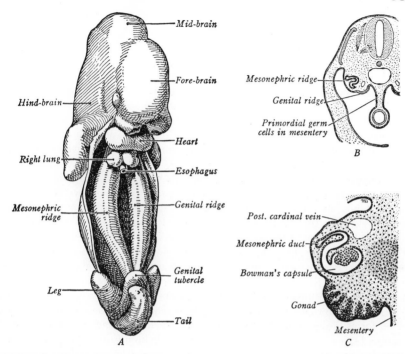

Fig. 279. *A*, Ventral dissection of a human embryo of 9 mm., digestive tract removed, to show genital ridge and kidney (mesonephric ridge) projecting downward into the (opened) celomic cavity. *B*,
Cross section of an embryo at an earlier stage (7 mm.); and *C*, a slightly later one (10 mm.). In the
latter the primary sex cords are forming in the still "indifferent" gonad, and capsule and glomerulus
are forming in the kidney tubules. (From Arey.)

an individual is to become a male or female depends for the most part upon the
chromosome complement of the fertilized egg. The egg has, so to speak, no
knowledge of which sex it will become, and the early embryo is prepared for
both possibilities. The influence of the sex chromosome mechanism is eventually
manifested in the gonad. Once this has become definitely either testis or ovary,
male or female patterns in other sexual organs appear in the later stages of embryonic life. Evidence suggests that these events are affected by hormones produced by the developing gonad, although it is thought that these hormones are
not identical with those produced by ovary or testis in later life. In many vertebrates the mechanisms of sex determination are so delicately balanced that the
gonads hesitate (so to speak) between male and female pathways, and both eggs
and sperm may tend to develop in a single individual. Intersexual conditions of
one sort or another may be present. In cyclostomes both eggs and sperm begin
development in different regions of the same gonad. For the most part one sex
or the other dominates in maturity, but a percentage of hagfishes remain sterile
intersexes throughout life. Among the teleosts, two families, the Serranidae (sea
bass) and Sparidae, exhibit in the young a development of both eggs and sperm
in the same gonad, and in these families alone among vertebrates, functional her-
maphrodites are reported. Amphibians show a delicate balance between sexes,
and variants of one sort or another are numerous. For example, in the common

toad (Bufo) the males have an ovary-like structure—Bidder's organ—in addition
to a testis. In the common frog genus Rana, young males show female tendencies,
and genetic females may in old age shift to the male side of the balance and produce sperm.

There is in vertebrates a great difference in the rapidity with which different organ systems develop. The nervous system, for example, grows exceedingly
rapidly in early stages; the genital organs, primary or secondary, are, on the other
hand, the slowest of any to develop. This is to be correlated with the fact that
whereas most of the bodily structures must be put to use at birth or even during
embryonic existence, the sex organs do not function until maturity of the individual has been attained.

Gonads.   The gonads make their appearance only at a stage in embryonic
history when most of the main features of other organ systems have been blocked
out, and when the celomic cavities are well developed. At this time paired longitudinal swellings, the *genital ridges,* are formed along the roof of the celom, lying lateral to the root of the mesentery and medial to the embryonic kidney (Fig.
279). Elongate to begin with, the gonads developed from such ridges often become relatively short and compact in later stages. Usually the definitive gonad
region is toward the anterior end of the abdominal cavity; fat bodies or other
structures may arise from abandoned portions of the genital ridge. The *germinal
epithelium* of the ridge, continuous with the mesodermal lining of the rest of the
celom, forms the more important structural elements of the gonad (Figs. 279, *B,
C,* 280, *A*); mesenchyme lying beneath the epithelium forms connective tissues
and in higher vertebrates, at least, gives rise to special *interstitial tissues.*

Before the end of the indifferent stage the gonad develops in many cases
into a compact, swollen structure extending out into the celomic cavity from its

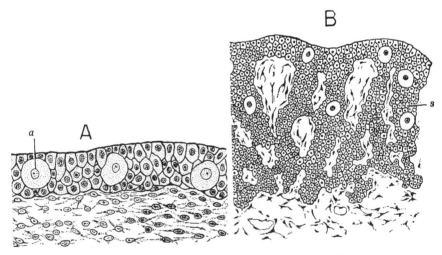

Fig. 280.   Early stages in mammalian gonad development. *A,* A section of the epithelium of the
gonad at an early indifferent stage; primordial germ cells are present (*a*), but sex cords are not developed. *B,* A somewhat later stage, with primary sex cords (*s*) growing inward from the epithelial layer. (From Maximow and Bloom.)

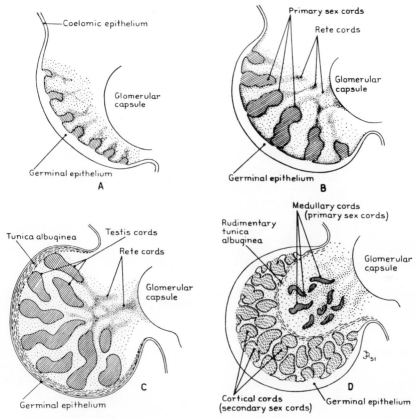

Fig. 281. Development of testis and ovary of a mammal. *A,* Genital ridge, with incipient primary sex cords growing inward from the germinal epithelium; the stage is slightly earlier than Figure 280, *B.* *B,* Gonad still in the indifferent state; the primary sex cords are well developed, and cords are forming which will become the rete testis if the gonad becomes a testis. *C,* Development of the testis; the germinal epithelium degenerates, and is replaced by a sheath around the testis; testis tubules and rete continue development. *D,* Early development of an ovary, with reduction of primary sex cords and rete rudiments with, on the other hand, great development externally of secondary cords in which eggs develop. (From Burns, in Willier, Weiss and Hamburger, Analysis of Development.)

dorsal wall in the neighborhood of the developing kidney and often supported by a special mesentery. From the germinal epithelium covering its surface, finger-like structures, the *primary sex cords* (Figs. 279, *C,* 280, *B,* 281, *A, B*), grow inward into the substance of the gonad. These cords contain germ cells as well as less specialized supporting elements.

Origin of Germ Cells. Germ cells from which eggs or sperm develop—large cells with a characteristic clear cytoplasm—may be identified at a relatively early stage in the germinal epithelium of the gonad, and it seems logical to assume that the germ cells are of local, mesodermal origin.

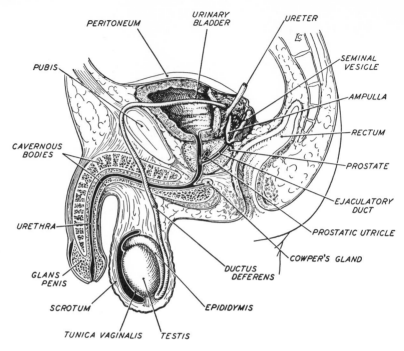

Fig. 282.   Male reproductive organs in Homo. (From Turner, General Endocrinology.)

There is, however, a peculiar quirk in the story. It may well be that the functional eggs and sperm of the adult do develop in this fashion. But a considerable body of evidence indicates that the first germ cells to appear in ovary or testis are actually derived in most cases from the endoderm. In embryos of many vertebrates, from cyclostomes to mammals, there have been observed in the lining of the gut or yolk sac, at an early stage, cells which histologically are quite distinct from the ordinary cells of the digestive tract. If a series of stages is followed through, these distinctive cells appear to leave the gut walls and migrate—either, in amoeboid fashion, through the intervening tissues (Fig. 279, *B*) or by way of the blood—into the celomic epithelium from which the genital ridges form. These cells are primary germ cells.

Biologists have often emphasized the fact that in animals in general the germ cells form an exceedingly independent tissue; the rest of the body, the "soma," is, on this point of view, merely a temporary structure shielding and conserving the potentially immortal germ plasm. In many invertebrates the future germ cells become distinct from the rest of the embryo at an early cleavage; this migration of vertebrate germ cells is, possibly, a demonstration of their equally distinctive nature.

But there are puzzling features in the vertebrate story. Most workers believe that the primordial germ cells, once arrived at the gonads, give rise to eggs or

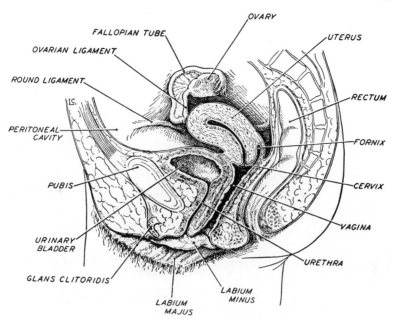

OVARY

FALLOPIAN TUBE

OVARIAN LIGAMENT

ROUND LIGAMENT

UTERUS

PERITONEAL CAVITY

RECTUM

PUBIS

FORNIX

URINARY BLADDER

CERVIX

GLANS CLITORIDIS

VAGINA

URETHRA

LABIUM MAJUS

LABIUM MINUS

Fig. 283.   Female reproductive organs in Homo. (From Turner, General Endocrinology.)

sperm. Some, however, believe that this is not the case, and that these cells degenerate after a fruitless migration. Many hold an intermediate viewpoint that these first germ cells give rise to a first-developed series of gametes, but that the functional eggs and sperm of the adult are derived from other germ cells, which arise *in situ* in the mesodermal epithelium of the gonad. Under this view the function of the immigrant primary germ cells may be merely the initiation and stimulation of the process of gamete formation.

Ovary: Egg Production (Figs. 284, 285).   In the development of an ovary beyond the indifferent stage there is generally found as a diagnostic feature the proliferation inward from the germinal epithelium of *secondary sex cords* (Fig. 281, *D*, p. 389). The primary cords, already formed, degenerate in the female, and it is in the succeeding series that the ova of the adult arise. In the developing ovary the germ cells contained in these cords divide repeatedly and develop eventually, by a complicated maturation process—*oogenesis*—into definitive egg cells. Each egg cell may become surrounded by a cluster of other cells derived from the sex cords to form a *follicle;* connective tissue cells may form a further external sheath. The follicular cells aid in the sustenance of the growing egg; in addition, the follicle is the major seat of estrogen formation. As maturity is approached, egg and follicle increase in size. In forms with large-yolked eggs the follicle comes to be relatively enormous, and to form a major expansion on the ovarial surface. In viviparous mammals the egg is small, but the follicle surrounding it nevertheless enlarges, causing the development of a liquid-filled space in its interior.

At seasons of reproductive activity follicles ripen at the surface of the ovary and burst, releasing the egg into the surrounding celomic space—the process of

Fig. 284. Diagrammatic section through a lobe of the frog's ovary. *1* to *5* Illustrate stages in the growth of the follicle; *6* and *7*, rupture of a follicle and emergence of egg; *8*, postovulatory follicle. (From Turner.)

ovulation. In most lower vertebrates the follicle material is quickly resorbed. In mammals, however, and in some elasmobranchs the follicle persists for some time after the egg has been released, its cavity filled with a mass of yellow material from which its name of *corpus luteum* is derived. This "yellow body" secretes the hormone *progesterone,* (cf. p. 567).

The number of eggs in a mature state in the ovary at any one time is, in most groups of vertebrates, small—from two to a dozen in many cases. In amphibians, however, hundreds or even thousands of ripe eggs may be present at breeding time, and in actinopterygians there may be hundreds of thousands or even millions (the codfish is estimated to lay 4,000,000 eggs in one season). At an early stage of ovarian development a large number of tiny eggs are produced as a stock from which those matured at successive seasons may be drawn. It was once believed that there is no further production of egg cells beyond this early stage; but the large number of eggs produced by many fishes and amphibians indicates that there must be later proliferations of germ cells from the germinal epithelium on the surface of the ovary. On the other hand, forms in which the number of eggs which mature is small, obviously do not use up the abundant supply of egg cells; in such types investigation shows that a large proportion of the eggs degenerate, even if far advanced in follicle construction, without reaching maturity.

The ovary is usually a paired structure, often with an oval shape when in a resting phase, but frequently distended and irregular in outline at the breeding period. In cyclostomes the pair of gonads fuse into a single median structure, and the two ovaries fuse in many teleosts as well. In some elasmobranchs the left ovary remains undeveloped; in nearly all birds and in the primitive mammal Ornithorhynchus (the duckbill) the left alone matures. In amphibians and reptiles the ovary is thin-walled and hollow, containing central lymph-filled cavities. In other cases the central part—the medulla—is mainly a connective tissue struc-

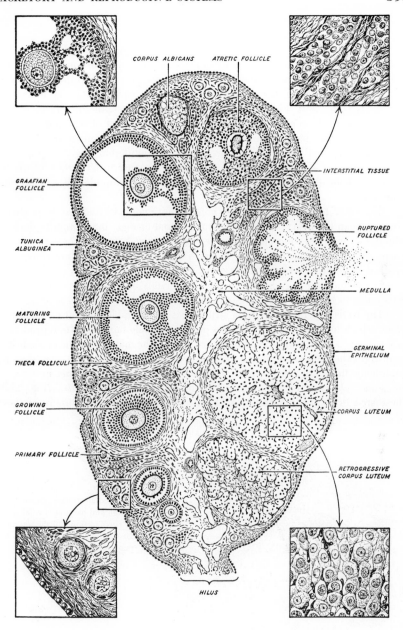

Fig. 285. Diagram of a composite mammalian ovary. Progressive stages in the differentiation of a follicle are indicated on the left. The mature follicle may ovulate and form a corpus luteum (*right*) or degenerate without ovulation (atretic follicle). (From Turner.)

ture; the eggs and their follicles, together with the germinal epithelium on the surface, form the cortex.

Testis.   The early history of the testis is, through the indifferent stage, identical with that of the ovary in its development from a portion (usually anterior) of the genital ridge, in the development of a germinal epithelium, and in the growth inward from this surface of primary sex cords containing germ cells (Fig. 281, *C*, p. 389). From this point onward, however, the history of the two organs diverges. In contrast to the ovary, no secondary set of sex cords is developed. On the other hand there is in amniotes further development, deeper in the gonad, of strands of tissue already present in the indifferent stage; these become the rete testis (p. 402). No germinal epithelium remains at the surface of the testis, which, beneath a normal celomic epithelium, is surrounded by a connective tissue sheath.

The testis tends to be, on the whole, a more compact and regularly shaped structure than the ovary; it is subject to seasonal change, but generally does not exhibit such marked differences between breeding and resting stages as does the female gonad. In cyclostomes the testis, like the ovary, is a median rather than a paired structure. In sharks the two testes may fuse posteriorly, and the right member of the pair may be the larger. In various birds and mammals the left testis tends to be moderately larger than the right.

The testis generally has in its structure a considerable amount of connective tissue, which includes interstitial cells producing male hormone. Its reproductive tissues are produced from the primary sex cords. The material of the cords breaks up in the substance of the testis into numerous hollow structures. In fishes and amphibians these are usually more or less spherical sperm *ampullae*; in amniotes and some teleosts there are formed elongate *seminiferous tubules* (Fig. 286). These structures are lined by epithelium in which countless numbers of sperm

Fig. 286.   A small area of a mammalian testis, showing one tubule and parts of several others in cross section and the intertubular tissue. (From Hooker in Fulton-Howell.)

are produced at each breeding season. The epithelium of tube or ampulla is stratified and contains both reproductive cells and relatively rare supporting cells—
Sertoli cells. At the base of the epithelium there are generally to be found germ
cells which are little differentiated, the *spermatogonia.* From these primary cells,
after repeated divisions, there are formed mature cells which are released at the
surface of the epithelium, as *spermatozoa.* They include in their structure little
except a head, containing the nuclear material, and a long, motile tail. Spermatozoa are exceedingly small but exceedingly numerous, and even in small animals the total production may be measured in billions.

In most vertebrates sperm production—*spermatogenesis*—like that of eggs,
is a cyclic phenomenon. The sperm ampullae of lower vertebrates are expendable
and are thus rather comparable to egg follicles. All the germinal materials of a
given number of ampullae ripen at a specific breeding season, the sperm are discharged, and the ampullae resorbed, to be replaced by others which have meanwhile developed more slowly. The seminiferous tubules of higher vertebrates, on
the other hand, are characteristically permanent structures, producing successive
crops of sperm and persisting little changed throughout the breeding life of the
individual.

Descent of the Testis (Fig. 287). In most vertebrates the gonads of the
adult retain their primitive position in the upper part of the celomic cavity. In a
majority of mammals, however, a radical change in the position of the testes occurs during embryonic development. Paired pouches form in the floor of the abdominal cavity and cause external swellings on the ventral surface of the body
just anterior to the pelvis. These are the *scrotal sacs,* lined internally with celomic
epithelium, and constituting separate portions of the celomic cavities. Each testis
moves posteriorly and ventrally from its original position, and descends into a
sac, accompanied, of course, by the ductus deferens for sperm transport, its
proper blood supply, and a fold of its proper mesentery—the *gubernaculum.* In
some cases the scrotal sacs remain in open connection with the abdominal cavity
through an *inguinal canal,* and the testes may be withdrawn from the sacs into
the body between breeding seasons through the action of a muscle (cremaster) developed in the gubernaculum. In other mammals the sacs may be closed off from
the abdominal cavity by a fold of tissue. Rupture of this fold—a weak spot in
the abdominal wall—may lead to the condition known in man as inguinal hernia.

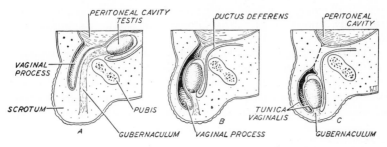

Fig. 287. Descent of the testis in mammals; ventral surface of body at left. A vaginal process develops from the body cavity; its peritoneum forms the vaginal tunic of the scrotal sac. Broken line in
C, position of inguinal canal in mammals in which sac is not completely closed. (From Turner.)

Most commonly the two scrotal sacs may push downward and backward to fuse externally below and behind the penis; more rarely, as in many marsupials, they may be anterior to that organ.

Experiments and the study of abnormalities have revealed the functional basis for this unusual phenomenon of testicular descent. The delicate process of sperm maturation cannot go on at high temperatures. The temperatures maintained internally in the bodies of mammals are in general too great for sperm formation; temperatures in the exposed scrotal sacs are several degrees lower.

The Oviduct and Its Derivatives in Lower Vertebrates (Figs. 272, 273, 274, pp. 378, 379, 381).

In Amphioxus the sex cells (formed in segmentally arranged gonads) are shed directly to the surface (via the cavity of the "hood" surrounding the gills). In cyclostomes both eggs and sperm are shed into the celom, and must find their own way to the posterior end of this cavity, whence a pair of abdominal pores afford them passage to the exterior. In all gnathostomes the sperm are conducted to the outside by way of closed tubes, but the eggs are still shed in most cases into the celom. They are not, however, really freed into this cavity, for they are (except by accident) received, through a funnel-like structure close beside the ovary, into a tube which cares for them on the remainder of their journey. This is the primitive *oviduct* (or müllerian duct), present, with various regional modifications, in most jawed vertebrates. Along the course of the oviduct there may be formed specialized enlargements for various purposes: storage of eggs before laying, the deposition of a shell, or the retention of the egg during embryonic development and a subsequent "live" birth—the *viviparous* condition.*

The oviduct and specialized structures derived from it arise in the dorso-lateral wall of the celomic cavity, and may come to be suspended in the celom by special mesenteries. The embryonic course of the oviduct parallels that of the archinephric duct. In elasmobranchs and urodeles it is formed by a splitting in two of this duct. In some tetrapod groups there are indications of a similar origin, and in some lower actinopterygians—sturgeons, paddlefishes—the oviduct continues, even in the adult, as a side branch of the archinephric duct. On the other hand, in a majority of land vertebrates the oviduct arises as a distinct structure, formed by an infolding of the celomic epithelium or the development of a cord of tissue closely associated with the archinephric duct. The evidence on the whole thus indicates that the female genital duct (like that of the male, described below) is derived from the urinary system, but has become so specialized that embryonic evidence of its origin may be lost. As would be expected, the oviduct, present in all embryos in the "indifferent" stage, usually disappears in males; exceptionally, however, it persists in the adult male in some amphibians and lungfishes.

The oviduct is seen in its simplest form in lungfishes and amphibians—groups with reproductive habits which apparently are primitive, the female laying at each breeding season a moderate number of shell-less eggs of modest size. It is here for the most part a simple ciliated tube, with glands or gland cells which secrete mucus or a gelatinous covering for the eggs. In the resting phase

---

* In contrast to the primitive *oviparous* method, in which the egg is laid and development takes place externally. Some distinguish from viviparity an intermediate *ovoviviparous* type, in which development is internal, but takes place without the formation of a placenta or other means of obtaining nourishment from the mother.

the egg tube is usually small in diameter and relatively straight; at the breeding season it may elongate to become highly convoluted, and its diameter may increase greatly.

There is no direct connection between ovary and oviduct in primitive forms (nor, for that matter, in most advanced types except teleost fishes). The anterior end of each oviduct, however, lies close beside the ovary; it consists of a ciliated funnel, the *infundibulum*, with a frilled margin. (The funnels are usually separate; in the Chondrichthyes, exceptionally, the two are fused.) Eggs released from the ovary are normally caught up by the funnel to begin their journey down the tube. We have noted that anterior kidney tubules in embryos and in lower vertebrates frequently connect with the celomic cavity by funnel-shaped openings; if the oviduct is derived from kidney structures historically, its funnel may have originated from a greatly enlarged opening of this sort.

In such vertebrate groups as the more primitive bony fishes and amphibians, there is little specialization of the oviduct posteriorly. There is generally an expanded distal part of the tube, an *ovisac*, which serves for the storage of eggs. A few salamanders and toads are viviparous; fertilized eggs are retained within this sac until embryonic development has been completed and the young are "hatched." The oviducts open posteriorly into the cloaca, when present, or to the surface of the body. In variable fashion the two tubes may remain separate over their entire length, as in salamanders and some anurans, or fuse into a common tube, as in other anurans and in lungfishes.

An exceptional situation is that which must be dealt with by the actinopterygians, and more especially the teleosts, in which countless thousands or even millions of eggs may be released during a short breeding season.* It is obvious that the normal system of egg reception through an open funnel would be inadequate; there would be the danger, or rather the certainty, that the entire body cavity would be hopelessly choked with eggs. In most teleosts (and in the related gar pikes as well) the difficulty has been solved by a complete enclosure of the ovary and an associated tube system so that no escape of eggs into the general body cavity is possible (Fig. 288, *g, h*). The ovary is enclosed in a fold of the celom and encloses a cavity within its substance. Into this the eggs are shed, and directly from it a funnel-like duct, not homologous with the usual vertebrate oviduct, leads backward to the exterior; there is no possible opportunity for the escape of eggs into the interior of the body.†

In other vertebrate classes—cartilaginous fishes, reptiles and birds—a large, shelled egg has been evolved, and special regions of the tube are developed which produce the egg white and shell. In elasmobranchs and chimaeras there is, part way down the tube, an enlarged and specialized region, the *shell gland* (nidamental gland). Although this usually appears to be a uniform structure externally, there are internally two types of epithelia present when the gland is well developed. In the upper part of the nidamental region of the tube albuminous material—"egg white"—is secreted about the egg; in the lower part a hard, horny egg case is formed. Fertilization must, of course, occur before the shell is added

---

* In a few viviparous teleosts, the eggs develop within the ovarian cavity. In such forms the number of eggs is secondarily reduced.

† In salmon and a few other forms the ovary is sheathed, but is not directly connected with the duct (Fig. 288, *h*).

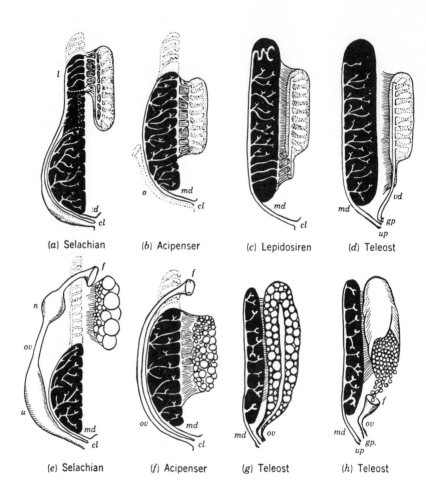

Fig. 288. Representative types of urogenital systems in fishes. Upper series, males, lower series, females. Acipenser is a primitive actinopterygian, Lepidosiren, the South American lungfish. Black structures, opisthonephros; testis stippled; organs with circles (representing eggs) are ovaries; mesenteries hatched; vestigial pronephros, and vestigial male oviduct (in *b*) in stippled lines. *a*, Vestigial oviduct; *cl*, cloaca; *d*, special duct draining kidney in advanced selachians; *f*, open funnel of oviduct; *gp*, genital papilla and pore of teleosts; *l*, gland in anterior region of selachian kidney analogous to epididymis; *md*, archinephric duct as kidney duct; *n*, shell gland; *ov*, oviduct; *u*, selachian ovisac, or "uterus"; *up*, urinary pore of teleosts; *vd*, sperm duct of teleosts, analogous to ductus deferens of amniotes. In male selachians, as in amniotes, the testis tends to take over the original archinephric duct for sperm transport (cf. Fig. 277, *D*), but in other fishes this duct continues to drain the kidneys, and in teleosts a separate sperm duct (*vd*) develops. Specialized methods of egg transport are present in teleosts. (After Portman and Goodrich, from Hoar, in the Physiology of Fishes, M. E. Brown, editor, Academic Press.)

to the egg,* and in the Chondrichthyes internal fertilization takes place. With the aid of claspers on the pelvic fins of the male the sperm are injected into the cloaca. Thence they travel "upstream" in the oviduct, and fertilize the egg before it descends to the shell gland.

We have noted that the young are born alive in a few amphibians and a fraction of the teleosts. Viviparity requires internal fertilization of the egg, and is hence the exception in vertebrates with primitive reproductive habits; for external fertilization appears to have been the original method of insemination. With the development of shelled eggs and consequent internal fertilization in cartilaginous fishes, opportunities for the development of viviparous conditions are increased. Distally, there is present in the elasmobranch oviduct an ovisac, which in many forms is simply a repository for eggs before discharge. In a variety of sharks and skates, however, viviparity has arisen; the shell fails to develop around the egg, and the ovisac serves as an organ in which the embryo is sheltered and nourished until its birth as a "pup." The ovisac in such forms supplies food materials in one fashion or another to the young. Most common is the development from the inner wall of the ovisac of highly vascular leaflike or filamentous outgrowths which gain contact with the embryo's yolk sac; a connection is formed somewhat comparable to the placenta of a mammal.

The Oviduct in Amniotes—Uterus, Vagina (Figs. 274, B, p. 381; 275, B, p. 382; 283, p. 391; 289). In amniotes, as in sharks, a shelled egg has brought about specializations of the tube for the production of albumen and shell. In reptiles and birds the successive divisions of the oviduct are given names comparable to those used in mammalian anatomy, although the functions differ. The greater part of its length is the oviduct proper, or *uterine tube.* This is a broad, muscular tube, capable of further distention at the breeding season. The *uterus* † lies close to the distal, cloacal end of the tube; it is in the resting phase somewhat greater than the tube in internal diameter and may be greatly expanded during the breeding season. Its walls contain a heavy coat of smooth muscle. Glands are present in the epithelia of both tube and uterus; those in the upper part of the tube secrete albumen or egg white in turtles and crocodilians, those of the uterus form the shell. Beyond the uterus a short terminal segment leads to the cloaca; this is often termed a vagina, although it lacks the special function of that region in mammals. The two tubes of reptiles open separately into the cloaca. Birds are universally oviparous, but various lizards and snakes bear their young alive, and in some cases have paralleled elasmobranchs and mammals in the development of structures through which nutriment may pass from mother to young.

In birds the right oviduct, like the right ovary, is absent, but the structure of that remaining has retained the reptilian pattern. Among mammals the monotremes, which produce a shelled egg, although one of small size, have a uterine structure essentially similar to that of reptiles.

Markedly different from those of more primitive amniotes are conditions in

---

* Hagfish eggs have a thin horny shell and yet have external fertilization; a soft spot (micropyle) in one end of the shell allows the sperm to enter. In the absence of any oviduct system the capsule is formed about the egg before it leaves the ovary.

† The distal expansion of the oviduct in elasmobranchs and amphibians, here termed the ovisac, is frequently called a uterus. Since its homology with the mammalian uterus is none too certain, it is probably better not to extend the use of this term to these lower vertebrates.

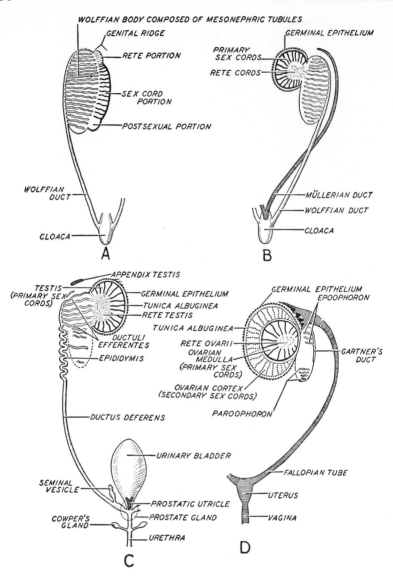

Fig. 289. Embryonic development of the genital system of amniotes. *A,* Early indifferent stage, showing sex cords, developing rete testis, mesonephric kidney and archinephric duct (wolffian body, wolffian duct). *B,* Somewhat later stage, in which the embryonic oviduct (müllerian duct) has appeared. *C,* The adult male (cf. Fig. 282). *D,* Adult female (cf. Fig. 283). (From Turner.)

marsupials and placental mammals, for here, with viviparity, shell formation has ceased; instead, the uterus becomes the site for the development of the embryo; and the ends of the two oviducts, usually conjoined, develop as the vagina for reception of the penis.

Since the mammalian ova are of small size, the upper part of the original oviduct, the uterine tube, is a slender structure, and lacks, of course, the albumen-secreting glands found in other amniotes. Fertilization of the egg usually takes place at the upper end of the tube, and the trophoblast (p. 102) has already developed before the uterus is reached.

The uterus, or womb, is a thick-walled muscular structure, within which the embryo is destined to pass its embryonic existence. It has a richly vascular epithelium, the *endometrium,* which may be relatively thin during resting phases, but is greatly thickened at seasons of reproductive activity; its growth rhythms are controlled by hormones of ovarian origin. The placenta, affording maternal nourishment of the developing embryo, is formed by a union of the uterine epithelium with the external membranes of the embryo. In the most primitive mammalian situation the two uteri are quite separate, a *duplex* condition; this is found, for example, in marsupials and in many rodents and bats (Fig. 290). In most mammals, however, the distal parts of the two uteri are fused together to give a *bipartite* or *bicornuate uterus;* and in higher primates there is a complete fusion to a *uterus simplex.*

Although the uteri may remain distinct, the terminal portions of the two egg tubes are invariably fused in placental mammals to form a vagina. The cloaca, into which the genital tubes opened in ancestral types, is absent in viviparous mammals, but is represented by a urogenital sinus (cf. Fig. 295, *E*, p. 407). This sinus is frequently shallow; when of some depth, as in a considerable number of mammalian types, it has the appearance of a further continuation of the vagina itself.

(The marsupials are in many regards structurally transitional between primitive reptilian and placental types in their reproductive system, but vaginal con-

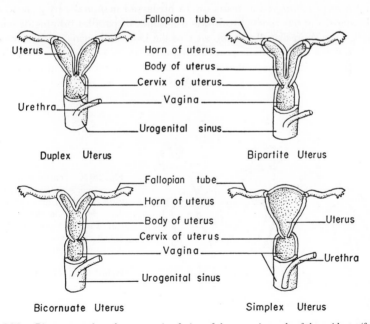

Fig. 290. Diagrams to show the progressive fusion of the posterior ends of the oviducts (fallopian tubes) in placental mammals. The uterus and part of the vagina have been cut open. (From Walker, after Wiedersheim.)

any event, however, the sperm pass through the erstwhile kidney tubules, now termed *ductuli efferentes,* and finally reach the archinephric duct.

Presumably the most primitive condition in gnathostomes is one in which the archinephric duct continues in the male to serve impartially both urinary and genital functions as, for example, in frogs and sturgeons (Fig. 288, *b*). As we have noted, however, in our discussion of the urinary system, most vertebrates have developed new ducts so that sperm and urine travel separate courses. The events in this history have been noted in discussing the urinary organs; they may be reviewed here from (shall we say) the point of view of the testis (Fig. 277, p. 383).

In most bony fishes the kidney has retrieved its original duct; the spermatozoa pass back to an external opening behind the anus by way of a sperm duct, probably developed from the central canal of the testis, which by-passes the kidney (Fig. 288, *d*). In all other groups of vertebrates, we have noted, sperm transportation has triumphed in deciding the fate of the archinephric duct. Parallel developments are witnessed in cartilaginous fishes and in land vertebrates. Urine conduction in elasmobranchs and many amphibians is found, at the most, only in the back end of the duct, and in all amniotes has been completely excluded. With such partial or total exclusion from urinary function, the archinephric duct has become a *ductus deferens,* a tube specific for sperm transport; the testicular connections are universally with the proximal, or anterior end of the duct.

For much of its length the ductus deferens remains a simple structure, but it may undergo major modifications in various regions and in various regards. Most notable are the modifications in the anterior portion of its length, where in both Chondrichthyes and amniotes it takes part in the formation of an appendix to the testis termed the *epididymis.* In sharks, skates, and chimaeras a limited number of efferent ductules from the testis enter the anterior end of the embryonic opisthonephros and reach the former archinephric duct (Figs. 270, *D*, p. 375; 277, *C, D,* p. 383). The anterior end of this duct is much convoluted and may be termed the *ductus epididymidis.* As it passes backward, before reaching the functional kidney, it is joined in sharks by a series of nephric tubules

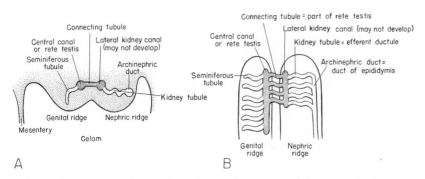

A   B

Fig. 292. *A,* Cross section of an amniote embryo, to illustrate the fact that testis and kidney are adjacent (cf. Fig. 279) and may thus readily come into connection by the development of tubules bridging the gap between sperm tubules and kidney tubules. *B,* Diagrammatic ventral view of a section of nephric and genital ridges to show mode of connection, usually with a central testis canal or rete testis between the sperm tubules with connecting tubules and frequently with a lateral kidney.

which have been modified into glandular structures; these secrete a fluid medium which is believed to stimulate the sperm.

A parallel development has occurred in amniotes; in them the epididymis forms, as its name implies, a compact body resting close beside or upon the testis. The ductules which cross from the testis to this former nephric structure enter, in reptiles, a longitudinal canal whence the efferent ductules continue on to the head of the former archinephric duct; in birds and mammals the longitudinal canal is absent, and the sperm continue directly via the much convoluted ductules to the head of the archinephric duct, which is, here, as in elasmobranchs, highly convoluted (Figs. 282, p. 390; 289, p. 400; 292).

Distally, the ductus deferens may expand into an ampulla for sperm storage before ejaculation; such a structure is common, but not universal, in Chondrichthyes, amphibians, and the amniote groups. In many mammals (Figs. 282, 289) there are further present *vesicular glands* (seminal vesicles) which do not store semen (as the alternative name implies), but secrete a thick liquid as part of the seminal fluid. In most mammals the *prostate gland,* surrounding the urethra and secreting a thinner fluid, and the more distally placed *bulbo-urethral glands* (Cowper's glands) are further secretory structures along the path of the sperm duct.

THE CLOACA AND ITS DERIVATIVES

In a great variety of fishes and tetrapods there is present at the back end of the trunk region a ventral pocket, communicating with the exterior, into which open the orifices of the digestive, genital, and urinary systems. This structure, appropriately termed the *cloaca* (the Roman name for a sewer) appears to have been a primitive vertebrate feature. We shall in this section follow, through the vertebrate groups, the history of the cloacal region and the varied disposition of the outlets of the systems concerned. Inseparable from this general story is that of the urinary bladder of the land vertebrates and of the external genitalia of the amniotes.

The Cloaca in Fishes.   The cloaca is typically developed in elasmobranchs (Fig. 293, *B*), where it forms a depression, which may be provided with a sphincter muscle, on the ventral surface of the body behind the pelvic girdle. The major opening into it is that of the posterior end of the intestine. Into it, further, open the urinary ducts and the vasa deferentia of the male or the paired oviducts of the female.

Embryologically, the cloaca has a twofold origin (cf. Fig. 295, *A*, p. 407). Its major part in the embryo of any vertebrate consists of an expansion of the posterior end of the endodermal gut tube. This cavity is, until a relatively late stage of development, closed off from the exterior by a membrane, external to which lies a depression of the ectoderm, the *proctodeum*. When the membrane disappears, this ectodermal area is incorporated into the cloaca. It is generally assumed that the ectoderm plays little part in cloacal formation. But once the membrane breaks, it is difficult to tell which part of the cloacal lining comes from ectoderm, which from endoderm; it is known in some cases, and suspected in others, that the ectodermal contribution to the cloaca and its derivatives may be of considerable magnitude.

Among other fishes we find a well developed cloaca only in the lungfishes (Fig. 293, *D*) and the male of the sole surviving crossopterygian, Latimeria. In

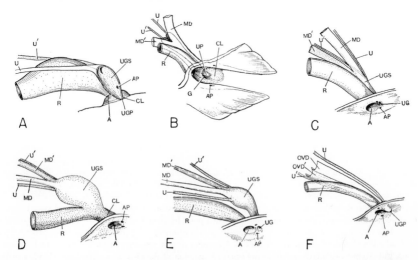

Fig. 293. Cloacal and anal region in fishes. *A,* The lamprey, Petromyzon; *B,* a female shark; *C,* a young female chimaera; *D,* the Australian lungfish, Epiceratodus; *E,* a female sturgeon; *F,* a female salmon. Abbreviations: *A,* anus; *AP,* abdominal pore; *CL,* cloaca; *G,* genital opening; *MD, MD′,* left and right oviducts (müllerian ducts); *OVD, OVD′,* left and right oviducts of teleost; *R,* rectal region of intestine; *U, U′,* left and right urinary ducts; *UG,* urinogenital opening; *UGP,* urinogenital papilla; *UGS,* urinogenital sinus; *UP,* urinary papilla. (From Dean.)

the chimaeras (Fig. 293, *C*) the cloaca has been entirely eliminated, anal, urinary, and genital openings all reaching the surface separately. Among cyclostomes, hagfishes have a cloacal pocket into which anus, urinary tube, and abdominal pore all open, but in lampreys the anus has an opening separate from that of the conjoined urinary and genital tubes (Fig. 293, *A*).

In actinopterygians (Fig. 293, *E, F*) the cloaca has likewise disappeared. In the female Latimeria, lower ray-finned fish types, and some teleosts urinary and reproductive tubes empty by a common sinus representing part of the cloaca, but the anus has a separate opening. In other teleosts we find that three quite distinct openings are present—anal, genital, and urinary.

The Cloaca in Lower Tetrapods (Fig. 294, *A*). In the amphibians a cloaca is present, presumably a direct inheritance from piscine ancestors. The archinephric ducts and, in the female, the oviducts open as paired structures into the inner end of the cloacal pouch. Ventrally, there develops from the cloaca a urinary bladder of varied shape, often distensible to large size (p. 385). In reptiles the cloacal structure is similar; the paired openings of the ureters are typically on the dorsal wall of the cloaca, above the anal entrance; the urinary bladder, usually present, is a distinct ventral pocket not connected, except in turtles, with the ureters. In birds, entrances into the cloaca are similarly placed, but no urinary bladder is present except for vestiges in a few forms.*

Fate of the Cloaca in Mammals. In mammals the lowly monotremes still have a cloaca. Higher types have done away with this structure and have a

---

* Birds have, uniquely, a pocket, termed the *bursa of Fabricius,* opening into the cloaca from above. In the young it is filled with thymus-like tissue; it degenerates in the adult.

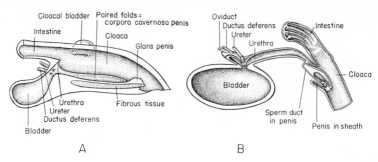

Fig. 294. Section of the cloacal region of *A*, male tortoise, *B*, a monotreme mammal (Echidna). In *A* a penis-like structure is contained in the floor of the cloaca; paired folds may meet to form a tube at the time of sperm emission. In the monotreme a formed penis is present within the cloaca; it contains a tube, divided into several branches, for sperm transport, but urine passes out via the cloaca. In most reptiles the ureter opens dorsally into the cloaca at a point far from the bladder; in its chelonian position there is a closer approximation to the mammalian condition in the ventral shift of this opening. The tube labelled "urethra" in the two figures is equivalent to that structure in the female of higher mammals, but is here essentially a ventral proximal subdivision of the cloaca. A turtle specialization is the presence of a pair of small "supernumerary" bladder-like structures in the side walls of the cloaca. (*A* partly after Moens; *B* after Keibel.)

separate anal outlet for the rectum. The monotreme cloaca shows the initiation of this subdivision (Fig. 294, *B*). The cloaca as such includes only the distal part, roughly comparable to the proctodeum. The more proximal part is divided into (1) a large dorsal passage into which the intestine opens, the *coprodeum*, and (2) a ventral portion, the *urodeum* with which the bladder connects. Ureters open into the proximal end of the urodeum, which is partially equivalent to the placental urethra (cf. Fig. 295) and the urine may thus enter the bladder without being associated with fecal material.

In marsupials the cloaca is persistently represented by a slight proctodeal depression, with a sphincter muscle, but in most higher placental mammals the cloaca has disappeared completely in the adult; coprodeum and urodeum have distinct orifices. The coprodeum becomes the rectal region of the gut, opening at the anus. The urodeum, however, has a more complex history and differs much in the two sexes. Conditions here are best understood by considering the developmental story; the development of the placental mammal recapitulates in many respects the phylogenetic story (Fig. 295).

In the sexually indifferent stage of a placental mammal there is a cloaca, formed as a simple, distal endodermal expansion of the gut. A membrane is present to separate the endodermal cloaca from the indipping ectodermal area which in ancestral types forms the proctodeal component of the cloaca. Into the walls of the endodermal cavity open paired archinephric ducts (paralleled later by the oviducts); out from its floor extends the stalk of the allantois.

While the indifferent stage still persists, a septum develops, and extends out to the closing membrane. This divides the cloaca into two chambers: a coprodeum continuous with the gut above, and a urodeum or *urogenital sinus* below. The archinephric ducts—that is, the ducti deferentes of the male—enter the lower division, as do the female genital ducts. As development proceeds, part of the allantoic stalk region enlarges as the beginning of the typical amniote bladder, and a narrower tubular region develops between the urogenital sinus proper and the bladder which forms part or all of the *urethra* of the adult. The sex tubes remain connected with the sinus. As the ureters develop, however, they separate from the parent archinephric ducts and gain separate distal openings. These openings migrate to the region of the bladder, their definitive position in placental mammals; urine in mammals (in contrast with most lower tetrapods) enters the bladder directly, without having to traverse any part of the cloaca or its subdivisions.

From this stage onward the course of development of the two sexes diverges as regards the structures associated with the urogenital sinus. In the female, when the cloacal membrane disappears, this ventral part of the cloaca becomes the *vestibule* of the urinary and genital organs. This may attain a considerable depth

Fig. 295. Embryology of the cloacal region of mammals; diagrammatic lateral views. *A*, Sexually indifferent stage, with intestine and allantois opening into undivided cloaca, archinephric duct and ureter opening together into base of allantois. *B*, Later indifferent stage; embryonic oviducts developed, ureter and archinephric duct separated, cloaca divided into rectum and urogenital sinus; phallic organ has begun development. *C*, Early stage of development of male, and *D*, adult male structure. In contrast to female, the oviduct disappears (broken line in *D*), the archinephric duct becomes the ductus deferens, and an extensive urethra includes, in addition, (1) the base of the allantois, (2) the urogenital sinus, and (3) a duct traversing the penis. *E*, Early stage of development of female, and *F*, adult female structure; disappearance of archinephric duct (broken line in *E*), development of bladder from base of allantois with short urethra distal to it, differentiation of uterus and vagina from embryonic oviduct, development of phallic organ as clitoris. *a*, Archinephric duct; *al*, stalk of allantois; *b*, bladder; *c*, cloaca; *cl*, clitoris; *dd*, ductus deferens; *gf*, genital fold; *i*, intestine; *o*, oviduct; *p*, penis; *ph*, phallic organ; *pr*, proctodeum; *pu*, penile urethra; *r*, rectum; *s*, scrotum; *u*, ureter; *ugs*, urogenital sinus; *ur*, urethra; *ut*, uterus; *v*, vagina; *v-a*, vestige of archinephric duct; *v-o*, vestige of oviduct; *vs*, vestibule.

(as in typical carnivores) or be a relatively shallow depression (as in primates). Into this vestibule open the conjoined distal ends of the oviducts, the vagina (the archinephric ducts degenerate); into the vestibule also opens a relatively short urethral tube from the bladder.

In the male the sinus has a different history. Instead of becoming shallow and broad, it becomes an elongate tube which continues into the penis. Into its proximal end open the ducti deferentes (the oviducts degenerate) and the tube from the bladder. In the female this short proximal tube constitutes the entire urethra, but in the male the entire extent from bladder to end of penis is termed urethra. Female and male urethrae are, thus, not comparable structures; that of the male includes the homologues of both female urethra and vestibule.

External Genitalia.   In primitive water-dwelling vertebrates with shell-less eggs external fertilization is the rule; sperm and eggs are shed into the water, and fertilization takes place in that medium. But in forms with shelled eggs or with viviparous habits—such types include the Chondrichthyes and all amniotes—internal fertilization takes place, for the sperm must reach the egg before it has descended the oviduct to shell gland or uterus. Special structures are usually formed to facilitate the entrance of the sperm into the female genital tubes.

In sharks, rays, and chimaeras—fishes with heavily shelled eggs—*claspers* are developed in the males to aid in fertilization. These are posterior extensions of the pelvic fins, which are stiffened by rods from the fin skeleton (Fig. 130, *C*, p. 197). The claspers are inserted into the cloaca of the female; rolls of skin folded into tubes along the clasper form a channel for the sperm. In a limited number of teleosts internal fertilization (and viviparity) is present; one specialization to facilitate this is that the anal fin may develop a clasper-like intromittent organ, a *gonadopium,* with a groove or tube to carry the sperm.

In the amniotes internal fertilization is rendered necessary, apart from the presence of the shelled egg or of viviparous type of development, by terrestrial life and the consequent absence of a watery environment for sperm and eggs at the time of breeding. In the ancestral amniotes direct contact of male and female cloacae would seem to have been sufficient for the transfer of sperm, for Sphenodon lacks copulatory organs, which are also absent in most birds (here their absence is perhaps secondary).

In many reptiles, however, the male has some type of accessory organ, a *penis,* to aid in sperm transfer. In snakes and lizards there are unique structures, the *hemipenes.* These are a pair of pockets, often containing thornlike spines, which lie in the skin adjacent to the cloacal opening; at the time of copulation the hemipenes may be turned inside out, extruded, and inserted in the female cloaca to guide the sperm. In turtles and crocodilians there are structures which may be morphologic forerunners of the penis of mammals (Fig. 294, *A*). In the ventral wall of the cloaca are a pair of longitudinal ridges, the *corpora cavernosa penis,* with a groove between them; they are composed (as the name implies) of spongy fibrous tissue. A further spongy structure, the *glans penis,* lies at the outer end of the groove. On excitation these structures are filled with blood and thus distended; the glans is protruded and inserted into the female cloaca; the cavernous bodies expand to meet one another and turn the groove between them into a tube for the passage of the sperm. These structures appear in the embryo in the sexually indifferent stage, and persist in the adult female in a relatively undeveloped and functionless state as the *clitoris.* The ratites, geese, and a few other birds

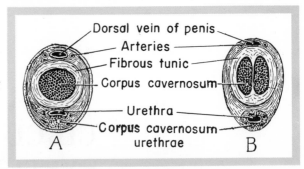

Fig. 296. Sections through the penis of a rhesus monkey; *A*, proximally, and *B*, distally. (From Wislocki.)

have modest development of penis and clitoris, but these structures have been reduced in most birds.

The phallic organs of typical mammals are more highly developed (Figs. 282, p. 390; 296); the monotreme penis, however, is transitional in some regards, and the mammalian clitoris is simpler than the penis in structure. Glans and corpora cavernosa are present and form the main erectile structures; they are, however, permanently fused in the adult penis, together with an additional erectile body continuous with the glans penis, the *corpus cavernosum urethrae*. These structures enclose a continuation of the urethra as a tube carrying both sperm and urine. The corpora cavernosa are in reptiles embedded in the walls of the cloaca; in typical mammals, however, the penis as a whole extends outside the body, and the glans is surrounded with a skin fold, the *prepuce*. As mentioned earlier, a bony structure, the os penis, may develop—most notably in carnivores —in the connective tissues of the penis.

14

CIRCULATORY
SYSTEM

In many small invertebrates a circulatory system is not necessary. Distances are short, structures are simple, and transportation of materials within the body may be effected by diffusion and by such flow of internal fluids as may result from body movement. With greater size and complexity a definite circulatory system is required. A comparison with human communities is a fair analogy. In a village a transportation system is unnecessary; stores, school, church are all close to the homes they serve. With growth of the community this is no longer the case, and an organized transportation system is a public necessity.

Among invertebrates we see the development of two types of circulation—open and closed systems. In the former a heart forms a pump whence blood is forced out through a series of vessels—arteries—to various parts of the body. From the point where the vessels terminate, however, the blood oozes back to the heart through tissue spaces; return vessels are absent. In the more advanced closed system—the type present in the vertebrates—the blood never leaves the vessels and thus lacks direct contact with the body cells which lie in the separate interstitial fluid. The blood serves the tissues by diffusion of materials through small, thin-walled terminal vessels—the capillaries—and returns to the heart again through a second series of closed channels, the veins. Amphioxus shows an intermediate stage in development, for although both outgoing and returning vessels are present, there are no capillaries, and in mid-course the blood is in direct contact with the body cells which it serves.

Functions. Foremost of functions served in vertebrates by the circulatory system are those of transportation to the cells (via the interstitial fluid) of the materials needed for their sustenance and activity, and of the removal of wastes. The tissues (as we noted in Chapter 4) must be constantly supplied with oxygen from gills, skin or lungs, and fed with a small but steady stream of food materials from intestine or from storage and manufacturing centers, notably the liver; these materials include glucose, fatty substances, amino acids, minor amounts of other chemicals, minute amounts of vitamins. Wastes must be removed: carbon

410

dioxide, destined for gills or lungs; nitrogenous wastes, to be excreted in the kidneys; excess metabolic water.

A second important function of the circulation lies in the influence which it exerts over the maintenance of the stable and narrowly defined internal environment necessary for cellular welfare. The constant circulation of liquid throughout the body in the blood stream makes for uniformity of composition in the interstitial fluids of every region, and aids in the maintenance of relatively uniform temperatures.

The vascular system has still further functions. It aids in the struggle against disease and in the repair of injuries; through the circulation of hormones, the blood acts as an accessory nervous system.

Components. The important gross structural features of the vertebrate circulatory system are familiar and readily demonstrated. A muscular pump, the heart, forces the blood stream by way of arteries to gills or lungs and to the varied body tissues. The tiniest circulatory units are networks of capillaries, through whose walls exchange of materials with the interstitial fluid surrounding body cells takes place. From the capillaries blood returns to the heart via veins; lymphatic vessels, originating in the tissues and unconnected with the arteries, form an alternative return route in most vertebrate classes. In certain instances blood from capillaries does not return directly to the heart, but is forced through an intervening second capillary "portal" along its venous course. The veins between two capillary systems are termed a *portal system*.

BLOOD

The blood, filling the vessels of the circulatory system, may be regarded as a tissue—a tissue with very remarkable properties, but one which is, in certain aspects, comparable to the connective and skeletal tissues, to which, ontogenetically, the blood system is closely related. Each of these tissues consists of cellular elements derived from mesenchyme and lying in a "matrix." In bone the matrix is a hard substance; in connective tissue it is gelatinous in consistency; in blood, there is a liquid matrix in which the cellular components float in free fashion. The blood in tetrapods may comprise 5 to 10 per cent of the body weight; the proportion is lower in fishes and in teleosts may be but ½ to 3 per cent.

Blood Plasma. The liquid part of the blood, plasma,* is a watery fluid of complex composition, of which—in mammals, for example—some 7 to 10 per cent of the total volume consists of materials in solution. We have previously (p. 89) noted the composition of the interstitial fluid surrounding the body cells, notably the complex and stable series of salts it contains in solution. The blood is to be regarded as essentially a part of this tissue juice enclosed within the walls of the blood vessels, and it has a practically identical salt content.

In addition, however, the blood contains materials peculiar to itself in the form of special *blood proteins*—albumin, globulin, and fibrinogen, formed, it is believed, by the liver cells and making up the greater part of the nonaqueous fraction of the plasma. These molecules are so large that they are normally unable to pass through capillary walls and thus leave the blood stream. Since the

---

* The term "serum" refers to the liquid remaining after the protein clot material (fibrin) has been removed from clotted blood plasma.

salt concentration of the blood is comparable to that of the interstitial fluids lying outside the blood vessels, the presence of these blood proteins—notably the *albumins*—raises the osmotic pressure of the blood above that of the interstitial fluids—a point of importance in capillary function. *Fibrinogen* makes up but a small percentage of the total, but is important as the material which, in modified form as fibrin, causes clot formation when a blood vessel is cut. Highly important are the varied *globulins*. One globulin type takes part in the formation of the blood clot from the fibrinogen proteins. Other globulins of a highly specific nature are sensitive to protein materials of "foreign" origin and will, for example, cause the clumping (agglutination) of red blood cells of another species or even (as in man) of individuals of another blood type if the bloods are admixed. Certain globulins are active agents in disease protection as the antibodies effective against invading viruses.

The salts and blood proteins are stable, permanent, plasma constituents. In addition, however, blood analysis reveals various materials in transit. A quantity of glucose, on its way to be used as cell fuel, is always present, as well as smaller amounts of fats and of amino acids for intracellular formation of proteins. Waste materials, on the way to kidney or to gills or lungs, are also present, particularly carbon dioxide, mainly as a bicarbonate, nitrogenous waste, usually in the form of urea or uric acid, and lactic acid. In more minute amounts enzymes may be identified in the plasma, and endocrine secretions—the hormones.

Blood Cells (Fig. 297).   Cellular blood components are absent in Amphioxus, but are almost invariably present in vertebrates. They normally include (1) red blood corpuscles or erythrocytes, (2) white blood corpuscles or leukocytes, (3) thrombocytes.

Constant transportation of oxygen is, on a percentage basis, the most important function of the circulatory system. Various metallic compounds, particularly of iron or copper, are found in the blood of almost every form with a developed circulatory system; these compounds have the property of attaching to themselves large amounts of oxygen, and thus vastly increase the oxygen load that the blood can carry. No such material is found in Amphioxus; in all vertebrates, however, there is present *hemoglobin*, a protein molecule which in most vertebrates includes in its complicated structure four iron atoms, each capable of

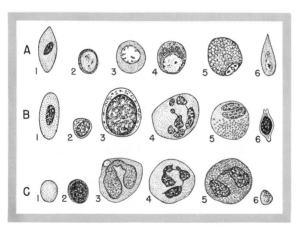

Fig. 297.   Blood cells of *A*, a teleost (Labrax); *B*, a frog (Rana); *C*, a mammal (man). *A1, B1, C1*, Erythrocytes; *A2, B2, C2*, lymphocytes; *A3, B4, C4*, neutrophile granulocytes; *A4*, fine-grained acidophile granulocyte; *A5*, coarse-grained acidophile granulocyte; *A6, B6*, thrombocytes; *B3, C3*, monocytes; *B5, C5*, acidophile granulocytes; *C6*, blood platelet. *A*, × about 1800; *B, C*, × about 1200. (*A* after Duthrie; *B* after Jordan; *C* after Maximow and Bloom.)

carrying an oxygen ion. (In addition to oxygen carriage, hemoglobin is a factor in the return of carbon dioxide from the tissues.)

In invertebrates the oxygen-carrying substances are loose in the blood stream; in vertebrates, the hemoglobin is carried by cells as blood corpuscles—almost necessarily so, for the presence of a large quantity of free hemoglobin in the blood would cause serious interference with other plasma functions. The hemoglobin carriers are the red blood corpuscles, the *erythrocytes*. In most vertebrates these corpuscles are properly nucleated cellular structures, flattened ovals in form, with their cytoplasm tightly packed with hemoglobin. The mammalian erythrocyte is unusual in structure. Except for camels and llamas, the shape is round rather than oval. Further, the mature mammalian erythrocyte extrudes its nucleus, thereby, it would seem, gaining greater efficiency in oxygen carriage in the total mass of the red blood cells.

There is great variation in the size of red blood corpuscles. In man, for example, the diameter of the erythrocyte is but 7 or 8 microns, and in a goat but half this figure; the erythrocytes are larger in all lower classes than in mammals and some amphibians have corpuscles with a volume 100 times or more as great as that of human red blood cells. Nevertheless, the amount of hemoglobin present in the blood is in general fairly constant in animals of any given volume, for the larger the corpuscles, the fewer their numbers. Exceptions are to be found among teleosts, however; some sluggish cold-water forms may have little or no hemoglobin or red blood cells.

The white corpuscles characteristic of the blood and lymph streams are the *leukocytes*. They are much fewer in number than erythrocytes. In amniotes they never compose more than 1 per cent of the blood corpuscles; in fishes, however, the figure may rise to 10 per cent or over. Leukocytes vary greatly, in appearance and in types present, from one group of vertebrates to another, and it is difficult to establish any classification of them which will hold throughout. In the body there appears to be a considerable interplay between the cells of the connective tissues and those of the circulatory system; white blood corpuscles when they leave the blood stream may play an active role in connective tissues, with a radical alteration of appearance. In general we may distinguish two major groups of white cells—lymphoid types, with a simple, single nucleus and a nongranular cytoplasm, and granulocytes, in which the nuclear materials are irregularly arranged and often subdivided, and the cytoplasm is granular in appearance.

Among *lymphoid leukocytes* the common forms are the *lymphocytes*, small, rounded cells with a large nucleus and a relatively small amount of clear cytoplasm. These are present in all classes of vertebrates and are especially abundant in the lower groups. They derive their name from the fact that in mammals they abound in the lymph nodes, but they are equally common in other classes of vertebrates where such nodes are few in number or absent. *Monocytes*, sometimes regarded as a separate category of white cells, are perhaps merely large lymphocytes, with a larger amount of cytoplasm and a nucleus that may become somewhat irregular or kidney-shaped.

The second characteristic group of leukocytes is that of the *granulocytes* or *polymorphonuclear leukocytes*. These, like the monocytes, are large cells. The nucleus, as the alternative name suggests, is irregular in structure and more or less subdivided into lobes. Most characteristic is the fact that the abundant cytoplasm is highly granular. In some cases the granules are stainable with acid dyes; in others basic dyes are effective; in still others both types of dyes take hold to some degree. These three types of "polys" are hence reasonably termed, respectively, *acidophilic* (eosinophilic), *basophilic,* and *heterophilic* (neutrophilic) *granulocytes.* Heterophilic elements are the most abundant granulocytes in all vertebrate classes except, apparently, reptiles; acidophils are rare in the individual, but widespread among vertebrate groups; basophils are generally still fewer in numbers and seldom identified in fishes.

Leukocytes appear to be essentially inert while in the blood stream, but are capable of ameboid motion and seem to be able to wriggle in and out of capillaries between endothelial cells. Despite much study, their functions are incompletely known. They tend, however, to accumulate rapidly in injured, inflamed, or infected tissues. The heterophile granulocytes are capable phagocytes, "eating-cells," and a major means of reducing bacterial infection. It is thought that mononuclear leukocytes and lymphocytes may become transformed into connective tissue elements of the repaired region.

Thrombocytes are blood elements associated with the process of blood clotting. In mammals these structures take the form of *blood platelets,* tiny discs, lacking a nucleus, which are formed by the fragmentation of giant cells—*megakaryocytes* (Fig. 298)—present in the blood-forming tissues. In most nonmammalian vertebrates the thrombocytes take the form of *spindle cells*—small, oval, pointed structures with a central nucleus, which appear to be related in origin to other white blood cells. When thrombocytes leave the environment of the blood stream (as in a cut vessel), they tend to disintegrate, and release a material which (through complicated chemical steps) causes the blood protein fibrinogen to change into fibers of fibrin, masses of which form the blood clot.

BLOOD-FORMING TISSUES

In most body tissues, cellular differentiation takes place in embryonic stages once and for all; in blood elements, proliferation and differentiation of cells continue throughout life. The life of an individual blood cell is short; mammalian erythrocytes, for example, appear to live, at the most, but a few months, and the life of leukocytes appears to be measured in days or even hours. In consequence, an animal must retain throughout its existence *hemopoietic* tissues in which blood cells are constantly formed, and must in addition provide for the removal of worn-out cells.

Students of the blood have devoted much study to blood cell formation, but many features of the process are in doubt, owing to the peculiar nature of the vascular system. Most other differentiated cells are parts of tissues which are fixed in position; their development takes place on the spot. But blood cells are free agents, and it is immaterial where they are formed, as long as the area is in communication with the blood vessels. A cell loose in the blood stream carries no clue in itself as to where it arose in the body, and blood-forming tissues are found in the most varied places in various vertebrates. Unlike most organ systems, no part of the circulatory system is derived from any of the epithelial sheets laid down in the early embryo. In its entirety it is derived from mesenchyme cells—vessels and blood corpuscles alike. The blood cells are thus formed from the same elements which give rise to the connective tissues; they frequently show comparable characteristics, and elements of one system can be demonstrated to transform into cells of the other category.

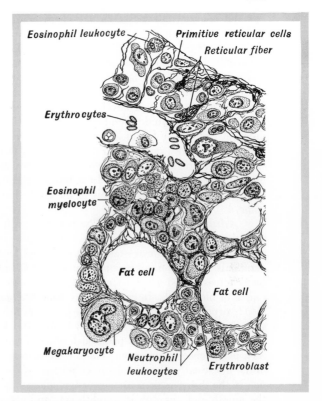

Fig. 298. A blood-forming tissue —bone marrow from a mammalian femur. Much of the reticular framework and two reticular cells are seen, as well as two types of granular leukocytes in process of differentiation, and erythroblasts from which erythrocytes are formed. The megakaryocyte is a giant cell type from which it is believed blood platelets may be formed. (After Maximow and Bloom.)

Except for certain sites utilized in early embryonic stages, areas in which blood cells arise have, in general, common structural features (Fig. 298). All are spaces which are enlargements of circulatory vessels or lie adjacent to such vessels. A network of fibers forms the "skeleton" of the tissue. Along the course of the fibers lie *reticular cells* which are responsible for the formation of the fiber network. They are part of the *macrophage* system of the body—cells of phagocytic nature, having the power of engulfing waste or foreign materials, such as bacteria or damaged blood cells. Macrophages are not restricted to blood-forming tissues, it may be noted, but may be found along the course of blood vessels, notably in the liver and spleen and we have mentioned that they occur as free, ameboid scavenging elements in the connective tissues.

Enmeshed within the reticular framework of a hemopoietic tissue are found masses of blood cells in process of multiplication and differentiation. The *hemocytoblast*—derived from the embryonic mesenchyme, and "cousin" to connective tissue cells—is a primary unspecialized cell type, from which blood corpuscles of all sorts (erythrocytes, leukocytes, megakaryocytes) are thought, by many students of the blood, to be derived. This is a cell of modest size, with a relatively small amount of clear cytoplasm.

Embryonic Blood-Forming Sites. The first blood vessels which form in the embryo are those engaged in bringing food materials into circulation, and the first blood cells are erythrocytes formed in connection with them. In forms with a mesolecithal egg type, the food lies in the yolk-filled gut, and the first vessels and blood cells form in the mesenchyme of the belly floor. In large-yolked eggs, vessels and cells form in the yolk sac, typically as clusters of cells termed *blood islands* (Fig. 248, *A*, p. 345), and in mammals vessels and cells are early formed in the tissues of the placenta as well. At a somewhat later stage, as vessels extend through the body, blood cells may form locally in the mesenchyme of various regions, and may long continue to arise from blood vessel walls. In later phases of embryonic development blood cell formation becomes more localized, but the embryonic blood-forming tissues are often situated in areas quite different from those found in adult life. The embryonic kidney is an important seat of this activity in many forms from sharks to reptiles and birds. The tissues of the throat region and the thymus in particular are an important source of blood cells in many embryos. In mammals the liver and spleen are no longer important as hemopoietic organs in the adult, but play a prominent role in the embryo.

Adult Blood-Forming Tissues. A great variety of organs are seats of such tissues in adult vertebrates of one group or another. In fishes, much of the maturation of erythrocytes takes place in the blood vessels. Except in birds and mammals the spleen is an important area of blood-cell formation. In lampreys, many teleosts, and amphibians the kidney continues throughout life as a great source of blood cells. In cartilaginous fishes the gonads are areas in which white blood corpuscles are formed. In teleosts, amphibians, and turtles hemopoietic tissue is associated with the liver, and in urodeles this is a large source of leukocytes. In the sturgeon and paddlefish blood-forming tissue surrounds the heart. As a persistence of embryonic conditions, masses of lymphoid tissue are present in the intestinal walls, and many vertebrates show in adult life blood cell formation in the throat region. Masses of lymphocyte tissue are present in the walls of the mouth and pharynx in amphibians, and are present in many mammals as *tonsils*, palatine and pharyngeal. The esophagus of sharks shows a large mass of lymphocyte-forming tissue, and similar esophageal "tonsils," as well as the thymus gland, may be found in a number of amniotes.

The *bone marrow* is a great center of blood cell formation in higher vertebrates. The hollowing out of large limb bones appears to be primarily an adaptation for greater efficiency in the use of bone tissue. The resulting "waste" space is, however, available for other purposes; fat storage and blood cell formation are the uses to which the marrow cavities are put. In frogs some hemopoiesis takes place here, especially in the males at the breeding season, and among reptiles the lizards are notable for considerable utilization of bone marrow. In birds and mammals this site is universally used and highly important as a source of blood cells. In reptiles and birds the bone marrow produces blood cells of all sorts; in mammals, however, lymphoid cell formation is practically absent from the bone marrow (the lymph nodules being the center for their proliferation), and production in marrow cavities is confined to erythrocytes and granular leukocytes. This mammalian specialization has led some histologists without a comparative background to a belief, probably erroneous, that lymphoid corpuscles are markedly different from other blood cells.

Spleen (Fig. 299). It is only in the spleen and in the lymph nodes characteristic of mammals that hemopoietic tissues assume the condition of discrete organs. The spleen is the largest mass of reticular tissue in the vertebrate body, and is an important organ in the formation, storage, and destruction of blood corpuscles; it is, further, of importance in defense against disease. In most verte-

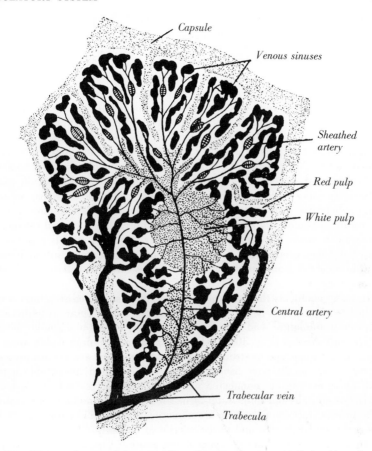

Capsule

Venous sinuses

Sheathed artery

Red pulp

White pulp

Central artery

Trabecular vein

Trabecula

Fig. 299. Diagram of a part of the mammalian spleen. Venous spaces in black; white pulp, heavy stipple; connective tissue capsule and trabeculae, light stipple; red pulp, unstippled. "Sheathed arteries" are surrounded by white pulp. (From Finnerty and Cowdry.)

brates it is a reddish body situated in the dorsal mesentery; it is surrounded by a connective tissue capsule. Extensions inward of connective tissue partitions form the major framework of the spleen. It contains an extensive reticular network, in the spaces of which are contained tissues of two types, a *white pulp* and a *red pulp*. As may be inferred, the former contains clusters of white corpuscles; the red pulp consists of thick masses of all the elements of the blood, including, of course, a large percentage of erythrocytes. In fishes and some amphibians the pulp is dominantly red; in higher tetrapods white pulp is often more common. The spleen is fed by an artery, and is drained by a vein; lymphatic vessels are never present. The internal circulation of the spleen is obviously complicated, and its nature much disputed. The white pulp clusters about the terminal arterioles; the red pulp lies near the venous outlets.

The spleen is always an important center of blood cell production. In the embryo of all vertebrates, erythrocytes as well as leukocytes are formed there, and this function persists in the adult in every group except mammals. In this last class, in which bone marrow has become the important seat of red blood cell formation, hemopoiesis in the spleen appears to be confined to lymphocytes alone. Red corpuscles are stored in great quantities in the spleen, and destruction of such cells occurs in this organ through the agency of numerous macrophages found there. The macrophages of the spleen are further of great importance in destroying infectious materials in the blood stream.

The spleen was developed early in the course of vertebrate history, for it is present in most fishes and universal among tetrapods. Historically, it appears to be connected with the primary seat of blood cell formation in the embryo, for it arises in connection with the gut tube. Cyclostomes and lungfishes lack a formed spleen. In the former it is represented by a layer of reticular blood-forming tissue surrounding much of the gut; in the latter by a mass of tissue of a somewhat more compact nature, but still ensheathed within the outer lining of the gut. In the remaining fishes—Chondrichthyes, actinopterygians—this tissue has separated to form a definitive spleen. Its form is variable, and it appears to modify its outlines readily in conformity with those of adjacent organs. An elongate shape, paralleling much of the gut length, is presumably primitive, and is retained in a majority of fishes, urodeles, and reptiles. A more compact structure is, however, present in some fish, some urodeles, anurans, many birds, and all mammals above the monotreme level.

In many mammals there are present occasional small red structures termed *hemal nodes*, interposed between arterioles and venules. Their structure is that of a spleen in miniature, and they may be accessory organs of a similar nature.

Lymph Nodes (Fig. 300).   For the most part, lymph nodes are a specialized mammalian type of structure. Although lymphatic vessels are present in all vertebrates from the bony fishes upward, we do not find any notable aggregation of blood cell tissues connected with them until we reach birds and mammals. In crocodilians and some water birds a few nodular lymphatic developments may be present; in mammals there are numerous and variable lymph nodes, both in the subcutaneous tissues and in the interior of the body.

These are small, rounded encapsulated masses of reticular tissue, comparable to a small spleen in general structure, but to be sharply distinguished from that organ by being situated along the course of lymphatic rather than blood

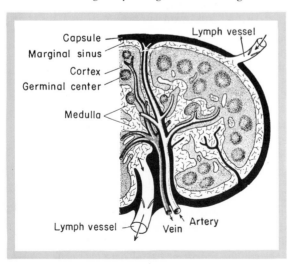

Fig. 300.   Diagram of the structure of a lymph nodule. In addition to the lymph vessels, a nodule is supplied by a small artery and vein. (After Portmann, Einführung in die vergleichende Morphologie der Wirbeltiere, Benno Schwabe & Co.)

vessels. Their cellular contents consist almost entirely of lymphocytes of various sizes. These nodes are, in mammals, a special seat of lymphocyte proliferation; in lower vertebrates the lymphocytes are developed in common with other types of corpuscles. Macrophages in the node reticulum deal with bacteria and other foreign or waste materials which have entered the body and reached the lymphatics; under such conditions, enlargement of the node may occur.

CIRCULATORY VESSELS

The vessels of the circulatory system, like the blood cells, are derived from the embryonic mesenchyme. As food-containing liquid begins to flow through the body of the early embryo, adjacent mesenchyme cells gather about such channels and surround them with a thin but continuous wall. All early formation of major blood vessels takes place in this fashion; later in development, minor vessels arise by outgrowths from the cells lining the blood channels already established and throughout the life of an animal new vessels arise frequently in correlation with changes in body tissues—after injury or damage, breaks may be repaired and circulation reestablished, and with growth of a tissue or organ there is a corresponding growth of additional circulatory vessels.

The inner lining of circulatory vessels is a special type of epithelium which arises *de novo*, and is not derived directly from any epithelial formation originally present in the embryo; it is termed the *endothelium*. It consists of a single layer of thin, leaf-shaped cells, continuous with one another at their margins. The absolutely continuous nature of the endothelial lining cannot be too strongly emphasized; in vertebrates, quite in contrast with various invertebrates and even Amphioxus, the circulating fluid is nowhere, under normal conditions, in continuity with the interstitial liquid and cells outside its vessels, although most of the plasma contents can freely interchange through the thin endothelial membrane.

The vessels of the circulatory system include (1) the heart; (2) arteries, by definition vessels carrying blood from heart to body tissues; (3) capillaries and comparable structures, typically small vessels, connecting arteries and veins; (4) veins, returning blood to the heart; and (5) lymphatics, auxiliary vessels, prominent in higher vertebrates, which aid in the return of fluid from the tissues.

Capillaries (Fig. 301). These smallest of vessels, typically with only the "bore" necessary to allow an erythrocyte to pass, are simple in structure. They deploy from the ends of the arterioles or the veins of portal systems, and twine in among the cells of most of the body tissues so that no cell is far from a capillary. The degree of "vascularization" of a tissue by capillaries is generally proportionate to the metabolic activity of the tissue concerned. At their distal ends the capillaries are recollected into larger vessels—usually veins—in which the circulatory path of blood flow continues onward. The capillary walls in most cases consist simply of a thin if absolutely continuous layer of endothelial cells, although connective tissue cells or other cells of mesenchyme type may adhere to them and in some instances a smooth muscle cell is occasionally present.

Capillaries are too small to be dissected by ordinary means and hence are neglected from the point of view of gross anatomy. But it must never be forgotten that functionally the capillaries are the most important part of the circulatory system. Elsewhere, blood is merely in transit; here it is at work. The endothelium

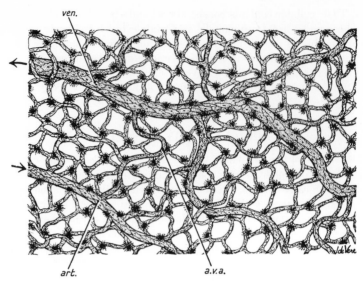

ven.

art.   *a.v.a.*

Fig. 301.   Portion of a capillary bed from the web of a frog's foot, showing small arteriole (*art.*) and venule (*ven.*), a capillary network, and a direct arterio-venous anastomosis (*a.v.a.*). (From Young, The Life of Mammals, Oxford University Press.)

is in general a barrier to cells and large molecules; smaller molecules and ions, however, pass through readily, and in the walls of the capillaries an active exchange of materials takes place. In typical body tissues the capillary in the proximal part of its course gives out oxygen and food materials; in its distal part it takes on waste and carbon dioxide from the tissues. This shift of direction of transit, vitally necessary, is made possible by a change of balance between physical and osmotic pressures in the blood as it passes through the capillaries. The presence of the special blood proteins creates a tendency for materials to flow from the interstitial fluid into the blood stream. At the proximal end of a capillary, however, the hydrostatic pressure put on the blood by the heart pump more than balances this tendency for inflow; food materials and oxygen are given off. Distally in the capillary network, the hydrostatic pressure has been decreased by the friction of the capillary walls; osmotic forces dominate over physical pressure, and waste materials flow inward to the blood vessels from the surrounding tissue fluid.

Capillary networks in most areas of the body tissues are interposed between arterial and venous vessels. But the breaking up of a blood stream into capillaries and its reconstitution into larger vessels may take place also along the path of either the arteries or the veins in special regions. In gill-bearing vertebrates the course of the arterial flow is interrupted by a capillary system for aeration of the blood in the gills.* The return of the venous blood from the tissues may be

* We are accustomed to think, in visual images, of arterial blood as oxygenated and hence "red"; but arterial blood between heart and gills in a fish is, of course, of the "blue" venous type; the arteries and veins leading to and from the tetrapod lung likewise have a reversal of "blue" and "red" blood types.

interrupted also by its forced passage through the capillary networks of a portal system. In all vertebrates blood from the gut passes by a venous portal system to capillaries in the liver; a majority of vertebrates (the highest and the lowest are exceptions) route part of the returning venous blood through a portal system to capillary networks in the kidneys.

Although capillaries are the major type of arteriovenous connection, there are other modes. Microscopic study sometimes reveals direct connections of larger caliber—anastomoses—between small arteries and veins which can vary the amount of blood passing through the capillaries of a given organ. Sometimes the exchange of materials between tissues and blood may take place in small, irregularly shaped, thin-walled "ponds" of blood termed *sinusoids*, which are essentially proximal parts of the venous system. In some instances, usually connected with special organ functions, a blood vessel breaks up into a complicated, coiled mass of tiny blood vessels reasonably termed "a marvellous network"—*rete mirabile*; a kidney glomerulus is such a structure, and others are found, for example, in the red body of the teleost air bladder and the heat-sensing organ of pit vipers. A special type of network may be present in the distal part of the limbs, particularly in wading birds and the "flippers" of aquatic mammals. A maze of tiny channels from the arteries leading to the foot or "paddle" may surround the returning venous channels. This appears to be a heat-conserving device, warmth being short-circuited from the arteries to the veins and back into the body, at the expense of the chilly limb. The tails of many mammals (such as dog, cat, rat) show small tissue masses, termed *caudal glomeruli*, which contain retia mirabilia; man retains one such structure as a *coccygeal glomus*.

Arteries and Veins (Figs. 302, 303).   Sheathing materials, in addition to the ubiquitous endothelium, surround not only the larger vessels of the body —*arteries* and *veins*—but also their smaller branches, the *arterioles* and *venules*, and likewise the major lymphatic vessels. Reinforcing elements include connec-

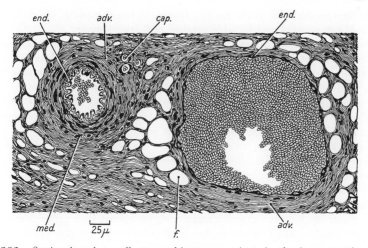

Fig. 302.   Section through a small artery and its accompanying vein, showing contrast in size and thickness of walls. *adv.*, Adventitia; *cap.*, capillary; *end.*, endothelium; *f*, fat cell; *med.*, media (muscle layer) of artery. (From Young, after Maximow and Bloom.)

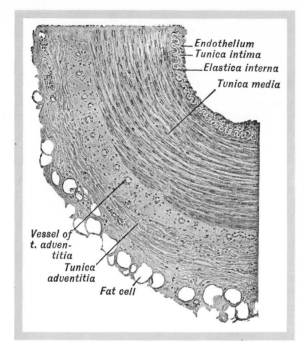

Endothelium
Tunica intima
Elastica interna
Tunica media

Vessel of
t. adven-
titia
Tunica
adventitia
Fat cell

Fig. 303. Section through an artery of a mammal. (After Schaffer.)

tive tissue fibers, elastic fibers, and smooth muscle cells in variable amounts and arrangements; nerve fibers for the smooth muscles are also present, and small nutrient blood vessels may be present in the walls of large arteries or veins.

The walls of blood vessels are customarily described as consisting of three layers or "tunics," the *tunica intima, tunica media*, and *tunica externa* or *adventitia*. As seen in simplest form in small arteries or veins, the intima may consist only of the endothelium, the media a few muscle fibers (absent in the smallest veins), the externa a bit of connective tissue. In larger vessels, however, thick sheaths of complicated and variable arrangement are present.

In a typical large artery the intima includes, besides the endothelium, a thin sheet of fibrous connective tissue just beneath it, and a sheath of elastic tissue which completely surrounds the vessel as an *internal elastic membrane*. The tunica media contains some connective tissue, but is dominantly the muscular layer, although smooth muscle fibers are sometimes found in the other two layers. When well developed, the muscle may be arranged in two layers, of circular and longitudinal fibers. The tunica media is often bounded externally by a second elastic tissue structure, an *external elastic membrane*. Beyond this is the adventitia—connective tissue, often rather loose, which binds the vessel to adjacent structures.

Veins have a somewhat similar but simpler build; in general there is much less muscle and elastic tissue in proportion to connective tissue. There are many further contrasts between arteries and veins, as regards both gross and minute structure; much of the contrast is due fundamentally to the fact that the blood flows under higher pressure in the arteries. That pressure may be better withstood, arterial walls are thicker and more complex than those of veins. Again, the lumen of an artery is much smaller than that of a vein of comparable importance; this is correlated with the faster flow of arterial blood (just as, for example, a high-speed through highway needs fewer lanes than a street where, with the same amount of traffic, the speed is slower). Frequently, in histologic sections, twin vessels can be seen beside one another (cf. Fig. 302), and artery and vein can be clearly distinguished by these criteria. The "bore" of an artery tends to remain constant, diminishing only as branches are given off; a vein—particularly in sharks and cyclostomes—may expand along its course to form a large sac, or *sinus*. Again associated with speed and pressure differences is the fact that the arterial system presents few individual anomalies, but veins are highly variable. A fast-flowing mountain stream tends to take a direct and undeviating course, whereas a sluggish stream meanders, branches and re-forms, produces islands; so in the embryo a vein often appears as a network of variable channels (cf. Fig. 329, p. 454). Which channels of the network are to form the definitive vein is not fixed; hence the frequent anomalies. In limbs, arteries are deeply placed; veins may in part be superficial in position.

Lymphatic Vessels.   The lymphatic system, well developed in the higher vertebrates as a return route from tissues to heart paralleling the veins, consists of vessels which are comparable to capillaries and veins of the blood system. Lymphatic capillaries, however, tend to be larger in diameter and more irregular than blood capillaries (Fig. 304). Larger lymphatic vessels, in which the lymph fluid flows but sluggishly toward the heart, have walls still thinner than those of veins, and may expand into thin-walled pockets, *lymphatic cisterns*.

Valves and Sphincters.   Expansion and contraction of blood vessels is controlled by the action of the muscular and elastic tissues present along their walls; more positive control of blood and lymphatic flow is frequently exercised by the development of sphincters and valves. In small arteries and veins, circular muscle fibers may be greatly developed in a sharply localized region to form a

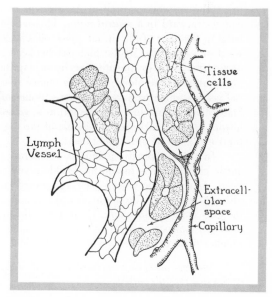

Fig. 304.   A small lymphatic and a neighboring capillary. (Ponder in Fulton-Howell.)

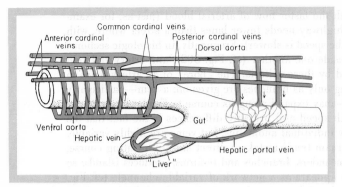

Fig. 305. Diagram of the major circulatory vessels of Amphioxus. Except for the absence of a heart at the posterior end of the ventral aorta, the system is closely comparable to that of vertebrates. Only a few of the numerous aortic arches are shown. Capillary systems are not shown except those concerned with the hepatic portal system. (The vessels are colored as if oxygen intake were entirely through gill walls, which is, of course, not the case.)

sphincter capable of closing off the blood flow in the vessel concerned. A backwash of blood or lymph through a vessel may be prevented by the presence of valves. These are folds of endothelium and connective tissue, behind which lie pocket-like depressions. A backward flow of liquid distends the pocket and pushes the valve flap out into the lumen of the vessel; two such valves generally suffice to close a vessel (three or four, however, are occasionally found). Valves are common in the veins in tetrapods (but not in fishes) and in the lymph vessels of birds and mammals (and are, of course, highly developed in the heart). Almost never is a valve found in an artery, since arterial blood cannot ordinarily work back against the strong pressure under which it flows from the heart.

ARTERIAL SYSTEM

Aortic Arch System in Fishes (Figs. 306, 309). In primitive, gill-breathing vertebrates (and in Amphioxus as well) all the blood from the heart courses forward in a *ventral aorta*. This median trunk, bifurcated anteriorly and lying in the floor of the throat, gives off a series of paired vessels which arch upward on either side of the pharynx between successive gill clefts. Each typical *aortic arch** breaks up into a series of capillary vessels on the gill membranes for aeration of the blood, which is thence re-collected dorsally into further arterial vessels which pass to the various tissues of the body and head. In land vertebrates the gills are lost, but the gill arch vessels are found in every embryo. The history of these aortic arches is one of the most interesting chapters in the structural evolution of the vertebrates.

In a diagrammatic primitive vertebrate (Fig. 209, *A*) we may picture the aortic circulation as including, beside a ventral aorta running forward from the heart, paired aortic vessels passing upward laterally in front of or between each gill slit or pouch. The major vessel reached by the blood after passage through the gills is the *dorsal aorta*. Posteriorly, the aorta is a single median trunk; anteriorly, it consists of a pair of vessels passing along either side of the head. The number of aortic arches was presumably high and variable in the ancestral verte-

---

* The triple use of the word "arch" in the gill region was commented on earlier; in this chapter *aortic* arch is generally implied.

Fig. 306. Diagram of the main blood vessels of a shark as seen in lateral view.

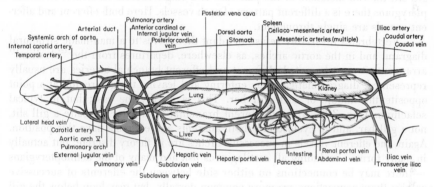

Fig. 307. Diagram of the main blood vessels of a urodele amphibian as seen in lateral view.

Fig. 308. Diagram of the main blood vessels of a mammal (rat) as seen in lateral view.

brates (it is very high in Amphioxus); in most living jawed forms, however, there are but five normal gill slits plus a spiracle, and hence potentially six pairs of aortic arches, usually designated by Roman numerals. In the vertebrate embryo these arches are, to begin with, continuous vessels passing without interruption from ventral to dorsal aorta; only as the gill slits open and become functional does the gill capillary system develop, with consequent interruption of the loop of the arch. In all vertebrates the aortic arches develop in order, in the embryo, from front to back. The first, or mandibular, arch is, in the early embryo, the only passage from ventral to dorsal aorta (Fig. 313, *A*, p. 432).

The circulation in the gills may be noted briefly. In the cyclostomes the gills are subspherical, pouchlike structures; the arches break up into smaller afferent vessels and capillaries beneath each pouch and collect into a series of efferent vessels above. In all other living fishes the gill openings are slit-shaped, and the afferent vessel of an aortic arch typically runs up between each successive pair of slits (Fig. 310, p. 428). In selachians and lungfishes the afferent vessel continues as a single structure far up the gill, giving off capillaries as it goes. The efferent vessels of each gill are a pair, anteriorly and posteriorly placed; at the top of the gill slit the two members of the pair fuse to a single efferent structure. In actinopterygians there is a different pattern of arch vessels. Here both efferent and afferent vessels are single throughout.

Vertebrates invariably refuse to adapt themselves to a man-made structural diagram, and in the aortic arches, as elsewhere, departures from the "idealized" arrangement must be noted. Afferent and efferent branchial arteries are usually represented, diagrammatically, as entering and leaving the gill region at a point opposite the middle of each gill bar. This is usually the case; but in typical selachians (Fig. 309, *B*) each efferent branchial artery lies opposite a gill slit, not a gill bar, and in cyclostomes both afferents and efferents have this position. Again, the efferent vessels in successive arches are in theory discrete; but actually in many forms—including all cartilaginous fish and many of the actinopterygians —there may be connections on either side between the efferents of successive arches; these connections are more common dorsally, but may loop below the gill slits as well. In all gnathostome fishes there is commonly a ventral *hypobranchial artery* (not illustrated) developed from the efferent system, which runs backward along the throat to supply that region and the heart with aerated blood. Characteristically this takes its root from the fourth arch. Still further, we find in fishes an artery running downward and forward from the efferent gill arteries to the mandibular region.

In cyclostomes all of the aortic arches are similarly developed; in jawed fishes, in which six arches are usually developed in the embryo, the posterior four usually attain a typical adult structure, but the first two may be highly modified. The first arch, the *mandibular*, runs upward in the embryo between mouth and spiracle; the second, the *hyoid arch*, lies between the spiracle and the first "normal" gill slit.

Presumably ancestral vertebrates had a well developed arch I running up the jaw region. But although a first aortic arch is found in the embryo, it is never present in typical form in the adult of any living form. Its afferent portion almost universally disappears. There is usually in fishes a gill-like structure on the anterior margin of the spiracle opening. In theory such a gill should be supplied by arch I. But its blood supply comes, in the adult, from the efferent system of the second arch or from a branch of the dorsal aorta. The blood which reaches it has, thus, already been aerated. The spiracular gill is therefore not a true gill, but a "false gill" or pseudobranch (cf. p. 320). The efferent portion of arch I persists in fishes and runs up from the pseudobranch into the orbital region, enters the braincase to connect with the arteries beneath the brain, and supplies the eye with blood (Fig. 306, spiracular artery; cf. Fig. 309, B).

The second aortic arch is somewhat variable but more persistent. It is generally present in typical fashion in Chondrichthyes and is also found in some

Fig. 309. Diagrams of the aortic arches and derived vessels in various vertebrate types. A, Theoretical ancestor of the jawed vertebrates with six unspecialized aortic arches; B, typical fish condition as seen in a shark; C, the lungfish Protopterus; D, a teleost; E, a terrestrial salamander; F, a lizard; G, a bird; H, a mammal. Various accessory vessels are omitted. The vessels of the right side are heavily shaded. In terrestrial forms the position of the vessels is made (for purposes of the diagram) to correspond more or less to that of the arches from which they are derived. Aortic arches in Roman numerals; s, spiracular slit; following gill slits in Arabic numerals. cd, Carotid duct; da, embryonic ductus arteriosus; ec, external carotid artery; ic, internal carotid artery; L, lung. The carotid duct shown in the lizard is absent in other reptiles; in turtles the carotids arise by a separate stem directly from the heart. In H the embryonic arterial duct by-passing the lungs is shown in broken lines.

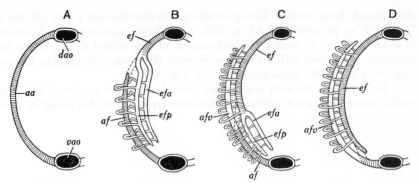

Fig. 310. Diagram of circulation in a fish gill, left side, from behind. *A*, Embryonic condition, with continuous aortic arch, *aa*, from ventral aorta, *vao*, to dorsal aorta, *dao*. *B*, Shark condition; the afferent gill vessel, *af*, is formed from the aortic arch; the paired efferent vessels, *efa*, *efp*, are new formations. *C*, Condition transitional to *D*, seen in sturgeons. *D*, Teleost condition. The embryonic arch gives rise to the efferent vessel, *ef*; the afferent vessel, *afv*, is a new formation. (After Sewertzoff, Goodrich.)

bony fishes. But in most actinopterygians it is lost, and the same is true of the lungfish Epiceratodus.

Arches III to VI are in general, as we have seen, both normally and fully developed in jawed fishes. In the lungfish Protopterus an interesting exception is that arches III and IV run without break past the gill region. This condition is associated with the reduced gills and developed lung of that genus and shows a partial parallel to developments in the amphibian relatives of the dipnoans.

The introduction of a lung into the circulatory system in certain bony fishes makes, for most forms still in the fish stage, no great change in the gill arch system. The lung in Polypterus and lungfishes (Fig. 309, *C*) is supplied by an artery from the efferent portion of the sixth aortic arch or the aorta beyond this point; hence the blood reaching it has already passed through the normal aerating device of the gill capillaries.

Aortic Arches in Amphibians (Figs. 309, *E*, 311, *A*). In the amphibian stage marked changes are present, even in the larval forms. Arches I and II disappear early in development, although a lingual (or external carotid) artery may continue forward ventrally to the jaw region. The remaining four arches may persist in the adult as continuous tubes in urodeles, since internal gills fail to develop (the external gills of the larva are supplied by accessory capillary loops). In frogs the extensive development of the peculiar gill leads to a larval interruption of continuity of the arches, which, however, is restored for the most part at metamorphosis. In the adult amphibian we generally find, in consequence, a system of complete tubular aortic arches, which always include the third, fourth, and sixth pairs; arch V often persists in urodeles, but is absent in frogs and all adult amniotes. In fishes the dorsal ends of all these arches connected with the uninterrupted dorsal aorta. Variations in these connections, however, are already present in amphibians. Even in fishes the blood flowing up through the third arch tended to pass forward toward the head region rather than backward with the main aortic flow, and cranial blood supply becomes the sole function of this arch in tetrapods. The part of the dorsal aorta between arches III and IV tends, in correlation, to disappear in adult tetrapods, thus completely separating cranial and body segments of the original aorta. However, this connection, termed the *carotid duct,* still persists in the adult in the Apoda, some urodeles and even in various reptiles. The third arch and the associated anterior part of the dorsal aorta is the *internal carotid artery;* the ventral aortic stem leading forward to it becomes the *common carotid* (cf. Fig. 314).

The fourth arch is always a large, bilaterally developed vessel in lower tetrapods; it is termed the *systemic arch,* since it is the main channel for blood flowing from heart to body. The fifth arch, on the other hand, tends to "lose out" in tetrapods; as was said above, it may persist in urodeles, but is found in no other land vertebrates beyond the embryonic stage; even in the embryo it is usually small and transient in appearance, and may fail to develop at all. Why the fourth arch is selected as the blood channel to the body rather than the seemingly shorter and more direct route via arch V is an unsolved puzzle.

As we have noted, the lung is supplied with blood via arch VI. The lung is functionless in the amphibian larva (as in the embryos of amniotes). During the larval period the major part of the blood in this arch travels straight on upward into the dorsal aorta as part of the main blood stream to the body. But when in the amphibian (or in the amniote at birth or hatching) the lung begins to func-

Fig. 311. Diagram of the heart and aortic arches in tetrapods. *A,* Amphibian; *B,* a mammal; *C,* typical modern reptiles; *D,* crocodilian. Ventral views; the heart (sectioned) is represented as if the chambers were arranged in the same plane; the dorsal ends of the arches are arbitrarily placed at either side. Solid arrows represent the main stream of venous blood; arrows with broken line the blood coming from the lung. Vessels with aerated blood are unshaded; those leaving heart with venous blood, hatched. The two vessels at the top of each figure are the internal carotid (laterally) and external carotid (medially). In amphibians without a ventricular septum the two blood streams are somewhat mixed; subdivision of the arterial cone tends to bring about partial separation, but some venous blood is returned to the dorsal aorta. In mammals ventricular separation is complete, the arterial cone subdivided into two vessels, and the arches are reduced to the left systemic and pulmonary. The mammalian condition has apparently arisen directly from the primitive type preserved in the Amphibia, for in modern reptiles the conus arteriosus shows a division into three vessels, rather than two; one, returning venous blood back to the body, leads only to the left fourth arch. In crocodilians the ventricular septum is nearly complete, and the elimination of the left fourth arch would give the avian condition. *asc,* Anterior subclavian; *d,* ductus Botalli; *da,* dorsal aorta; *la,* left atrium; *lsa,* left systemic arch; *lv,* left ventricle; *p,* pulmonary artery; *pv,* pulmonary vein; *r,* portion of lateral aorta remaining open in some reptiles; *ra,* right atrium; *rsa,* right systemic arch; *rv,* right ventricle; *spa,* interatrial septum; *spv,* interventricular septum; *sv,* sinus venosus; *v,* ventricle; *vc,* anterior vena cava; *vci,* posterior vena cava. (From Goodrich.)

tion, the dorsal part of this arch should, for the sake of efficiency, be eliminated to prevent admixture of blood streams. This connection, the *ductus arteriosus* (or duct of Botalli), persists in reduced form in the adult among urodeles and Apoda, in Sphenodon, and some turtles; in frogs and most amniotes it disappears after metamorphosis or birth.

The original ventral aorta, as a result of the processes just described, tends to be reduced to a channel of supply for arches III, IV, and VI. The last, as a bearer of venous blood to the lung, merits a separate channel from the heart. We find that in living amphibians the ventral aorta as such is done away with; it has been split to its base to separate the *pulmonary trunk* from the remainder of the original aorta.

In urodeles there persists a relatively complete and "fishy" arch system, but in anurans, as a result of the changes discussed, we find an arch system of a sort characteristic of a majority of reptiles and, indeed, more advanced than in many of that group. In this pre-amniote stage we have remaining (1) a carotid system, including the anterior end of the ventral aorta, the third arch, and the anterior end of the paired dorsal aorta; (2) a paired systemic arch, including the major basal stem of the ventral aorta and the fourth pair of arches; (3) a pulmonary system, including a basal stem split off from the ventral aorta, part of the sixth arch, and a *pulmonary artery* leading from arch to the lung.

Amniote Aortic Arches. In the amniotes further developments in the aortic arch system have to do mainly with variations in the fourth arch. In earlier evolutionary stages the arch structures were in general strictly bilaterally symmetric; in the amniotes asymmetry appears.

It is probable that in the ancestral reptiles (as in the frog) there were two ventral trunks from the heart, one to the lungs, the other a common trunk to both systemic arches and both carotids. In living reptiles, however, we find that three vessels, rather than two, open forward from the heart (Fig. 311, *C*, *D*). These include (1) the pulmonary arch; (2) a separate tube leading only to the left systemic arch; and (3) one for the right systemic arch, with which both carotids and arteries to both front legs have come to be associated. The three are so situated that in the ventricular cavity of the heart, incompletely divided in most reptiles, the vessel for the left fourth arch tends to receive much of the venous body blood and hence has little function as an oxygen carrier. When, in crocodiles, the two ventricles are well separated, the left fourth arch definitely receives "blue" blood from the right ventricle. This recirculation of "venous" blood is useless except as a "shunt" to relieve the lungs of too great a volume of blood; the birds, descended from reptiles related to the crocodiles, have eliminated this vessel completely (Fig. 309, *G*). Apart from the pulmonary stem from the right ventricle, there thus remains in birds only a single trunk leaving the heart—that from the left ventricle. This carries aerated blood to both the carotids and thence to the head, to both front legs, and to the body by a single systemic arch—the right member of the original pair. In correlation with the length and slenderness of the bird neck, the two carotids run close beside one another below the neck vertebrae, and one of the pair is often reduced and may be absent.

The history of the mammalian arches seems to have been simpler (Figs. 309 *H*, 311, *B*). Mammal ancestry diverged from that of other reptiles at an early date, and there is no reason to believe that the system of three heart orifices seen in modern reptiles was ever present in the mammalian line. Presumably, as in anurans, the early reptilian ancestor of mammals had, beside a pulmonary arch, a single trunk leading from the left side of the ventricle to the two carotids and the two systemic arches. But a double systemic arch is unnecessary and ineffi-cient; somewhere along the line of development to mammals, the right fourth arch disappeared from the picture (except that its base remained as a connection with the subclavian artery to the arm), and the entire blood supply to the trunk follows the curve of the left member of the embryonic pair. The mammal, like the bird, has simplified the systemic blood supply; but the two groups are in con-trast as to which member of the pair of fourth arches is retained.

In mammals there is great variation in the way in which the pairs of caro-tids and front leg vessels (subclavians) branch off from the arch of the aorta (Fig. 312). The carotids may leave the aorta separately, by a common stem, or jointly with the neighboring subclavian; and as a final variant, all four vessels may de-part as a single, large trunk.

The embryonic development of the aortic arches of a mammal recapitulates to a considerable degree the phylogenetic story outlined above (Fig. 313). The first blood channels established from heart to body in the embryo are a pair of anteriorly placed arches which, subsequent history shows, are the first pair—the mandibular arches—of the fish series. Gill pouches develop in sequence behind this point, and successive aortic loops are formed between them as arches II, III, and IV. As the more posterior arches develop they tend, each in turn, to become the most prominent pair; synchronously, the more anterior arches tend to be re-duced in importance, so that the first two cease to be functional in a short time. Behind arch IV, arch VI presently develops, but the fifth arch is sometimes ab-sent and at the best is small and transitory. In the embryo, arch VI runs directly upward to the dorsal aorta, and little blood passes through the pulmonary artery branching from it. At birth, however, the upper part of this arch—the ductus arteriosus—becomes almost immediately occluded, and the full flow of blood passes to the lung.

Blood Supply to the Head (Fig. 314).   Though the main dorsal flow of arterial blood is in a posterior direction, to the trunk, tail, and limbs, an impor-tant element in the circulation, if a minor one in quantity, is a forward flow to the head region.

The anterior part of the dorsal aortic system is a paired vessel which, in the skull region, primitively runs along either side of the braincase, receiving the

Fig. 312.   Diagrams, in ventral view, to show variations in the branching of the main blood vessels from the mammalian aortic arch. *A*, Embryonic condition, with ventral trunk of aorta and third (caro-tid) and fourth pairs of arches, of which the right fourth arch is later lost beyond the point of departure of the subclavian. By differential growth of the vessels the various arrangements shown in *B* to *F* are brought about (*D* is the human type). *lc*, Left carotid; *ls*, left subclavian; *rc*, right carotid; *rs*, right sub-clavian arteries. (After Hafferl, in part.)

Fig. 313. Development of the aortic arches of a mammal (Homo). The outline of the gut cavity, gill pouches, and lung buds are shown in addition to blood vessels; in *A*, the cavities within the heart are included. Arch I is developed. *B*, Arch I already reduced, II and III formed. *C*, Arch II reduced, IV (systemic) formed, VI (pulmonary) arch and pulmonary artery forming (Arch V does not develop in man). *D*, Pulmonary arch well developed. *E*, Carotid arch (III) separated dorsally from aorta, pulmonary arch becoming distinct at root from ventral aorta. *F*, Diagram to show reduction at birth of upper end of arch VI (ductus arteriosus). P^1 to P^5 = pharyngeal pouches. (After Streeter.)

efferent branchial arteries from more anterior members of the gill series. Posteriorly, this vessel is considered a paired part of the dorsal aorta; anteriorly, it is an obvious homologue of the internal carotid artery of higher vertebrates above the fish level. If we follow this artery forward in fishes, we find that after giving off a major branch—the *orbital* (temporal) *artery*—to supply much of the general face and jaw region, its main stem passes upward into the braincase in front of the pituitary. Here it furnishes the main blood supply for the brain, gives off an artery to the eyeball, and connects with the efferent pseudobranchial artery mentioned earlier.

The condition just described is a primitive one, which holds, with little variation, among the various fish groups. In amphibians the system tends to be modified in relation to the disappearance of the internal gill system; all that remains of the aortic arch system anterior to the fourth arch is the proximal part of the carotid system, and the pseudobranchial artery of fishes is absent.

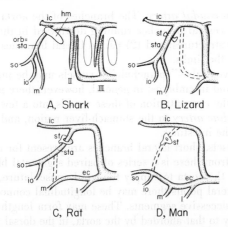

Fig. 314. Diagrams of the left side of the head to show the evolution of the carotid system. In a relatively primitive fish stage (*A*) the direct forward continuation of the aorta is the internal carotid artery, which enters the braincase near the pituitary. This gives off a major branch, the orbital artery, which, passing close to the hyomandibular, supplies most of the more superficial features of the skull and jaws. (An accessory blood supply to the head from the spiracle is omitted from the diagram.) In many tetrapods (*B*) a similar situation persists, the orbital artery being commonly called the stapedial, since it passes close to or through the stapes (= hyomandibular). However, a small branch present near the root of the carotid extends forward, and as the external carotid of mammals may take over part (*C*) or all (*D*) of the functions of the stapedial. *ec*, External carotid; *hm*, hyomandibular; *ic*, internal carotid; *io*, infraorbital artery; *l*, lingual artery; *m*, mandibular artery; *orb*, orbital artery; *so*, supraorbital artery; *st*, stapes; *sta*, stapedial artery; II, III, second and third aortic arches. In *B* to *D* modified aortic root = common carotid.

In typical reptiles and amphibians the carotid gives off near its base, while ventral in position, a small *external carotid* (lingual) *artery* which supplies tissues of the tongue and throat (and may exceptionally reach the lower jaw region). The main carotid stem, much as in fishes, passes upward and forward as the internal carotid, to the middle ear region of the skull. Here the internal carotid artery continues forward toward its opening into the braincase; but it gives off, close by the stapes, a major branch, a large *stapedial artery*, which supplies all the structures of the outer parts of the head and most of the area of the jaws. This last artery is identical with the orbital artery of the fish ancestors.

In primitive mammals and all mammalian embryos the arterial system of the head persists in much the same fashion. In most mammals, however, major changes occur. The originally small external carotid grows forward and taps the branches of the stapedial artery. As a result the external carotid is large in most mammals, the stapedial artery reduced or absent; a new and shorter route has developed for supplying blood to the face and jaws. The process is analogous to "stream piracy," whereby one river taps the headwaters of another.

Blood Supply to the Body and Limbs (Figs. 306–308, p. 425; 315). In every vertebrate the major blood supply to the trunk, tail, and limbs is furnished by the dorsal aorta and its branches. Its most anterior, cranial, part may be paired, but in the trunk the aorta becomes a median vessel, lying beneath notochord or vertebrae and above the root of the mesentery; posteriorly, it continues as a median *caudal artery*. The branches of the aorta tend to be of two types: (1) median ventral branches running downward in the mesentery to the gut and associated structures; and (2) paired lateral branches to the outer areas of the body and to the limbs.

The median ventral—"splanchnic"—vessels may be numerous in certain lower vertebrates and in embryos; in general, however, there is a somewhat variable tendency for the concentration of these vessels into a few main trunks, usually including a *celiac artery* to the stomach-liver region, and one or more *mesenteric arteries* to the intestines.

Of paired vessels, short lateral branches are present for the gonads and the kidneys. Separate from these is a series of paired segmental blood vessels which run laterally from the aorta to supply the trunk musculature, the skin, and the spinal cord. At several points there may be longitudinal connections between the paired vessels of successive segments. These may form lengthwise arterial channels, supplementary to that afforded by the aorta, in the dorsal region of the body and the skin of the back and flanks. These channels may, further, afford the opportunity for originally segmental arteries to coalesce into a smaller number of large vessels stemming from the dorsal aorta, so that in higher vertebrates the segmental arrangement is increasingly obscured.

In the embryonic development of paired fins or legs, there is seen, at an early stage, a network of small arteries continuous with the segmental arteries of the neighboring region of the trunk (Fig. 329, p. 454). During ontogeny one or another of these tends to become dominant and to form a main channel from aorta to limb. In the pectoral limb this main trunk is usually given its mammalian name of *subclavian artery*, although it is improbable that it is exactly the same vessel in every case. Giving off branches to the shoulder and chest region, this same main trunk is termed the *axillary artery* as it enters the limb, and the *brachial artery* as it proceeds down the "arm." The point of departure of the sub-

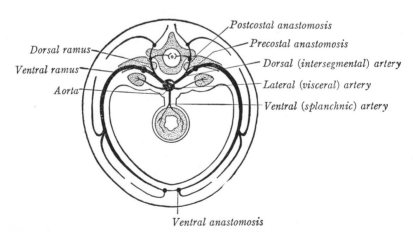

Fig. 315. Diagrammatic cross section of the body of a higher vertebrate to show various types of branches which may be given off by the aorta. Most prominent are median ventral branches descending in the mesentery to the gut, and so forth, and paired intersegmental arteries, the main ventral ramus of which descends the flanks between the myomeres or adjacent to successive ribs. Longitudinal anastomoses may occur between successive segments in various regions. (From Arey.)

clavian from the primitive aortic trunk seems to have been rather variable; in consequence, its relation to carotids and main aorta varies in tetrapod types (Figs. 307, 308, 312, pp. 425 and 431). Subclavians may arise from the unpaired stem of the dorsal aortic trunk (salamanders), or from the paired systemic arch (frogs), or from the right systemic (reptiles, birds). In mammals the right systemic arch is done away with, but the base of the arch is retained as a proximal part of the right subclavian. In crocodiles the origin of the subclavians is still farther forward, from a point near the top of aortic arch III, and hence in the adult the subclavians and carotids have a common trunk (Fig. 311, *D*, p. 429); the same situation persists in their avian relatives.

In the pelvic appendage, as in the pectoral, there is a tendency for the concentration of the blood supply to the limb into a single vessel. Primitively this was an *ischiadic artery* running outward behind the ilium; in mammals the major stem becomes the *femoral artery*, emerging in front of the girdle. Further down the limb the main trunk is termed the *popliteal* at the knee region and the *peroneal* in the shin.

VENOUS SYSTEM

The veins—vessels bringing blood from capillary systems to the heart—have a complicated and variable arrangement. If, however, their embryonic history is studied, it is seen that they can be logically sorted out into a small number of systems. The discussion of the venous system here will be based largely on the developmental story. So treated, we may consider the following principal components of the venous system (Fig. 316):

1. An embryonic *subintestinal system* of veins flowing forward below the gut, forming in the adult the *hepatic portal system* running from the gut to the liver and the *hepatic veins* from liver toward the heart.

2. Veins situated dorsal to the celom or gut and carrying blood toward the heart from the dorsal parts of the body and the head (and generally from the paired limbs as well); they include the *cardinals* or the *venae cavae* which replace them, and their affluents.

3. A relatively minor group, the *abdominal vein* or veins, draining the ventral part of the body wall.

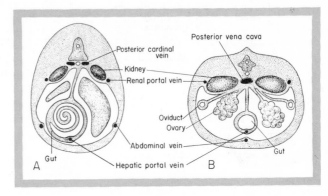

Fig. 316. *A*, Cross section of the abdominal region of a shark, to show the position of the main veins. *B*, The same in a urodele amphibian.

4. In typical lung-bearing vertebrates, the *pulmonary veins* from lungs to heart.

The first and fourth of these four components forms the drainage of the gut tube and its outgrowths; it is essentially a visceral venous system. The second and third components are, on the contrary, mainly somatic venous systems, draining the outer wall of the body.

Hepatic Portal System and Hepatic Veins (Figs. 306–308, p. 425). The *hepatic portal system,* common to all vertebrates, is composed of veins which collect blood from the intestine and transport it to the sinusoids of the liver. Functionally the system is of great importance, for the intestinal capillaries take in all the food materials absorbed from the gut (with the exception of part of the fats),

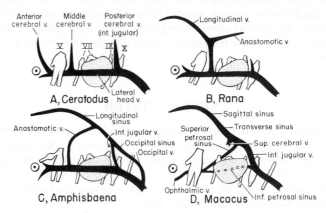

Fig. 317. Diagrams of the left side of the head region to show stages in the evolution of the venous drainage. Roots of some of cranial nerves are indicated; the position of the eye is shown, and the otic capsule is stippled. In lower vertebrates the main drainage is by a lateral head vein, which forms in the orbital region and runs backward to become the anterior cardinal. This primitively receives several successive veins from the interior of the skull. A series of sinuses develops within the braincase; the lateral head vein is abandoned in mammals, and blood from the orbital region enters the sinus system, all finally draining from the skull as the internal jugular vein. *A,* Lungfish; *B,* frog; *C,* lizard; *D,* mammal (macaque monkey). (After van Gelderen.)

Fig. 318. Ventral views of the veins anterior to the heart region in successive developmental stages to show the formation, in man and certain other mammals, of a single anterior (or superior) vena cava from the two anterior cardinals (precardinals). An intercostal vein (*I*) and a small vein from the wall of the left atrium (*O.V.*, oblique vein) are persisting vestiges of the original left anterior cardinal. (From Arey.)

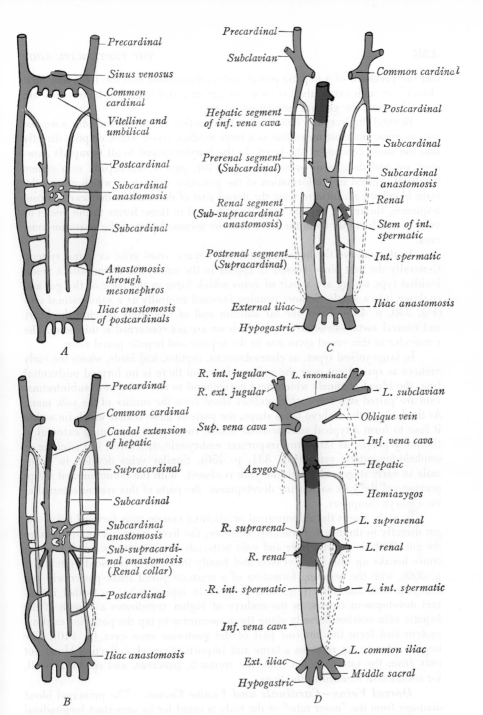

A

- Precardinal
- Sinus venosus
- Common cardinal
- Vitelline and umbilical
- Postcardinal
- Subcardinal anastomosis
- Subcardinal
- Anastomosis through mesonephros
- Iliac anastomosis of postcardinals

B

- Precardinal
- Common cardinal
- Caudal extension of hepatic
- Supracardinal
- Subcardinal
- Subcardinal anastomosis
- Sub-supracardinal anastomosis (Renal collar)
- Postcardinal
- Iliac anastomosis

C

- Precardinal
- Subclavian
- Common cardinal
- Postcardinal
- Hepatic segment of inf. vena cava
- Subcardinal
- Prerenal segment (Subcardinal)
- Subcardinal anastomosis
- Renal segment (Sub-supracardinal anastomosis)
- Renal
- Stem of int. spermatic
- Postrenal segment (Supracardinal)
- Int. spermatic
- External iliac
- Iliac anastomosis
- Hypogastric

D

- R. int. jugular
- L. innominate
- R. ext. jugular
- L. subclavian
- Sup. vena cava
- Oblique vein
- Inf. vena cava
- Azygos
- Hepatic
- Hemiazygos
- L. suprarenal
- R. suprarenal
- L. renal
- R. renal
- R. int. spermatic
- L. int. spermatic
- Inf. vena cava
- Ext. iliac
- L. common iliac
- Hypogastric
- Middle sacral

Fig. 319. Development of the posterior vena cava of man, showing embryological processes roughly paralleling the evolutionary history. The original postcardinal system is shown in blue. Presently there develop subcardinal vessels, corresponding to the veins draining the kidney when a portal system is established in sharks. In *B*, this venous system is tapped (as in lungfishes) by a branch of the hepatic veins (purple). A third system of embryonic veins, the supracardinals (yellow) is not exactly paralleled in phylogeny. In green are vessels which develop in amniotes to bypass the kidney and eliminate the renal portal system. As seen in *D*, the definitive posterior vena cava includes fractions of all these structures. (From Arey, after McClure and Butler.)

437

and the presence of a hepatic portal system guarantees that the liver has "first chance" at such materials, for their storage or transformation, before they are turned out into the general circulation.

Beyond the liver the blood from the intestine is re-collected into a *hepatic vein* or veins. In most fishes this is a large median vessel which empties directly into the sinus venosus of the heart. In the lungfishes and in all tetrapods ,however, we find that, as discussed later (p. 440), part of this hepatic vein system has been utilized in the formation of the posterior vena cava, which carries the main blood stream forward from the dorsal part of the trunk to the heart. In consequence, the term "hepatic vein" is restricted in these forms to the vessel or vessels which empty from the liver into the terminal part of the posterior vena cava.

In the embryo the hepatic portal and hepatic veins arise as a unit system. Generally the first blood vessels to appear in the embryo in forms with a meso-lecithal type of egg are a pair of veins which form in the floor of the gut and coalesce into a single channel running forward ventrally as a *subintestinal vein* (Fig. 330, p. 455). From the far anterior end of this trunk develop the heart and ventral aorta—structures with which we are not concerned at this point. The remainder of this vessel gives rise to the hepatic and hepatic portal veins.

In large-yolked types, as elasmobranchs, reptiles, and birds, where the early embryo is spread out over the yolk surface and there is no formed midventral line, the blood channels which here correspond to the embryonic subintestinal vein are paired structures which collect blood from the surface of the yolk mass. As the body of the embryo takes shape, the parts of these vessels which lie within it fuse to form a typical subintestinal vessel; those parts remaining external to the body persist as large and important embryonic structures, the *vitelline* or omphalo-mesenteric *veins* (Fig. 331, p. 456). Similar veins develop in mammals in early stages, although the yolk is absent. With the reduction and disappearance of the yolk sac during development, the parts of this system external to the embryo disappear.

In early stages the subintestinal or vitelline system runs forward below the gut directly to the heart. Presently, however, the liver grows out ventrally from the gut. With its growth, liver and vein materials become intermingled; the vein trunk breaks up into small vessels and finally into a liver sinusoid system (cf. p. 360), with the resulting formation of a separate portal trunk posteriorly and a hepatic vein anteriorly (Fig. 332, p. 457). In typical fishes no further important development occurs; in the embryo of higher vertebrates a branch of the hepatic vein reaches dorsally along the mesenteries to tap the posterior cardinal system and form the anterior part of the posterior vena cava (p. 440). The hepatic portal vein remains a large and important vessel, collecting blood not only from the intestine, but from the stomach, pancreas, and spleen as well, for conduction forward to the liver.

Dorsal Veins—Cardinals and Venae Cavae. The principal blood drainage from the "outer tube" of the body is cared for by important longitudinal vessels situated dorsally above the gut and mesenteries. In lower vertebrates these veins are the cardinals; in higher forms major modifications of these vessels produce the venae cavae.

In the embryo of every vertebrate (and of Amphioxus as well) paired veins appear at an early stage in the tissues above the celomic cavity, one on either side of the midline (Fig. 331). These are the primitive *cardinal veins*. The *poste-*

rior cardinals run along the trunk on either side of the dorsal aorta to a point in the body wall dorsal to the heart. Paired *anterior cardinals* begin as head veins on either side of the developing braincase and run back dorsally along the neck region to meet their posterior mates. From this point of junction on either side a major vessel descends to enter the sinus venosus of the heart; this is the *common cardinal* (or duct of Cuvier).* This characteristic embryonic cardinal system is retained in almost diagrammatic form in the adult of elasmobranchs (Fig. 306, p. 425), and is retained in ray-finned fishes as well. We may discuss separately the history of the anterior and posterior parts of this system.

In all vertebrate classes except the mammals the main stem of each anterior cardinal (or anterior vena cava) is the *lateral head vein* (Fig. 317). This characteristically arises in the space behind the orbit, where it may be present as an expanded sinus, and receives vessels from various areas of the anterior part of the head. Traveling posteriorly along the side of the braincase and ear region, the lateral head veins receive tributaries from the brain and, continuing backward, enter the common cardinals. In lungfishes and tetrapods (where the posterior vena cava has taken the place of the posterior cardinals) the common cardinals are incorporated in the trunk of the anterior cardinals, including in their course, therefore, the openings of the subclavian veins from the pectoral limbs. With this modification the anterior cardinals come to resemble the vessels termed anterior venae cavae in mammals, and are frequently called by this name.

In mammals there is an important change in the cranial circulation. A system of intercommunicating venous sinuses is set up within the expanded brain cavity. The lateral head veins disappear, and the blood from the deep vessels of the front part of the head enters the braincase, to leave posteriorly on either side, after collection of the venous blood from the brain, as the *internal jugular veins.* As these travel posteriorly they are joined by vessels, the *external jugulars,* which gather blood from the more superficial parts of the head, to form *common jugulars;* joining the subclavian vein, the further course of each of these vessels to the heart is a trunk termed an *anterior vena cava.* Such veins are easily recognizable as the old anterior cardinals and common cardinals, except that intracranial channels supplant the lateral head veins which originally formed the most anterior part of the cardinal stems.

In many mammals (including man) the terminal part of the system is further modified (Fig. 318). In the embryo a cross connection develops between the two trunks, a short distance anterior to the heart, and the left common cardinal disappears. All the blood from the left cardinal then flows over to enter the heart through the right cardinal, so that in the adult only a single anterior (or superior) vena cava is present. A comparable development is seen in birds.

The story of the *posterior cardinals* is more complex (Figs. 320, 321). It begins with a pair of rather simple dorsal trunk vessels draining forward into the heart via the common cardinals; it ends in mammals with the draining of the same region by a single but complex vessel, the posterior vena cava. In between lies a considerable history.

In cyclostomes the posterior cardinals are simple paired vessels, receiving blood from a median caudal vein, kidneys, gonads, and dorsal parts of the body musculature and running forward uninterruptedly to the common cardinal region.

* The adult lamprey retains only a single common cardinal (the right).

Fig. 320. Diagrams in lateral view to show the evolution of the posterior cardinals and the development of a posterior vena cava. *A,* Lamprey (larva); *B,* typical fish condition; interjection of renal portal system. *C,* Lungfish or primitive tetrapod; a shortened route to the heart is established by utilizing part of the hepatic vein system in the initiation of a posterior vena cava. *D,* Mammal; the renal portal eliminated. (Vessels of the right side are shown in deeper shading.)

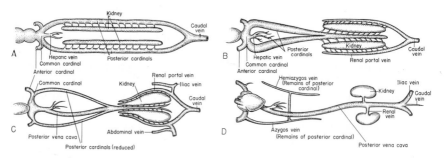

Fig. 321. Diagrams in ventral view to show the evolution of the posterior cardinals and the development of a posterior vena cava. Stages as in Figure 320.

In the Chondrichthyes, however, a new feature appears in the system which was destined to persist upward into the reptilian stage—the development of a *renal portal system.* The blood from the posterior part of the trunk and from the tail no longer flows directly to the heart. The cardinal channels are interrupted forward of the kidneys, and this blood is diverted into a network of capillaries around the kidney tubules (but not through the glomeruli). After this passage the blood is received by new vessels which carry it forward to the truncated stumps of the two posterior cardinals and thus to the heart. It is customary to term the vessels from kidney to heart in fishes the posterior cardinals over their entire length; but it is, of course, only the more anterior part which is truly homologous with the "original" cardinals of the cyclostomes or of the fish embryo before the renal portal system was established.

In the Sarcopterygii, as shown by the living lungfishes, a second progressive change initiates the development of a *posterior vena cava.* A branch of the hepatic veins draining the liver grows upward past that organ along a pulmonary fold (cf. p. 293) to the dorsal side of the body cavity and taps the right posterior cardinal vein some distance back of its entrance into the common cardinal. Once this is done, blood from the right cardinal may follow this new short cut to the heart; further, since there tends to be fusion in the kidney region between the vessels draining the two kidneys, blood from the left vessel may be shunted over and follow the same course. In lungfishes and urodeles part of the blood stream still utilizes the old cardinal entrances to the heart, but in frogs and all higher tetrapods both posterior cardinals lose connection with their more posterior trunks; they remain (one or both) merely as outlets for the small and variable series of *azygous veins*, draining the blood from part of the flanks. The new major trunk, from kidneys down past the liver to the heart, may be properly termed the posterior vena cava from the lungfish stage upward.

Among reptiles, and even in some amphibians, the renal portal system begins to degenerate, and much of the portal blood may be shunted through or past the kidney without entering the tubule circulation. In birds, it is commonly stated that the renal portal still exists; but actually nearly all the blood reaching the kidney plunges straight through that organ on its way to the heart without entering a capillary system. And in mammals the renal portal system has been completely abandoned. Blood from the hind legs (and tail, if any) passes directly forward, into the posterior vena cava; the posterior part of this vessel may be paired, but for most, if not all, of its length, the posterior vena cava is a single major vessel extending without interruption forward from the sacral region to the heart.

The posterior vena cava of the mammal is a vessel of seeming simplicity. As its history shows, however, it is a composite patchwork structure, including part of the original posterior cardinals, much of the veins draining the kidneys in the renal portal stage, and anteriorly, a branch of the original hepatic veins. In its evolutionary development from the primitive posterior cardinals, there have been three main steps: (1) introduction of a renal portal; (2) tapping of the right cardinal by the hepatic vein, and consequent degeneration of much of the anterior ends of the cardinal system; (3) subsequent reduction and abandonment, in amniotes, of the renal portal.

As might be expected from this complicated evolutionary story, the embryology of the posterior vena cava in higher tetrapods is likewise complicated. Since, however, the circulatory system must remain functional throughout development of the individual, the story is far from an ideal recapitulation of the phylogenetic history (Fig. 319). Postcaval development has been studied with care in several mammals, and while there is considerable difference from form to form, the general outline of development history is the same. Three successive pairs of longitudinal veins appear in the dorsal region of the trunk: (1) a pair representing the original posterior cardinals; (2) a second pair, situated more ventrally and medially, termed *subcardinals*, and representing the veins seen, from elasmobranchs upward, draining the kidneys forward into the stumps of the cardinals; (3) finally, *supracardinals*, mediodorsal in position (these do not appear clearly in the phylogenetic story). As in cyclostomes, there arise full length posterior cardinals; then, through the intervention of the subcardinals a renal portal system is established and, almost concomitantly, the connection with the hepatic veins is made as in lungfish. The role of the supracardinals is variable. In some forms they contribute little except drainage of the flanks through the system of azygous veins; in other cases, as in man, they contribute a fair length of the posterior part of the vena cava trunk.

Abdominal Veins; Limb Veins.   In the Chondrichthyes longitudinal *abdominal veins* are present low down in the body wall on either side (Figs. 306, 316, *A*, pp. 425, 435), draining blood from the lower part of the trunk musculature and run forward to empty into the common cardinals. Anteriorly each receives a small vein draining the pectoral fin, posteriorly a still smaller one from the pelvic fin. Abdominal veins are absent in ray-finned fishes, but a single median ventral abdominal vein is found in lungfishes and persists in amphibians (Figs. 307, 316, *B*) and in reptiles. In these tetrapods, however, it does not reach the heart directly, but runs upward anteriorly into the liver, to become essentially part of the hepatic portal system (Figs. 307, 316, *B*).

The abdominal vein system persists in the embryos of all amniotes, even when absent in the adult, for the significant reason that the veins from the allantois empty into paired abdominals. In reptiles and birds these veins are important for bringing oxygenated blood from the allantoic "lung" into the body; in placental mammals they are the carriers of the entire food supply from the placenta (Fig. 331, p. 456). They are in the mammalian embryo termed the *umbilical veins*, since, fused into one vessel for part of their course, they form the one venous afferent in the umbilical cord of the late embryo. As in the abdominal veins of adult amphibians and reptiles, the embryonic umbilical veins drain into the liver (Fig. 332, p. 457).

We may mention here in passing a pair of anterior veins in fishes which perform for the anterior end of the body the same function as the abdominal veins in the trunk; they are found in sharks and other lower vertebrates, as paired ventrolateral structures draining the walls of the "throat" region and running back into the common cardinals (Fig. 306). They are frequently termed external jugulars but appear not to be homologous with the vessels of that name in tetrapods, which are part of the anterior cardinal system.

Of the limb veins, those from the pectoral fin lose their slight affiliation with the abdominal vein in actinopterygians, to enter the common cardinals directly, and in tetrapods the pectoral limb drainage becomes associated with the anterior vena cava system as the *subclavian veins*. The veins from the pelvic appendages have a more complex history. As the vessels termed the *iliac veins* in tetrapods, they drain dorsally into the renal portal system in actinopterygians and from this point on a dorsal connection is retained with the renal portal and the vena cava which succeeds this system in birds and mammals. There is, however, a curious situation regarding the iliac vein connections. The ventral as well as the dorsal drainage route persists in lungfishes, amphibians, and reptiles. As a consequence, blood from the limb can travel toward the heart by either one of two routes in lungfishes, amphibians, and reptiles. But more than this, the connection may work "in reverse"—blood from the tail and sacral region may, instead of entering the renal portals, be shunted downward and follow the abdominal vein forward to the heart in lungfishes or to the liver in amphibians and reptiles. We have noted that there is no abdominal vein in ray-finned fishes, and there is none in birds. In both these groups, however, a vein, perhaps derived from the old abdominal, runs downward and forward from the renal portal system in the pelvic region to enter the hepatic sinus system, and thus gives the same choice of routes for blood from hind limbs and the hinder part of the body. In mammals neither abdominal vein, nor any substitute for it, exists; the posterior vena cava is the sole exit.

Pulmonary Veins.   These veins are, of course, absent in most living fishes, in which lungs are nonexistent. In the actinopterygian Polypterus, where a functional lung exists, the pulmonary veins empty into the hepatic vein; hence their blood mixes with the general blood stream from the body.

In the lungfishes, however, the pulmonary trunk by-passes the sinus venosus and enters the atrial cavity of the heart directly and at the left side. This separate course of the aerated blood from the lungs to the heart persists in all tetrapods. The entrance of the pulmonary veins into this heart region is a causal factor in the subdivision of the atrium and the final subdivision of the entire heart.

LYMPHATICS

In all except the lowest vertebrate groups we find, supplementary to the venous system, a second series of vessels returning fluids from the tissues to the heart—the *lymphatic system*. Although paralleling the veins in many functions (and often paralleling them topographically), the lymphatics differ from them in major respects. A fundamental difference is that the lymphatics are not connected in any way with the arteries, but arise from their own capillaries which are blind at their tips (Fig. 304, p. 423). Although the nature of the tips of the lymphatics was once debated, it is now generally agreed that they are closed throughout. There is thus no arterial pressure behind the fluid contained in the lymphatics; the flow of materials in them is generally sluggish.

The contained liquid, the *lymph*, gains entrance into the lymphatic vessels by diffusion through their walls and hence is essentially similar to the general tissue juice and (except for the absence of blood proteins) to the plasma of the blood vessels into which the lymphatics empty. There are, in most cases, few blood corpuscles in the lymph, since there is no flow of corpuscle-bearing blood into their distal ends; ameboid white blood cells, however, may make their entrance from adjacent tissue spaces. The lymphocytes owe their name to the fact that in mammals the main site of their formation is in the lymph nodes placed in the course of the lymphatic vessels. This, however, is almost exclusively a mammalian peculiarity, and in other vertebrate groups there is little or no special association of the lymphocytes with the lymphatic system.

Related to the low pressure under which lymph travels is the fact that the walls of lymphatics are thin (they are consequently difficult to find and dissect unless specially injected). Even the largest of lymph vessels have but a thin coat of musculature and connective tissue comparable to that of the smaller veins. In general, movement of the lymph is brought about by movement of the body and its various organs; in mammals and birds the lymphatics are supplied with numerous valves, preventing a backward flow. In amphibians the lymphatic system is supplied with *lymph hearts*—small, two-chambered, muscular structures which lie at points where lymph vessels empty into veins and actively pump lymph onward into the general circulation. These hearts are usually but few in number, but in the Apoda there may be 100 or so in a paired series. A pair in the pelvic region is prominent in both anurans and urodeles, and persists in reptiles and some birds (notably the ostrich), and lymph hearts are found in the tail of teleosts. No lymph hearts are, however, found in most birds or in mammals.

In the Agnatha and Chondrichthyes there are no lymphatics, although the presence of thin-walled sinusoids which drain into veins, but have little or no arterial connections, are suggestive of a stage in the evolution of these structures. Lymphatics are present, however, in bony fishes and all tetrapods. They are highly developed in amphibians, where they are remarkably abundant in the subcutaneous tissues as a protection against potential desiccation; owing to the development of the lymph hearts, amphibians have a relatively active lymph circulation.

Lymphatic vessels in higher vertebrates penetrate most of the body tissues; the nervous system, liver, spleen, and bone marrow are exceptions. They are highly developed in the gut region. The intestinal lymphatics are of great importance in metabolism in that, while carbohydrate and protein food materials pass into the hepatic portal vein, much of the fats enters the circulation by way of the lymphatics; this is perhaps associated with the relatively large size of the molecules involved and difficulties encountered by them in entering against pressure the intestinal capillaries of the blood vessels.

In their arrangement the lymphatic vessels (Fig. 322) vary greatly from group to group. Terminally, the lymphatics enter the veins—generally the dorsal veins, cardinals or venae cavae. Primitively, the points of entrance may have been numerous and even more or less metameric; conditions of this sort prevail in urodeles and apodous amphibians, and even in amniotes small lymphatics enter the veins at a variety of points. In general, however, there tends to be a concentration of lymph discharge in three areas: (1) Anterior. There are always one or more main entrances into the anterior cardinals or jugulars near the heart (where pressure in the veins is, of course, lowest and unopposed entrance easiest). (2) Middle. Entrances along the course of the posterior cardinals or posterior vena cava are variable; they are rare in mammals, numerous in urodeles. (3)

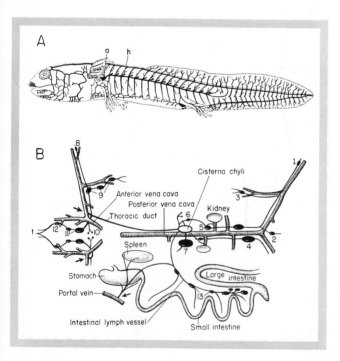

Fig. 322. *A*, Side view of a salamander, showing superficial lymph vessels. Dorsal, lateral, and ventral longitudinal vessels are present; a series of lymph hearts (*h*) is present along the lateral vessel. Lymph from this vessel enters the venous circulation through an axillary sac (*a*); lymph from the ventral vessel enters through an inguinal sac. *B*, Diagram of the deep vessels of the lymphatic system of the rat, anterior end at left. Lymphatics in solid black; the neighboring veins also shown. Nodes are numbered according to the region in which they lie: *1*, knee; *2*, tail; *3*, inguinal; *4*, lumbar; *5*, kidney; *6*, nodes about the cisterna chyli; *7*, intestinal node; *8*, elbow; *9*, axilla; *10*, thoracic; *11*, cervical; *12*, submaxillary; *13*, mesenteric nodes; *t*, plexus of lymphatics around tongue and lips. Arrows indicate the point of entrance of lymph into the veins near the junction of jugular and subclavian and into the portal vein. (*A* after Hoyer and Udziela; *B* after Job.)

Posterior. In fishes and birds (but not mammals) there may be a major flow of lymph into the veins in the pelvic region.

The fatty lymph, or *chyle*, leaving the intestine runs up the mesenteries in vessels termed *lacteals* from their milky appearance when distended. There tends to develop a pair of longitudinal lymphatics, *thoracic ducts*, along the back of the body cavity, paralleling the posterior cardinals or vena cava, with anterior and sometimes posterior openings. These ducts serve as collectors for the lacteals. Paired ducts are common in fishes, reptiles, and birds, but in some fishes and reptiles and in mammals generally the pair tend to fuse into a single asymmetric duct; a large cistern—*cisterna chyli*—may develop along its course in the lumbar region.

The lymphatic vessels frequently run parallel to the veins and have been thought to represent a part of the embryonic venous system. This, however, is debated, and in postembryonic life growth of lymphatics is independent of the veins.

The functional explanation of the development of lymphatics would appear to be suggested by the fact that they are most highly developed in tetrapods, in which the gills have been eliminated from the arterial circuit, and the blood, hence, courses at a higher pressure than in lower fishes. In consequence, entrance of tissue liquids into the capillaries, against pressure, is more difficult than in the original fish condition. The lymphatics offer a relatively low pressure system of drainage into the veins, where the blood pressure is at its lowest.

THE HEART

Some type of muscular pumping device is necessary for the efficient circulation of the blood. A variety of heart structures are found in invertebrates, and in Amphioxus there is a whole series of paired "heartlets." In true vertebrates, however, the heart is a single structure, situated ventrally and well anteriorly in the trunk, drawing in posteriorly venous blood from all regions of the body and pumping it anteriorly, in lower vertebrates, to the aortic arch system and the gill circulation. Primitively, it consisted of four successive chambers, termed, from back to front, sinus venosus, atrium, ventricle, conus arteriosus; in advanced groups the first and last lose their identity, but atrium and ventricle tend to subdivide.

The heart is situated ventral to the gut in a special anterior region of the celomic cavity; it is in the adult attached to the walls of this cavity only at the points of entrance and departure of the blood vessels and thus is able to change its shape readily during its powerful pumping movements. This pericardial cavity (Fig. 325, p. 448; also p. 290) is usually completely separated from the general body cavity in the adult, but connections persist in the cyclostomes and Chondrichthyes.

The heart is essentially a series of expansions developed along the course of a main blood trunk; its histologic structure, although much modified, is essentially comparable to that seen in other blood vessels. There is a thin internal lining, the *endocardium;* an outer covering is a thin, mesodermal epithelium, the *epicardium,* similar to that lining the rest of the celom. The main bulk of the heart consists of connective tissues and muscle—the *myocardium.* The connective tissue may be compact (particularly about the ventricles) and become essentially a type of skeleton; in some instances there may even be a development of cartilage or bone. There are frequently cross strands of connective tissue across the cavity of the ventricle (and sometimes of the atrium as well), preventing undue expansion under pressure. The muscular tissue has been discussed earlier. Between the heart chambers and at the points of entrance or exit of blood vessels lie a series of heart *valves*, similar basically to those in veins or lymphatics, but usually powerful and of complex structure. These yield freely to the forward propulsion of blood, but prevent a backflow when a chamber contracts. Frequently there are tendinous strands of tissue which limit the extent to which the valves may be pushed backwards into (or beyond) the orifice to be closed; in some higher vertebrates the valves may even be furnished with small muscles.

The heart is, of course, itself supplied by blood vessels which ramify in its muscular walls. Though small, these vessels are of crucial importance; we are familiar with the fact that occlusion of the little coronary artery which supplies the heart in man may result in sudden death through heart stoppage.

Heart Beat.   Fibers from the autonomic nervous system reach the heart (at the sinus venosus or atrium) and may affect the rhythm of its beat; the heart, however, is essentially "on its own," as is shown by the fact that heart muscle will continue a rhythmic contraction even when cultured apart from the body. In lower vertebrate classes the four successive chambers present contract in sequence in posteroanterior order: the beat starts with a contraction of the sinus venosus; the wave of contraction of the sinus musculature acts as a "pacemaker," stimulating the atrium to activity and so on down the remaining chambers. An accessory center of stimulation in fishes lies in the atrioventricular valve muscles, and in teleosts, where sinus venosus stimulation is generally unimportant, an accessory pacemaker is present in the atrium. In amniotes continuity between the muscles of atria and ventricles is broken and there develops a unique conducting system for this stimulus, the *sinoventricular system*—essentially a local simulation of a nervous system (Fig. 323). It consists of strands or aggregations of fibers which are specialized muscle fibers—specialized not for contraction, but carriage of an impulse and thus simulating nerves. A *sinus node* of these tissues, situated

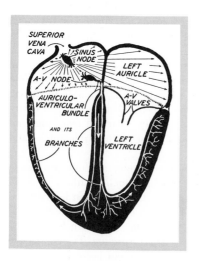

Fig. 323.   Diagram of a mammalian heart opened from the ventral surface to show the conducting system. (From Carlson and Johnson, The Machinery of the Body, University of Chicago Press.)

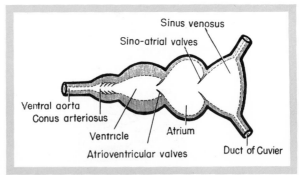

Fig. 324. Diagram of the chambers of the primitive vertebrate heart. (After Ihle.)

in the right atrium, initiates the beat. The stimulus is in the main transferred to a second node in the septum between the atria, whence a fiber bundle—the *atrio-ventricular bundle*—descends to disperse among the muscles of the ventricles and set up a contraction of these chambers. The asymmetric point of origin of the beat is correlated phylogenetically with the fact that the sinus venosus, in which the stimulus began in the primitive heart, is incorporated in the right atrium.

The Primitive Heart. The heart of typical fishes is a single tube consisting of four consecutive chambers. The heart of a bird or mammal is also four-chambered, but the four chambers do not correspond to the original four; it is, rather, a double pump, with two chambers in each of its two parts. Great changes have occurred in the history of the heart, changes correlated with the shift from gill breathing to lung breathing and the necessary changes associated in the course of the circulation.

In the more primitive vertebrate heart (Figs. 324, 325, *A*) the four chambers are:

1. *Sinus venosus*, a thin-walled sac, with little muscular tissue, essentially a place for the collection of venous blood, lying posteriorly, in the region of the septum between heart cavity and general celom. It receives the hepatic vein or veins, posteriorly, and laterally the paired common cardinal veins.

2. *Atrium* (or *auricle*), the next anterior chamber, still relatively thin-walled and distensible.

3. *Ventricle*, thick-walled; the main contractile portion of the heart.

4. *Conus arteriosus*,* thick-walled, but small in diameter and frequently lined by several sets of valves.

These four chambers are arranged in posteroanterior series in the embryo of lower vertebrates. But during development the anterior part of the heart tube tends to fold back ventrally (and somewhat to the right) in an S-shaped curve, thus combining length with compact structure. As a result, the more posterior heart chambers tend, even in a fish heart, to be situated dorsal to the anterior ones, and the atrium may be anterior as well as dorsal in position with regard to the ventricle. The ventricle tends to be so placed that it forms a pocket with a "free" posterior end and with both atrial entrance and arterial exit via the

---

* Often confused with the *bulbus arteriosus*, developed as a proximal part of the ventral aorta just in front of the heart. The term *bulbus cordis* is frequently used for the embryonic equivalent of the conus in mammals.

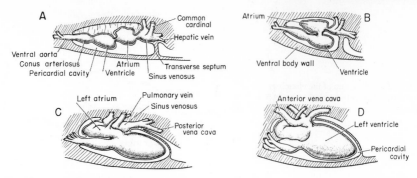

Fig. 325. Diagrammatic views of left side of heart in various vertebrates, to show its position in the peri-cardial cavity and phylogenetic modification of the heart chambers. *A*, Hypothetic ancestral condition, found essentially repeated in embryos (cf. Figure 324). The four primitive chambers are in line antero-posteriorly, and a dorsal mesentery is still present. *B*, Selachian stage; the mesentery is gone; the atrium has pushed forward above the ventricle, but the sinus venosus is still posteriorly placed. *C*, Amphibian stage; the sinus and accompanying blood vessels have moved anteriorly. *D*, Amniote stage; sinus and conus arteriosus have lost their identity; the heart attaches to the walls of the pericardium only anteriorly. (After Goodrich, 1930.)

conus placed near one another anteriorly. The folded position makes it difficult to visualize heart construction, and frequently (as in Figs. 311, p. 429; 324) diagrams of heart structure arbitrarily represent the organ as if "pulled out" into its embryonic longitudinal arrangement.

The primitive type of heart here described is typically developed in the cartilaginous fishes, and most other fishes have a heart similarly constructed. There may be, however, minor modifications. In cyclostomes, for example, the sinus venosus tends to be reduced in size; in teleosts the conus is much reduced and practically absent and is more or less replaced by an arterial bulb.

Evolution of the Double Heart Circuit (Fig. 311). In the lungfishes, and more fully in the amphibians, a major problem arises connected with the substitution of lungs for gills as breathing organs. The heart now receives blood of two different types: "spent" venous blood from the body, and "fresh," oxy-genated blood from the lungs. These two streams should be kept separate, as far as possible, and sent to two different destinations—the venous blood to the lungs, the "fresh" blood to the body. Beyond the heart a splitting of the arterial chan-nels is made for these two destinations. But how to keep the two streams distinct in a single-barreled pump?

The perfect solution of this difficulty was not attained until the avian and mammalian stages were reached, but the lungfishes and amphibians have made some progress toward attainment of a separation of the two blood streams. In the lungfishes we find that the blood coming from the lungs by way of the pulmonary veins does not enter the sinus venosus, as does the typical venous blood (and, indeed, the pulmonary veins of Polypterus), but enters the atrium directly and separately. The sinus venosus, thus, is restricted to the typical venous blood cir-cuit; the sinus remains large in lungfishes and urodeles, but is reduced in size in anurans, represented by a vestige, at the most, in some reptiles and birds, and completely absorbed into the atrial structure in mammals.

A second change lies in the gradual subdivision of the originally single atrium.

The pulmonary venous trunk enters the left side of the atrial chamber. A partition develops which cleaves the atrium in two in such a fashion that the left chamber contains only pulmonary blood; the right (with which the sinus becomes confluent), typical venous blood. In lungfishes there is a partial septum between the two sides of the atrium; in typical amphibians the division is complete. In these forms, however, there is still a single opening from the atrial chamber into the ventricle. Primitively, this was guarded by a pair of valves. In lungfishes, instead of valves, a special cushion of tissue from the posterior (originally ventral) wall of the heart helps close this opening (now functionally double); in amphibians four valves are present, although the opening is still single.

But atrial subdivision is in vain if the two blood streams meet and mix in the ventricle. In lungfishes and amphibians (Figs. 311, *A*, 326, *A*) the ventricle is single, but complete mixture of the two blood streams is prevented by adaptations of one sort or another. Modern lungfishes have developed a partial septum, essentially a continuation of that in the atrium, along the posterior wall of the ventricle. But this seems to be an independent development in this group, probably not present in the ancestors of tetrapods, for amphibians have failed to develop a septum. There is, however, a functional separation of blood streams to some limited extent in amphibians. The spongy, cavernous structure of the cavity of the ventricle tends to prevent too free a mixing of the blood received from the two auricles. But in most living amphibians much of the "breathing" is done through the skin, the oxygenated blood from which enters the right ventricle; there is hence little point in separation of the blood streams.

A septum is developed between two parts of the ventricle in reptiles. In most forms, however, a major gap persists near the points of entrance and exit of the blood streams, so that admixture can still take place. The position of the septum and atrial orifices is such that it is mainly "spent" blood from the right atrium which enters the (smaller) right ventricle; the left ventricle receives a portion of this venous blood plus all the oxygenated blood from the lungs via the left atrium. Despite the incomplete nature of the septum, there tends to be a separation of blood supplies to the three vessels leaving the reptilian heart—the right ventricle sends "spent" venous blood into the pulmonary arch; the left ven-

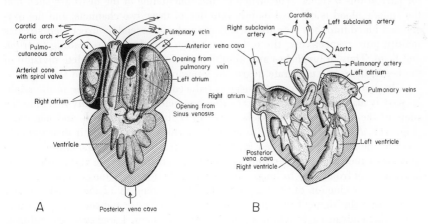

A   B

Fig. 326. Diagrammatic section through the heart of *A*, a frog; *B*, a typical mammal. (Partly after Jammes.)

tricle supplies aerated blood to the right systemic arch; and a mixed, mainly venous, supply goes to the left arch (Fig. 311, *C*, p. 429; cf. p. 430). The crocodilians have, technically, a complete ventricular septum, with venous blood entering the pulmonary and left systemic arches from the right ventricle, and aerated blood supplied to the right systemic from the left ventricle. But even here there is a gap, with possible leakage, at the base of the arterial trunks (Fig. 311, *D*).

The two most progressive vertebrate classes, the birds and mammals (Figs. 311, *B; 326, B*), have completed the ventricular septum and at long last have completely separated the two blood streams along the length of the major heart chambers. This development has obviously been brought about independently in the two cases, since mammals and birds have evolved independently from primitive reptiles.

There is no point in establishing separate heart circuits unless the blood, when it leaves the heart, is directed into appropriate arterial channels—aerated blood to head and body, venous blood to the lung. We have earlier (p. 430) noted subdivisions which occur in the ventral arterial trunk and separate these two streams. We must now, finally, consider the history of the most anterior region of the heart, that of the *conus arteriosus,* which is the primitive connecting piece between ventricle and aorta.

Primitively, as seen in a shark, the well developed conus was a valved, tubular structure with a single terminal opening into the ventral aorta, and the aorta itself was a single stem. The aorta, as noted previously, becomes subdivided in tetrapods so that at least the pulmonary arteries of the sixth aortic arch are separated from the more anterior arches which circulate blood to head and body. There remains as a problem the course of the blood through the conus arteriosus, most anterior of heart chambers. In lungfishes and amphibians we find that there occurs a change in the nature of the conus. Originally it contained simple, typical heart valves; in these primitive lung bearers there develops, instead, a twisted "spiral valve" which runs the length of the conus. This valve partially subdivides the conus for its entire length into two channels (Figs. 311, *A*, 320, *A*), and in the South American lungfish and amphibians the conus is completely subdivided for part of this distance. The structure and functioning of the heart are such that the venous blood is directed mainly into one of these two channels, and the oxygenated blood into the other; distally, the two channels tend to direct their streams mainly into, respectively, the pulmonary arch and the arches leading to trunk and head. Thus in lungfishes and amphibians, despite the incomplete division of the heart, there is a moderate degree of separation of the two blood streams.

In amniotes the conus arteriosus is reduced and not identifiable in the adult. In part it may be incorporated into the ventricles, in part subdivided into the roots of the discrete aortic vessels, three in reptiles, two in birds and mammals (Fig. 311, *B–D*). With this splitting of the aortic vessels and their direct attachment to the completely divided ventricles in birds and mammals, complete separation of the two blood streams is attained, that through the right side of the heart flowing from body to lungs, that through the left from lungs to body.

The introduction of the lung into the blood circuit in advanced fishes threw out of order the simple heart plan of primitive vertebrates and furnished a "problem" which advanced vertebrates found difficult to solve. Lungfishes, amphibians, and reptiles even today have not solved it completely, although their partial solutions are satisfactory enough to allow them to survive. In birds and mammals alone is the complete solution seen and complete separation of circuits attained. The result is surprising in its efficiency. The single pump of the original heart has become a double one; each half of the heart performs effectively its own distinct task.

Heart Development (Fig. 327).   We have noted that the first blood vessels to develop in the typical vertebrate embryos are paired vitelline vessels, which fuse to form a subintestinal vein running forward beneath the gut. The heart is a development in the course of this longitudinal tube, strategically situated in the embryo and in the adult of lower vertebrates, near its anterior end, just behind the gill region. The necessity for a circulatory pump develops at an early stage of embryonic history, and in large-yolked types heart function may begin even before the two vitelline veins have fused; the heart may thus appear in transitory fashion as a paired structure. Celomic cavities develop within the lateral plate mesoderm lying on either side of the embryonic heart. The peritoneal linings of the two cavities come to surround the heart tube; they supply it with its epicardial outer coat, furnish mesenchyme, from which the heart muscle later forms, and form dorsal and ventral mesenteries—*mesocardia*. A ventral mesocardium, if developed at all, is short-lived, and the dorsal mesocardium disappears at an early stage, so that a single pericardial cavity is created. Posterior to the heart a transverse septum is presently formed (p. 290) which in most vertebrates shuts off the pericardial cavity from the general celom. With this septum is associated the entrance into the subintestinal vessel of a pair of veins— the common cardinals—descending from the dorsal regions of the body. Their entrance causes an enlargement at the back of the heart region which becomes the sinus venosus. Meanwhile the more anterior part of the heart tube shows a series of enlargements and intervening constrictions which delimit, in linear order from back to front, atrium, ventricle, and conus. Simultaneously there begins the elongation and twisting of the tube noted in the description of the adult chamber, so that the ventricle comes to lie below and behind the atrium, and somewhat to the right, rather than in its morphologically primitive anterior position.

With these developments the embryo heart has attained the general structural features found in typical fishes, and needs little but valvular development to reach the adult piscine condition. In higher vertebrates, however, further differentiation is needed. We have noted phylogenetically a series of progressive stages in the subdivision and rearrangement of heart chambers in adjustment to lung

Fig. 327.   Cross sections of a mammalian embryo to show an early stage in heart formation, before the fusion of the two subintestinal vessels from which the heart forms. In the atrial region, *A*, the two are still widely separated; farther forward, in the ventricular region, *B*, the two tubes are apposed inside a single pericardial sac, but are not yet fused. (From Arey.)

breathing and the consequent necessity of separating two blood streams. In the various tetrapod classes ontogenetic events essentially recapitulate the phylogenetic stages. In a mammalian heart, for example, principal developments include subdivision of both atrium and ventricle and of the original single opening between them; absorption of the sinus venosus into the right atrium and the segregation of the pulmonary veins so that they open into the left atrium; subdivision of the conus arteriosus into a pulmonary trunk leading from the right ventricle and a major aorta leading from the left. As noted later, however, the different breathing mechanisms before and after birth in amniotes cause certain embryologic developments in the heart which have no phylogenetic significance.

BLOOD CIRCUITS

In earlier sections of this chapter the components of the blood circuit have been described piecemeal. We shall here briefly review the general evolutionary history of the circulation as a whole with especial reference to blood pressures and capillary nets (Fig. 328).

As in any passage of liquid through tubes, the friction of the liquid on the vessel walls tends to lessen the pressure given by the "pump," and the capillaries are, of course, the parts of the system in which the loss of pressure is the greatest. In fishes, in general, every drop of blood which leaves the heart must pass through at least two capillary systems before its return to that organ, for blood first passes through a capillary network in the gills, where there is a sharp drop in pressure, before it can reach the aorta and thence to the capillary system of the ordinary body tissues. But before its return to the heart much of the blood

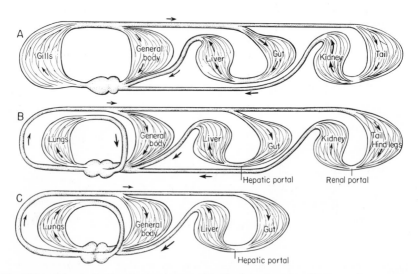

Fig. 328. Diagrams showing the general nature of the blood circuits and capillary networks encountered in *A*, a typical fish; *B*, a terrestrial amphibian or a reptile, with elimination of gill circulation and introduction of pulmonary circuit; *C*, a mammal or a bird, with elimination of renal portal system.

passes, in addition, through a portal system—the hepatic portal in all forms, and a renal portal system in fishes above the cyclostome level. In this situation the blood passes through three, rather than two, capillary systems, losing much pressure in each.

With the introduction of the lung circuit into the circulatory system and the abolition in adult amphibians of gill breathing, circulatory efficiency is greatly promoted. The gill capillary system is eliminated; hence all body tissues may be reached directly with little loss of pressure. Blood passing from heart to lungs and much of the body tissues completes the circuit back to the heart without encountering more than the one capillary system en route. Blood to the posterior end of the body or to the intestine, however, still has to pass through a portal system, renal or hepatic, on its return; but even here there are only two capillary drops in pressure, rather than three.

With reduction of the renal portal system in reptiles and its abolition in both birds and mammals, the efficiency of the circulation is further increased. In these last classes only the intestinal circulation passes two capillary networks; blood to every other region goes directly from and to the heart, the only capillary system encountered being that in the tissues supplied.

The substitution of lungs for gills has, seemingly by a happy accident, brought about, in the long run, the development of a more efficient circulatory system. On the other hand, lymphatic development in higher vertebrates may perhaps be a response to the increased difficulties in tissue drainage with increased pressure in the vessels of the blood-vascular system.

EMBRYONIC CIRCULATION

In earlier sections of this chapter we mentioned the formation of this or that blood vessel in the embryo. Here we may attempt to gain a general picture of the development of the circulatory system (although this necessarily involves some repetition), this with attention to certain of the vessels not retained in the adult but necessary in the sacs and membranes of embryos of large-yolked types. It must be emphasized that the circulatory system cannot develop in the embryo merely with the "aim" of producing the adult structure; it must be functionally effective at every moment of every embryonic or larval period. In general, too, we may note that in many areas (as in the limbs, Fig. 329) the circulation first develops in the form of a diffuse network, in which major vessels are "sorted out" only at a later stage.

A generalized pattern of vessel development (Fig. 330) is that in such lower vertebrates as amphibians and lungfishes, in which the egg is not heavily yolked, normal body form is soon attained, and the picture is not complicated by the presence of intricate extra-embryonic membranes. The basic plan of the vertebrate circulation is one in which (in contrast with the annelid scheme) the blood flows forward ventrally beneath the gut, turns dorsally, and then runs backward above the gut tube. The earliest blood vessels to appear in an amphibian or lungfish are portions of the ventral part of this system. Beneath the yolk-laden gut small vessels form and run forward, assembling into a pair of vitelline veins which fuse, anteriorly at least, to form a subintestinal vessel. The most anterior part of this vessel forms the ventral aorta; the succeeding section early develops into a heart structure. Posterior to this point the ventral vessel is later invaded

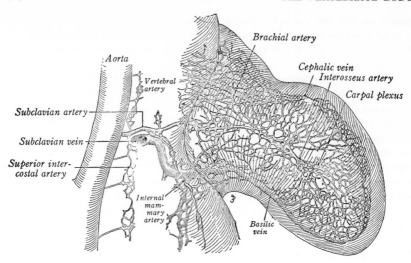

Fig. 329.   An early stage in the development of the forelimb of a pig embryo, to show the manner of formation of patterns in limb circulation. There is a network of interweaving small vessels from which the main adult vessels develop. Choice of one definitive channel or another allows for the occurrence of variants as anomalies. (From Woollard.)

by liver tissue and disrupted here into a system of sinusoids. Between this liver "portal" and the heart the ventral trunk becomes the hepatic vein; posterior to it there develops the hepatic portal system, which continues to drain the gut in the adult.

But before the ventral vessels have proceeded far in their differentiation there appears a dorsal arterial trunk which, coursing backward, completes the return circuit of the blood to the gut walls. From the front end of the subintestinal vessel, in front of the developing heart, blood vessels arch upward around either side of the foregut to the dorsal part of the body. Here, below notochord and nerve cord, they turn backward above the gut and send off branches by which the blood descends around the digestive tube to enter once more the vitelline system. The anterior part of the ventral vessel becomes the ventral aorta. The pair of loops ascending around the foregut are the first of the aortic arches of the pharynx (Fig. 313, p. 432). As development proceeds, additional aortic loops develop more posteriorly. These may break up along their course into capillary systems as the gills develop; the anterior arches may atrophy or undergo modification even in early stages of development. The dorsal vessel is the dorsal aorta, and its anterior continuation becomes the carotids. At its first appearance the aorta may be a paired structure, and its derivatives remain paired in the most anterior cephalic region in the adult; for most of the body length the two vessels fuse, however, at an early stage to form a single median longitudinal aortic vessel. Its first branches, which descend around the gut walls, are paired, to begin with; but as the gut diminishes in size relative to the body as a whole, these vessels fuse to descend the mesentery as median arteries which become the celiac, mesenteric, and so on, of the adult.

With the development of the subintestinal and aortic vessels and their connections a primary circulatory system is completed. This, it will be noted, is essentially a "visceral" circulation, associated primarily with the gut tube region.

With growth of mesodermal structures and of the nervous system there develops the necessity for circulatory vessels in the outer body tube—a "somatic" circulation. The afferent arterial supply in this new system is still the dorsal aorta, which sends out lateral branches into the trunk musculature, kidneys, and gonads, and upward to the neural tube. From the capillary networks developed at either side of the aorta arise return venous vessels as the paired cardinal veins, anterior and posterior; these gain a discharge into the heart by forming a descending trunk, a common cardinal, down either side of the thoracic region. In higher vertebrates the anterior cardinals are modified to some degree to form the anterior (superior) vena cava—double or single. The posterior cardinals, we have noted, undergo important changes in lungfishes and tetrapods to become the posterior (inferior) vena cava; these changes include, in every embryo, the interpolation of a renal portal system, which is eliminated again in the adult stage of higher amniotes. Other elements in the "somatic" circulation include an arterial supply and venous return from the fins or limbs, and, in lower vertebrates, the development of abdominal veins which drain the ventral part of the body wall.

In large-yolked types—elasmobranchs, amniotes—we find an extra-embryonic circulation composed of vessels which run from and to the yolk sac and, in amniotes, connect the embryo with allantois or placenta. The presence of these two structures complicates the embryonic story (Fig. 331).

In elasmobranchs and amniotes alike there is at first no "floor" of yolk-filled cells to the gut cavity, but instead a mass of nutritive yolk; in consequence, the paired *vitelline veins* carrying nutriment inward to the body arise on either side in the roof of the yolk sac. There can be no formation of a single ventral subintestinal trunk until a relatively late stage in embryonic development; the heart and ventral vessels persist for a time as paired elements. The return vessels from the dorsal aorta likewise long remain paired structures as *vitelline arteries*. A highly developed system of vitelline veins and returning vitelline arteries is present throughout embryonic life in elasmobranchs, reptiles, and birds. In mammals, despite the absence of yolk in the yolk sac, similar vessels early develop and persist for some time.

In amniotes a second series of embryonic vessels of note are those which extend along the stalk of the allantois, which in reptiles and birds serves as an embryonic lung. Paired *allantoic* or *umbilical veins* enter the body of the embryo

Fig. 330. Diagram of the general circulation in a young frog tadpole. The food supply still lies in the yolky gut cells, and the vitelline circulation is of great importance.

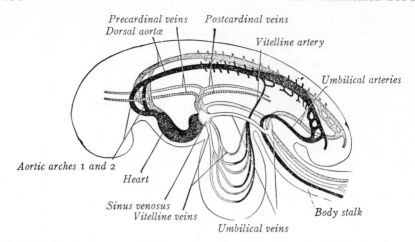

Fig. 331.   The circulatory vessels in a mammalian embryo. (From Arey, after Felix.)

and course forward in the ventral part of the lateral body walls; they appear to represent, within the body, the lateral abdominal veins of lower vertebrates. In the early embryo these veins course directly to the heart, as do the abdominal veins of a shark. In later development, however, they turn inward anteriorly to enter the liver and become (together with the vitellines) part of its portal system (Fig. 332), as does the abdominal vein of the adult amphibian or reptile. Apparently, however, the flow of blood of the combined vitelline and umbilical veins is too great for proper handling by the liver capillaries, and in embryonic amniotes much of the blood passes through the liver by a direct channel—the *ductus venosus*. Corresponding to the umbilical veins, paired *allantoic* or *umbilical arteries* arise from the dorsal aorta posteriorly and, in strong contrast to the vitelline vessels, descend to the allantoic stalk in the body walls rather than via the gut. In mammals the allantoic stalk becomes the connection between placenta and embryo, and the allantoic vessels are of the utmost importance, bringing food as well as oxygen to the embryo; in this class of vertebrates the yolk sac circulation diminishes with the gradual absorption of the yolk, and the vitelline vessels disappear.

The allantoic or umbilical vessels of amniotes persist until birth, but abruptly cease their function at that time. They are shut off at the points where they leave the body, and their internal courses are soon obliterated, as is the ductus venosus channel through the liver.

In amniotes oxygen is supplied to the embryo by the umbilical veins. The abrupt entrance of the lung circuit into the picture at the time of hatching or birth calls for special modifications in the embryonic circulation. In the embryo the pulmonary arteries and veins develop at a fairly early stage, but the blood for the most part by-passes these vessels. We have noted that the upper part of the pulmonary arch, from which the pulmonary arteries proper take origin, remains open in amniote embryos so that blood which takes this course from the heart need not enter the lungs, but instead may proceed to the dorsal aorta and enter the general body circulation. This vessel, we have noted, is the ductus arteriosus —paired in reptiles and bird embryos, present only on the left side in mammals

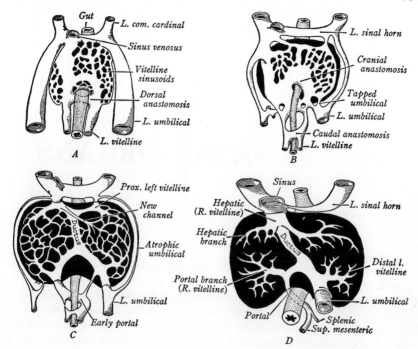

Fig. 332. Diagrams of the liver region of human embryos at successive stages (4.5, 5.6, and 9 mm. in length), seen from the ventral surface, to show developmental changes in the vitelline and umbilical veins. (The gut tube is stippled.) In *A* the vitelline vessels from the yolk sac are well developed and pass through the liver tissue; in *B-D* their transformation into the portal system is seen. The umbilical veins (from the placenta) are already well developed in *A*, but run directly to the sinus venosus. In later stages this blood flow is diverted to the liver circulation, much of it flowing through this organ via a hepatic duct. The right umbilical vein is reduced; the left persists until birth, when this vessel and the hepatic duct undergo reduction. (From Arey.)

(Fig. 313, *E, F,* p. 432). At the other end of the circuit we find that in the amniote heart the left atrium has no proper blood supply in the embryo, for the only vessels entering it are the pulmonary veins, which carry almost no blood. This situation is remedied by the fact that in all amniotes the septum between the two atria is imperfect in the embryo: blood from the right atrium may cross over and fill the left atrium sufficiently to enable it to function properly.

At birth there is a sharp change in the lung circuit. The ductus arteriosus closes rapidly in birds and mammals and most reptiles, so that all blood entering the pulmonary arch is forced into the lungs. The return of this blood to the heart furnishes the left atrium with its proper share of the blood stream, and the opening between the two atria is soon closed.

15

SENSE ORGANS

All cells, one may believe, are capable of receiving and responding to stimuli which measure, so to speak, some condition in the environment or a change in such condition. If, however, in a vertebrate the proper response to a sensory stimulus is one that should be performed by a distant region of the organism, or by the organism as a whole, its reception is in vain unless there is some channel of communication between the sensory receptor and the organs—muscles or glands—which should make the appropriate response. Such communication may be made by hormonal action, but in general the mechanism used is that of the nervous system. The tips of nerve fibers are themselves capable of direct excitation, but more often the reception of sensation in vertebrates is the function of specialized *sensory cells*, generally grouped in organs of lesser or greater degree of complexity. These are attuned to physical or chemical stimuli of specific types and are associated with nerves which relay these stimuli to specific centers in the brain or to the nerve cord.

Anatomists divide such nerves, sensory in nature, into two groups: the *somatic sensory nerves*, carrying impulses of a sort which in ourselves usually reach the level of consciousness, from the "outer tube" of the body—the skin and body surfaces and the muscles; and *visceral sensory nerves*, whose impulses, seldom reaching our consciousness, arise from the viscera. The physiologist customarily classifies sensory receptors in a fashion which for the most part fits readily into the neurologic scheme. *Exteroceptors* are those sensory structures of the skin and special senses which receive sensations from the outer world; *proprioceptors* include those situated in the striated voluntary muscles and tendons; *interoceptors* are those located in the internal organs. The first two of these correlate fairly well with the somatic system of sensory nerves, the third with the visceral sensory system of the anatomist.

SIMPLE SENSE ORGANS

One ubiquitous sensation—that of *pain*—seems not to need any special organ for its reception. Pain, as it appears in our own perception, is not specific,

458

but may be due to a variety of physical and chemical causes. This sensation is produced, as far we know, by direct stimulation of the end fibers of sensory nerves. Such nerve endings, in the skin at least, appear to be also sensitive to touch in vertebrates generally. In fishes and amphibians most skin sensations, apart from those from the special sensory organs, appear to be picked up by free nerve endings.

Sense Corpuscles. Many "simple" sensations are received by small sensory structures which may be present in almost any part of the body—in skin, muscles, viscera. These are most highly developed in mammals and birds; in contrast amphibians and fishes have but a few sensory corpuscles, these presumably responding to touch. Most corpuscles are of such tiny size that their study lies in the realm of the histologist with his microscope rather than that of the dissector with his scalpel. Their appearance and structure vary greatly (Fig. 333). In general we see a series of specialized cells with which are associated tangled skeins of terminal nerve fibrils. Such corpuscles are commonly present in the connective tissues, but similar sensory structures may be present in epithelia (special tactile cells in the mammalian epidermis, for example).

With small and varied bodies of this sort, accurate determination of function is difficult. Some knowledge can, of course, be gained from our own sensory experience, and can be extrapolated to give us some idea of the sensory situation in other mammals and, with lesser chance of correctness, in other vertebrate classes. Among mammals, some four types of sensations, in addition to pain, may be distinguished in the dermis—warmth, cold, touch, pressure. It has been

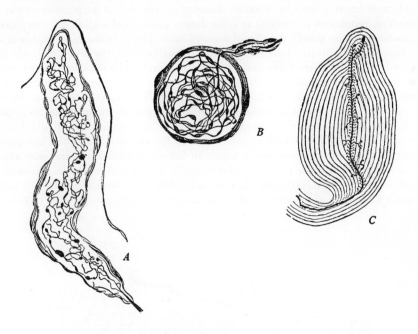

Fig. 333. Some types of sensory organs from mammalian tissues. *A*, Tactile corpuscle (Meissner's corpuscle) from the connective tissue of the skin; *B*, an end bulb of Krause, sensitive to cold; *C*, a pacinian corpuscle, which registers pressure and tension. (From Ranson, after Dogiel, Sala, Böhm-Davidoff, Huber.)

thought that these types of reception are associated with corpuscles of different sorts, but this conclusion appears to be uncertain. A number of types of interoceptive corpuscles are present in and among the viscera, but it is difficult to tell the nature of the sensations to which they respond. Structures may be present along vessels of the aortic arch system (particularly the carotids in mammals) which "sense" the blood, probably responding to both pressure and chemical (carbon dioxide) stimuli.

Proprioceptive sensations, of the physiologist's terminology, include those obtained from sensory structures located in the striated muscles and tendons as *muscle spindles* and *tendon organs*. Proprioceptive organs are absent in fishes, but are present in tetrapods generally. In lower tetrapods sensory nerve fibrils simply twist about individual muscle fibers or tendon fibers. In mammals, however, muscle spindles consist of small and somewhat specialized muscle fibers surrounded by a tangle of sensory nerve endings and enclosed in an elongate connective tissue sheath (Fig. 334). These muscle and tendon structures are the seat of "muscle sense." They furnish to the central nervous system a report on the state of contraction of the muscles—data necessary before any further action of the muscle can be properly "ordered" by way of motor nerves. In addition, these spindles are the source of the animal's information concerning the position in space of the various parts of the body—information, as we are ourselves well aware, which can be furnished without the aid of other sensory structures, but confined (in the absence of contact with other objects) to parts of the body containing striated muscles or their tendons.

Taste. Most of the simpler senses are responses to physical stimuli; taste and smell are responses to chemical stimulation. The skin of all primitive water-dwelling vertebrates is sensitive to some degree to chemical stimuli, the receptors apparently being simply the tips of sensory nerve fibers. In the more highly developed sense of taste, there are developed small organs, the *taste buds*, which usually consist of barrel-like collections of elongated cells sunk within the epithelium, usually ectodermal (Fig. 335). Two cell types are present, supporting and sensory. Each taste cell has a sensitive, hairlike projecting process. Taste buds are for the most part confined to the mouth, and in mammals are in great measure concentrated on the tongue. They may be more widely distributed, however. Even in mammals they may be found in the pharynx and larynx and pharyngeal taste buds are common in fishes. In fishes and amphibians they may also develop in the skin. In a sturgeon, for example, they are abundant on the under side of the projecting rostrum, so that as the fish glides over the bottom it can obtain a foretaste of potential food before the mouth reaches it. In some catfishes

Fig. 334. A muscle spindle. (After Windle, Textbook of Histology, McGraw-Hill.)

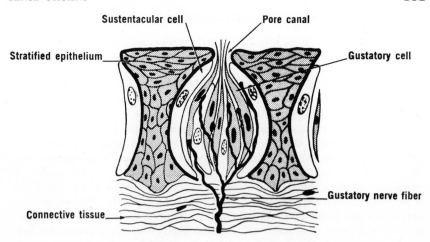

Fig. 335.   Microscopic section through a taste bud. (From De Courcey, Medical Physiology.)

—notably the "bullhead" Amiurus—there is a tremendous spread of taste buds over the surface of the body, giving a phenomenal possibility of pleasant (or unpleasant) gustatory sensations. It must be noted that much of what we casually think of as taste is actually a smelling of mouth contents (foods do not "taste" as well when a head cold clogs the nose) and, in addition, the "feel" of the food in the mouth. All taste buds look alike, but in such animals (including ourselves) as have been experimentally tested, a limited number of types, distinct as regards reception, are present. Their differences lie in their responses to specific sorts of molecules or ions in solution in the liquids of the mouth (or body surface). In ourselves, for example, sensations of sour, salty, bitter, and sweet can be distinguished and some fishes, at least, have similar discriminatory powers; but the frog, it seems, distinguishes sour and salty only.

In sections which follow are described the more prominent of the complicated sensory structures of vertebrates, including nose, eye, ear, and lateral line organs. The first three of these are familiar as part of our own sensory apparatus; the last type of organ we do not ourselves possess, but it is so distinctly developed in fishes that it cannot be overlooked.

Presumably there is a variety of still other sensory structures in other vertebrates, particularly the lower classes of them, which give responses of types unfamiliar to us and hence difficult for us to understand. One such sense, about which we do have data, lies in the *pit organ* of the so-called pit vipers among snakes, of which the rattlesnake is a familiar (although not popular) example. Between eye and nose on either side of the face is a pit filled with a peculiar, highly vascular tissue with numerous nerve endings. Experiments show that this is a heat-sensitive organ; a pit viper can perceive the movement of a moderately warm body past its head at a distance of several feet—a sensory power extremely useful to an animal (such as a rattlesnake) which makes its living mainly by capturing warm-blooded rodents and is not too well endowed with "normal" sense organs. A series of tiny pits along the jaw margins of pythons and some boas appear to have similar sensory properties.

THE NOSE

In tetrapods the nose, with an internal opening, has become associated with breathing, but its primary function, of course, is that of olfactory reception. In certain vertebrate groups smell is relatively unimportant; it is not in general highly developed in teleost fishes, and is feeble in birds (apart from some oceanic forms), in marine mammals, and in higher primates, including man; most are groups in which the eyes have become the dominant sense organs. These cases, however, are the exception; among vertebrates in general smell is in many ways the most important of all senses. From cyclostomes and sharks up through the more primitive bony fishes, amphibians, reptiles, and especially among most mammals, smell is a main source of information concerning the outside world—the location of enemies, friends, food—and produces responses based on "memories" of previous olfactory experiences established in the forebrain. That we ourselves have this sense feebly developed should not blind us to its general importance; the fact that, as we shall later see, the most highly developed mammalian brain centers arise in a brain area primarily connected with smell is testimony to the part olfaction plays among the vertebrates.

In a majority of fishes the nasal structures consist of a pair of pockets placed well anteriorly on the head and without any internal opening to the mouth. Typically, they are lateral in position; in sharks they are placed on the under surface of the snout. The external opening of each sac is paired, as in typical teleosts, where water may flow inward through an anterior and out through a posterior opening, or partially subdivided into two openings by a fold of skin, as in sharks. Within the nasal sac is a highly folded epithelium of simple columnar type. This epithelium contains, in all vertebrates, *olfactory cells*, interposed with supporting elements (Fig. 336). Each olfactory cell has a rodlike extension to the surface which at its tip bears a radiating brush of short, hairlike sensitive processes. In one remarkable feature these cells differ from any other receptor organs in vertebrates. All others depend upon nerve fibers to relay inward the sensations received. The olfactory cells, on the contrary, do their own work; a long fiber extends from each cell into the olfactory bulb of the brain. This type of organiza-

Fig. 336.   Section through the nasal mucosa. (From De Courcey, Medical Physiology.)

tion, with a sensory cell itself serving for nerve conduction as well, is found in various instances among invertebrates and even in Amphioxus, and is suggestive of the antiquity of the sense of smell in vertebrate history.

The surface brushes of the olfactory cells are sensitive to minute amounts of chemical materials, derived from distant objects, which come to be present in solution in the liquid covering the nasal epithelium. Despite much work on the part of physiologists, we have little data as to the precise nature of olfactory sensations of different sorts; our lack of success in analysis may be due in considerable measure to our lack of subjective appreciation of the delicate nuances of smell perceived by vertebrates more fortunate in their olfactory powers.

The jawless vertebrates present a puzzling structural situation. In contrast to that of all other living vertebrates, the cyclostome olfactory organ is a single median pouch, opening either at the tip of the snout (hagfishes) or far back on the upper surface of the head (lampreys) (Figs. 17, 231, pp. 37, 324). A further peculiarity, already noted, is the fact that the hypophyseal sac is combined in a common opening with the nostril. In the hagfish the nasal pouch breaks through internally into the pharynx, presumably aiding olfaction by a flow of water.

Is the cyclostome dorsal single-pouched structure primitive or specialized? The answer is none too clear. In the ancient ostracoderms two out of three main groups show the lamprey condition; but in a third group the nostrils were presumably ventral and paired, so that both situations were present at an early stage in vertebrate history. Some embryologic evidence can be adduced for a belief that the cyclostome condition is not primitive. In the embryo lamprey, we have seen (Fig. 207, p. 299) that the nasal pocket is at first ventral in position and only later migrates dorsally; and in the larval lamprey the nasal sac is bilobed, although not distinctly paired.

In earlier chapters we commented upon the evolution in the typical crossopterygians of a type of nostril with an opening into the roof of the mouth as well as to the exterior, and the utilization, in tetrapods, of this passage as an adjunct to air breathing. In typical fishes the nasal sac is filled with water; in tetrapods, air replaces water, but the air-borne chemical particles are absorbed into a film of liquid which covers the olfactory mucous membranes. Specific glands are generally developed which function in keeping the membranes moist with water and fatty material, and liquid brought from the eye by the lacrimal ducts aids as well.

In amphibians (Fig. 337, *A, B*) the main air channel is usually simply constructed. Each small *external naris* opens into a somewhat elongated sac; posteroventrally, a large opening, the *choana*, or internal naris, opens directly into the front part of the roof of the mouth. In fishes practically the entire surface of the olfactory pouch is covered with sensory epithelium, which is thrown into numerous small folds. These folds are absent in amphibians; the surface of the main nasal sac, used in great measure as an air passage, is nearly smooth, and part of the surface is covered by a nonsensory epithelium. (We may note, parenthetically, peculiar olfactory tentacles developed from the nostrils of the apodous amphibians.)

In typical reptiles the nasal region begins to assume a more complicated structure (Fig. 337, *C*). The air passage is longer, the choana generally more posteriorly placed, and there is usually a distinct, small anterior sac, or *vestibule*, through which inspired air passes before it reaches the main olfactory chamber.

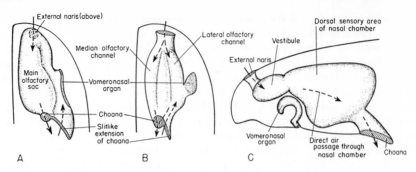

Fig. 337.   *A,* Ventral view of anterior part of the left side of the palatal region of the salamander, Triton, with the nasal channels shown as solid objects, remainder as transparent structures (cf. Fig. 208, *A,* p. 300). *B,* Similar view of the toad Pipa. *C,* Longitudinal section of the nasal region of a lizard, cut some-what to the right of the midline, to show the cavities of the nasal apparatus. In the embryo lizard the vomeronasal organ was a lateral pocket of the main nasal channels, as in an amphibian; in the adult (as in many mammals) this organ has separated to open independently into the roof of the mouth by a naso-palatine duct. Arrows show the main air flow inward in all figures and the outward flow toward the vomeronasal organ in the amphibians. (*A* after Matthes; *B* after Bancroft; *C* after Leydig.)

Of this main chamber, the ventral part, the direct air passage to the choana, is usually lined by a nonsensory epithelium. The expanded dorsal part contains the sensory area; here we find typically developed a swollen, curved ingrowth, a *concha* or *turbinal* from the lateral (never the medial) wall of the chamber; this increases the surface over which sensory epithelium may form. In chelonians there may be some development of a secondary palate and, in relation to this, a development of a short air duct leading from the nasal chamber back to the cho-ana. In the crocodilians, with a long snout and an elongate secondary palate, the nasal chamber, containing three conchae, is itself considerably elongated, and there is a long tube leading back to the pharynx.

In birds, generally, smell appears to play but an exceedingly small role in sensory reception—as would be expected, vision is dominant, smell being of little possible value to a flier. The nasal structures, built on the general reptilian plan, are of modest size, and the olfactory epithelium is generally restricted to a small area in the upper back part of the nasal chamber. The birds, however, retain the three nasal conchae seen in their crocodilian relatives, and these may develop into complicated scrolls. The external nares, generally situated at the base of the beak, are of varied form and, as in fowls and doves, are often protected by a horny structure something like a small eyelid. (We have mentioned previously [p. 370] the presence of salt secreting glands in the bird nose.)

The nasal structures reach the peak of their development, as far as size is concerned, among the mammals (Fig. 208, p. 300, 338). In lower vertebrates they are generally confined to a short stretch of territory at the anterior end of the head; in typical mammals (higher primates are exceptional) they push far backward to the orbital region, and may occupy up to half of the skull length. Their size is augmented through the fact that there has developed in mammals a secondary palatal structure. As a result, the original vault of the mouth is in-cluded in the nasal area; this mouth region anteriorly forms the ventral part of the main nasal cavity and posteriorly forms the *nasopharyngeal duct,* carrying air backward to the pharynx.

These new additions to the nasal area function primarily as aids to respiration. There is, however, a considerable development of olfaction. We have seen that in reptiles there tended to be a concentration of sensory epithelium in the upper part of the nasal chamber. This is true in mammals as well. The lower part of the system, forming a straight passage from external naris to nasopharyngeal duct and choana, is an air passage; the sensory areas are concentrated in the upper and posterior parts of the chamber.

The nasal chamber is, however, by no means a simple sac. We have noted the development in reptiles and birds of folded ingrowths from the lateral wall of the nasal chambers, the conchae or turbinals. In mammals these are developed to a high degree as coiled scrolls of bone, covered with epithelium, which subdivide the air passage into a series of semitubular channels. Typically there are two to four turbinals developed from the ethmoid bone, and one each from the maxilla and nasal. Ventrally, these structures act as "air conditioners," filtering and warming incoming air; dorsally and posteriorly, they afford, as in reptiles, additional sensory surface.

In placental mammals there occur, generally, extensions of the nasal air cavities into the adjacent bones as *sinus pneumatici* (plural), frequently present in the adjacent maxillary, frontal, ethmoid and sphenoid regions, and reaching to the occiput in the high-domed head of the elephant and in the heads of a variety of other mammals. These sinuses effect a lightening of the skull; other human attributes are perhaps all too familiar to some readers.

In numerous tetrapods there is a specialized part of the olfactory system termed the *vomeronasal organ* (organ of Jacobson, Fig. 337), which in most cases appears to have as its main function the picking up of olfactory sensations from the food in the mouth cavity. Its predecessor is seen in simple form in urodele amphibians. There a partially separated grooved channel runs along one side of each nasal sac and opens out into the roof of the mouth in a slit continuous with the choana. This groove bears an area of olfactory epithelium quite separate from that of the main part of the nose and served by a distinct branch of the olfactory nerve. In the other two amphibian orders this pocket is nearly completely separated from the rest of the nasal system and comes to lie in a blind pouch.

Fig. 338. A section through the nasal region of a guinea pig, slightly to the right of the midline, to show the development of the turbinals, including the maxilloturbinal, *MT*, nasal turbinal, *NT*, and ethmoturbinals (I–IV). *CP*, Choanal passage; *LT*, lamina transversalis separating sensory area of the nasal fossa from the choanal passage. (After Cave.)

In Sphenodon the organ likewise forms a club-shaped blind pouch which opens into the choana, and it is not distinct in chelonians. Adult crocodilians have lost it, and it is absent or vestigial in birds as well. In lizards and snakes, on the other hand, it is well developed and completely separated from the normal nasal structures; the two vomeronasal organs are separate pouches which open independently into the roof of the mouth anterior to the choanae. Use here is peculiar. The tongue, cleft into two prongs and darting in and out of the mouth, serves as an accessory olfactory organ. When the tongue is withdrawn, the tips are inserted into the vomeronasal pockets; chemical particles which adhered to them in the air are transferred to the moisture on the sensory epithelium of these pouches.

Among mammals the vomeronasal organ is absent in man and other higher primates, in many bats and in various aquatic forms. In almost all other groups of mammals, however, it persists as a functional organ. It is a small, cigar-shaped structure, buried in the floor of the nasal region toward the midline. In many rodents it opens into the main nasal cavity. In other cases, however, the vomeronasal organs connect independently with the mouth, much as in lizards and snakes, by paired *nasopalatine ducts* which pierce through the secondary palate and appear to retain their original mouth-smelling functions.

THE EYE

The vertebrate body is subjected constantly to radiations which may vary from the extremely short but rapid waves of cosmic rays and those from atomic disintegration to the long, slow undulations utilized for radio transmission; in figures, from waves with as high a frequency as some quintillion vibrations per second and a length of a fraction of a billionth of a centimeter, to others with only a few hundreds or thousands of oscillations per second and a theoretic wavelength measurable in miles. Many of these radiations affect protoplasm, but specific sensitivity to them appears to be limited to a narrow band part way between the two extremes; for knowledge of other wavelengths we must resort to mechanisms which transform their effects into terms receivable by our own limited senses. It is not unreasonable to find that the animal band of sensitivity corresponds in great measure to the range of radiations reaching the earth from the sun, since that body is the source of the vast bulk of the radiations that normally reach us. Of this band, slower waves are received as heat, faster, shorter waves perceived as light—the process of *photoreception*.

Specific sensitivity to light is widespread through the animal and plant kingdoms. In many simple invertebrates such sensitivity is concentrated in special cells, or cell clusters, frequently with associated pigment, which form "eye spots." Often there is evolutionary progress to an organized photoreceptive structure, with a lens for concentrating light upon sensitive cells contained in a closed chamber. Many such organs are merely receptors for light "in bulk"; with better organization and the arrangement of the sensory cells in a definite pattern so that they receive light from specific external areas, true vision results. Well developed eyes with many common features, but surely independently evolved, are found in forms as far apart as molluscs, arthropods of various sorts, and vertebrates.

The general composition of the vertebrate eye (Figs. 339, 340) may first be noted before consideration of details. Leaving aside for the moment various ac-

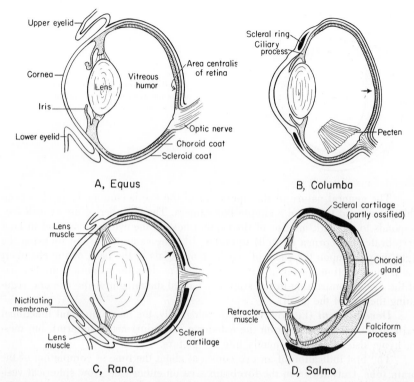

Fig. 339. Diagrammatic vertical sections through the eye of *A*, a horse; *B*, a dove; *C*, a common frog; *D*, a teleost (salmon). Connective tissue of sclera and cornea unshaded; scleral ring or cartilage black; choroid, ciliary body, and iris stippled; retina hatched. Arrows point to the fovea. In *B* is shown the pecten, lying to one side of the midline. In *D* the section is slightly to one side of the choroid fissure through which the falciform process enters the eyeball. (After Rochon-Duvigneaud, Walls.)

cessories, we find that the essential structure is the roughly spherical *eyeball*, situated in a recess, the *orbit*, on either side of the braincase, and connected with the brain by an *optic nerve* contained in a stalk emerging from the internal surface. The eyeball has an essentially radial symmetry, with a main axis running from inner to outer aspects. Internally, there is a set of chambers filled with watery or gelatinous liquids. In the interior, well toward the front, lies a *lens*. The walls of the hollow sphere are formed basically of three layers, in order, from the outside inward, the *scleroid* and *choroid* coats, and the *retina*. The scleroid is a complete sphere; choroid and retinal coats are incomplete externally. The first two are of mesenchyme origin and are essentially supporting and nutritive in function; the retina (actually a double layer) includes the sensory part of the eye system where visual stimuli are received and transferred to the brain via the optic nerve. At the outer end of the eyeball the scleroid coat is modified to form, with the overlying skin, the transparent *cornea*. Externally, choroid and retinal layers are fused and modified. Opposite the margins of the lens the conjoined layers usually expand to form a *ciliary body*, from which the lens may be suspended. Forward beyond this point the two fused layers curve inward parallel to the lens to form the *iris*, but leave a centrally situated opening, the *pupil*.

Fig. 340. Diagrammatic section of an eye to show the arrangement of the successive embryonic layers.

The general nature of the operation of the eye is commonly (and reasonably) compared to that of a simple box camera. The chamber of the eyeball corresponds to the dark interior of the camera box. In the eye the lens (and in land vertebrates the cornea as well) operates, like the camera lens, in focusing the light properly upon the sheet of sensitive materials in the back of the chamber; the retina functions in reception of the image as does the camera film. The iris of the eye is comparable to the similarly named diaphragm of the camera, regulating the size of the pupil.

Development (Fig. 341). Embryologically, the most important functional parts of the eyeball arise from the ectoderm (including neurectoderm), but mesenchyme also enters prominently into the picture.

The first indication of an eye comes at about the time of completion of the brain tube. Outward from the forebrain area on either side grow spherical vesicles which remain connected by a stalk with the brain. As each *optic vesicle* develops, its outer hemisphere folds into the inner to form a double-layered *optic cup*; ventrally, however, there is a slit in the cup, the *choroid fissure*, through which blood vessels enter during development (normally, except in teleosts, this fissure is later obliterated). The optic cup becomes the retina, which is thus primarily a two-layered structure; from the retina comes part of the ciliary body and iris.

The lens is the second main eye structure to put in its appearance. As the optic vesicle approaches the surface, the overlying ectoderm of the skin thickens, and a spherical mass or pocket of ectoderm detaches itself to sink into the orifice of the cup and forms the lens body. It has been proved in a number of amphibians that the stimulus for lens formation is provided by the approach of the optic vesicle to the epidermis. If the optic vesicle in these forms is removed experimentally, no lens forms; if the vesicle is transplanted to (say) the flank, formation of a lens from the ectoderm of that region occurs. (In certain other forms, however, induction by the optic vesicle is not necessary for lens formation.)

The mesoderm contributes the further structures of the eyeball. From the mesenchyme arises an inner sheathing layer, primarily vascular, to enclose the retinal cup as the choroid, and to form much of the ciliary body and iris. Subsequently an external coat of connective tissue forms a complete sphere about the organ as the sclerotic coat (or sclera) and cornea. These sheaths correspond in great measure to the wrappings (meninges) which surround the brain—a condition which we might reasonably expect, since the developmental picture shows that the retina is in reality a peculiarly developed part of the brain itself.

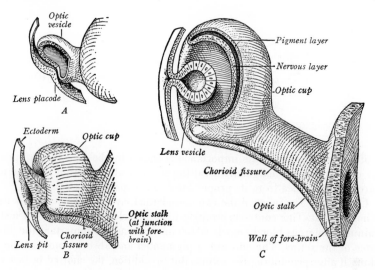

Fig. 341. A series of diagrams to show the embryonic development of the optic cup and lens. (From Arey.)

Sclera and Cornea. The most external eye sheath is that of the scleroid coat, or sclera, a stiff external structure which preserves the shape of the eye ball and resists pressure, internal or external, which might modify this shape. In cyclostomes and mammals, at the two extremes of the scale of living vertebrates, it consists entirely of dense connective tissue. In most groups, however, this is reinforced by the development of cartilage or bone. Often there is a cartilaginous cup enclosing much of the eyeball posteriorly; in birds this sometimes ossifies. Further protection against pressures is afforded by the frequent presence of a *scleral ring* (Fig. 342), a series of bony plates, fixed in position, lying in the sclera in front of the "equator." Fossil evidence shows that such a ring was present in ancestral vertebrates and continued onward along all the main lines of vertebrate evolution. It has, however, disappeared in many groups, and is found today only in actinopterygian fishes, numerous reptiles, and birds. Primitively, it appears, the ring consisted in fishes of four plates, but it is reduced in living ray-finned forms to two elements (or to one or none). In the crossopterygian ancestors of land vertebrates and the older fossil amphibians the number of plates was greatly increased, often to a score or more, and a high count is still present in reptiles and birds.

The superficial, external part of the sphere of sclerotic tissue is the translucent cornea, through which light enters the eyeball. Primitively, the cornea appears to have lain beneath the skin as a distinct structure, and this is still the case in lampreys. In all gnathostomes, however, the scleral coat and skin fuse inseparably in the adult; the skin component of the cornea and the sensitive skin area beneath the lid folds constitute the *conjunctiva*.

The refractive index of the cornea—its ability, that is, to deflect the course of light waves—is practically the same as that of water. Hence in primitive water-dwelling vertebrates the cornea has no power to act as a lens structure. In air, however, the curved cornea does much of the work of focusing and relieves the

Fig. 342. A skull of a bird (Aquila), showing the scleral ring in place. (From Edinger.)

lens of much of this task. Its importance is shown by the fact that in ourselves many defects such as astigmatism calling for optical correction are due to departures of the cornea from its proper form as a segment of a sphere.

Choroid. The inner of the two mesodermal layers of the eyeball is that of the choroid coat. This contrasts strongly with the sclera, for it is a soft material containing numerous blood vessels which are particularly important for the sustenance of the retina. The choroid is pigmented and absorbs most of the light reaching it after penetrating the retina. But in addition, the choroid of many vertebrates, from elasmobranchs to a variety of mammals, includes a light-reflecting device, most familiar to us as seen in the ghostly eyes of a night-prowling cat illuminated by automobile headlights. This phenomenon is due to the *tapetum lucidum,* generally developed in nocturnal terrestrial animals and in fishes which live deep in the water. With plenty of light coming to the eye, internal reflection is not needed and is in fact harmful, since it may confuse the details of the visual image. Where light is scarce, however, conservation of light rays, turned back to the retina by this mirror, more than makes up for the disadvantages.

Tapeta are variously constructed. In one type, common in hoofed mammals, the inner part of the choroid develops as a sheet of glistening connective tissue fibers which act as a mirror of sorts. In a second type, exemplified in carnivorous mammals, elasmobranchs, and some marine teleosts, the cells of this part of the choroid form an epithelium filled with fiber-like crystals of guanine (a material already mentioned in connection with skin pigmentation). Although the tapetum when present is normally formed in the choroid, some teleosts develop a guanine mirror in the pigment layer of the retina.

Iris. This structure, universally present, is formed by a combination of modified segments of both choroid and retinal layers of the eyeball. Both layers have in this region lost their most characteristic functions—vascular supply and photoreception, respectively. In attenuated form, they join to furnish an "external" covering for the lens and retinal cavity, and outline the pupil—the restricted opening through which light penetrates into the inner recesses of the eyeball. The iris is universally pigmented. Its inner (retinal) layer, for example, gives in man a blue effect, while brown pigments which may mask the blue are added by the outer (choroid) component. In a number of fish groups the iris is fixed in dimensions, except where forward or backward movement of the lens may affect its distention and the consequent size of the pupil. In sharks, however, some teleosts, and in tetrapods generally, muscle cells are present—striated fibers in reptiles and birds, smooth in amphibians and mammals. Arranged in circular and radial patterns, these fibers may contract or expand the pupillary opening. This gives the iris the function of a camera diaphragm; the pupil may be expanded in dim light for maximum illumination, contracted in bright light for protection of the retina and for more precise definition. Nocturnal forms tend to have a slit-shaped pupil which closes more readily to exclude bright light.

The nature of the muscle fibers in the iris is of theoretic interest. They are formed from the retinal component of the iris. This is a derivative of the neural ectoderm of the embryo. But muscle, smooth or striated, is supposedly formed by the mesoderm alone, and an ectodermal origin of muscle fibers is unorthodox, improper, and shocking to a right-minded embryologist. However, these cells in the iris have all the attributes of muscle fibers, structurally and functionally. The embryo eye has never read a textbook on embryology, and in its innocence violates the rules laid down for it.

The Lens and Accommodation. In land vertebrates light rays are strongly refracted as they enter the cornea, which consequently does much of the work of focusing. In fishes this is not the case, and the entire task is thus performed by the lens itself. In consequence, we find that the fish lens has a spherical shape, which gives it the highest possible power, and is situated far outward in the eyeball to afford the maximum distance for the convergence of rays on to the retina. In land vertebrates, in which the cornea relieves it of its optical task except for "fine adjustment," the lens is less rounded (the primate lens is exceptionally flat) and is situated farther back in the eye cavity. The lens is formed of elongated collagen fibers, wound about in a complicated pattern of concentric layers; it nevertheless has excellent optical properties and is completely transparent. It is firm in shape and, in lower vertebrates, resistant to distortion.

In cyclostomes the lens is not attached to the walls of the eyeball; pressure from the "vitreous humor" behind it and the cornea in front fix it in place. In all other groups, however, the lens is attached peripherally by a belt of tissues of some sort. This may be (as in elasmobranchs) a circular membrane or zonule, shaped like a washer; in most cases, however, the suspensory structure consists of a circular belt of zonule fibers. The area of attachment of these fibers is a ring-shaped region of conjoined choroid and retinal layers, the *ciliary body*, lying opposite the equator of the lens. The inner surface of this body is an epithelium formed by retinal tissue; its substance is derived from the choroid.

As every user of a camera is aware, it is impossible to obtain exact "definition" of objects at varied distances without adjustment of the lens focus. Such adjustment in the eye is termed *accommodation*. The eyes of most vertebrates are capable of accommodation; but, curiously, it is attained in a different fashion in almost every major group. The methods used may be broadly classified as follows:

A. Lens moved to achieve accommodation:
  1. Fixed position for near vision; moved backward to accommodate for distant objects (lampreys and teleosts)
  2. Fixed position for far vision; moved forward to accommodate for near objects (elasmobranchs, amphibians)
B. Shape of lens modified; fixed form for far vision, expanded shape for near objects (amniotes)

In lampreys and teleosts the lens is normally at its most "forward" position and is thus adjusted for nearby objects. For distant vision the lens is, in lampreys, pushed back by a flattening of the cornea, which it directly underlies (the flattening is accomplished by an external somatic muscle peculiar to this animal). In teleosts there is an unusual situation in that the embryonic choroid fissure in the floor of the eye remains open. Through it projects an elongated vascular structure, the *falciform process* (Fig. 339, *D*, p. 467), serving a nutritive function for the interior of the eyeball. From the front edge of this process there generally takes origin a small *retractor lentis muscle* (of mesodermal origin) which attaches to the lower edge of the lens and pulls it backward.

In elasmobranchs the lens is fixed for distant vision; for close sight it is swung forward (most strongly suspended by a dorsal ligament) by a forward pull of a small protractor muscle attached to the ventral rim of the lens. This muscle is, like those of the iris, of ectodermal (retinal) origin, and thus presents another worry for the embryologist.

The amphibian lens movement is the same as that of sharks—a forward pull of the lens for close-up focus. All amphibians have a small ventral muscle which pulls forward on the lens, and in anurans there is a second, dorsal muscle as well. These muscles form in the substance of the ciliary body and hence are (respectably) of mesodermal derivation.

In all amniotes the second principal mode of accommodation is present. The lens is somewhat flexible and capable of changing its shape from a flattened condition adjusted to far vision to more rounded contours for near sight. These changes in shape are accomplished by smooth muscles of mesodermal origin situated in the ciliary body. But despite this basic agreement among amniotes, we find that (perversely) reptiles and birds, on the one hand, and mammals on the other, do the trick in two different ways. In typical reptiles and in birds the greatly developed ciliary body has a ring of padlike processes which extend inward to gain a contact with the periphery of the lens. When circular muscle fibers of the ciliary body contract, these processes push in on the lens and force it to bulge into the more rounded shape suitable for near vision.

In reptiles and birds the zonule fibers are unimportant. In mammals, however, the ciliary body does not touch the lens; this is suspended by the fibers which attach at the back edge of the ciliary region (Fig. 343). The pull of the fibers holds the lens, under strain, in a flattened condition. Contraction of the ciliary muscles brings the region to which the fibers attach inward, closer to the

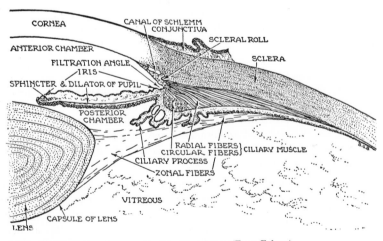

Fig. 343.   Details of the outer segment of the human eye. (From Fulton.)

lens; the fibers relax, and the elastic lens, released from tension, takes a more "natural" rounded shape. The amniote type of mechanism is efficient in many regards, but is effective only if the lens retains its elasticity. In man, as older readers know, it stiffens with age, accommodation diminishes, and without artificial aids a book can be read only at arm's length, if at all. Further, the ciliary musculature is poorly developed in many mammals, and a large variety of forms, ranging from rats to cows, lack powers of accommodation and are permanently far-sighted.

Why this great variety of methods to attain a single result? One may more than suspect that it is due to the absence of any device of this sort in the ancestral vertebrates (some fish still have none today). Over the long course of hundreds of millions of years various major vertebrate groups have all solved the problem of accommodation, but have solved it independently of one another, each in its own fashion.

Cavities of the Eyeball. Much of the eyeball is, as far as function goes, merely a blank space which needs only be filled by some substance which will not block or distort light rays passing through. This filling is in the form of liquids, here known under the old-fashioned name of humors. The principal cavity of the eyeball, between lens and retina, is filled by the *vitreous humor,* a thick, jelly-like material. In front of the lens is the *aqueous humor,* a thinner watery liquid (as it needs particularly to be in lower vertebrates where the lens moves to and fro in this area). The cavity filled by aqueous humor between the cornea and iris is termed the *anterior chamber* of the eye; the *posterior chamber* is not, as one might think, that filled by the vitreous humor, but the area—never of any great dimensions—which the aqueous humor may occupy between iris and lens (Fig. 343).

Intrusive structures are sometimes found in the eye cavity occupied by the vitreous humor. We have already noted the intrusion of the falciform process of teleosts. In reptiles a *papillary cone* projects into this cavity from the region of attachment of the optic nerve. This is a highly vascular structure which presumably aids in the supply of nutritive substances to the retina by diffusion through the vitreous humor. In birds it has developed into the *pecten* (Fig. 339, *B,* p. 467), a characteristic structure of this class. The pecten is, like its reptilian homologue, a source of nutritive or oxygen supply, but its usual shape, with pronounced parallel ridges, leads to the belief that it is, in addition, a visual aid. It is suggested that the shadows of these ridges, falling on the retina, act as a grille ruling, and that small or distant moving objects are more readily discerned as their images pass from one component to another on this grille. The presence of a pecten may be responsible, in part at least, for the high visual powers attributed to many birds.

Retina. All other parts of the eye are subordinate in importance to the retina; their duty is to see that the light rays are brought in proper arrangement and focus to this sensory structure for its stimulation and the transfer of these stimuli inward to the brain. We have noted that embryologically the retina is a double-layered structure; in the adult, however, the two layers are fused. The outer one is thin and unimportant; it contributes nothing but a set of pigment cells to reinforce the pigment present external to it in the choroid. The complex sensory and nervous mechanisms of the retina all develop from its inner layer.

The nature of the retina varies greatly from form to form and from one part to another of a single retina. Frequently, however, a sectioned retina has the general appearance seen at the left in Figure 344. Externally, next to the choroid, there is the thin pigmented layer; just inside this, a zone showing perpendicular striations; inside this, again, three distinct zones containing circular objects recognizable as cell nuclei. Special methods of staining reveal the nature of this stratification. The striated zone contains the elongated tips of the light-receiving cells, the rods and cones; the outer nuclear zone contains the cell bodies and nuclei of these structures. The nuclear zone next in order is that of the bipolar cells, which transmit the impulses inward from the rods and cones, and of accessory types of retinal nerve cells. The innermost nuclei are those of ganglion cells which pick up the stimuli from the bipolar elements and send fibers along the optic nerve to the brain.

The *rods* and *cones* are the actual photoreceptors of the system. They receive their names from their usual shape in mammals. Each cell includes a sensory tip

Fig. 344. *Left*, Vertical section through the retina of a mammal; *Right*, retinal connections are revealed by silver impregnation. *a* and *h*, Nervous elements of more or less uncertain function. Other abbreviations: *b*, bipolar cells associated with single cones; *c*, cones; *cb*, bipolar cells, connecting with a series of rods; *g*, ganglion cells; *r*, rods. (From Walls, partly after Polyak.)

directed outward toward the choroid, a thickened section and (beneath a membrane lying at this level of the retina) a basal piece containing the nucleus. In most mammalian eyes the two types are readily distinguishable: the rod cell is slenderly built throughout; the cone cell has generally a short broad tip and broad "body." In other groups, however, rods and cones vary greatly in shape and are sometimes difficult to tell apart.

One is immediately impressed by the fact that rod and cone cells in the vertebrate retina are *pointing the wrong way!* In a "logically" constructed retina, the tips of the photoreceptors should point toward the light source, and the parts of the retina which carry the impulses inward toward the brain should be farther removed. Some invertebrate eyes are so built, but not those of vertebrates, in which the light has to plunge through the full depth of the retina before reaching the point of reception. Various theories have been made to account for this anomalous situation—theories based mainly on the fact that the retina is a brain outgrowth. A reasonable assumption is that visual cells first appeared in the floor (or side wall) of the brain cavity and were able to function with upwardly (and inwardly) pointing tips, owing to a nonopaque build of the head in ancestral chordates. (Such cells appear to be present in the Amphioxus spinal cord.) When such cell groups became outfolded optic vesicles, the retinal elements simply retained their original orientation.

Considerable data are currently at hand regarding the chemistry of photoreception. All sensitive retinal cells contain substances consisting of special retinal proteins plus some type of carotenoid pigment related to vitamin A. The tips of the rods in land-living vertebrates and most marine fishes contain a substance known as visual purple, chemically termed *rhodopsin*. Light reception causes a breaking down of the visual purple and nerve stimulation; in the dark rhodopsin is reconstituted. A more primitive vertebrate rod chemical, however, is a "visual red," *porphyropsin*, formed from a vitamin A of somewhat different composition than that of rhodopsin; this is present in lampreys, fresh water fishes, and larval amphibians. (The history of visual pigments has, curiously, paralleled the story of kidney tubules as told in Chapter 13.) The cones have visual pigments, *iodopsin* and *cyanopsin*, of violet and bluish tints, closely comparable to the two types in the rods.

Rods and cones differ markedly in their functions, as one can determine from his own eyes, where the cones are concentrated in the center of the field of vision, the rods situated, in the main, peripherally. (1) Good illumination is necessary before the cones come into play; rods are effective in faint light, and it is calculated that rod stimulation can be produced by a single quantum, the smallest theoretic unit of energy. At night one can often catch a glimpse of a faint star in the margin of the field of vision, but fail to see it if looking directly at it. (2) Cones as a group give good visual details; rods give a more blurred picture. For accurate detail we focus the cone-bearing center of the eye on the object; things seen peripherally with the rods are blurred and indistinct. (3) Cones give color vision; rods give black-and-white effects only. In one's visual field, peripheral objects are gray and colorless.

The difference in acuity of vision between cones and rods is explained by the nerve fiber connections of these two types, noted below. We do not know what makes the difference between the high and low "thresholds" of cone and rod cells.

Cell morphology offers little aid in the interpretation of color vision. The visual radiations are measured in terms of wavelengths based on Ångström units of 1/10,000,000 of a millimeter. The longest, and slowest, vibrations perceptible to the eye are those on the order of 7000 such units, producing the sensation of the color red (longer waves—infra-red—are discerned as heat). Shorter and shorter waves give color sensations of orange, yellow, green, blue, indigo, and at about 4000 units, violet; beyond this lies the invisible ultraviolet region. A dominant modern theory holds that the cones are of three main types which pick up sensations in the red, green, and violet regions of the spectrum, and that intermediate color sensations are due to a combination within the brain of the relative proportion of stimulation of these cone types. Thus, stimuli of red and green-perceiving cones in various proportions produce orange or yellow sensations; green and violet produce shades of blue; violet and red produce purple—a color not in the spectrum at all. There is, however, little anatomical evidence for this. In turtles and birds colored oil globules in the cones may filter light for reception of one or the other of the assumed basic colors; but in other groups all cones in a given animal appear to be anatomically of a single type.

Color vision is widespread in vertebrates, but very far from universal. Obviously there is little if any color vision in forms in which cones are rare or absent. But it is none too certain that color vision is present, or if present is similar to our own, even where cones or cone-like structures are found in the retina. Observation and experiment on living animals are necessary to determine whether color sensitivity is present. Many teleosts have color vision, as do many reptiles and most birds, but there is no proof of color vision in elasmobranchs and amphibians. In mammals as a whole relatively few of those tested show much response to color; the ancestral mammals, it is believed, were mainly nocturnal forms, with rods predominating in the eyes. The high color sensitivity of higher primates, including man, is an exceptional situation in mammals; to a dog or cat the world is probably gray, or has at the most faint pastel tints.

The distribution of rods and cones in different animals and in different retinal regions is highly variable. As would be expected, rods dominate in nocturnal animals, or fishes dwelling in deeper waters; cones are more abundant in forms active by day. Since, however, members of a given order or class may differ widely in their habits, the distribution of rod and cone types of retinas does not sort out well taxonomically. In an "average" vertebrate probably not over 5 per cent or so of the total photoreceptive cells are cones. Retinas containing rods alone are found in many sharks and some deep sea teleosts, and a relatively few nocturnal forms in the amniote classes. Eyes which, on the other hand, have cones only are also known in a few amniotes of each class. A majority of reptiles and birds have eyes relatively rich in cones and hence mainly suited for daytime life. In teleosts there are to be found "twin" cones, with partially fused cell bodies.

Rods and cones may both be present in any retinal region. Often, however, in forms in which both types of cell are common, there develops a distribution such as that in our own eyes. In this pattern the cones are but sparingly present over most of the retinal area and concentrated, to the practical exclusion of rods, in a central region in which vision is most acute and perception of detail best developed. This is the *area centralis* (sometimes termed macula lutea because, exceptionally, the area has a yellow tinge in man). Frequently there is present here a *fovea* as well, a depression in the surface of the area centralis from which blood vessels and the inner layers of cells have been cleared away.

In many birds (and in some lizards as well) there is, curiously, a development of two central areas in each eye, one centrally situated, the other well toward the posterior or outer region. The bird's eye normally is pointed well to the side, and the primary central area is aimed at this lateral visual field. In bird flight, vision straight ahead is of great importance; the secondary center gives each eye a perception of detail in the anterior part of each visual field.

Inward from the rods and cones is a layer which consists for the most part of *bipolar cells;* and, well to the inner surface of the retina, a third cell layer is that of *ganglion cells.* The bipolar cells have short processes serving to connect with rods and cones on the one hand and with ganglion cells on the other; the latter cells are neurons from which long fibers relay on into the brain the impulses initiated by light reception. Both bipolar and ganglion layers include in addition peculiar types of cells which appear to make cross connections between the various direct pathways. It appears that often (although not always) one cone cell alone connects with a given bipolar cell, and only one such bipolar cell connects with an associated ganglion cell; thus each cone may have an individual pathway to optic nerve and brain. On the other hand, a considerable number of rods always converge into a single bipolar cell. In consequence, the brain obtains no information as to which of the group of rods has been stimulated, a condition which accounts for the lack of precision in rod vision as compared with that of cone areas.

Optic Nerve. Although the brain and nerves are the subject of the next chapter, we may perhaps permit ourselves to violate proper order and discuss the central connections of the eye in relation to vision. The ganglion cells of the retina produce long nerve fibers which travel inwardly along the course of the original optic stalk to the forebrain region. The fibers originate on the inner surface of the retina, converge to a point opposite the attachment of the stalk, and there plunge through the substance of the retina. At this point there can, of course, be no rods or cones, and there is, hence, a *blind spot* in the field of vision. In ourselves, at least, this blank area is "fudged" by the brain, which fills it in with the same materials seen in the surrounding region.

While the connection of retina with brain proper is customarily called a nerve, it differs from any normal nerve in two regards. Here, somewhat as in the olfactory nerve, we are dealing with fibers running inward toward the brain rather than outward from cells in or near that organ. Further, since the retina is, from an embryologic point of view, properly a part of the brain itself, the optic "nerve" is to be thought of not as a true external nerve, but rather as a fiber tract connecting two brain regions.

Reaching the floor of the forebrain, the optic nerve fibers enter via the X-shaped *optic chiasma* (Fig. 345). We find that frequently fiber bundles cross from one side to the other within the substance of the brain, without any immediately obvious reason, and this is the case also with the optic nerves. In the crossroads of the chiasma, in primitive vertebrates, nearly all the fibers of the right optic nerve cross to the left side of the brain, and vice versa; such a crossing of fibers is termed a *decussation.* The two sets of fibers in lower vertebrates run to the paired roof structures of the midbrain (tectum); in mammals they are relayed to special areas in the gray matter of the cerebral hemispheres. Details are little known in lower vertebrates, but it appears that, as is known to be the case in mammals, the points in the brain receiving sensations from the different parts of the retina are arranged topographically in many if not all cases in such a fashion

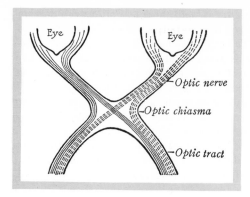

Fig. 345. Diagram of the optic chiasma in a mammal with good stereoscopic vision. All fibers from the corresponding half of each eye pass to the same side of the brain. (From Arey.)

as to give a brain pattern—and a resulting mental "picture"—reproducing the arrangement of objects as "seen" by the retina.

In a majority of vertebrates the eyes are directed nearly straight laterally, and the two fields of vision are partially or totally different; the brain builds up two separate pictures of two quite separate views. In a number of higher types, however—such as birds of prey and many mammals—the eyes are turned forward, the two fields of vision overlap to a greater or lesser degree, and the two sets of impressions transmitted to the brain are more or less the same. Most notable is the case in primates, where, from Tarsius to man, the two fields of vision are practically identical.

In such cases the formation of two duplicate mental pictures seems an unnecessary procedure. Nevertheless, this is done, as far as can be discovered, in birds and other nonmammalian forms with overlapping visual fields. In mammals, however, we find a new development. *Stereoscopic vision* appears. The field of vision is unified; sensations from objects received in common by the two eyes are superposed. As a result such a form as man is aided, by the slight differences in point of view of the two eyes, in gaining effects of depth and three dimensional shape of objects—effects otherwise impossible of attainment.

An important anatomic phenomenon concerned with this development is *incomplete decussation* at the optic chiasma. In many mammals—and in mammals alone—we find that, for overlapping parts of the field of the two eyes, fibers from the areas which in both retinas view the same objects go to the same side of the brain. In consequence, certain groups of fibers do not cross (i.e., decussate), but turn a right angle at the chiasma, to accompany their mates from the opposite eye. In man, for example, where the overlap of visual fields is nearly complete, practically all the fibers from the left halves of both retinas enter the left side of the brain, and all fibers from the right halves of the retinas enter the right side of the brain (Fig. 345). As a result, the visual area of each brain hemisphere builds up a half-picture of the total visual field as a "double exposure"; by further complicated interconnections between the hemispheres, the two halves of the picture are welded together to emerge into consciousness as a single stereoscopic view.

Accessory Structures. External to the eyeball are various visual aids. We have described earlier the six striated eye muscles which move the eyeball. This muscle group may form additional muscles upon occasion; notably in many tetrapods a *retractor muscle* which pulls the eyeball inward. We may note that in some vertebrates there develops in the orbit a derivative of the jaw musculature which, when contracted, bulges with the effect of popping the eye outward.

In fishes there may be present folds of skin around the margins of the orbit, but there is little further development of *eyelids* in most fishes. In some teleosts, however, the cornea may be partly covered by fixed skin folds, and in some sharks there are upper and lower lids, the latter movable.

All tetrapods have the lids movable in some fashion. A dry cornea would become opaque; the lids, by closing at intervals, moisten and clean the corneal surface. Upper and lower lids are always present; they are usually thick and opaque. In most groups the lower lid is more prominent than the upper; in mammals (and in crocodilians) the upper lid is the major structure. In birds, and in many reptiles and mammals, there is a third eyelid, the *nictitating membrane,* a transparent fold of skin lying deep to the other eyelids and drawn over the cornea from anterior (or medial) to posterior margins.

No muscles were originally present in the region of the eyelids, and various methods have been evolved to effect their movements. In many tetrapods, as noted above, the eyeball can be withdrawn and again protracted outward; such motions may produce a passive closing and opening of the lids. The operation of the nictitating membrane is effected by the development of a tendon which passes inward from it around the eyeball and becomes associated in variable fashion with the eyeball muscles; a similar tendon may arise in connection with the lower lid. Slips from the eyeball muscles proper in some cases grow forward to attach to the lids. In mammals use is made of a new development in that class. We have noted that facial muscles have here grown forward over the head; a ring of these muscle fibers operates as a sphincter to close the eye (Fig. 194, p. 286).

In snakes and some lizards there lies external to the cornea a second superficial eye-covering of transparent tissue. This pair of protective "spectacles" is formed from a fusion of the eyelids, giving the snake its unwinking stare.

In land vertebrates are developed "tear glands," *lacrimal glands* whose function is to furnish liquid for moistening the cornea. As seen in some urodeles, there is primitively a row of small glands running the length of the eyeball within the lower lid. In most groups, however, there is a concentration of glandular development at either the front (medial) or the back (lateral) margin of the orbit. Characteristic of the former position is the *harderian gland,* which tends to secrete a rather oily liquid, in contrast to the true lacrimal gland. The latter is typically developed at the back or outer corner of the eye. In amphibians, reptiles, and birds the harderian glands are usually prominent, the lacrimal glands often poorly developed or absent; in mammals, on the other hand, the lacrimal gland proper is characteristic, and a harderian gland relatively rare.

A minor if useful adjunct to the tetrapod eye is the *tear duct* (lacrimal duct), not generally developed in fishes, which carries surplus fluid from the anterior or medial corner of the eye to the nasal cavity. The lacrimal fluid has thus an accessory function in moistening the nasal mucosa and, in lizards and snakes, of reaching the mouth via the nose and forming an addition to the salivary fluid. (The duct is lacking in turtles.)

Eye Variations. Our previous comments on optic structures have given some faint idea of the great amount of adaptive variation seen in vertebrate eyes as a whole. Throughout the vertebrate series the basic eye pattern persists with remarkable consistency; nevertheless, entire volumes could be (and have been)

480   THE VERTEBRATE BODY

devoted to an account of the wealth of changes rung on the basic eye structures in different groups. A few additional notes on variations may be given here.

Eyeballs are generally nearly spherical, but there are striking departures from this. "Tube eyes"—deep and narrow—are seen in deep-sea teleosts on the one hand, and in owls on the other. Both these forms operate in dim light; in this eye type all available illumination is concentrated on a narrow patch of sensory retina to bring the light intensity up to the minimum necessary for visibility. Typical day birds, in contrast with owls, have a broadly expanded retinal surface (as in Fig. 339, *B*), making perception of small details possible. A curiosity is the little "four-eyed fish" Anableps of the American tropics, which has two separate corneas and retinal areas in each eye, so that, floating at the surface, it can simultaneously see both above and below water.

Eyes are relatively small in large animals, relatively large in little forms. This one might reasonably expect, for if an eye of a certain size furnishes satisfactory vision for a given animal, there is no selective advantage in a larger eye even if general body size has increased.

Eyes have degenerated and lost much of their structural niceties in a variety of forms from hagfishes to mammals. Such degeneration is, of course, usually correlated with a mode of life in which light is dim or absent. Among marine teleosts, those living at fairly considerable depths universally have large and specialized eyes which make the most of the faint illumination present; but in the great deeps some fishes have, so to speak, abandoned the struggle, and the eyes have degenerated. Cave life, too, has led to eye degeneration in various fishes and amphibians, some closely related to forms with normal eye structure. In land vertebrates burrowing forms usually exhibit a similar tendency. Snake eyes are in general well developed, but are peculiarly built and lack various structures, such as the scleral ring and certain of the usual eye muscles. It is suggested that the ancestral snakes were burrowers with reduced eyes, and that the typical ophidian eye of today has been secondarily built up from the remains of the degenerate ancestral organ.

Median Eyes.   Our attention thus far has been exclusively directed to the paired laterally placed eyes common to all vertebrates. In their early history, however, the ancestral vertebrates had a third eye, medially situated on the forehead and directed upward. In the oldest ostracoderms (Fig. 19, p. 38) a socket which obviously contained such an eye is universally present and often conspicuous, although always much smaller than the paired eyes. This eye opening was generally present in placoderms, but not in the sharklike fishes. It is found in the Devonian in primitive representatives of all three major groups of bony fishes and was especially common in crossopterygians (Fig. 154, p. 226). In early land animals this third eye persisted; it was present in almost all the older amphibians and early reptiles, including most of the mammal-like types (Fig. 158, *A*, 163, *A*, *B*, pp. 231, 235). But by Triassic times median eyes had apparently gone out of fashion. Even in fishes they disappeared at an early stage in most groups, and in modern amphibians, most reptiles, and all birds and mammals they are likewise absent. Today we find median eyes present only in lampreys, on the one hand, and Sphenodon and some lizards on the other (Fig. 393, p. 532); buried beneath the skin, they can do little more than detect the presence or absence of light, although a miniature cornea, lens, and retina may be developed. In frogs there may be a vestigial external structure of dubious nature;

in all other groups the remains of such organs are no more than glandular materials in the braincase.

A functional interpretation of this story can be made in terms of the habits of the vertebrate ancestors. Presumably they were bottom-dwelling mud strainers. In this mode of life, knowledge furnished by a median eye of what threatened from above was vital. With the development of a more active mode of life, vertical vision lost its importance.

Such dorsal eyes spring from the roof of the diencephalon and hence, like lateral eyes, are essentially parts of the brain. There is a curious quirk in the story: the median eye, it appears, is not the same structure throughout, but may develop from either of two outgrowths, the *parietal organ* (or parapineal organ) and *pineal organ.* Both may be present in the same animal and, although adjacent, are readily distinguishable through differences in the position of their stalk attachments. In lampreys both form eyelike structures, but the pineal is the dominant element. In Sphenodon and lizards, however, the parapineal is the functional eye. The situation suggests that possibly the remote ancestor of the vertebrates may have had paired dorsal eyes as well as paired lateral ones and conditions in some fossil placoderm skulls tend to strengthen this belief.

Despite loss of eye function, the pineal organ persists in higher vertebrates as a glandular structure. It is possibly an endocrine gland, but there is little more positive evidence that it functions in this fashion than there is for the suggestion, made by Descartes some centuries ago, that it is the seat of the soul.

LATERAL LINE ORGANS

A highly developed sensory system of a type quite unknown in land vertebrates is that of the lateral line organs (Figs. 346, 347) found in fishes and in aquatic larval amphibians. The receptors are clusters of sensory cells termed neuromasts; these may be found distributed in isolated fashion in the skin, but are generally located along a series of canals or grooves on the head and body.

A main element of the system is the *lateral line* in the narrower sense of the term. In typical fishes this is a long canal running the length of either flank (parallel secondary lines sometimes develop). The canal continues forward onto the head, where similar canals form a complex pattern. Generally, a major canal runs forward over the temporal region, then curves downward and forward beneath the orbit to the snout as an infraorbital canal. A second cranial canal is supra-

Fig. 346. Section through the skin of a teleost, to show the lateral line canal, *lc,* piercing a series of scales, and opening at intervals to the surface. The canal is followed by the lateral line nerve, *ln,* which sends branches to the sensory organs, *so; ep,* epithelium. (After Goodrich.)

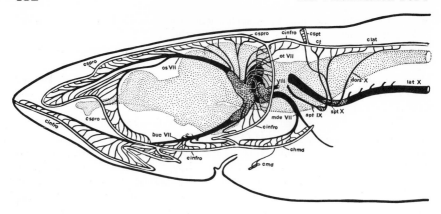

Fig. 347.   Left side of the head of a shark to show the lateral line canals (parallel lines) and the nerves (black) supplying them. Pit organs are not shown: *buc VII*, buccal ramus of nerve VII; *chmd*, hyomandibular canal; *cinfro*, infraorbital canal; *clat*, lateral line canal proper; *cmd*, mandibular canal; *cspro*, supraorbital canal; *cspt*, supratemporal (or occipital) canals; *ct*, temporal canal; *dors X*, dorsal ramus of nerve X; *lat X*, lateral line ramus of nerve X; *mde VII*, external mandibular ramus of nerve VII; *os VII*, superficial ophthalmic ramus of nerve VII; *ot VII*, otic ramus of nerve VII; *spt IX*, supratemporal ramus of nerve IX; *spt X*, supratemporal ramus of nerve X. (From Norris and Hughes.)

orbital in position in its forward course. The canals of the two sides may have a transverse connection across the occiput; a canal generally crosses the cheek and then runs downward and forward along the lower jaw. Other accessory canals may be present on the head and gill region, and in some cases there are accessory body lines. Isolated neuromasts, *pit organs*, may also be found on the head, often in linear arrangements.

In most fishes the lateral line organs are contained in closed canals, opening at intervals to the surface. In many bony fishes this canal system may be sunk within the substance of the head plates and within or below the body scales; in cyclostomes the neuromasts, on the contrary, are in isolated pits, although the pits are arranged in roughly linear order. In a few cartilaginous and bony fishes open grooves take the place of canals, and the same appears to have been true among the ancient fossil amphibians. In modern amphibians the neuromasts lie in the skin in more or less isolated fashion, although preserving in part a linear arrangement.

The sense organs of the lateral line system are the *neuromasts*, consisting of bundles of cells, often with much the appearance of taste buds. The neuromast cells are elongated, and each bears a projecting hairlike structure. Invariably there is present above the "hairs," and enclosing their tips, a mass of gelatinous material which may be termed a *cupula*, secreted by the neuromast cells, which waves freely in the surrounding water (Fig. 348). Lacking structures at all comparable ourselves (except, as we shall see, in the internal ear), the nature of the sensations registered has been difficult for us to determine. It appears that the neuromasts respond to waves or disturbances in the water through movement of the cupula and consequent bending of the hairlike processes, and supplement vision by making the fish aware of nearby moving objects—prey, enemies—or of fixed "obstructions to navigation." A fish seldom has visible "landmarks" against

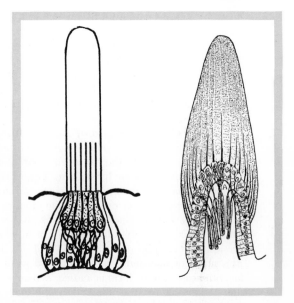

Fig. 348. Neuromast sensory organs. *Left*, an organ from a lateral line canal; *right*, the crista from a semicircular canal. In both are seen supporting cells and sensory cells, the latter with hairlike processes extending into the flexible, gelatinous cupula. (Partly after Fulton.)

which to measure its progress through the water; sensory structures of this sort will at least tell it of water movements and the pressure of currents against its body and thus be of great aid in locomotion.

The neuromasts and their nerve cells are derived embryologically (as are certain other nervous and sensory structures) from thickenings of the ectoderm on either side of the neural tissues of the head, termed *placodes*. The lateral line placodes become associated with three of the cranial nerves. Much of the system of head canals is formed from an anterior placode associated with cranial nerve VII. A short segment in the temporal region is formed from a small placode related to nerve IX. A posterior placode forms the posterior part of the head system and grows backward the length of the trunk; it is associated with cranial nerve X (the vagus), which sends a branch along the flank to accompany it.

Although the lateral line system is present in larval amphibians, it was lost, it seems, in the earliest reptiles. Many reptiles and mammals have returned to a water-dwelling life, but, useful as it would be to them, this sensory system, once lost, never reappears.

Related to the lateral line system in development and probably in phylogeny, although differing in structure and probable function, are the *Ampullae of Lorenzini,* clusters of jelly-filled little tubules scattered over the head region— particularly the snout—of elasmobranchs and containing at their bases sensory cells innervated by the facial nerve. It is possible that, like the proper lateral line organs, they are sensitive to hydrostatic pressure; they appear, however, to be most especially highly sensitive receptors for temperature changes in the water.

THE EAR

First thoughts as to the primary anatomic or functional aspects of the vertebrate ear are liable to be misleading when based on familiar human features. One tends to think, when the word is mentioned, of the ornamental pinna of the mammalian external ear, or, perhaps, of the middle ear cavity behind the drum, with its contained ear ossicles. These items, however, are entirely lacking in fishes; the basic ear structures of all vertebrates are those of the internal ear, the sensory organs buried deep within the ear capsule. We naturally think of hearing as the proper ear function; but in the ancestral vertebrates audition was apparently unimportant and perhaps absent; equilibrium was the basic sensory attribute of the "auditory" organ.

The Ear as an Organ of Equilibrium.   Before considering the hearing function, which becomes increasingly important as we ascend the scale of vertebrates, we may discuss the ear as an organ of equilibrium, a basic and relatively unchanged function from fish to man. Equilibrium is a type of sensation produced by the internal ear alone; all accessory ear structures are related to the hearing sense and need not concern us for the moment.

In a variety of fishes, amphibians, and reptiles the paired internal ears are built upon a relatively uniform pattern in which most of the structures present are related to equilibration (Fig. 349, *A–D*). The *membranous labyrinth* consists of a series of sacs and canals contained within the otic region on either side of the braincase. These form a closed system of cavities, lined by an epithelium and containing a liquid, the *endolymph,* not dissimilar to that of the interstitial fluid.

Two distinct, major saclike structures are generally present in jawed vertebrates, the *utriculus* and the *sacculus.* A slender tube, the *endolymphatic duct,* usually extends upward and inward from them to terminate within the braincase in an *endolymphatic sac.* In general, the sacculus lies below the utriculus. In both there is found a large oval "spot" consisting of a sensory epithelium associated with branches of the auditory nerve; these areas are the *utricular macula* and *saccular macula.* The utricular macula lies on the floor of that sac, in a horizontal plane; the saccular element is typically in a vertical plane on the inner wall of the sacculus. A pocket-like depression is found in the floor of the sacculus near its posterior end; this is the *lagena,* which contains a smaller *lagenar macula.*

The sensory cells of these maculae (and, indeed, of the entire internal ear) are comparable to the neuromasts of the lateral line system. During development there forms over the combined tips of the sensory hairs of these cells a gelatinous membrane or cupula. In the utricular and saccular maculae, and often that of the lagena as well, this material becomes a thickened structure, weighed down by the deposition in it of a mass of crystals of calcium carbonate termed an *otolith.* The nature of this "ear stone" varies. It may remain a rather amorphous mass of crystals. In ray-finned fishes, however, the otoliths develop into compact structures. The saccular otolith is generally the best developed; in teleosts it is so large as practically to fill the sacculus and reflect in its outlines the shape of that cavity. This shape varies from genus to genus and from species to species; a single tiny otolith will often furnish positive identification of the fish which bore it.

The utricular macula and, to a much lesser degree, those of the sacculus and lagena, register by the tilt of the otolith and its enclosed sensory "hairs," the tilt of the head and linear acceleration; somewhat similar organs are found in a number of invertebrate types. They do not, however, furnish data as to turning movements. This is the function of another series of structures, the *semicircular canals.*

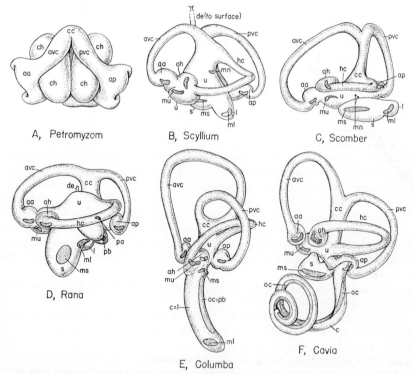

Fig. 349. Membranous labyrinth of *A*, lamprey; *B*, shark; *C*, teleost; *D*, frog; *E*, bird; *F*, mammal; all external views of the left ear. Sensory areas are shown (except in *A*) as if the membrane were transparent. *aa*, Ampulla of anterior canal; *ah*, ampulla of horizontal canal; *ap*, ampulla of posterior canal; *avc*, anterior vertical canal; *c*, cochlear duct; *cc*, crus commune with which both vertical canals connect; *ch*, chambers in the lamprey ear lined with a ciliated epithelium; *de*, endolymphatic duct; *hc*, horizontal canal; *l*, lagena; *ml*, macula of lagena; *mn*, macula neglecta; *ms*, macula of sacculus; *mu*, macula of utriculus; *oc*, organ of Corti; *pa*, papilla amphibiorum; *pb*, papilla basilaris; *pvc*, posterior vertical canal; *s*, sacculus; *u*, utriculus. (After Retzius.)

These tiny tubes are dorsal elements of the endolymphatic system, springing out from the utriculus and connected at either end with this sac. In every jawed vertebrate, without exception, three such canals are present; each of the three lies in a plane at right angles to the other two, so that one is present for each of the three planes of space. Two canals lie in vertical planes, an *anterior vertical* (or superior) *canal*, angled forward and outward from the upper surface of the utriculus, and a *posterior vertical canal*, running backward and outward; a *horizontal canal* extends laterally from that body. Often the two vertical canals arise at their proximal ends by a common stalk, a *crus commune*, from the upper surface of the utriculus. Each semicircular canal has at one end a spherical expansion, an *ampulla*. The vertical canals bear these ampullae at their distal ends, anteriorly and posteriorly; the horizontal canal (for no known reason in particular) has its ampulla anteriorly placed. Within each ampulla is a sensory area, usually elevated, termed a *crista* (Fig. 348, *B*). Here we find again the familiar hair cells, or neuromasts; their tips are embedded in a common membrane or mass of gelatinous substance, a tall *cupula*, which nearly blocks the ampulla and can move to and fro like a swing door.

The arrangement of the canals and their sensory structures makes it seem clear that their function is to register turning movements of the animal in the several planes of space. Displacement of liquid in one or more of the canals displaces the cupulae, with a consequent bending of their sensory hairs.

The organization of the parts of these ear sacs and canals is in general constant through the jawed vertebrates, high or low. There are, however, certain variables in the system. As in many other features, the cyclostomes exhibit an unusual and puzzling condition. The lamprey has but two semicircular canals, equivalent, apparently, to the vertical canals of other vertebrates, and, in addition, a peculiar system of ciliated sacs beneath them; the hagfish has but a single canal, presumably representing a combination of these two. As in the case of the nose, we cannot be sure whether this is a primitive or a degenerate condition. The lamprey type of ear (as well as nostril arrangement) is known to have been present in some of the most ancient fossil vertebrates. In cartilaginous fishes, sacculus and utriculus are merely two lobes of a common cavity from which canals and endolymphatic duct arise, and the posterior vertical canal may be associated, at its ampullar end, with the saccular region. In these forms the crus commune is commonly absent, and in skates the canals are connected only by narrow ducts with the remainder of the system.

The endolymphatic duct usually terminates in a sac of modest proportions lying within the braincase. In Chondrichthyes—presumed to be primitive in this regard—the endolymphatic ducts may extend upward to open on the top of the head. The endolymphatic sac is absent in some teleosts. In some bony fishes, the reptiles, and particularly in the amphibians, the endolymphatic sacs may be of great size and contain calcareous matter; those of the two sides may connect either above or below the brain in some lower tetrapods, and in the typical frogs may extend the length of the cavity of the spinal cord as well.

Origin of the Vertebrate Ear.   Embryologically, the internal ears first appear, like lateral line organs, as ectodermal thickenings—placodes—on either side of the head (Fig. 350). These sink inward to form a pair of sacs, which for some time may retain a tubular connection with the exterior (as do the endolymphatic ducts in the adult shark). Typically, each sac then subdivides into utricular and saccular portions; from the former the canals are gradually separated off, and from the latter arise further structures, discussed later.

This embryologic story, together with the nature of the sensory endings of the ear, suggests that the internal ear originated phylogenetically as a specialized, deeply sunk part of the lateral line system. Its sensory maculae and ampullae are typical neuromast organs, with hair cells embedded in a gelatinous cover and responding to pressure or to movements in the liquid-filled spaces in which they lie. The nerves from the two sets of organs are closely associated (as will be noted in the next chapter) to form an acousticolateralis system. Functionally also the two sets of sensory structures are closely knit; together they offer a primitive fish the major part of the data by which its locomotion is regulated; still further, there is even some slight evidence of hearing function in the fish lateral line organs themselves.

Hearing in Fishes.   Whether or not fish hear is a topic that was long disputed. A considerable body of evidence, however, indicates that hearing is certainly present in many teleosts, but in elasmobranchs there is merely indication of response to very low vibrations. Localization of the sensory uptake of vibra-

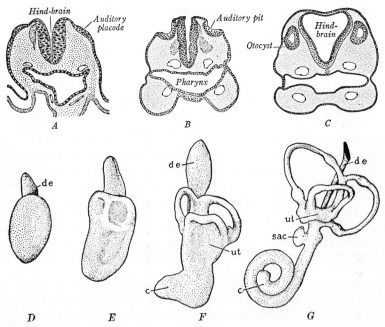

Fig. 350. Diagrams to show the development of the internal ear in mammals. *A* to *C,* Cross sections of the head of early embryos; an ectodermal placode sinks inward on either side to form an otic vesicle. *D* to *G,* Successive stages in the development of the various parts of the membranous labyrinth from the otic vesicle: *c,* cochlear duct; *de,* endolymphatic duct; *sac,* sacculus; *ut,* utriculus. (*A* to *C* from Arey; *D* to *F* after His and Bremer.)

tions is difficult. In most cases the saccular macula appears to be the major receptor, but in some forms the utriculus is apparently concerned as well. A suspect is the *macula neglecta* (Fig. 349, *B, C*), a small sensory spot found in the utriculus in a variety of fish and lower land vertebrates. The hearing organs of land vertebrates develop in connection with the lagenar pocket, but in fishes the macula of the lagena appears to be concerned only with gravity.

Fishes in general lack the various accessory devices by which in higher vertebrates sound waves reach the internal ear. But, as shown by studies on men with hearing deficiencies, the conduction of vibrations through the head skeleton to the internal ear may produce some degree of hearing. In most fishes water vibrations, to be heard, must set up head vibrations, and these in turn produce endolymphatic vibrations which can be picked up by the hair cells of the internal ear.

Some bony fishes, however, have accessory structures which parallel in a way the "hearing aids" found in land vertebrates, although evolved quite independently and along other lines. In these fishes, it appears, the swim bladder is utilized as a device for the reception of vibrations. In herring-like teleosts this air bladder sends forward a tubular extension which comes to lie alongside part of the membrane system of either ear and can thus induce vibrations in the endolymph. In a group of teleosts termed the Ostariophysii, which includes the catfishes, carp and relatives, in which hearing is unquestionably developed, another method is used. Processes of the most anterior vertebrae develop on either side as small detached bones termed the *weberian ossicles* (Fig. 351). These articulate in series to form a chain extending from the air bladder forward to the ear region. The ossicles operate somewhat in the fashion of the little ear bones of a mammal, transmitting air bladder vibrations to the liquids of the internal ear system.

The Middle Ear in Reptiles and Birds. Hearing is an important sense in tetrapods. A different problem in sound reception exists in land vertebrates as contrasted with the fish situation. The sounds to be heard are relatively faint air waves which can have ordinarily little direct effect in setting up endolymph vibrations in the internal ear. Devices for amplification of these waves and their transmission to the internal ear are a necessity; these form the middle ear structures.

The developments found in the living amphibians are specialized and degenerate, and will be considered later. A more generalized type of middle ear structure was present, however, in the ancient labyrinthodonts, and numerous modern lizards show a middle ear structure not far removed from this primitive tetrapod condition (Fig. 352). The spiracular gill cleft and the hyomandibular bone are the sole elements concerned. The spiracular pouch of the embryo never breaks through to the surface; the corresponding surface depression, where developed, becomes an *external auditory meatus*. A thin membrane between external depression and pouch becomes the eardrum or *tympanic membrane*, which picks up air vibrations. The spiracular pouch is the *middle ear cavity;* its connection with the pharynx is the *eustachian tube*. The hyomandibular bone of fishes changes its function to become a rodlike *stapes* (or columella) which crosses the middle ear cavity. Externally, it attaches to the eardrum and picks up the vibrations received by it. Internally, an expanded footplate of the stapes fits into an opening in the ear capsule, the *fenestra ovalis;* through the agency of the stapes, air vibrations are carried inward to set up vibrations in the liquids of the internal ear and eventually reach its sensory structures.

The fish spiracular opening lies high up on the side of the head (Fig. 353, *A*), the position in which the eardrum lay in the older fossil amphibians (Fig. 353, *B*). The eardrum position in the skull is shown by the presence of an otic notch (Fig. 353, *E*). In amniotes, however, the drum usually lies farther posteriorly and ventrally; it is not at all certain that the drum is strictly homologous

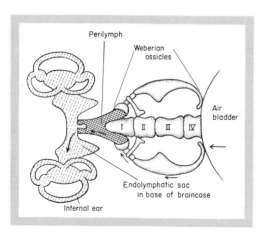

Fig. 351. Diagrammatic horizontal section of the posterior part of the head and anterior part of the body of a teleost with weberian ossicles. Vibrations in an anterior subdivision of the air bladder set up corresponding vibrations in a series of small ossicles which in turn set up waves in a perilymphatic sac. This, again, sets up vibrations in an endolymphatic sac at the base of the braincase. Arrows show the course of transmission of the vibrations. Roman numerals indicate the vertebrae from which the weberian ossicles are derived. (After Chvanilov.)

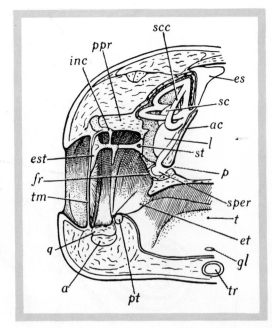

Fig. 352. Posterior view of the left side of a lizard head to show the auditory apparatus. A shallow external depression leads to the ear drum (*tm*). Internal to the drum, the stapes is seen, divided into two parts, the "extracolumella" (*est*), and columella or stapes proper (*st*); processes from the former articulate above with the skull (*inc*) and below with the quadrate anterior to the middle ear cavity. This cavity opens by a broad eustachian tube (*et*) to the throat. The internal ear is shown in diagrammatic fashion. Other abbreviations: *a*, articular bone of lower jaw (= malleus); *ac*, inner wall of auditory capsule; *es*, endolymphatic sac; *fr*, fenestra rotunda; *gl*, glottis; *l*, lagena; *p*, perilymphatic duct connecting inner ear with brain cavity; *ppr*, paroccipital process of otic region; *pt*, pterygoid; *q*, quadrate (= incus); *sc*, sacculus; *scc*, semicircular canals; *sper*, position of perilymphatic sac; *t*, tongue; *tr*, trachea. (From Goodrich, after Versluys.)

in all cases (Fig. 353, *F*). Primitively, the drum was nearly flush with the surface of the head. It is still in this position in anurans and turtles; in some reptiles and in birds, however, it attains some protection by being placed at the inner end of a short external meatus.

The eardrum is in general a thin membrane capable of rapid vibration in response to air waves. It contains a sheet of fibrous tissue and is bounded outside and inside by epithelia derived from the skin and from the lining of the first gill pouch, respectively. Its presence is due to the "failure" of the spiracular pouch to break through to the surface. The pouch itself expands lateral to the braincase to form the air-filled middle ear cavity—a cavity which, in crocodiles, birds, and mammals, may extend its air spaces into the neighboring bones of the skull (as in the mammalian mastoid). Primitively, as in anurans and many lizards, the middle ear cavity opens broadly into the pharynx; in most amniotes, however, the connection is narrowed to form the eustachian tube. In many amphibians (as noted later) the drum and middle ear cavity have degenerated, as is true of snakes and many lizards—mainly burrowing forms. A specialization of the turtles and snakes is the development of a secondary outer wall of the ear capsule around the shaft of the stapes; in the space beneath this is an extension of the fluid-filled cavities of the inner ear.

In the fish ancestors of the tetrapods the hyomandibular, once part of the gill apparatus, functioned as a jaw prop, bracing the quadrate on the otic region of the skull and lay just behind the spiracular pouch. In land vertebrates jaw suspension is adequately taken care of by the skull itself, and the hyomandibular, as the stapes, functions in transmitting vibrations from eardrum to internal ear and comes to lie within the bounds of the expanded middle ear cavity. The stapes,

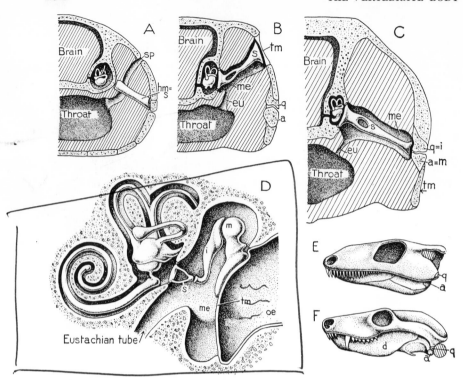

Fig. 353. Diagrams to show the evolution of the middle ear and auditory ossicles. Diagrammatic sections through the otic region of the head of *A*, a fish; *B*, a primitive amphibian; *C*, a primitive reptile; *D*, a mammal (showing the ear region only); *E*, side view of the skull of a primitive land vertebrate; *F*, of a mammal-like reptile to show the shift of the eardrum from the otic notch of the skull to the region of the jaw articulation. *a*, Articular; *d*, dentary; *eu*, eustachian tube; *hm*, hyomandibular; *i*, incus; *m*, malleus; *me*, middle ear cavity; *oe*, outer ear cavity; *q*, quadrate; *s*, stapes; *sp*, spiracle; *tm*, tympanic membrane. (From Romer, Man and the Vertebrates, University of Chicago Press.)

essentially a rodlike structure, has its main outer attachment to the eardrum; medially, there has developed, underneath an original attachment to the braincase, an opening into the internal ear capsule, the fenestra ovalis. In reptiles and birds the stapes often has a complicated build. The structure as a whole is often called the *columella*, and the stapes proper considered to be the proximal part of the shaft. The latter is always ossified, sometimes pierced by an arterial foramen, and ends in an expanded footplate in the oval window. The outer part, often termed the *extracolumella*, may remain cartilaginous and may have a complicated structure. The direct outer termination lies, of course, on the eardrum, but there may be extra processes connecting, as in fishes, with the quadrate region of the jaw articulation, with the skull dorsally, and, ventrally, with the hyoid arch (of which the stapes was originally a part).

External and Middle Ear in Mammals (Fig. 353, *D*). In mammals the external ear region is well developed. There is a deep, tubular external meatus. In some reptiles the meatus may be surrounded by cartilage; this is expanded in mammals, and in addition there is almost always a projecting ear *pinna* of elastic cartilage; this structure, often elaborately folded, may be of value as a collector of sound waves.

The mammalian middle ear is, as noted in an earlier chapter (p. 241), generally enclosed in a bony bulla. Instead of a single auditory bone, the stapes, it contains an articulated chain of three *auditory ossicles* leading from eardrum to oval window—*malleus, incus, and stapes* (hammer, anvil, and stirrup)—named in relation to their fancied shapes.

The origin of this series of auditory ossicles was long debated. It was thought at one time that they might be due to a subdivision into three parts of the reptilian columella or stapes. Embryology, comparative anatomy, and paleontology combined have, however, revealed the true story. The inner element, the stapes, although much shortened, is equivalent to the whole columellar apparatus of a lower tetrapod. The other two elements are homologous with the articular and quadrate bones which in lower vertebrates form the jaw joint. Mammals have evolved a new joint system for the jaw, and the older skeletal elements of this region have become superfluous. They have been put to new use. The reptilian eardrum lies close to the old jaw joint. The articular has kept an attachment to the membrane and become the malleus. The quadrate, connecting in reptiles with articular on the one hand, and stapes on the other, has become the incus, and the homologue of the jaw articulation of a reptile lies in mammals at the joint between two ear ossicles. These bones, originally gill bar elements, afford a good example of the changes of function which homologous structures can undergo. Breathing aids have become feeding aids and finally hearing aids.

The Internal Ear in Reptiles (Fig. 354). In tetrapods, as already indicated, the parts of the internal ear devoted to equilibrium remain little changed from the fish condition. The auditory apparatus, however, gradually develops into structures which attain such size and importance that the older regions of the sacs and canals are often termed (rather slightingly) the *vestibule* of the internal ear.

It is the lagenar region in which this expansion takes place. The macula of the lagena, mentioned earlier as present in fishes, persists in all tetrapods, except mammals above the monotreme level, but never develops to any degree; if it has an auditory function in land vertebrates, this function cannot be significant. The lagena itself, however, is important as a basal structure in the development of the cochlea.

The sensory area vital in the development of hearing in tetrapods is that termed the *basilar papilla* (Fig. 349, *D, E,* p. 485). This area is unknown in fishes, but is characteristically developed in many amphibians and in typical reptiles. In these forms it is an area of hair cells, covered by a common gelatinous membrane, situated on the posterior wall of the sacculus at the base of the lagena. It is here that vibrations, brought in from without by the stapes, are received.

In general the sacs and canals of the inner ear are not adherent to the skeletal walls of the auditory capsule that surround them. They are separated from them by spaces filled with liquid and crossed by connective tissue strands. This liquid is the *perilymph* (Fig. 355). It surrounds the membranous labyrinth and thus is quite distinct from the endolymph within. From the perilymph, there develops in land vertebrates a conduction system which leads from the fenestra ovalis to the basilar papilla and forms the last link in the chain of structures by which potentially audible vibrations reach the auditory sensory areas.

Internal to the oval window in lower tetrapods there develops a large *peri-*

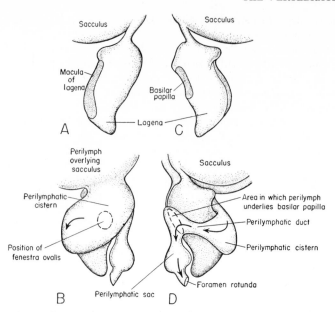

Fig. 354. The ear of a late embryo of a lizard (Lacerta). *A,* Left ear, lateral view of the membranous labyrinth in the floor of the sacculus and the lagena. *B,* The same with the perilymphatic system shown in addition. *C, D,* Medial views comparable to *A* and *B*, respectively. Arrows indicate course of conduction of vibrations from stapes to basilar papilla and on to the "round window" at the distal end, beyond the perilymphatic duct.

lymphatic cistern, against which the stapes plays (Figs. 354; 355, *B*; 356, *A*). Vibrations received here are, in typical reptiles, carried around the lagena to its posterior border in a perilymph-filled canal. This duct passes just outside the area of the basilar papilla, and is separated from the base of its sensory cells only by a thin *basilar membrane*. Vibrations in this membrane agitate the hair cells and at long last, in this roundabout fashion, the sensory organ is reached. This situation—an auditory sensory structure agitated by vibrations of the membrane at its base—is a fundamental feature in the construction of the hearing apparatus in all amniotes. We shall find it repeated, and capable of description in much the same words, in birds and mammals.

As a final point here, it must be noted that for vibrations set up by the stapes in the perilymph and carried along by the perilymphatic duct, some release mechanism, allowing a corresponding vibration, must be set up at the far end of the perilymph system. In many amphibians this consists of a *perilymphatic sac*, which projects from the auditory capsule into the braincase. In some amphibians and reptiles (except the turtles) a further development takes place. There is a large, rather tubular foramen (primarily for the vagus nerve) in the braincase wall which runs out from a point near this sac. We find that the perilymphatic duct system may, instead of terminating in a sac, run outward through this foramen—or a separate one formed close by, the *fenestra rotunda* (Fig. 352, p. 489)—and terminate in a membrane which vibrates in phase with the impulses received through the fenestra ovalis at the other end of the perilymph system. Primitively, this

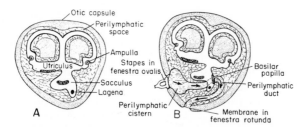

Fig. 355. *A*, Schematic section through the ear capsule of a fish, to show the perilymphatic space surrounding the membranous labyrinth containing endolymph. *B*, Similar scheme of a tetrapod, in which a part of the perilymph area (arrows) is specialized to conduct sound from the fenestra ovalis to and past the auditory sensory area. The maculae are darkly shaded. (After de Burlet.)

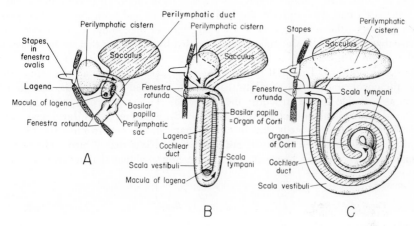

Fig. 356. Diagrammatic sections through the saccular region to show the evolution of the cochlea. *A*, Primitive reptile with a small basilar papilla adjacent to the perilymphatic duct. *B*, The crocodile or bird type; the lagena has elongated to form a cochlear duct, the basilar sense organ with it, and a loop of the perilymphatic duct follows the cochlear duct in its elongation. *C*, The mammalian type; the cochlea is further elongated and coiled in a fashion economical of space.

membrane is buried in the tissues at the margin of the skull; in more advanced forms this round window opens back into the middle ear chamber.

Development of the Cochlea. Both birds and mammals have greatly extended their hearing ability by the evolution of a *cochlea*—a highly developed structure for auditory reception. The crocodilians, related to the birds, demonstrate the manner in which the cochlea was developed. Three structural features are involved: the lagena, the perilymphatic duct, and the basilar papilla.

In the crocodiles and birds (Fig. 356) the finger-like lagena has become expanded into a long but essentially straight tube, filled of course with endolymph; this is the *cochlear duct* or *scala media*. At the tip in these forms (and monotreme mammals) persists the original macula of the lagena, of doubtful function. The important sensory structure is the basilar papilla, which is here greatly expanded into an elongate area running the length of the cochlear duct, and generally termed the *organ of Corti*. It has a complicated series of sensory hair cells and supporting cells; over them folds a membranous flap, the *tectorial membrane,* corresponding to the cupula in other neuromast structures; beneath is an elongate fiber-supported and vibratile basilar membrane. With the lengthening of this sensory organ the perilymphatic duct, which remains closely applied to its base, expands in a double loop. The part of this tube leading inward from the oval window is termed the *scala vestibuli* (so called because the fenestra ovalis is considered to lie in the vestibular part of the inner ear). The distal limb of the tube, leading to the round window with its membrane, or "tympanum," is the *scala tympani.* It is in this distal segment of the loop that the perilymphatic duct underlies the basilar membrane and the sensory organ.

These modifications of the primitive reptilian system result in the development, in birds and their crocodilian relatives, of a true, although simply constructed, cochlea. This consists of three associated tubular structures—one endolymphatic, and two filled with perilymph—and, in the central duct, the organ of Corti. This sensory organ is separated from the distal perilymphatic tube —the scala tympani—only by the basilar membrane and from the proximal perilymph duct—the scala vestibuli—by a still thinner membrane. Crudely one may visualize the formation of this type of cochlea by imagining that he has grasped the region of the lagena and the perilymphatic duct crossing its base and pulled this area outward. This pull has stretched the lagena out into a long blind tube as the cochlear duct; the perilymphatic duct, attached at both ends, has pulled out as a double-looped structure, the two scalae.

The mammalian cochlea (Figs. 357, 358), we believe, has developed independently of that of birds, but in closely parallel fashion. In monotremes it is still a simple, uncoiled structure, readily comparable to that of birds. The typical mammalian cochlea is, however, much more elongated than that of birds or croco-

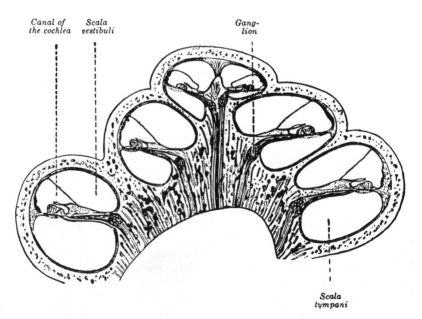

Fig. 357.   Diagrammatic section through a mammalian cochlea. (After Finnerty and Cowdry.)

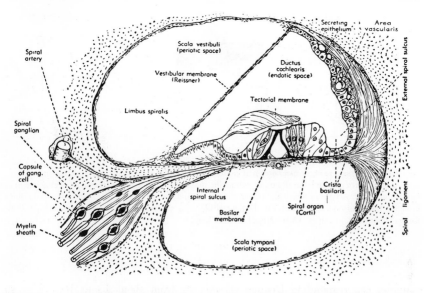

Fig. 358. A much enlarged section through a mammalian cochlea to show details of the organ of Corti (cf. Fig. 357). (From Ruch and Fulton, Medical Physiology and Biophysics.)

diles. If it were to remain straight, it could not be comfortably accommodated within the ear capsule, and in relation to this we find that (as the name implies) the mammalian cochlea of three tubes has been coiled into a tidy spiral structure.

The mammalian organ of Corti is, like that of a bird, readily derivable, by elongation and increased complexity of structure, from the primitive basilar papilla. Beneath it, adjacent to the scala tympani, is the basilar membrane, crossed by numerous fibers. Above is, as in birds and crocodiles, a tectorial membrane in which, as always, the tip of the hair cells are engaged. Rows of supporting cells lie along the medial and lateral areas of the organ; centrally there is a curious little triangular tunnel, braced by pillar cells on either side; on either side of this structure are rows of sensory hair cells, running the length of the cochlea—three or four rows medially, a single row laterally. As in lower tetrapods, vibrations in the basilar membrane caused by waves in the perilymph system cause hearing sensations through displacement of the hairs of the sensory cells above the membrane. Although in a primitive tetrapod hearing system the vibrations reach the basilar membrane and basilar papilla (organ of Corti) only from below (cf. Fig. 356, *A*), here vibrations entering this triple system via the scala vestibuli can "short circuit" the double loop and send impulses through the vestibular membrane and down to the basilar structures through the liquid of the cochlear duct. The functional "reason" for elongation of the basilar papilla into the formed organ of Corti appears to be the discrimination of sounds of different pitch—i.e., of different wavelengths. Differences in the transverse span of the basilar membrane, which grades in width from one end of the cochlea to the other, appear to result in making the membrane sensitive to different wavelengths at different parts of its extent and thus render tone distinctions possible. Even in the relatively short avian cochlea, there is excellent discrimination of tone, and in mammals the range of vibrations heard may be extremely wide. The human ear, for

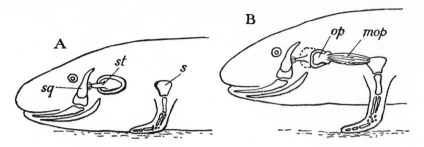

Fig. 359.   Diagram to show mechanism of communication between exterior and inner ear in urodeles. *A*, An aquatic form in which the stapes, or columella, picks up vibrations by a ligamentous attachment to the squamosal. *B*, A type in which the stapes is reduced, and the operculum picks up ground vibrations through a muscular connection with the shoulder girdle. *mop*, Opercular muscle; *op*, operculum; *s*, scapula; *sq*, squamosal; *st*, stapes. (After Kingsbury and Reed.)

example, can respond to frequencies ranging from about 15 to 16,000 or so cycles per second. The apex of the cochlea, where the basilar membrane is broadest, is most sensitive to the lowest tones, the narrow region of the membrane at the base of the cochlea to high notes.

   The Middle Ear in Amphibians.   We have above omitted any reference to ear construction in living amphibians, for the reason that conditions in these forms are not, in general, primitive. They are specialized and seemingly degenerate in most cases, and are, further, extremely varied. Three main points may be noted: (1) the drum and middle ear cavity are often missing; (2) the stapes is frequently reduced or absent; (3) a second ossicle, the operculum, is frequently present in the oval window.

   A majority of frogs and toads have a well-developed middle ear region, with a large, superficially placed eardrum and a good stapes* carrying vibrations inward from drum to oval window. But in urodeles and the Apoda, and even in a number of anurans, there is no drum or middle ear cavity, and typical sound transmission is impossible. The stapes may persist in the absence of drum and cavity, and is well developed in the Apoda and some salamanders. Its outer end articulates with the quadrate region of the skull, and it may in some fashion pick up for transmission vibrations in this region of the head (Fig. 359, *A*). In a great number of both urodeles and anurans, there is present a second ear ossicle, the *operculum*, peculiar to amphibians. This is a flat plate fitting into the oval window. It may be present in the fenestra in company with a well-developed stapes, as in typical frogs and toads; in many forms, however, the stapes is reduced, and the operculum replaces it functionally as a hearing aid. The operculum has no homologue in the skeleton of other groups of vertebrates; it is thought to be a separate part of the wall of the otic capsule itself. In most urodeles, and in those anurans in which the eardrum is lost, the operculum is connected with the shoulder blade by a small *opercular muscle*, a specialized axial muscle (Fig. 359, *B*). It is suggested that when this muscle is tensed, ground vibrations are carried from the limb along the muscle to the operculum and thence to the inner ear.

---

   * The stapes, or columella, is sometimes termed the plectrum in anurans.

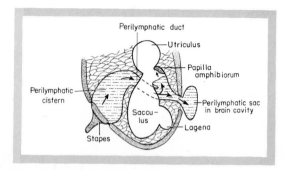

Fig. 360. Schematic section of the internal ear in a salamander. The basilar papilla is absent here, but is found in addition to the papilla amphibiorum in anurans. (After de Burlet.)

The Inner Ear in Amphibians. In inner ear as in middle ear, the amphibians were passed over earlier because they tend to exhibit specializations which obscure the general story. There is typically developed in modern amphibians, as in reptiles, a perilymphatic cistern, perilymphatic ducts, and a perilymphatic sac or release mechanism at the base of the skull. But though many amphibians have a basilar papilla, this is often absent. Instead, there may develop a special amphibian sensory structure, the *papilla amphibiorum,* which appears to play the main role in hearing in this class of vertebrates (Fig. 360). This is situated near the upper margin of the sacculus. It is structurally similar to the simpler types of basilar papillae. However, the perilymphatic duct does not lie beneath the base of this structure; instead, it approaches it, so to speak, laterally, being separated from the endolymph in a neighboring region by a thin membrane through which vibrations are transmitted to the latter fluid. (The same condition holds for the relations of the perilymph to the basilar papilla in amphibians.)

Evidently, auditory structures were in an experimental stage in the ancestral amphibians. Here, as in many other features, the ancestors of the modern amphibians chose a series of less progressive paths than did their ancient relatives who gave rise to the amniotes.

16

THE NERVOUS SYSTEM

In a protozoan the single cell in itself receives sensations and responds to them. In higher, metazoan organisms there tends to be, to an increasing degree, a differentiation between cells specialized for the reception of sensations—*receptors*—and those which make the appropriate response—the *effectors*. In lowly multicellular organisms the relations between these two types of cells may remain relatively simple, and cells receiving sensations may, by their physical and chemical activities, arouse their neighbors to respond. Even in the vertebrates the circulation of hormones in the blood stream is a retention of such essentially primitive methods of stimulation. But such a method of arousing responses tends to be slow, is often nonspecific, and is relatively ineffective for swift and precise reaction. With the development of a nervous system there are formed special tissues designed to transmit stimuli from sensory structures directly and rapidly to specific end organs (muscles or glands) which furnish the response.

In primitive metazoans, such as coelenterates, the nervous system may be a diffuse network of cells and fibers spread through the tissues. But in most animals of any degree of complexity, the system is an integrated, well organized one. Instead of scattered cells and fibers, we find collections of fibers formed into nerve trunks, and centers where transfer of nerve impulses between fiber systems takes place, much as a telephone system brings its numerous lines into major cables and central exchanges. In most groups a dominant center, a brain in some fashion or other, makes its appearance, usually in a situation strategically located with regard to major sense organs. In bilaterally symmetric animals there is usually a brain structure situated anteriorly and one or more main longitudinal nerve trunks. In the vertebrates there is a well-organized tubular brain and a single dorsal hollow nerve cord—the spinal cord—running backward from this along the body. These form the *central nervous system*. Running outward from brain and spinal cord are numerous paired nerves, along which ganglia—clusters of nerve cells—are found at specific regions; these nerves and ganglia constitute the *peripheral nervous system*.

STRUCTURAL ELEMENTS

The Neuron. Nervous tissues, in the brain, spinal cord, and ganglia, contain numerous cell bodies. Prominent in the nervous system, however, are slender but elongate nerve fibers, making up the nerves and much of the substance of the central nervous system as well. It was once thought that the cell bodies and the fibers, conveyors of the nervous impulses, were separate structures, independent of one another. Most nerve fibers are exceedingly long, and connections between them and cell bodies were not often observed. But as it gradually became clear, through the decades, that all the vital materials of the body were cellular, it was realized that these fibers are universally processes of cells rather than independent structures. The basic units of the nervous system are *neurons;* each consists of a cell body and its processes, long or short.

Most of the cell bodies of the neurons (Figs. 361, 362, p. 500) are situated within the walls of the central nervous system, a relatively small number in the peripheral ganglia. The shape of the neuron body is variable; in many cases, however, it is stellate, owing to the fact that a number of processes extend out from it. With appropriate stains, microscopic preparations show in the protoplasm of the nerve cell various characteristic structures not present in other tissues. Notable are clusters of darkly staining materials, *Nissl bodies;* these contain large amounts of the nucleic acid RNA, and it is clear that the chemical "manufacturing" work for the entire neuron is performed in the cell body, the products formed here flowing outward to supply the various processes. In the adult there is no evidence of mitosis in the neurons, indicating, as a notable peculiarity of the nervous system, that a full complement of nerve cells has been attained, for the most part at least, by about the time of birth or hatching. In consequence, destruction of nerve cells through injury or disease is a permanent loss; cell processes may regenerate if the cell body is intact, but a nerve cell, once lost, cannot be replaced.

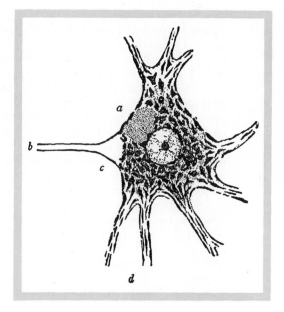

Fig. 361. The cell body of a motor neuron from the spinal cord of an ox; *a*, a mass of pigment. At *b* is the axon, with a clear cytoplasmic area (the "axon Hillock"), *c*, at its base; the remaining processes, *d*, are dendrites. Much of the cytoplasm is filled with readily stainable masses of material, the Nissl bodies. The large nucleus contains a prominent cluster of chromatin, the nucleolus. (From Herrick, after von Lenhossék.)

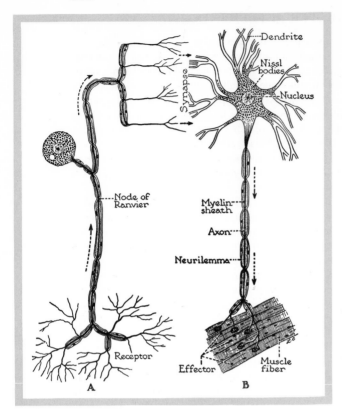

Fig. 362. Two types of nerve cells. *A*, Afferent (sensory) neuron of spinal and cranial nerves; long axon-like processes run from sensory receptor to cell body in spinal ganglion and thence into cord, where ramification occurs. *B*, Efferent (motor) neuron, with cell body in cord and a long axon (abbreviated in the figure) extending out to the effector (muscle fiber). (From Millard, King and Showers, Human Anatomy and Physiology.)

Nerve Fibers. Extending outward from the cell body of the neuron are slender processes along which the nerve impulses pass; the cell body is to be regarded mainly as a center for their maintenance and nutriment. The distribution and length of such processes are quite variable. Most often thought of as typical are such neurons as those which innervate striated body muscles (Fig. 362, *B*). In these motor neurons short processes—slender, numerous, and branching—which carry impulses inward toward the cell body, are termed *dendrites*, from their treelike appearance. There is a single *axon*, a relatively stout and elongate process, which may be in large animals as much as several yards in length, carrying impulses away from the region of the cell body. A second common type (Fig. 362, *A*) is that of the afferent neurons which carry sensory stimuli inward to the central nervous system; here both the long process leading in from the point of reception to the cell body adjacent to the cord, and a second long process which enters the cord are comparable in structure to the axon of a motor neuron.

Functionally, the most important part of a major nerve fiber is its central structure, the *axis cylinder*, a thin strand of protoplasm continuous with that of the cell body. Its appearance is homogeneous in unstained materials; however, appropriate stains, or study under the electron microscope, show the presence within it of numerous threadlike longitudinal neurofibrils. The axis cylinder is bounded by a very thin sheath proper to it; beyond this, however, are further wrappings. Cyclostomes apart, all fibers except the very smallest, central or peripheral, are covered by a *myelin sheath* of fatty material. When the sheath is well formed it gives a shiny, glistening appearance to the fibers. In some cases (as the postganglionic fibers of the autonomic system described later) the sheath is thin, not ordinarily observed and hence (incorrectly) assumed to be absent. In the case of fibers within the spinal cord or brain a continuous myelin sheath is laid down by adjacent supporting cellular elements. In peripheral fibers, it is special *sheath cells—Schwann cells—*derived from the neural crest which produce the sheath; this is a multilayered structure, the sheath cells wrapping themselves around segments of the axis cylinder in a fashion crudely comparable to a jelly roll (except that the "rolls" are very numerous and very thin). In the intervals between the territory of two successive sheath cells, the myelin sheath of peripheral fibers is interrupted, and there is found a *node of Ranvier.* In fibers outside the nervous system there is a further and continuous covering, a tough, inelastic membrane, the *neurilemma,* also produced by the sheath cells.

If nerve fibers are cut, the part distal to the cut degenerates, and the proximal region and cell body may show evidence of damage. But frequently peripheral fibers regenerate, growing out again from the stump still connected with the cell body. It appears that they are aided in retracing their former paths by the persistence of the sheath cells which surrounded the former axis cylinder. Fiber degeneration is a feature of great value in neurological work. Particularly in the central nervous system it is difficult to trace groups of long fibers through from origins to termini. However, a group of problematical fibers may be cut experimentally and allowed to degenerate. If the material is stained in appropriate fashion and sectioned, microscopic study enables one to distinguish the degenerating fibers from their normal neighbors and to trace them to their destination.

The Nerve Impulse. Investigation of the nature and properties of the impulses transmitted by nerve fibers has been the object of a vast amount of physiologic work. By analogy one tends to compare nerve transmission with an electrical impulse, and it can be demonstrated that as an impulse travels along a fiber there is a change of the electric potential at the fiber surface: a "ripple of leakiness" in the surface membrane associated with a shift in sodium and potassium ion concentration within and without the membrane. The energy needed immediately for this "work" is obtained (as in the case of muscle contraction) from ATP breakdown in the axis cylinder. Hence electric and metabolic phenomena go hand in hand in the promulgation of the impulse.

A nerve impulse, though rapid, cannot be compared for speed with an electric impulse. On the whole, mammalian fibers give speedier transmission than do those of lower vertebrates—about twice the speed of frog fibers, for example. But even in mammals the highest recorded speeds are at the rate of only 130 meters per second, and some mammal fibers have a speed of only about a foot or two a second. The faster speeds are found in the fibers with greater diameter; these diameters range in general from 1μ to 20μ. Although the speed of transmission along some fibers is not inconsiderable, there is, nevertheless, a distinct if small time lag between stimulation and response, and there are potential difficulties in coordination in such a large animal as an elephant, for example, because of the time necessarily consumed by the stimulus in even the simplest reflex in travelling many yards of fiber length.

A nerve impulse is anonymous and nonspecific. The nature of a sensation "felt" in the brain depends upon the centers which received it, not on any difference in the type of impulse received. Could the "wiring" be changed, nerve impulses from the nose, for example, if received in an auditory center, would give a hearing effect, and vice versa.

Nerve impulses normally travel in only one direction along the fibers. But the fiber is equally capable of transmitting impulses in either direction, as can be shown experimentally. The unidirectional transmission actually found in the working nervous system is due to the pattern of fiber connections; neurons are morphologically "polarized."

A nerve impulse is an "all or none" phenomenon. There are no "strong" or "weak" impulses; either the fiber reacts fully, or it does not react at all.* True, there may be variations in the strength of the nervous impulses sent along a nerve, but these variations are due to factors of other sorts. One is that there may be differences in the number of fibers in a nerve which are stimulated at one time or another. Most important is the fact that impulses do not come singly, but follow one another in variable rapid series, so that their effect may be cumulative.

The Synapse.   Never, among vertebrates, does a single neuron span the entire distance between the sensory organ (receptor) and the motor or glandular structure stimulated (effector). The action takes place through a chain of neurons, always two and usually more. The point of transfer between successive neurons is termed a *synapse*. When studied under the microscope, the end of the axon of the first of the two neurons is seen to break up into fine branches, often with knoblike ends, which intertwine with the dendrites of the second neuron or else twine about the cell body of that element. Many once believed that there is an actual protoplasmic connection between the neurons at the synapse; however, it is now certain that, among vertebrates, no such direct continuity exists, although processes of the two cells concerned may be closely appressed. The timing of nerve transmission shows that a distinct—although very small time interval—is taken up by the bridging of a synapse. It has in the past been thought by many that the time lag was due to an electrical situation, comparable to the building up of enough current for a "spark" to bridge the gap. But while there may be, exceptionally, direct electric stimulation of one neuron by another, it is becoming increasingly probable that the normal means of bridging a synapse is a chemical one, minute amounts of neurohumoral material given off by the tips of terminal branches of the "incoming" fiber diffusing across the gap to stimulate the second neuron. That synapses are bridged in this fashion in the peripheral nervous system seems rather certain, and evidence is accumulating that central nervous system synapses operate in similar fashion, acetylcholine being the neurohumoral material most generally concerned.

The Reflex Arc.   Before considering more complex anatomic structures, we may note the general nature of a simple type of nerve action of the sort known as a *reflex* (Figs. 363, 364, *A*). Reflex actions are those of such type as the "automatic" withdrawal of a bare foot that has trod on a tack, or of a finger that has touched a hot stove. In general a sensory stimulus is picked up from receptor cells and carried in toward the central nervous system by a long *afferent* nerve fiber. The cell body of the *sensory neuron* to which this fiber belongs lies, along with many others, in a ganglion close to cord or brain; the fiber, however, continues directly onward into the central nervous system. Here, normally, it does not connect simply with one successive neuron, but branches so that a stimulus may be caused in whole series of neurons, with which the sensory neuron syn-

---

* In the higher brain centers, special types of neurons may act, exceptionally, in different fashion.

Fig. 363. Diagrams to show simple reflexes. Area between broken lines is part of arc lying within the cord (cf. Fig. 364). *A*, Two-neuron reflex; *B*, association neuron interpolated, increasing the number of possible paths.

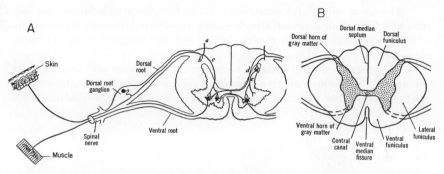

Fig. 364. *A*, Diagram of mammalian spinal cord and nerve to show path of reflex arc. A sensory fiber entering by the dorsal root may send branches, *a*, *b*, up and down the cord. At various levels the sensory fiber may connect with motor neurons of the same side, *c*, or opposite side of the cord, *d*; or with association neurons, *e*. *B*, Diagrammatic section of a mammalian spinal cord, to show distribution of white and gray matter and funiculi. (After Gardner.)

apses. Conversely, each neuron with which it connects may receive impulses from numerous afferent fibers, so that a considerable amount of interplay between receptors and effectors may take place. (Rather surely no one single incoming impulse will "set off" the second neuron; excitation only occurs when impulses arrive from a number of sources.)

In the simplest of reflexes the neurons stimulated by incoming impulses may be *efferent*—usually *motor neurons*. Their cell bodies lie within the central nervous system, and long axons run out from them to the effector end organs (usually muscle fibers). But even a simple reflex is frequently one stage more complicated than this, and is a three-neuron rather than a two-neuron chain. In this the afferent fibers entering the central nervous system do not synapse directly with motor cells, but with neurons contained entirely within the central nervous system. These *association neurons* (or internuncial neurons) send out, like the afferents, branched processes which synapse with numerous motor cells. This further multiplies the number of possible responses which a sensory impulse may cause and, conversely, also increases the number of sensory impulses which might produce any given motor effect. Summations of stimuli may occur, and "choices," so to speak, may be made as to possible reactions to stimuli. Still further, even at this relatively simple level of nervous activity, there are quite surely "feedback" mechanisms which increase complexity. The interposition of a single association neuron in the system is apparently as far as any normal spinal reflex usually goes in building up end-to-end neuron chains, but gives to a considerable degree a clue to the way in which more complicated brain mechanisms may have been evolved. By assuming the intercalation of still further association neurons and more complex feedbacks, modulations, and reverberating circuits, one can gain some idea of the mode of building up of higher association centers, into which a wide variety of sensory impressions may drain, and from which may come a wide variety of responses.

SPINAL NERVES

As contrasted with the central nervous system, the peripheral nervous system, which we shall first consider, is simply constructed. It consists essentially of the nerves which penetrate to almost every region of the body: groups of fibers, sheathed by connective tissues, along which the sensory "raw material" of nervous action is brought into the spinal cord and brain by afferent pathways, and out through which resulting efferent impulses pass, as the result of central actions, to affect muscular or glandular structures. Included, too, in the peripheral system

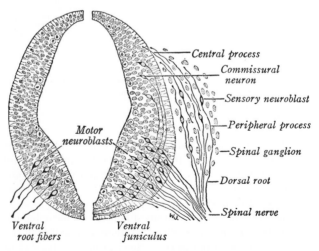

Fig. 365.   Sections of the spinal cord of early mammalian embryos. *Left,* axons are growing outward from motor nerve cells. *Right,* association or commissural neurons are developing within the cord; sensory neurons are developing externally from neural crest cells (cf. Fig. 64, p. 116). These sensory neuroblasts are at this stage bipolar, i.e., with separate proximal and distal processes; later the two processes fuse proximally in higher vertebrates to give a unipolar condition to the mature ganglion cell. (From Arey.)

Fig. 366. *Left,* nerve plexus supplying the left pelvic fin of a chimaera, showing interchange of fiber bundles between members of the series of spinal nerves concerned. The two roots and the dorsal ganglia of the nerves concerned are shown at the top of the figure; the base of the fin is at the bottom. *Right,* on a larger scale, the brachial plexus supplying the pectoral limb of a mammal. The nerve roots are not shown, and the branches of the plexus are cut short of their terminations; the largest trunk is that of the radial nerve supplying most of the forearm and front foot. The number of nerves involved is less than in the case of the fish fin, but the pattern of the plexus is complex. (Right figure, partly after Walker.)

Fig. 367. Diagrams to show the distribution of nerve components in dorsal and ventral spinal roots. Somatic sensory, blue; visceral sensory, green; visceral motor, yellow; somatic motor, red. *A,* Mammalian condition; the dorsal root is almost purely sensory, and almost all motor fibers are in the ventral root. *B,* More primitive type, common in lower vertebrates; some visceral motor fibers emerge through the dorsal root. *C,* Probable primitive condition; dorsal and ventral roots are separate nerves, visceral motor fibers are part of the dorsal nerve, and the ventral nerve is purely somatic motor (cf. Fig. 368).

Fig. 368. Diagram of the spinal cord and nerves of the left side of a lamprey seen in dorsal view (anterior end to the left), to show the alternating arrangement of separate dorsal and ventral spinal nerves, related to intermyotomic spaces and myotomes. Nerve components colored as in Fig. 367.

are the ganglia found along the course of the nerves and containing the cell bodies of peripheral neurons. We shall treat of spinal nerves, relatively simple and
uniform in structure, before considering the more specialized nerves of the cranial region.

The typical spinal nerves of most vertebrates (Fig. 364, *A*) are paired
structures present in every body segment. Each nerve arises from the spinal cord
by two roots, dorsal and ventral (posterior and anterior in a specialized human
terminology). The *ventral root* runs straight outward from the ventral margin of
the side wall of the cord; the *dorsal root*, which bears a prominent ganglion, enters the cord on its side wall. In most vertebrates the ventral and dorsal roots
are united to form the main trunk of the nerve leaving the canal of the vertebral
column. Emerging from the vertebral column, the nerve divides into a variety of
branches, or rami. Neglecting for the time a ramus running toward the viscera,
we may note the frequent presence of a major *dorsal ramus* supplying fibers to
the dorsal part of the axial musculature and the skin of the back, and a *ventral
ramus* to the more lateral and ventral parts of the skin and musculature of the
body wall.

The main spinal nerve trunk and its principal branches carry both afferent
and efferent fibers. The two roots, however, show a sharp division of functions in
higher vertebrates. The ventral roots carry only outward bound impulses through
efferent fibers, whose cell bodies are contained within the cord (Fig. 365). In all
typical spinal nerves of higher vertebrate groups the dorsal root, in contrast,
mainly carries afferent fibers with incoming impulses. The cell bodies of these
neurons generally lie in the dorsal root ganglion; they send out a stem which, almost immediately, branches in a T-fashion; one process brings impulses inward
from sensory structures, a second carries them onward centrally into the cord.

Spinal Nerve Plexuses. *   In many typical segments of the trunk each
spinal nerve is a discrete structure, without connections with its neighbors fore or
aft; it innervates the trunk muscles which have arisen from the myotome pertaining to this segment, and on the sensory side supplies a corresponding strip of
skin, although often with some overlap with the nerves of the adjacent segments.
In certain regions, however, there is an interweaving of branches of a number
of successive spinal nerves to form a *plexus* (Fig. 366). In forms with well developed paired limbs there is associated with each a well developed nerve plexus
—the *brachial plexus* and *lumbosacral plexus* for front and hind legs, respectively.
As a result we find that the muscles of any limb region may be supplied by fibers
from several spinal nerves. This condition is perhaps to be associated functionally with the development of complex limb reflexes, and structurally with the fact
that the limb musculature in tetrapods has lost all trace of its original segmental
nature.

Constancy of Innervation; Nerve Growth.   Even in complicated limb
plexuses we find that there is a high degree of constancy in the innervation of a
given muscle in various animals by twigs from seemingly comparable nerve stems
—a feature of practical value in the study of muscle evolution. This and other
facts tended to create the doctrine that innervation is an absolutely constant feature—that a given muscle is always, in every generation and over long evolutionary lines, innervated by the same nervous elements and by similar pathways.

* In Latin, singular and plural forms of the word plexus are identical in spelling; we use an anglicized plural here for the sake of clarity.

Actually, however, there are notable (although relatively rare) cases where such a doctrine cannot be maintained. Any discussion of this problem leads to a consideration of nerve growth.

The peripheral nerves are derived embryologically from two sources (Fig. 366). The fibers of efferent neurons emerge from cell bodies within the cord and grow out from the cord toward the muscles which they innervate. In the vertebrate ancestors the afferent fibers may have had cell bodies in the cord; neurons of this sort are found in the young of many anamniotes, and even in the adult of cyclostomes and some teleosts we find cell bodies of afferent neurons in the dorsal part of the cord rather than in a dorsal root ganglion. Generally, however, these cells do not develop in the cord, but in the neural crest, a structure versatile in the end products which derive from it, and which we have noted in Chapter 5 to have been produced along the line of closure of neural tube from skin ectoderm. Cells from the neural crest migrate downward to form the spinal ganglia and grow fibers both inward to the cord and outward to the periphery. In addition the crest supplies part at least of the cells sheathing peripheral nerve fibers and the cells in the ganglia. The neural crest represents, in a sense, a "spilling over" of nervous system materials from the restricted area which forms the cord. In the head region there is a still further expansion of the area of origin of nervous tissues, for the sensory cells of many of the cranial nerve ganglia may arise from thickenings—placodes—in the ectoderm lateral to the forming neural tube and crest.

As can be observed experimentally, peripheral nerve fibers grow out as long processes which finally reach their end organs—sensory structures, muscle fibers, or gland cells. How do they do this? Some have assumed that there is a sort of specific, mystic affinity between a special nerve fiber and a special organ to which it attaches, so that the nerve fiber "finds its mate." That there is a degree of specific association is certain, for efferent fibers do not attach to sensory structures, nor afferent fibers to muscle cells. Experimental work demonstrates that the presence of materials to be innervated does attract nerve fibers in some broad way; but such work also furnishes good evidence against precise specific affinities. For example, a salamander limb bud, moved in the embryo to an unusual position, may become connected with nerves; but these may be nerves arising from body segments quite different from those which normally supply it. Though the manner of growth of nerve fibers is not completely understood, it seems certain that in great measure fibers tend to push out from the nerve cord along paths of least resistance in the microscopic structural pattern of surrounding materials. Since in successive generations the topography of a region will tend to be the same, given nerve fibers will tend to find and follow similar courses and hence reach and innervate similar structures. Essential constancy of innervation may thus be explained without the necessity of postulating precise specificity.

Nerve Components and Spinal Nerve Composition (Fig. 365). Highly useful in the study of both peripheral and central nervous systems is the doctrine of nerve components. This points out that both afferent and efferent types of nerve connections can be divided into two types—*somatic* and *visceral*. We have, in discussing sensory structures, noted this type of subdivision. *Somatic afferent fibers* are those carrying impulses in from the skin and the sense organs of muscles and tendons—the exteroceptive and proprioceptive groups of the physiologist. *Visceral afferents*, on the other hand, carry sensations from sensory endings (interoceptive) in the gut and other internal structures. On the motor side, *so-*

matic efferents are the motor fibers to the somatic musculature—striated voluntary muscles of the body and limbs derived (directly or, at any rate, phylogenetically) from myotomes (cf. Chap. 9). *Visceral efferents,* on the other hand, carry stimuli primarily to the muscles of the gut (the visceral musculature) and to other smooth muscles and glands in various regions. There are thus four components present in most spinal nerves: the two afferents in the dorsal root, two efferents in the ventral. All four components are present in the trunk of a typical spinal nerve as it emerges from the vertebral column. Beyond this point, however, the larger and more characteristic trunks are composed mainly of the two types of somatic fibers; visceral fibers turn ventrally in a visceral ramus, and their further distribution will be discussed in the next section.

The root arrangement of the spinal nerve described above is usually assumed to be that present in vertebrates as a whole. As a matter of fact, however, as we descend the scale, we find increasing evidences of a different structure which give us a clue to some of the peculiar features of the cranial nerves studied later.

In higher vertebrate classes both afferent components are present dorsally in every known case, and both efferent components are in general confined to the ventral root. But in some cases, at least, among amniotes, a limited number of efferent visceral fibers are carried by the dorsal root as well as the ventral, and in amphibians and jawed fishes, where investigated, visceral fibers in the dorsal root appear to be common (Fig. 367, *B*). In the higher vertebrates the two roots emerge from the column at about the same level of the cord, one above the other; but in the lower fishes there tends to be an alternation of dorsal and ventral roots, and in sharks and hagfishes the union of the two roots is less intimate than in higher forms. The lowest evolutionary stage appears to be that seen in the lampreys and Amphioxus (Fig. 367, *C*). Here dorsal and ventral roots do not connect, and they are quite separate nerves. Further, visceral efferent fibers in Amphioxus are confined to the dorsal roots; these roots may thus carry three components, and the ventral root is purely somatic motor in nature; in lampreys some visceral efferents emerge with the ventral roots, but a majority form a dorsal root component. Still further, dorsal and ventral roots alternate in position in both Amphioxus and lampreys.

Probably this condition of separate roots was that present in vertebrate ancestors; the union of the two roots may not have occurred until some stage in early fish history. That the visceral efferent fibers were primitively carried by the dorsal root and only later tended to shift to emerge by the ventral root is suggested by the stages cited; further, we will see later a retention of the seemingly primitive three-to-one split of components in various cranial nerves in all vertebrates.

In the alternating position of the separate dorsal and ventral spinal nerves of the lamprey or Amphioxus, the ventral roots emerge opposite the middle of each body segment, and the dorsal roots are intersegmental in position (Fig. 368). This is a logical, primitive situation as regards somatic components, at least. The sole function of the primitive ventral root is the innervation of somite musculature, and the most effective position for the emergence of a group of fibers is opposite the middle of a somite. On the other hand, the most important primitive function of the dorsal root was innervation of the skin; the body surface is best reached by a path between successive somites, with an intersegmental position a logical point of origin of the nerve from the cord. Spinal nerves are segmentally arranged; but it would seem that this segmental arrangement is not inherent in the nervous system, but has, historically, been imposed upon it by the mesodermal somites. (We shall see, in the case of the brain, a partial imposition of a second type of "segmental" nerve arrangement in the brain stem because of the presence of the gill structures.)

VISCERAL NERVOUS SYSTEM

In the remote ancestors of the vertebrates the nervous system presumably consisted (as in acorn worms) of two parts which were but loosely connected with one another: one, a lowly organized set of superficial structures which responded to external stimuli, the other a net of cells and fibers around the gut and other internal organs which enabled them to adjust themselves directly to internal stimuli. In the vertebrates the more superficial portion of the nervous system—the central nervous system—has become highly organized and dominant. The old nerve nets of the gut still persist, however, and there is evidence that to some degree in all vertebrates the gut may still make its own responses to internal stimuli. But with the rise of the central nervous system of cord and brain, these new structures have tended, so to speak, to conquer the nerve system of the viscera and in great measure to do away with its independence. Efficient connections, both afferent and efferent, have been established and much visceral activity is mediated by cord or even hypothalamic centers in the brain. But, as we are well aware from personal experience, visceral sensations and motor responses to them are not generally associated with the higher centers of the brain; we "know" little of what our viscera feel and have little control over them. The hypothalamic region of the brain (p. 543) is the highest center directly related to visceral sensations and motor responses to them.

The afferent pathways of the visceral system call for little remark. Visceral sensory endings are present in internal organs, blood vessels, and so forth. Fibers from these ascend to the spinal cord and brain through special visceral trunk nerves, discussed below, or through the vagus nerve of the cranial system, which extends over much of the length of the gut cavity.

The Autonomic System (Figs. 369–372). Certain special efferent visceral pathways from the brain to the striated muscles of the branchial arch system by cranial nerves will be discussed later. More complicated in structure and function are the efferent fibers which innervate the smooth muscles and glands of the body. This system of efferent fibers was formerly called the sympathetic system; the term "sympathetic," however, is now commonly restricted to one subdivision of the visceral efferents,* and the efferents as a whole are usually referred to as the *autonomic system*, with reference to the generally self-governing nature of the reflexes affecting smooth muscles and glands. A classification is as follows:

$$\text{Visceral nervous system} \begin{cases} \text{Afferent} \\ \text{Efferent} = \\ \text{Autonomic} \end{cases} \begin{cases} \text{Sympathetic} \\ \text{Parasympathetic} \end{cases}$$

---

* But there is still wide variation in usage of the term sympathetic. By various authors it may be defined (*a*) narrowly, as here; (*b*) as equivalent to autonomic; (*c*) as equivalent to the entire visceral ("vegetative") system, both afferent and efferent. As still another confusing variant in terminology, "autonomic" is sometimes used for the entire visceral system, afferent as well as efferent.

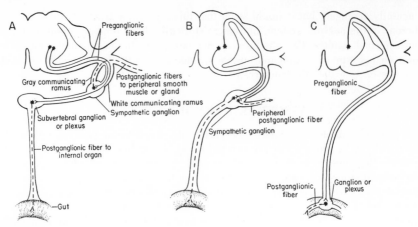

Fig. 369. Diagrammatic cross sections to show the path of autonomic fibers. *A*, Sympathetic (thoracolumbar) distribution in a mammal, with autonomic ganglia both in a lateral chain and in a subvertebral position. Preganglionic fibers may be relayed in either position and run either to superficial structures via the major nerve trunks or to the viscera, in both cases with a long postganglionic neuron. *B*, Sympathetic distribution as found in many lower vertebrates; there is little development of a sympathetic chain, and no distinction of ganglia into two groups; fibers to peripheral structures course independently or with blood vessels, rather than with the major (somatic) nerve trunks. *C*, Course of parasympathetic fibers; the preganglionic fiber makes the entire run from cord or brain to a point in or near the organ concerned, where there is a relay to a short postganglionic neuron.

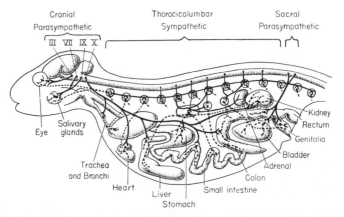

Fig. 370. Diagrammatic representation of the autonomic system of a mammal. Only a fraction of the true number of trunk segments is represented. A sympathetic chain is developed, allowing exchange of fibers between segments. Sympathetic ganglia are represented by circles; short nerves projecting from them represent gray rami rejoining the main segmental nerve trunk and running to peripheral structures. There is here a regional sorting out of autonomic nerves into parasympathetic elements associated with cranial and sacral nerves, and sympathetic nerves arising from trunk segments. The two systems nearly completely overlap, both reaching nearly every organ. In the sympathetic system, the relay to postganglionic fibers takes place in the sympathetic ganglia for peripheral structures and those in the head and chest; the relay to abdominal viscera occurs in a series of ganglia—celiac, superior mesenteric, inferior mesenteric—which are more ventrally situated. Preganglionic nerves or fibers in full line; postganglionic in broken line.

The fiber pattern followed by autonomic impulses from the spinal cord differs in one notable regard from that described earlier as typical for motor impulses to striated muscles (including the striated muscles of the special visceral system in the head and branchial region). Somatic motor impulses are carried from cord to effector by the long axon of a single neuron. The typical visceral efferent is, in contrast, a two-neuron chain. The first neuron is one whose cell body lies in the cord, termed a *preganglionic neuron.* Its axon is typically myelinated. This axon, however, does not extend the full length of the pathway to the effector organ, muscular or glandular. At some point along its course it enters a ganglion of the autonomic system. Here the impulse is relayed to a second series, *postganglionic neurons,* whose axons (with little of a myelin sheath) complete the passage to the end organ. Although this second neuron series is often far removed ventrally from the region of the cord, it appears to be derived (like dorsal root ganglion cells) from cells of the neural crest; these descend in the embryo along the developing nerves. The only exception to a two-neuron chain in autonomic innervation is the very special case of the adrenal medulla (cf. p. 564).

A combination of physiologic and anatomic investigations indicates that in mammals the autonomic system may be sorted out into two subdivisions, termed (1) the *sympathetic* (in a narrow sense) or *thoracolumbar system* and (2) the *parasympathetic* or *craniosacral system* (Fig. 370, 371). The two differ both functionally and topographically.

Stimulation of true sympathetic nerves tends to increase the activity of the animal, speed up heart and circulation, slow down digestive processes, and, in general, to make it fit for fight or frolic. On the other hand, the action of the parasympathetic tends to slow down activity in general, but promotes digestion and a "vegetative" phase of existence. This functional difference is associated with known differences in the way in which these systems affect the end organs. In both cases neurohumors are produced by the tips of the nerve fibers. In the sympathetics proper the materials produced are two amines of similar composition, *noradrenaline* (norepinephrine) and, to a much lesser degree, *adrenaline* (epinephrine). These neurohumors are identical with the materials put into the blood stream by the medulla of the adrenal gland (see pp. 564–565), except that there it is adrenaline which is the major secretion. In the case of the parasympathetic, the substance given off (as appears to be the case in most other parts of the nervous system) is *acetylcholine.* Warning must be given, however, that this pretty picture of clear cut differentiation, chemical and functional, of sympathetic and parasympathetic systems does not fully hold even in a mammal.

Anatomically, the two autonomic types can be distinguished in mammals as to (*a*) the point along the nerve course at which the relay to the postganglionic fiber occurs, and (*b*) the point along the length of the neural tube at which the nerves leave the central nervous system. In true sympathetic fibers the relay typically takes place close to the spinal cord, and the preganglionic fibers are in consequence short, the postganglionic long (Fig. 369, *A, B*). In the parasympathetic system, in contrast, the preganglionic axons are long, the postganglionics short, and the relay occurs in or close to the organ concerned.

Topographically, it is seen that in a mammal (Figs. 370, 371) the sympathetic system proper (as its alternative name, thoracolumbar, suggests) is confined at its origins to the thoracic and lumbar regions of the cord. The parasympathetic fibers emerge from the central nervous system both anteriorly and posteriorly. Anteriorly, they are associated with certain cranial nerves, most par-

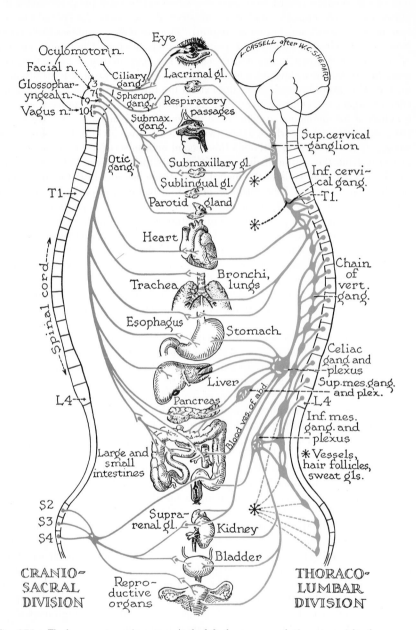

Eye
Oculomotor n.
Facial n.
Ciliary gang.
Glossophar-
yngeal n.
Sphenop. gang.
Vagus n.
Submax. gang.
Lacrimal gl.
Respiratory passages
L.CASSELL after W.C.SHEPARD
Sup. cervical ganglion
Inf. cervi- cal gang.
T1.
Otic gang.
Submaxillary gl.
Sublingual gl.
Parotid gland
T1
Heart
Bronchi, lungs
Trachea
Chain of vert. gang.
Spinal cord
Esophagus
Stomach
Celiac gang. and plexus
Sup. mes. gang. and plex.
Liver
Blood ves. of abd.
Pancreas
L4
Inf. mes. gang. and plexus
L4
Large and small intestines
* Vessels, hair follicles, sweat gls.
S2
S3
S4
Supra- renal gl.
Kidney
Bladder
CRANIO- SACRAL DIVISION
Repro- ductive organs
THORACO- LUMBAR DIVISION

Fig. 371.   The human autonomic system. At the left, the parasympathetic system; right, the sympathetic system. (From Millard, King and Showers, Human Anatomy and Physiology.)

Fig. 372. Diagrammatic representation of the autonomic system of a shark. As in Figure 370, only a fraction of the true number of trunk segments is represented, and "samples" only of types of innervation of abdominal viscera and blood vessels are given. Trunk sympathetic ganglia are developed—indicated by white circles—and are usually associated with renal bodies (stippled). There is no development of a sympathetic chain, no development of gray rami to peripheral structures, and no regional sorting out of sympathetic and parasympathetic systems (cf. Fig. 370). Preganglionic autonomic nerves in full line, postganglionic nerves or fibers in broken line. (After J. Z. Young, modified.)

ticularly the important vagus nerve; posteriorly, they are present in the spinal nerves of a few segments in the sacral region. From their origins both sets of nerves spread out widely, so that glands and smooth muscle* receive, in every major body organ, a double innervation from the two antagonistic systems.

The true sympathetic fibers in mammals leave the vertebral canal in the main trunk of the nerve of each segment. Just beyond the vertebra, however, they leave this trunk and turn ventrally in a short *visceral ramus* (white ramus,† ramus communicans) to enter a small *sympathetic ganglion*. In most mammals, as in all other tetrapods and in teleosts, the ganglia on either side of the vertebral column are connected by lengthwise strands of fibers to form a *sympathetic chain* along which preganglionic fibers may course some distance before reaching the level at which they terminate. In the sympathetic ganglia occurs the relay to postganglionic neurons in the case of impulses destined for the smooth muscles of peripheral blood vessels and for smooth muscles and glands in the skin. In mammals such an outward-bound axon rejoins the main spinal nerve trunk from the ganglion by way of an accessory communicating ramus, gray because of the paucity of myelin in its fibers. In many lower vertebrates, however, the peripheral sympathetic nerves pursue an independent course, running outward along the blood vessels.

But the sympathetic fibers relayed in the ganglia of the chain are only a part of the sympathetic system in mammals. Most of those bound for the deep internal organs pass uninterruptedly through these ganglia and turn ventrally and inward. Beneath the vertebral column, sympathetic fibers from the two sides meet in an interlacing network of fibers and ganglion cells, the *subvertebral ganglia* or subvertebral plexuses (such as the celiac plexus, lying beneath the anterior lumbar vertebrae of mammals, and the mesenteric plexuses, situated farther posteriorly). Here each preganglionic fiber may relay its impulses to much more numerous

* Including heart muscle as a specialization from the smooth type.
† Termed this because the included preganglionic fibers have a thick myelin sheath giving a glistening white appearance to the ramus.

postganglionic cells whose long axons extend downward, mainly via the mesenteries, to reach the various gut organs.

The greater part of the parasympathetic distribution is by way of the vagus nerve, a major branch of which follows the gut tube for much of its length; apart from minor elements associated with other cranial nerves, the remaining parasympathetic nerves come from a few segments in the sacral region. In this system there are no proximal ganglia; long, myelinated preganglionic fibers extend the entire distance to, or nearly to, the various viscera; the relay takes place in plexuses generally embedded in the organ concerned.

Our knowledge of the autonomic system has been gained chiefly from a study of mammals. Autonomic structure in lower vertebrates is relatively poorly known, for the reason that both anatomic and physiologic studies are needed to elucidate conditions in any animal, and both types of work are difficult in this system. But although the story of autonomic evolution is still imperfectly known, some major points in its development seem clear. We shall cite conditions seen in three types which appear to represent some of the principal evolutionary stages.

(1) In Amphioxus connections between central nervous system and gut organs are already established, but the system is a diagrammatically simple one. For the entire length of the "head" and trunk, every dorsal segmental nerve sends fibers to the viscera, in which there exists a plexus of nerve cells. There are, however, no relays in the system until the organs concerned are reached and thus the autonomic nerves resemble anatomically those of the parasympathetic type. There are no known functional distinctions between sympathetic and parasympathetic types. Further, there is no known autonomic innervation of the skin or blood vessels, and hence there is no need for proximal ganglia, corresponding to those in the mammalian "chain."

(2) In a shark (Fig. 372) there is, again, no known functional distinction between two nerve types, but the topography of the autonomic system is of a somewhat more specialized type than in Amphioxus. Autonomic fibers emerge from the cord in nearly every segment from head to pelvic region; but there is a short break in continuity in the cervical region, and in the head the autonomic fibers emerge (with one exception) with nerves of the dorsal root type described later. Most cranial fibers are associated with the vagus nerve, which reaches to the stomach and may even reach the intestine. In the case of the cranial and in part of the trunk autonomic fibers, the relay still takes place at the organ concerned in the fashion of mammalian parasympathetic fibers; but in part of the trunk autonomics, the relay takes place close to the backbone, as in mammalian sympathetics. There is still no motor innervation of the skin, but there are autonomic fibers to the blood vessels. We consequently find developed a series of small ganglia, essentially segmental in disposition, along the trunk where the relays to these fibers take place; but there is little development of a sympathetic chain connecting them, and there are no gray rami, the fibers running to the blood vessels proceeding independently of the somatic nerve trunks.

(3) Although teleosts are a side branch, these forms show advances comparable to those found in typical lower land vertebrates. Here autonomic fibers to the skin are present, and gray rami developed; further a sympathetic chain is developed connecting the trunk segments. In a shark there was little overlapping of areas innervated by cranial and trunk nerves, but in teleosts postganglionic fibers from the trunk chain "invade" the stomach, pharynx and even the head region, formerly served exclusively by the vagus and other cranial nerves. In the

teleost trunk most nerves to the viscera are relayed proximally, in the fashion of mammalian sympathetics. Posteriorly, however, the urinary bladder is innervated by long preganglionic fibers whose relays are in a plexus in the bladder walls; this is suggestive of the mammalian sacral parasympathetic. Viewed as a whole, the teleost type of organization, repeated essentially in amphibians, is one which with further anatomic and functional specialization could lead to that seen in mammals.

CRANIAL NERVES

In the head region of vertebrates there is present a special series of varied nerves which are, particularly at first sight, difficult to compare with those of the body (Fig. 373). They deserve close consideration and analysis. The cranial nerves were first studied in man and were early given names and numbers based on their mammalian functions and positions. Although, as we shall see, the human arrangement does not hold throughout, we shall introduce the study of cranial nerves by listing them:*

    I. *Olfactory:* sensory, from the olfactory epithelium.

    II. *Optic:* sensory, from the eye.

    III. *Oculomotor:* innervates four of the six eye muscles.

    IV. *Trochlear:* to the superior oblique muscle of the eye (sometimes termed the trochlear muscle).

    V. *Trigeminal:* a large nerve with three main branches, mainly bringing in somatic sensations from the head, with motor fibers to the jaw muscles.

    VI. *Abducens:* to the posterior rectus muscle (which abducts the eye).

    VII. *Facial:* partly sensory, but mainly important as supplying the muscles of the face.

    VIII. *Acoustic:* sensory, from the internal ear.

    IX. *Glossopharyngeal:* a small nerve, mainly sensory, and innervating (as the name implies) much of the tongue and pharynx.

    X. *Vagus:* a large nerve, both sensory and motor, which (as the name suggests) does not restrict itself to the head region, but runs backward to innervate much of the viscera—heart, stomach, and so forth.

    XI. *Accessory:* a motor nerve accessory to the vagus.

    XII. *Hypoglossal:* a motor nerve to the tongue muscles.

One can brutally memorize such a list of cranial nerves and their functions, but no one interested in the nervous system can stop at this point. We have here a series of nerves which are amazing in variety and seemingly haphazard in distribution, and one cannot but attempt to "make sense" out of them. Is there any logic in their distribution? Can they be grouped in any sort of natural categories?

Stimulus to attempt this is added through the fact that comparative study shows that the fixed, orthodox mammalian scheme just presented is not found in all vertebrates. Even the number of cranial nerves varies. The hypoglossal, for

---

* The initial letters of the names of the cranial nerves are the initial letters of the words of the following choice bit of poetry: "On old Olympus' towering top a Finn and German viewed a hop."

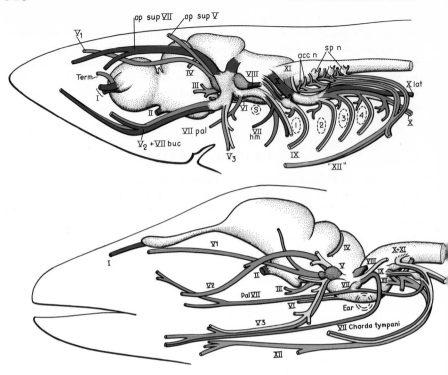

Fig. 373. *Above,* diagram of the distribution and components of the cranial nerves of a shark (Squalus). *Below,* diagram of the distribution and components of the cranial nerves of a lizard (Anolis). Special somatic sensory nerves (I, II, lateral line, VIII), purple; somatic sensory components, blue; visceral sensory, green; visceral motor, yellow; somatic motor, red. Roman numerals refer to the cranial nerves. *buc,* Buccal; *hm,* hyomandibular; *lat,* lateral line trunk; *occ n,* occipital nerves, *op sup,* superficial ophthalmic; *pal,* palatine; *S,* position of spiracle; *sp n,* anterior spinal nerves; *Term,* terminal nerve; *1* to *4,* position of gill slits; V_1, ophthalmic (profundus) ramus of trigeminal; V_2, maxillary division; V_3, mandibular division of trigeminal; *Pal* VII, palatine ramus of facial. "XII," Trunk of conjoined occipital and anterior spinal nerves corresponding to amniote hypoglossal XII. In Squalus, special somatic sensory components of VII and X = lateral line nerves. (Squalus after Norris and Hughes; Anolis data from Willard, Watkinson.)

Fig. 374. Diagrams showing the distribution of branchial (dorsal root) cranial nerves. *A,* Hypothetic primitive condition, with typical nerves to each of two anterior gill slits lost in jawed vertebrates, and a terminal nerve to anterior end of head. *B,* Condition in jaw-bearing fishes. *M,* Mouth; *O, O',* anterior gill slits lost in gnathostomes; *S,* spiracular slit; *T,* terminal nerve; *1* to *5,* typical gill slits of gnathostomes.

Table 3.   Table of Nerve Components of Cranial Nerves

Nerve Types	Special Sensory	Branchial (Dorsal)						Ventral
Components	Special Somatic Sensory	General Somatic Sensory	General Visceral Sensory	Special Visceral Sensory	Special Visceral Motor	Visceral Motor (Autonomic)	Somatic Motor
O. Terminalis		X					
I. Olfactory	X						
II. Optic	X						
III. Oculomotor						(X)	X
IV. Trochlear							X
V_1. Profundus		X				(X)	
$V_{2, 3}$. Trigeminal proper		X			X		
VI. Abducens							X
VII. Facial	L	(X)	X	X	X	X	
VIII. Acoustic	A						
IX. Glossopharyngeal	L	(X)	X	X	X	X	
X and XI. Vagus (and accessory)	L	X	X	X	X	X	
XII. Hypoglossal							X

Proprioceptive fibers (muscle sense) are not included. *L*, Lateralis sensory components of lower vertebrates (in X, the vagus, alone in amphibians); *A*, acoustic component of lateralis-acoustic system. Components in parentheses: variable or negligible. The three areas between vertical double-ruled lines indicate the components proper to each of the three nerve types. Except for the usual presence of autonomic fibers accompanying the oculomotor nerve, the distinctions are clear-cut.

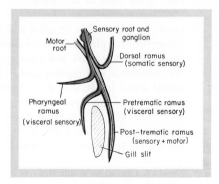

Fig. 375. Diagram showing the composition of a typical branchial nerve, such as the fish glossopharyngeal. The three nerve components colored as in Figs. 367 and 373.

example, is absent as such in fishes, and the accessory is in lower vertebrates an integral part of the vagus; on the other hand, most vertebrates have anteriorly a small "terminal" nerve absent in man, and one main branch of the mammalian trigeminal appears originally as a quite distinct element; in fishes there is frequently a variable series of extra "occipital" nerves which emerge at the back of the braincase.

A clue to a possible classification of cranial nerves lies in a consideration of nerve components (cf. Table 3). We have noted that, in the postcranial region, components of four types are present. In the head region these can be made out together with three further subcategories. In addition to the ordinary smooth visceral muscles found in the trunk, the head and throat have special striated visceral muscles connected with the gill bar system, and a *special visceral motor* category has been established for nerve components supplying them. A *special visceral sensory* component is distinguished for fibers from the taste organs. Further, there are found in the head special somatic sensory structures—nose, eye, and acustico-lateralis organs; their nerves merit a *special somatic sensory* category. We can group cranial nerves into three types which (as indicated by the double vertical rulings in the table) show essentially clean-cut distinctions as to the components present. These three types are (*a*) *special sensory nerves* of somatic type— I, II, VIII, and lateral line nerves; (*b*) complex *dorsal root* or *branchial nerves* which may contain sensory components both somatic and visceral, and visceral motor elements, including both autonomic and special visceral motor components associated with the branchial region; (*c*) *ventral root nerves,* containing almost exclusively somatic motor fibers. The first category is peculiar to the cranial region; the other two are comparable to the dorsal and ventral roots of spinal nerves of lower vertebrates, and especially comparable to the separate dorsal and ventral spinal nerves of lampreys and Amphioxus.

Special Sensory Nerves.   In all vertebrates the three main sense organs —nose, eye, and ear—are innervated by special nerves; in primitive aquatic vertebrates we find in addition nerve trunks, intimately associated with that for the ear, which innervate the lateral line organs.

Olfactory (I).   As mentioned previously (p. 462), the olfactory is not a typical nerve. A normal sensory nerve usually has the cell bodies of its neurons located in a ganglion close to the spinal cord or brain. In this case, however, the nerve fibers are not formed by nervous system elements at all; they are, instead, formed by the cells of the sensory epithelium, and run inward to the olfactory bulb at the front of the brain.*

In mammals the olfactory is not a compact nerve; rather, it consists of a number of short fiber bundles which pass back from the olfactory organ through the cribriform plate of the ethmoid bone. In many other vertebrates, nose and brain are farther apart, and a distinctive pair of olfactory nerves is formed. In typical amphibians and reptiles and in many mammals with a well-developed vomeronasal organ (p. 465), a discrete branch of the olfactory nerve develops for the innervation of this structure.

Optic (II).   The optic nerve, entering the brain at the chiasma, was discussed in connection with the eye (p. 477). It is, properly, not a nerve at all, but a brain tract, since the retina is formed as an outgrowth of the brain tube; the

---

* Prior discussion of cranial nerves is necessary for a proper consideration of brain structure, but, conversely, some mention of prominent brain landmarks is necessary in the description of cranial nerves.

fiber-forming cells are situated peripherally—in the ganglion cell layer of the retina.

Acoustic (VIII).   More normal in construction is the acoustic nerve, connected with the internal ear. Here the nerve fibers are formed by true ganglion cells which (as in the cochlear branch of the nerve in mammals) may be situated peripherally, in the otic capsule, close to the sensory structures. The acoustic nerve is not, of course, visible in an external dissection of the braincase region, since its fibers run directly from the capsule into the endocranial cavity, where it enters the medulla oblongata at a far dorsal position. Two main branches are present in higher vertebrates, each with a separate ganglion. The *vestibular nerve* serves the anterior parts of the system of canals and sacs; the *cochlear nerve* is so named because in mammals it serves the auditory organ of the cochlea as well as the posterior part of the organs of equilibrium.

Lateral Line Nerves (cf. Fig. 347, p. 482).   The lateral line organs of primitive water dwellers are, we have noted, intimately related to the auditory sense; hence it is reasonable to find that the nerves innervating these structures are closely associated with the acoustic nerve. In fishes a pair of stout lateral line nerves flank the root of the acoustic nerve anteriorly and posteriorly on either side of the medulla. These nerves enter the braincase with certain of the branchial nerves and, therefore, frequently are reckoned as part of these nerves. This association, however, seems to be merely one of "convenience," and the essential independence of the lateral line nerves should be emphasized.

The *anterior lateral line nerve* enters the skull in company with the facial nerve and supplies the lateral line organs of much of the head region; its main branches—superficial ophthalmic, buccal, hyomandibular—are often quite independent of the branches of the facial nerve. Some fibers of the *posterior lateral line nerve* may fuse with the glossopharyngeal (IX), but most or all of the posterior nerve accompanies the vagus. It innervates the neuromast organs of the occipital region, but primarily forms a stout trunk accompanying the lateral line the length of the body.

Branchial Nerves.   We have noted evidence that primitively (as in Amphioxus and the lamprey today) dorsal and ventral roots were quite distinct nerves; the dorsal roots contain all sensory components and in addition appear to have carried originally part, and perhaps all, of the visceral motor fibers as well. If Table 3 is inspected, it will be seen that a large series of cranial nerves appear to belong to this category of dorsal root nerves, all containing sensory fibers and in most (but not all) cases visceral motor components as well. This series includes the terminal nerve, profundus nerve, trigeminus proper, facial, glossopharyngeal and vagus (Fig. 374).

These dorsal cranial nerves all, however, differ in various regards from dorsal root nerves of the trunk. Most of the differences are obviously due to their close association with the gill system, prominently developed in this region of the body in lower vertebrates. The presence of the gill slits tends to bring about a serial pattern of distribution of these nerves. This is enhanced by the serial pattern of the striated branchial muscles which are innervated by special visceral sensory components.

Most typical of these dorsal root or branchial nerves is perhaps the glossopharyngeal in fishes (Fig. 375), which is associated with the first typical gill slit. Like all members of this series, it arises from the upper part of the medulla oblongata and bears a prominent ganglion on its sensory root. A major trunk, containing both sensory and motor fibers, runs down behind this slit as a *post-trematic ramus*. A smaller, *pretrematic ramus* runs down in front of the gill slit, and a *pharyngeal ramus* turns inward and forward beneath the lining of the pharynx; these two branches contain visceral sensory fibers only. A small *dorsal ramus*, often absent, may bring in somatic sensations from the skin.

Posterior to the first, each of the gill slits has a similar pattern of associated nerve branches; all, however, unite to connect with the brain via a single large compound nerve, the vagus. Anteriorly, the development of the jaw apparatus has greatly modified in gnathostomes the branchial nerve pattern which may have been present in the ancestral jawless vertebrates. The facial nerve, associated with the spiracular slit, is not too atypical, but has reduced or lost its somatic sensory component. Jaw development, it is thought, may have eliminated two anterior gill slits. The trigeminal nerve complex appears to have been originally associated with this lost gill region, and the little terminal nerve may be a vestigial anterior member of this series.

These dorsal root nerves may be described in anteroposterior sequence.

Terminal Nerve.   In many vertebrates, representing every class except cyclostomes and birds, there is found a tiny nerve which parallels the olfactory in its course inward from the nasal epithelium; its fibers run back to the diencephalon. Little is known of its nature; it is apparently sensory in function, but has nothing to do with olfactory reception. Quite possibly it is the last remnant of a most anterior member of the branchial series which innervated the primitive small mouth area.

Profundus Nerve (V_1).   The *ophthalmicus profundus* nerve* is a stout trunk which runs forward through the deeper part of the orbit and functions as a somatic afferent, receiving sensations from the skin of the "snout" region. In mammals this nerve is intimately associated with the trigeminus and counted as one of its three main trunks. In lower vertebrates, however, it has frequently a separate ganglion and may emerge independent of the trigeminus from the brain. In consequence, it is generally held that it was originally a separate nerve of the branchial series, associated with an anterior gill slit which has been lost with the development of the jaws and expansion of the mouth region.

Trigeminal Nerve (V_2, V_3).   The trigeminal nerve proper is believed to have been originally associated, like its profundus component, with an anterior gill slit lost with the expansion of the mouth gape. This nerve has not, however, been reduced; it has become the main nerve of the mouth region in all jawed vertebrates. Two main branches, somewhat comparable to pretrematic and post-trematic rami of a typical branchial nerve, are always present in the trigeminus proper: a *maxillary ramus* (V_2) to the upper jaw region, and a *mandibular ramus* (V_3) to the lower jaw. Both branches include somatic sensory elements which supply much of the surface of the head and mouth cavity. The fibers innervating the jaw muscles are typically associated with V_3. Because of its anterior position the trigeminal has no visceral sensory component.

Facial Nerve (VII).   This is the nerve proper to the spiracular gill slit. Its main, post-trematic trunk in fishes is the *hyomandibular nerve*, which descends behind the spiracle alongside the hyomandibular cartilage or bone. This supplies the branchial muscles proper to the hyoid arch and contains visceral sensory fibers

---

* In mammals termed simply the ophthalmic; in most vertebrates, however, it is termed the deep ophthalmic to distinguish it from a more superficial nerve in the same general region.

as well. Anterior branches are purely visceral sensory in nature, and include a *palatine ramus* which corresponds to the pharyngeal rami of more posterior nerves. As we have noted, the anterior lateral line nerve is associated with the facial. The visceral sensory fibers innervate much of the mouth, including part of the taste bud series.

In tetrapods the nerve preserves its various branches in modified form. The main ventral trunk, after looping through the middle ear region, turns forward as the *chorda tympani* to give a sensory innervation to taste buds and lower jaw. In mammals, we have noted, the musculature of the hyoid arch has become expanded over the surface of the head as the facial muscles, and branches of the facial nerve spread over skull and face to innervate them—a feature to which the nerve owes its name.

Glossopharyngeal Nerve (IX).   As noted, this small nerve is associated in fishes with the first typical gill slit; it is never of any great size or importance. A somatic sensory element is absent except in certain fishes and amphibians. A small amount of striated visceral musculature of the throat and larynx and part of the salivary glands are innervated by this nerve, and it carries visceral sensations from the back part of the mouth (and tongue) and part of the taste buds.

Vagus Nerve (X, XI).   The vagus is the largest and most versatile of all cranial nerves. The *accessory nerve* of mammals is essentially a motor portion of the vagus which continues its area of origin back from the medulla into the cervical region of the spinal cord, and in lower groups appears to be an integral part of the vagus. Usually there is a minor skin sensory component from the neck region; for the most part, however, the vagus is a visceral nerve. The vagus nerve supplies, in fishes, a typical series of branches to each of the gills behind the first, innervating the pharynx and the striated gill muscles. This branchial part of the vagus survives, in modified form, in the tetrapod pharynx and its musculature. In fishes the vagus carries (like VII and IX) taste sensations, but this function is reduced in land forms. In every vertebrate the main trunk of the vagus runs on backward into the body as an *abdominal ramus* which extends in all forms to the stomach and heart, to the lungs, when present, and in some cases may run the entire length of the gut. This nerve carries visceral sensations to the brain and (as noted previously) is the main route of the fibers of the parasympathetic system. In fishes the posterior lateral line nerve emerges from the braincase with the vagus.

Somatic Motor Nerves.   The nerves in this category—III, IV, VI, and XII of the human series—are highly comparable in most regards to ventral roots of spinal nerves. They are almost entirely composed of somatic motor fibers which emerge ventrally from the brain stem. Their arrangement is closely correlated with the distribution of the myotomes in the head region. As we have seen earlier (p. 264; Fig. 179, p. 257), the myotome succession found in the trunk is interrupted anteriorly in the otic region; farther forward, three further somites form the muscles of the eyeball. Nerves III, IV, and VI innervate the eye muscles formed by these somites (Fig. 182, p. 264); nerve XII, when present, supplies musculature arising from somites formed in the occipital region.

Since both the branchial and the somatic motor nerves of the brain show a serial arrangement, it is but natural that students of the cranial nerves have attempted to arrange them, theoretically, in pairs corresponding to dorsal and ventral roots in trunk segments. Such attempts, however, have been none too successful; and on consideration it is clear that no such arrangement need ever have been present. The serial arrangement of the somatic motor nerves corresponds to the segmental arrangement of the somites which they innervate. The linear arrangement of the dorsal, branchial nerves, on the other hand, is based on the serial arrangement of the gill slits, which develop in the embryo quite independently of the somites.

Oculomotor (III).   The greater part of this nerve, which arises ventrally from the midbrain, consists of somatic motor fibers innervating the four eye muscles developed from the first cranial somite—the superior, anterior, and inferior rectus, and the inferior oblique. (An exception is the innervation in cyclostomes of the inferior rectus muscle by the abducens nerve.) Autonomic fibers, partly derived from nerve V_1 and hardly to be considered an integral part of the oculomotor, generally accompany the nerve to the eyeball and enter it to innervate the smooth muscle fibers of the ciliary body and iris; they are associated with accommodation and pupil reflexes.

Trochlearis (IV).   The trochlearis is a small nerve with a most unusual course. It arises ventrally within the midbrain on either side; but instead of emerging directly outward, its fibers turn upward within the substance of the brain and cross to emerge dorsally on the opposite side. It innervates solely the superior oblique muscle of the eyeball, derived from the second head somite.

Abducens (VI).   This small nerve emerges ventrally from the anterior end of the oblongata and supplies the posterior rectus muscle, derived from the third head somite. A muscle retracting the eye is developed in many forms from the same somite and is also innervated by the abducens.

Hypoglossal (XII).   In fishes (particularly among the sharks) the posterior end of the skull—and hence of the cranial nerve series—is not a fixed point. The number of potential vertebrae which are incorporated in the occipital region of the skull is variable; hence we find a variable number of would-be spinal nerves emerging from the occiput. Such *occipital nerves* tend to lose their dorsal roots and are mainly motor nerves supplying muscles formed from the somites of the occipital region. In amniotes the condition is stabilized; back of the vagus-accessory region there is a final cranial nerve, the hypoglossal, usually formed from three ventral roots which represent three body segments fused into the occiput. There is no hypoglossal nerve in modern amphibians. But fossil amphibians and crossopterygians show a foramen for it in the skull; it would seem that a definitive hypoglossal was formed in the ancestors of the tetrapods and that its absence in frogs and salamanders today is one of the many degenerate characters of these forms.

The myotomes in the region close to the back of the skull migrate in the embryo backward and downward around the gill region to form the hypobranchial muscles in fishes and the tongue musculature of higher vertebrates (Fig. 179, p. 257). Trunks of the occipital nerves of fishes follow this migration route to innervate the hypobranchial muscles, and the hypoglossal nerve of amniotes follows a similar path, back, down, and then forward around the pharyngeal region to innervate the tongue musculature.

CENTRAL NERVOUS SYSTEM—ACCESSORY ELEMENTS

Besides the functionally important neurons, other types of cells are developed as part of the nervous system. We have already noted the cells sheathing nerve fibers and ganglion cells; within the central nervous system are various

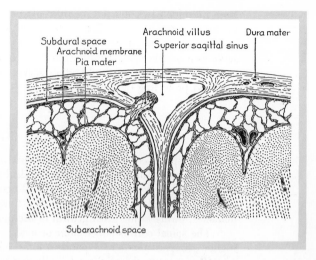

Fig. 376. Transverse section of a portion of the brain of a mammal to show the meninges. The section is taken through the partition (falx cerebri) between the two cerebral hemispheres. The superior sagittal sinus is a prominent venous channel following a longitudinal course backward between the hemispheres; sections of smaller blood vessels are seen in meninges and brain. The subarachnoid space is occupied by cerebrospinal fluid; the arachnoidal villi offer a minor means of transfusion of material between this fluid and the blood. (After Weed.)

other cell types termed, in a broad sense, the *neuroglia.* In most body organs supporting functions are performed by connective tissues. These are not present, to any degree at least, in the central nervous system, and the neuroglial cells take their place as protective and supporting structures.

The neuroglial elements arise embryologically as a part of the true nervous tissues, from which they become differentiated during development. They are found throughout the brain and spinal cord as relatively small but numerous elements scattered among the neurons. Typically, there is a rather small cell body from which radiate numerous fine processes, giving the neuroglia a starlike appearance. One type, the *ependymal cells,* retain the epithelial character true of all the tissue of the embryonic nerve tube, and persist in a layer of epithelium (the ependyma), frequently ciliated, lining the cavities of the brain and spinal cord.

The brain and spinal cord, enclosed within the braincase and the neural arches of the vertebrae, are further protected and sustained by one or more wrappings, or *meninges* (Fig. 376). In most fishes there is but a single meninx of compact tissue, external to which a loose mucous or fatty connective tissue lies between cord or brain and neural arches or braincase. In all tetrapods at least two meninges are present. The outer, the *dura mater,* is a stout sheath, mainly of connective tissue origin, connected by numerous slender ligaments with an inner membrane, mainly, it seems, of neural crest origin applied to the brain or cord. In mammals there is a separation of the softer, inner wrapping into two delicate structures, an outer *arachnoid* and an inner, vascular *pia mater,* the two separated by a fluid-filled *subarachnoid space,* which is crossed by a spidery cobweb of delicate tissue threads.

The vertebrate nervous system develops as a hollow tube, and this tubular arrangement persists in the adult; within the brain are the ventricles and in the spinal cord a central canal. Present in these cavities, and also found between arachnoid and pia mater in the brain wrappings, is a clear liquid, the *cerebrospinal fluid.* This is similar in composition to the interstitial fluid or the perilymphatic liquid of the ear. Nutrient or other materials reach the cerebrospinal fluid from the blood through the medium of special vascular structures, the choroid plexuses of the brain (p. 536). These are more impervious to large molecules or other structures of any magnitude than are ordinary capillary walls, and thus serve as a barrier against the introduction of foreign materials into the brain tissues. The cerebrospinal fluid further serves as a water-bed suspending brain and cord and protecting them from injury.

SPINAL CORD

The spinal cord (Figs. 364, 367, pp. 503, 505; 377, *A*), extending most of the length of the body, is a little-modified adult representative of the nerve tube formed in the early embryo. It still contains, as did that of the embryo, a centrally situated, fluid-filled canal; this, however, has become relatively tiny in diameter, owing to the great growth of the nervous tissues surrounding it.

The spinal cord is subcircular or oval in section in lower vertebrates, but in higher groups it tends to expand in bilateral fashion, and pronounced grooves may be present in the midline dorsally and ventrally. Two layers of material can be readily distinguished, a central area of *gray matter* surrounding the canal of the cord, and a peripheral region of *white matter*. The former consists mainly of cell bodies, the latter of countless myelinated fibers coursing up and down the cord.

Primitively, the gray substance was, it seems, arranged in a fairly even fashion about the central cavity; in most vertebrates, however, there is a bilaterally symmetric arrangement, as seen in section, into an H-shape, or that of a butterfly's wings. Such a pattern gives the appearance of a pair of "horns" on either side, dorsally and ventrally. Actually, of course, each "horn" is merely a section of a longitudinal structure, and we should speak rather of a dorsal column and a ventral column.

The *ventral column* is the seat of the cell bodies of the efferent or motor neurons of the spinal nerves, their axons typically passing out through successive ventral nerve roots. The number of neurons in any given part of the cord will, naturally, vary with the volume of musculature at that level of the body, and in land vertebrates the ventral column (indeed, the entire cord) may be much expanded in the regions supplying the limbs. Most of the motor supply is to so-

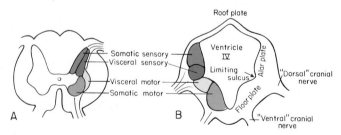

Fig. 377. Diagrams showing the distribution of sensory and motor columns. Somatic sensory association column, blue; visceral sensory, green; visceral motor column, yellow; somatic motor, red. *A*, The spinal cord of the adult of certain lower vertebrates. *B*, The embryonic medulla oblongata; the embryonic spinal cord shows a similar arrangement of the columns. The plate of tissue lying below the limiting sulcus is termed the floor plate; from this, motor centers arise. The sensory region above is the "wing" or alar plate. (Partly after Herrick.)

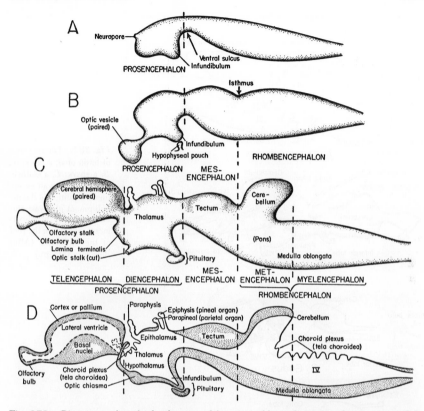

Fig. 378. Diagrams to show the development of the principal brain divisions and structures. *A,* Only prosencephalon (primitive forebrain) distinct from remainder of neural tube. *B,* Three main divisions established. *C,* More mature stage in lateral view. *D,* The same in median section. (Partly after Bütschli.)

Fig. 379. Diagram to show the relation in lower vertebrates of the three major sense organs to the three dorsal areas of gray matter in the three major subdivisions of the brain. (In mammals the midbrain tectum is reduced and optic sensations are relayed to the cerebrum instead.)

Fig. 380. Diagram showing position of brain ventricles. (From Gardner.)

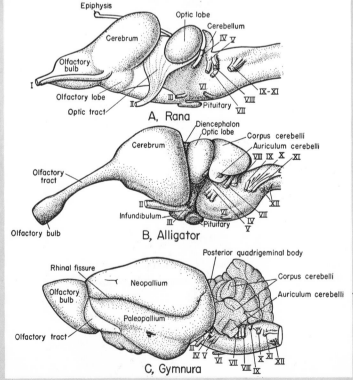

Fig. 381. Lateral views of brain of *A*, a lamprey; *B*, a shark; *C*, a codfish. In the lamprey an exceptional condition is the development of a vascular choroid area, the plexus mesencephali, on the roof of the midbrain. (After Bütschli, Ahlborn.)

Fig. 382. Lateral views of brain of *A*, a frog; *B*, an alligator; *C*, an insectivore representing a primitive mammalian type. (In normal head posture the front end of the alligator brain is tilted upward. (After Bütschli, Clark, Crosby, Gaupp, Wettstein.)

A, Anser

B, Equus

Fig. 383. Lateral views of brain of *A*, a goose; *B*, a horse. (The goose brain, like that of the alligator, is tilted upward anteriorly in life.) (After Bütschli, Kuenzi, Sisson.)

Fig. 384. Right half of the brain of a shark (Scyllium) in median aspect. Unshaded areas are those sectioned. (After Haller, Bruckhardt.)

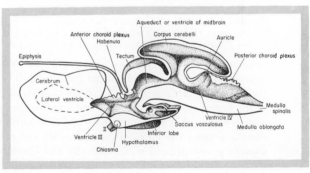

matic muscles; but visceral efferents may be present over much of the length of the cord. The cell bodies of these latter neurons are situated above and lateral to those of the somatic motor type, and sometimes are distinguishable as a *ventro-lateral column*.

The *dorsal column* of the gray matter is associated with the dorsal, sensory root of the spinal nerves; it is the seat of the cell bodies of association neurons through which impulses brought in from sense organs may be relayed and distributed. These neurons have processes which may ascend and descend the cord

A, Didelphys

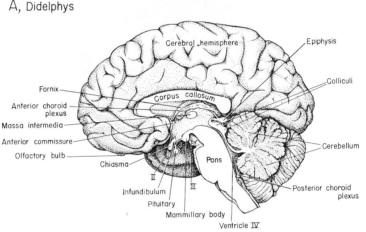

B, Homo

Fig. 385. Right half of the brain, in median aspect, of *A*, an opossum; *B*, man. Unshaded areas are those sectioned. The internally bulging side walls of the diencephalon may meet and fuse in the midline, forming a "massa intermedia," which, however, has no functional importance. (*A* after Loo.)

to connect with motor neurons of the same side, may cross to connect with motor neurons of the opposite side of the cord, or, still further, may ascend the cord to the brain. The arrangement of various clusters of these sensory association cells in the dorsal column is complex and variable, but in some cases (particularly in certain embryos) it appears that we can distinguish a larger series associated with somatic sensory reception, situated dorsally and medially, and a smaller, visceral sensory group situated more ventrally and laterally. There thus appear to be in the gray matter four areas on either side related to the four nerve components, the four being in sequence, from dorsal to ventral: somatic sensory, visceral sensory, visceral motor, and somatic motor. It is of interest that the same arrangement is found in the gray matter of the brain stem (Fig. 377, *B*).

The *white matter* is composed, as has been said, of innumerable myelinated fibers. These include ascending and descending fibers of sensory nerve cells which enter the cord through the dorsal nerve roots, and of similar fibers taking origin from association cells. Present as well are fibers which carry sensory stimuli forward to the brain, and fibers returning from brain centers to act (usually via association neurons) on motor neurons. Fibers of these latter categories are especially

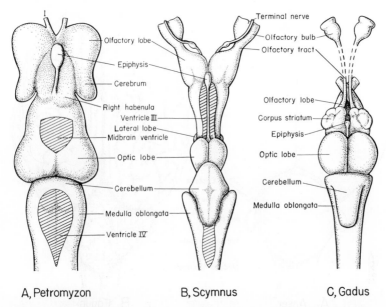

Fig. 386. Dorsal views of the brain of *A*, a lamprey; *B*, a shark; *C*, a teleost (codfish). Hatched areas are those in which a choroid plexus has been removed, exposing the underlying ventricle. (After Bütschli, Ahlborn.)

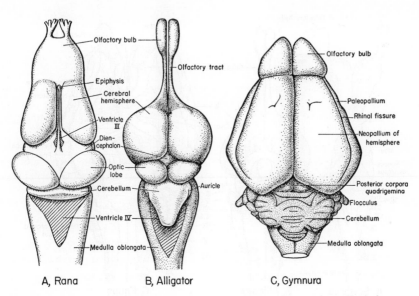

Fig. 387. Dorsal views of the brain of *A*, a frog; *B*, an alligator; *C*, a tree shrew. Hatched areas are those in which a choroid plexus has been removed, exposing the underlying ventricle. (After Gaupp, Crosby, Wettstein, Clark.)

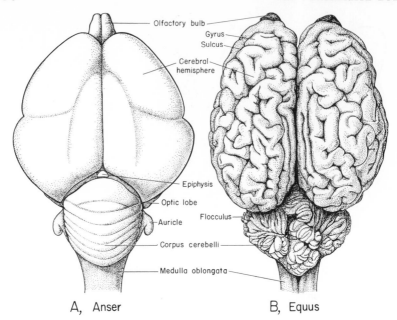

Fig. 388.   Dorsal views of the brain of *A*, a goose; *B*, a horse. (After Bütschli, Kuenzi, Sisson.)

Fig. 389.   Ventral views of the brain of *A*, a shark; *B*, an alligator; *C*, a horse. (After Bütschli, Wettstein, Sisson.)

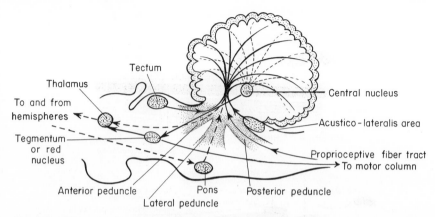

Fig. 390.   Diagram to show the main connections of the cerebellum. The connections with the cerebral cortex, peculiar to mammals, are shown in broken line.

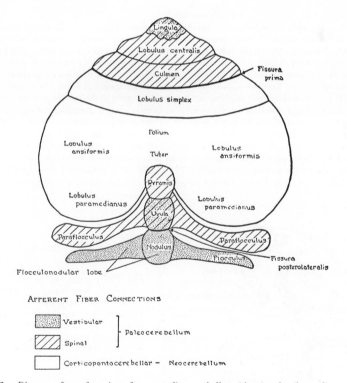

Fig. 391.   Diagram of a surface view of a mammalian cerebellum (showing details not discussed in the text). The stippled and hatched portions, associated with equilibrium (vestibular) and with muscle sensations (spinal), are the phylogenetically oldest parts of the cerebellum; the white area is a mammalian addition associated with the cortex of the cerebral hemispheres. (From Fulton, after Larsell.)

Fig. 392. Diagrams of midbrain and hindbrain regions in lateral view to show the arrangement of sensory and motor nuclei. Somatic sensory, red; special somatic sensory, stippled; visceral sensory, green; special visceral sensory, hatched; visceral motor, yellow; special visceral motor, stippled; somatic motor, red. *A*, Hypothetic primitive stage, in which brain stem centers were continuous with one another and with the columns of the cord. Even at such a stage, however, it would be assumed that special somatic centers would have developed for eye and ear. The brain region includes a special visceral motor column for the branchial muscles. *B*, Comparable diagram of the mammalian situation. The somatic sensory column is still essentially continuous (almost entirely associated with nerve *V*, but the other columns are broken into discrete nuclei. The visceral sensory column includes both a general visceral nucleus (mainly for afferent fibers from the viscera via the vagus) and a special nucleus for the important sense of taste. Of efferent visceral nuclei, there are small anterior ones for autonomic eye reflexes and the salivary glands, and a large nucleus for parasympathetic fibers to the viscera via the vagus. There are important branchial motor nuclei for *V*, *VI*, and *IX*, *X* (ambiguus). The somatic motor column includes small nuclei for eye muscles anteriorly and a hypoglossal nucleus posteriorly.

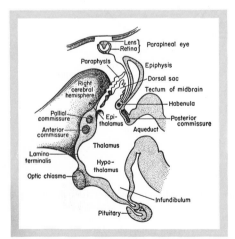

Fig. 393. Right half of the diencephalon, midbrain and neighboring structures of a lizard to show, particularly, the various outgrowths. The arrow indicates the position of the interventricular foramen leading from ventricle III into the right lateral ventricle. (After von Kupffer, Nowikoff.)

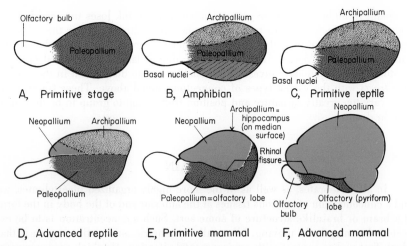

Fig. 394. Diagrams to show progressive differentiation of the cerebral hemisphere (cf. Fig. 395). Lateral views of left hemisphere and olfactory bulb. In *A* the hemisphere is merely an olfactory lobe. *B,* Dorsal and ventral areas, archipallium (= hippocampus) and basal nuclei (corpus striatum) are differentiated. *C,* The basal nuclei have moved to the inner part of the hemisphere. *D,* The neopallium appears as a small area (in many reptiles). *E,* The archipallium is forced to the median surface, but the neopallium is still of modest dimensions, and the olfactory areas are still prominent below the rhinal fissure (as in primitive mammals). *F,* The primitive olfactory area is restricted to the ventral aspect, and the neopallial areas are greatly enlarged (as in advanced mammals). The various cellular components of the hemispheres are distinguished by color.

Fig. 395. Diagrammatic cross sections of left cerebral hemisphere to show stages in the evolution of the corpus striatum and cerebral cortex. *A,* Primitive stage, essentially an olfactory lobe; gray matter internal and little differentiated. *B,* Stage seen in modern amphibians. Gray matter still deep to surface, but differentiated into paleopallium (= olfactory lobe), archipallium (= hippocampus), and basal nuclei (= corpus striatum), the last becoming an association center, with connections from and to the thalamus (indicated by lines representing cut fiber bundles). *C,* More progressive stage, in which basal nuclei have moved to interior, and pallial areas are moving toward surface. *D,* Advanced reptilian stage; beginnings of neopallium. *E,* Primitive mammalian stage; neopallium expanded, with strong connections with brain stem; archipallium rolled medially as hippocampus; paleopallial area still prominent. *F,* Progressive mammal; neopallium greatly expanded and convoluted; paleopallium confined to restricted ventral area as pyriform lobe. The corpus callosum developed as a great commissure connecting the two neopallial areas. *a,* Archipallium; *b,* basal nuclei; *cc,* corpus callosum; *n,* neopallium; *p,* paleopallium; *V,* ventricle. The different types of "gray matter" colored as in Fig. 394.

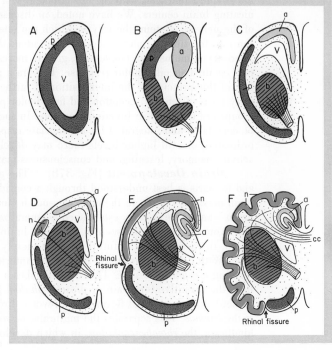

abundant in higher vertebrate groups, in which the trunk loses the semi-autonomous nature which it has in fishes and comes more directly under the influence of the brain. Topographically, the white matter is more or less subdivided by the dorsal and ventral "horns" into major areas: dorsal, lateral, and ventral *funiculi.* Anatomic and physiologic investigation enables one to distinguish in these areas *fiber tracts* with the varied types of connections noted above. These tracts, however, vary too greatly in nature and position from group to group to be described here in detail.

THE BRAIN

In all vertebrates, as well as in the more highly organized invertebrates, we find a concentration of nervous tissues at the anterior end of the body in the form of a brain or brainlike structure of some sort. Such a concentration is to be expected. In an actively moving, bilaterally symmetric animal this region is that which first makes contact with environmental situations to which response must be made. It is, in consequence, the region in which the major sensory structures come to be situated, and in which, hence, it is most advantageous to locate correlation of sensory impulses.

Primitively, we may believe, the vertebrate brain was merely a modestly developed anterior region of the neural tube in which, in addition to facilities for local reflexes to the head and throat region, special sensory stimuli were assembled and "referred for action" to the semi-autonomous body region via the spinal cord. Within the vertebrates, however, there has occurred a strong trend for the concentration in the brain of command over bodily functions (except for the simplest reflexes), with the development of a series of complex, intercommunicating brain centers. We have noted, in discussing the elementary composition of the nervous system, the way in which the intercalation of an association neuron into the simple reflex arc greatly broadens the field of possible responses to a sensory stimulus and, conversely, greatly increases the variety of stimuli which may excite a specific motor response. The brain pattern is essentially an elaboration of this principle—the interposition of further series of neurons between primary areas of sensory reception and final motor paths. These intermediate neuron groups are clustered in functional centers. In such centers afferent impulses may be correlated and integrated for appropriate responses, or motor mechanisms coordinated; on still higher levels there may develop association centers of whose activity memory, learning, and consciousness may be the products.

Brain Development (Fig. 378). The general topography of the brain and its parts is best understood through a consideration of its development. The brain develops rapidly in the embryo—much more rapidly than almost any other organ—and there is early established a generalized structural pattern upon which the numerous variations seen in the adult brains of different groups are superposed. In early stages the future brain is merely an expanded area of the neural tube. With continued increase in size, its anterior end tends to fold downward, forming a *cephalic flexure.* This distinguishes a median, terminal saclike structure, the primitive forebrain or *prosencephalon,* from the remainder of the tube. Somewhat later a second flexure, in a reverse direction, is found more posteriorly at the *isthmus.* This separates the midbrain, or *mesencephalon,* from the primitive hindbrain, the *rhombencephalon,* in which develops the *medulla oblongata* of the adult. Posteriorly, the rhombencephalon tapers gradually, without any abrupt change, into the spinal cord.

Prosencephalon, mesencephalon, and rhombencephalon are the three primary subdivisions of the brain. The three successive "segments" of the brain tube which constitute them in early stages are still recognizable in the adult, where they are termed collectively the *brain stem*—that part of the brain which is presumably phylogenetically the oldest and in which are persistently located centers for many simple but basically important reactions within the nervous system.* Subdivision of the brain stem into three parts would have been pointless were it not that there presumably appeared at an early stage in phylogeny three major sense organs: nose, eye, and ear + lateral line. In primitive vertebrates each of the three becomes associated with one of the three brain subdivisions, and for each of the three there tends to develop a dorsal outgrowth of laminated "gray matter" from its proper section of the stem (Fig. 379). These three outgrowths are respectively cerebrum, midbrain roof (tectum), and cerebellum.†

At the three-vesicle stage midbrain and hindbrain regions are simple in construction, but in the primitive forebrain region special structures appear early. Most notably, the optic vesicles (whose history was discussed in the last chapter) push out at either side; the optic stalks, in which the optic nerves later develop, remain attached anteriorly to the base of the primitive forebrain at the optic chiasma. More posteriorly, there is a down-growing median projection from the diencephalon, the *infundibulum.* Concomitantly a pocket of epithelium, the *hypophyseal pouch* (Rathke's pouch) grows upward from the roof of the embryonic mouth. In later stages modified infundibular tissues and those derived from the pouch combine to form the pituitary gland. Dorsally there grows presently from the roof of the primitive forebrain a series of median processes, the paraphysis and a median "eye stalk" (sometimes two) which are described elsewhere.

Further developments occur to transform the tripartite brain stem into a brain of five regions. The midbrain shows little important change except for paired dorsal swellings which form the *tectum* (prominent in lower vertebrates), but both hindbrain and forebrain regions become subdivided. In the hindbrain a dorsal outgrowth from the roof of the front of the rhombencephalon becomes the *cerebellum.* The region of the medulla oblongata beneath the cerebellum is little changed in most vertebrates, but in mammals is expanded into the structure termed the *pons.* Pons and overlying cerebellum are distinguished as the *metencephalon* from the more posterior part of the oblongata, the *myelencephalon.*

Still more striking is the development anteriorly of paired outgrowths from the primitive forebrain. These are hollow pockets of brain tissue (at first somewhat analogous to the optic cups) which grow forward toward the nasal region; from them develop the *cerebral hemispheres* and, still farther anteriorly, the *olfactory bulbs.* These structures constitute the *telencephalon,* the anterior terminal segment of the brain; the unpaired part of the forebrain is the *diencephalon.* (It must be noted, however, that, by definition, the most anterior tip of the median

---

* The cerebellum and the cerebral hemispheres are "new additions" not developed at this stage and not included in the brain stem. Also excluded by neurologists in defining the brain stem are certain structures (such as the pons, p. 539), lodged in the brain stem, but intimately connected with the functioning of cerebellum or hemispheres.

† In mammals the eye, as we shall see, has "deserted" the midbrain in favor of the hemispheres as a major brain connection.

forebrain pocket, between the foramina leading to the paired vesicles of the hemi-spheres, is reckoned as part of the telencephalon.)

The principal brain structures of the adult may be tabulated according to the divisions established in the embryo:

Prosencephalon	Telencephalon............	Cerebral hemispheres, including olfactory lobes, basal nuclei (corpus striatum) and cerebral cortex (pallium); olfactory bulbs
	Diencephalon...........	Epithalamus; thalamus; hypothalamus; and appendages
Mesencephalon.........................		Tectum, including optic lobes (corpora quadrigemina in mammals); tegmentum; crura cerebri (cerebral peduncles) in mammals
Rhombencephalon	Metencephalon..........	Part of medulla oblongata; cerebellum; pons of mammals
	Myelencephalon.........	Part of medulla oblongata

Ventricles (Figs. 380, 384, 397, pp. 525, 527, 548).   The original cavity of the embryonic neural tube persists in the adult brain in the form of a series of cavities and passages filled with cerebrospinal fluid. A cavity, or *lateral ventricle,* is present in each of the cerebral hemispheres. These cavities connect posteriorly through an *interventricular foramen* (foramen of Monro) with a median *third ventricle,* situated in the diencephalon. Within the midbrain there is in lower verte-brates a well developed ventricle, but in amniotes this becomes a narrow chan-nel termed the *cerebral aqueduct.* Within the medulla oblongata is a *fourth ventricle;* this tapers posteriorly into the canal of the spinal cord. Over most of the extent of the brain the ventricles are surrounded by thick walls of nervous tissue. The walls are commonly thin, however, in two roof regions, one at the junction of the hemispheres with the diencephalon, the other forming the roof of the fourth ven-tricle. In each of these areas there develops a *choroid plexus* (or tela choroidea) —a highly folded area of richly vascular tissue. Through these plexuses exchange of materials takes place between the blood and cerebrospinal fluid.

Brain Architecture.   In the present elementary account of the vertebrate brain our attention will be mainly centered on external features and gross struc-tures (Figs. 381–389). But while such superficial aspects of brain anatomy are significant, an adequate understanding of the working of the brain can no more be gained from them than a knowledge of the working of a telephone system can be had from an acquaintance with the external appearance and room plan of the telephone exchange. What is of importance in a telephone system is the arrange-ment of switchboards and wiring; in a brain it is the centers which act as switch-boards, in a sense, and the tracts of fibers which form the wiring between them.

It may well be that the brain "wiring" was primitively much like that of the spinal cord—a general crisscross of fibers interconnecting all areas. Such types of connection still persist in the brains of all vertebrates as the *neuropil,* a maze of interlacing fibers diffusely distributed through the brain. Generally, however, there is a strong tendency for the clustering together of nerve cells of specific functions in centers, and the assembling of fibers with like connections into defi-nite bundles.

Although certain special centers have special names, most are termed *gan-glia* or *nuclei* (making an unfortunate, duplicate, biologic use of this latter word). Nuclei, or centers, in a broad sense, range in size from tiny clusters of cells embedded in the gray matter of the brain stem and discernible only on microscopic study, to such massive structures as the cerebellum. Fiber bundles connecting nuclei with one another are in general termed *tracts;* the fibers constituting such a tract are, of course, axons of neurons whose cell bodies lie in the nucleus of origin. A tract is generally given a compound name, the two parts of which designate its origin and termination; thus the corticospinal tract carries impulses from the cortex of the cerebral hemispheres to or toward the motor cells of the spinal cord.

Despite the general tendency of brain cells and fibers to organize into clean cut centers and tracts, a primitive condition persists in the *reticular system.* This is a band of interlacing cells and fibers associated with the motor columns in the brain stem and anterior part of the spinal cord, and particularly well developed in the anterior part of the brain stem. This system is important in motor coordination. Still further, the reticular network appears to function in carrying stimuli downward from the anterior brain regions to the motor centers of the oblongata and cord. This function is an essential one in lower vertebrates, in which motor tracts giving the brain control over trunk activities are poorly developed (cf. Figs. 399, 400, pp. 550, 551); the reticular system is still important in mammals, not only as a persistent "low level" path to motor centers, but also (working in the opposite direction) as an agent which tends to promote activation of the higher centers of the cerebral cortex.

The brain is constructed on a bilaterally symmetric pattern; in consequence, cross connections must be established in order that an animal may not have a literally dual personality. We have noted that even in the spinal cord there are numbers of association neurons whose fibers cross to the opposite side, and in the brain such connections are numerous. There are a number of *commissures,* fiber tracts which connect corresponding regions of the two sides. In addition, there are cases where tracts in their course along the brain cross over from one side to the other (i.e., decussate), sometimes without apparent reason. We have described such a decussation in the case of the optic nerves (which are really brain tracts). Another example is recalled by the well known fact that movements of one side of the body are controlled by the gray matter of the brain hemisphere of the opposite side—a situation caused by a decussation of the corticospinal tracts of the two sides as they pass backward along the brain stem.

The discussion above of the "wiring" of the brain was stated in terms comparable to those of a telephone system, a pattern of end-to-end connections of series of neurons straight through the system from receptor to effector. But actually, as has been increasingly realized in recent years, the general patterns of brain activity are far more intricate in nature, and include "feedbacks," resonating systems associated with memory and learning, and other complexities—into which we shall not attempt to enter here—which are being increasingly approached in the development of computing machines and of the science of cybernetics.

Medulla Oblongata. Approach to the study of brain architecture is best made by first considering those brain parts which are simplest in construction and most closely resemble the spinal cord. The brain stem, including the three primary vesicles of the embryo, is simpler than its specialized outgrowths, the cerebral hemispheres and cerebellum. Even in the stem, however, the anterior part appears to have been the seat of complex nervous centers from the beginning of vertebrate history. It is in the hindbrain region, the medulla oblongata, that we find the closest structural approach to the cord. Further, from the oblongata and the adjacent parts of the midbrain arise all the cranial nerves except the atypical ones from nose and eye.

The medulla oblongata is, particularly in lower vertebrates, closely comparable to an anterior section of the spinal cord—enlarged, however, through the expansion of the central canal to form the fourth ventricle, and with the columns of gray matter of either side widely separated dorsally as a consequence. For most of its length the roof of the oblongata is thin, membranous, and infolded to form the posterior choroid plexus; anteriorly, the oblongata is covered by the cerebellum.

In the gray matter of the oblongata and the posterior part of the midbrain, there is found a series of columns or nuclei of gray matter basically similar to those present in the cord (Figs. 377, B, p. 524; 392). In that region we have noted the presence of a dorsal column, containing association centers for the reception and distribution of sensory impulses, and a ventral column containing motor neurons; we have further noted evidence that both columns may be subdivided into somatic and visceral components. A similar situation is found in the oblongata and the posterior part of the midbrain, although the widely expanded ventricle makes for a somewhat different appearance. A horizontal groove, running along the inner surface of the brain stem on either side, separates a dorsal sensory region from a ventral motor region. Further, here, as in the cord, each of these two can be subdivided into somatic and visceral components.

In the embryo each subdivision appears to be formed as an essentially continuous fore and aft column. Most ventrally is a somatic motor column. Dorsal to this, but still below the limiting sulcus, are visceral motor columns for both branchial muscle and autonomic efferents. Above the sulcus are, in order, visceral sensory and somatic sensory columns, the primary areas of reception for sensations from gut and skin, respectively. The ventralmost column is that from which the ventral cranial nerves—III, IV, VI, XII—arise; the others are the areas of central connection of the dorsal root or branchial nerves—including V, VII, IX, X.

In the adults of lower vertebrate groups much of the embryonic continuity of the column is preserved; in higher types, however, there is a strong trend for a breaking down of the columns into discrete nuclei for the cranial nerves concerned and as centers for various body activities which are controlled or influenced by the brain stem. Thus in mammals the somatic motor column is fragmented into (1) several small anterior nuclei in the midbrain and in the anterior end of the oblongata for the eye muscle nerves, and (2) a more posterior nucleus for the hypoglossal. The special visceral motor column for branchial musculature is broken up into separate special visceral motor nuclei for nerves V, VII, and IX and X (*nucleus ambiguus*), and in this column there develops a center concerned with respiratory rhythm. Small autonomic nuclei are present in the midbrain for eye reflexes, farther back in the oblongata for salivary glands, and still farther back for the autonomic component of the vagus. In vertebrates generally the nuclei associated with the normal visceral sensory fibers remain concentrated in a *nucleus solitarius* of the oblongata, but a parallel *gustatory nucleus* is present for the special visceral sense of taste. The somatic sensory column remains as a single elongate nucleus which, primarily associated with the trigeminal nerve, extends much of the length of the brain stem and even back into the cord.

In mammals a great mass of fibers connecting with the cerebellum bridge over the base of the oblongata anteriorly, causing so prominent a swelling that this region is termed the pons. Even apart from this, the gray matter of the oblongata is thickly sheathed, in amniotes, with white tracts of fibers passing between body and more anterior brain centers. In lower classes the sheathing is relatively thin, for trunk and tail are semi-autonomous and perform most movements reflexly, without referring them to the brain. In fishes generally a limited number of sensory fibers from the body reach the brain stem, cerebellum and midbrain; in amniotes such fibers reach forebrain centers. Conversely, there is little positive control by the higher brain centers over body movement below the stage of birds and mammals except through the rather indirect means of the reticular system mentioned above. A striking exception is the presence in fishes and tailed amphibians of a pair of spectacular *giant cells* (cells of Mauthner) in the medulla whose large fibers extend the entire length of the cord. As discussed before (p. 179), locomotion in fishes and primitive tetrapods is mainly accomplished by rhythmic undulations of the body. To some extent this could be (and presumably is) regulated by local cord reflexes. This pair of cells, however, appears to exercise general control over these movements. In frogs, typical reptiles, and higher forms this type of locomotion disappears and these giant cells disappear likewise.

The series of motor and sensory columns or nuclei of the medulla give us all the elements required for reflex circuits in the brain between sensory reception and the responding effector organs of the head and gill region. But brain mechanisms are not built solely on such a simple plan. In addition to ordinary sensory receptors in the skin, muscles, and gut tube, such as are found throughout the body, we have in the head region special sensory organs. Centers must be present for the primary reception of sensations from these organs; and higher centers must be built up for the association and correlation of these sensations before final "directions" can be issued to the motor columns of brain stem and cord. Much of this apparatus is situated elsewhere in the brain. But even in the relatively simple brain stem region here considered we find the primary area of reception of one of the main sensory systems—the acustico-lateralis system.

The lateral line organs and the ear, a special development from them, are somatic sensory structures; as such, sensations from them were primitively received in the somatic sensory column of the oblongata. So special are they, however, that in fishes a specific *acustico-lateralis* area, often of considerable size, develops above the normal somatic sensory column in the anterior part of the oblongata. In land vertebrates the lateralis system disappears, but acoustic nuclei persist; in mammals there are distinct centers for the vestibular and cochlear parts of the ear.

Cerebellum (Figs. 390, 391).   Rising above the brain stem at the anterior end of the medulla oblongata is the cerebellum, a brain center, often of large size, which is of extreme importance in the coordination and regulation of motor activities and the maintenance of posture. The cerebellum acts in a passive, essentially reflex fashion in the maintenance of equilibrium and body orientation. In addition it plays a major positive role—particularly in mammals—in locomotion. Its function in regulating muscular activity may be compared to that of "staff work" in the movement of an army. To carry out the general orders of an army commander it is necessary that there be in hand information as to the position, current movements, condition, and equipment of the bodies of troops concerned. A "directive" from the higher brain centers (hemispheres or tectum) for a muscular action—say, the movement of a limb—cannot be carried out efficiently unless there are available data as to the current position and movement of the limb, the state of relaxation or contraction of the muscles involved, the general position of the body, and its relation to the outside world. Such data are assembled in the cerebellum and synthesized there, and resulting "orders" issued by efferent pathways render the movement effective.

The data upon which the cerebellum acts are derived from two main sources. One is the acoustic area of the medulla—acustico-lateralis area of lower vertebrates—in which are registered equilibrium sensations from the ear and lateral line sensations. The base of the cerebellum lies immediately above this area, and the cerebellum originated as a specialized part of this sensory center. The second main source of cerebellar data is the system of muscle and tendon spindles. Into the cerebellum are directed fibers of this proprioceptive system carrying data regarding the position of the body parts and the state of muscle tension.

In addition to these two primary sources, the sensory picture assembled in the cerebellum is rounded out by additional fiber relays from skin sensory areas, from the optic centers, and, in lower vertebrates, even from the nose. Information, further, is supplied regarding muscular movements which are directed by higher brain centers, but upon which the cerebellum has influence. In lower vertebrates these data are furnished by fibers from the midbrain, where such impulses in great measure originate; in mammals, where the cerebral cortex dominates motor functions, strong fiber tracts connect cortex with cerebellum via the pons.

After integration of data by the cerebellum, outgoing fiber tracts carry impulses forward and downward on either side of the brain stem to the side walls of the midbrain (the tegmental region), whence they continue (in part after a relay there) to the appropriate motor nuclei of head or body or, in mammals, to the thalamus and thence to the cerebral cortex also.

In forms in which the cerebellum is well developed the fiber tracts leading to and from it are prominent features in the architecture of the brain stem. In mammals, for example, these fibers form three pairs of pillar-like structures, the *cerebellar peduncles* (or brachia, Fig. 390). Anterior peduncles, mainly composed of efferent fiber tracts, connect cerebellum and midbrain. A middle, or lateral, pair of peduncles rise straight upward along the sides of the metencephalon from the pons; these carry fibers running from cerebral cortex to cerebellum, which cross and are relayed ventrally in the pons. Posterior peduncles rise up through the oblongata and carry proprioceptive fiber bundles from the cord.

The cerebellum varies greatly in size and shape from group to group. Its degree of development is correlated with the intricacy of bodily movements; it is large and elaborately constructed in many fishes and in birds and mammals, small in reptiles, little developed in cyclostomes and amphibians, where it is little more than a pair of small centers lying just above the acustico-lateralis nuclei and hardly distinct from them. This most ancient part of the cerebellum persists in all groups as the *auricles* (or flocculi), especially concerned with equilibrium and closely connected with the inner ear.

Even in lampreys and amphibians, however, there is some development of a median cerebellar region between the two auricles above the front end of the fourth ventricle. To this come fibers from the organs of muscle sense and from sensory centers in the brain for integration and correlation with stimuli from the organs of equilibrium in the ear. This primary structure, the *corpus cerebelli*, constitutes the main mass of the cerebellum in typical fishes, reptiles, and birds.

In mammals the rise of the cerebral cortex to command of motor functions, and the development of powerful tracts from motor cortex to cerebellum and return, is correlated with the appearance of large paired and convoluted structures— "cerebellar hemispheres"—which make up much of the bulk of the mammalian organ.

In contrast to every other area of the central nervous system except the cerebral hemispheres and midbrain roof, the cerebellum is a region in which the gray cellular material is superficially placed as a laminated cortex, the white matter internal. In a well developed cerebellum the gray matter is spread out as a surface sheet which is often highly convoluted and thus gains greater area. Beneath this is the white matter, principally a fan-shaped radiation of incoming fibers spreading out in all directions to the surface, and of fibers returning from the gray matter. (The latter are relayed through a central nucleus.) The cerebellar cortex contains cells of several quite distinctive types, arranged in layers, between which sensory data are interchanged by a complex fiber network. There is evidence of some degree of localization of function in the cerebellum, but in many respects the corpus cerebelli appears to act as an integrated unit.

Midbrain and Diencephalon. In contrast with the posterior part of the brain stem, the mesencephalon and diencephalon show specialized functional features in vertebrates of all classes. Sensory and motor nuclei connected with cranial nerves extend some distance into the midbrain from the oblongata. Farther forward, however, such structures are absent. The anterior brain stem centers have in general no direct connection with afferent or efferent impulses apart from those of the optic nerve. This region serves two main functions. In higher vertebrates, more particularly, it is a principal way station between "lower" brain areas and the cerebral hemispheres. In all groups it is important to at least some degree as a locus of centers of nervous correlation and coordination. In mammals these latter functions are overshadowed by those of the cerebral cortex, but in many lower groups the most highly developed association mechanisms lie in the midbrain and thalamus. In a mammal, destruction of the hemispheres results in functional disability; a frog, on the other hand, can go about its business in nearly normal fashion without cerebral hemispheres as long as the brain stem and the structures surmounting it are intact.

The topography of the midbrain and diencephalon and their annexes may be described before dealing with the functions and connections of the various nuclei of their gray matter (Fig. 393).

The midbrain is that part of the brain tube traversed by the cerebral aqueduct; the diencephalon is a region lying about the third ventricle. Diencephalon and midbrain lie on the lines of communication between anterior and posterior brain areas. In mammals the diencephalon is buried below and between the expanded hemispheres, and fiber tracts of white matter form the greater part of the midbrain walls and floor, these including great motor fiber bundles (the pyramidal tracts descending from the hemispheres) which form the *cerebral peduncles* (crura cerebri).

In the midbrain the gray matter above the aqueduct is greatly thickened to form the mesencephalic *tectum*; thinner areas of gray matter in the side walls are termed the *tegmentum*.

Of the areas bounding the third ventricle, the anterior wall, the *lamina terminalis* in which the brain stem ends, is technically considered to form part of the telencephalon; the remainder forms the diencephalon. Accessory structures, described below, are present in the roof and floor of the diencephalon; the main substance of this brain subdivision consists of the lateral walls of the ventricle, which contain in their gray matter a host of nuclei. These wall areas are termed collectively the *thalamus*, because of the fancy that the diencephalon forms a "couch" upon which rest in higher vertebrates the great cerebral hemispheres. Dorsal and ventral parts—roof and floor—of the diencephalon are called the *epithalamus* and *hypothalamus*. Thickened parts of the hypothalamus may cause swellings of the brain surface as *inferior lobes* in fishes (Fig. 381, p. 526) or *lateral lobes* in amphibians and reptiles. The thalamus proper is further divided, on the basis of the centers contained within it, into a *dorsal thalamus* and a *ventral thalamus*.

The roof of the third ventricle is for the most part a thin, non-nervous structure. In it develop a varied series of outgrowths. Most anteriorly, in that part of the roof which pertains to the telencephalic region, there grows upward in embryos of most groups a thin-walled sac, the *paraphysis*, of unknown function; this structure disappears in the adult in most cases. Adjacent to it, in the anterior part of the diencephalic roof, is the region of the anterior choroid plexus. In higher vertebrate classes this is typically invaginated into the cavity of the ventricles; in lower groups, however, it is more generally an extroverted dorsal sac. Still more posteriorly in the diencephalic roof there may develop one or both of a pair of median, stalked eyelike structures, the parietal and pineal organs, discussed elsewhere (pp. 480–481).

In the floor of the diencephalon the *optic chiasma* is a prominent feature anteriorly. Posteriorly, we find in most fishes the *saccus vasculosus*, a thin vesicle which may reach considerable size. Its function is unknown. Possibly it may register fluid pressure, internal and external; the sac is generally best developed, it may be noted, in deep sea fishes (Fig. 381, p. 526). Below the diencephalon lies the *pituitary gland* or *hypophysis cerebri*, most important of all the endocrine structures of the body; it is described in the following chapter.

The eyes appear to have been responsible in great measure for the development, in lower vertebrates, of important association centers in the anterior region of the brain stem (just as the acustico-lateralis system is related to cerebellar development in the hindbrain and the olfactory sense to cerebral development). The optic nerves enter ventro-anteriorly at the chiasma. In all vertebrates except mammals, however, their fibers do not tarry in the diencephalon, but proceed, almost without exception, upward and backward to the roof of the midbrain, where the primary visual center is located. The midbrain roof, the tectum, became, early in vertebrate history, the seat of an important association center; it is the dominant brain region, it would appear, in fishes and amphibians, but became of lessened importance in amniotes with increased development of the cerebral hemispheres (cf. Figs. 399–401, pp. 550–552).

This center developed in connection with visual reception. A greater part of it develops as a pair of *optic lobes*, varying in size with the importance of the eyes, and becoming particularly large in birds and many teleosts. The histologic pattern of the optic lobes of nonmammalian vertebrates is complex, with successive layers of cell and fiber areas, giving them a structure broadly comparable to the laminated gray matter of the cerebellar or cerebral cortex. It appears probable that a visual pattern is here laid out in a fashion similar to that developed in our own case in the cerebral gray matter.

The presence of this visual center in lower vertebrates was, it would seem, responsible for the attraction to the tectal region of stimuli from other sensory areas. Fiber paths lead hither from the acustico-lateralis area, from the somatic sensory column, and from the olfactory region via the diencephalon, and connections with the cerebellum are developed. Sensory stimuli from all somatic sources are here associated and synthesized, and motor responses originated. Primitively, these motor stimuli were relayed, it would seem, by way of the reticular formation lying more ventrally in the tegmental region of the midbrain. In amphibians and reptiles, however, direct motor paths are developed, with the formation of a definite tract from the tectum to the motor columns of the brain stem and cord.

In fishes and amphibians the tectum appears to be the true "heart" of the nervous system—the center which wields the greatest influence on body activity. In reptiles and birds the tectum is still an area of great importance, but is rivaled, particularly in birds, by the development of the basal nuclei of the hemispheres.

In mammals the midbrain has undergone a great reduction in relative importance; most of its functions have been transferred to the gray matter of the cerebral hemispheres, and most of the sensory stimuli which are integrated in the midbrain in lower vertebrates are, instead, projected to the hemispheres in mammals. Most auditory and other somatic sensations which reach the midbrain are, in mammals, relayed onward by way of the thalamus to the hemispheres. It is especially notable that few of the optic fibers in mammals follow the original course to the midbrain; most are interrupted in the thalamus, and visual stimuli are shunted forward to the hemispheres. The tectum retains little function except that of serving in a limited way as a center for visual and auditory reflexes. In mammals it takes the form of four small swellings of the midbrain roof, the *corpora quadrigemina*. Of these the anterior pair deal with visual reflexes and represent the main part of the tectum of lower vertebrates. In amphibians, with the development of hearing functions in the ear, secondary auditory centers develop on either side of the midbrain adjacent to the optic tectum. These develop into the posterior pair of elements of the corpora quadrigemina, which attain considerable size in some groups of mammals; they function as a relay station for auditory stimuli on their way to the thalamus and thence to the cerebral hemispheres.

The region on either wall of the midbrain termed the tegmentum is essentially a forward continuation of the motor areas of the oblongata. As such it functions as a region in which varied stimuli from diencephalon, tectum, and cerebellum are coordinated and transmitted downward to the motor nuclei of the brain stem and spinal cord. In lower vertebrate groups it consists in general of the rather diffuse series of nerve cells and fibers of the reticular system (p. 537). In some instances, however, well defined nuclei may be formed; we may note, for example, the presence in this region in mammals of the *red nucleus* through which are forwarded efferent impulses from the cerebellum.

Of diencephalic regions, the epithalamus is of little importance as a brain center. We may note the constant presence here in all vertebrates of the *habenular body*, a group of small nuclei through which olfactory stimuli pass on their way back from hemispheres to brain stem.

The hypothalamus contains olfactory centers, notably the *tuber cinereum* and, in mammals, the *mammillary bodies* adjacent to the pituitary region. Its main importance, however, is that of a visceral brain center; other major centers are almost exclusively somatic in their activities. Much of the visceral nervous functions are carried out by reflexes in the cord or medulla, but the hypothalamus is in all vertebrate classes a region which serves as a major integrative center for the body's visceral activities. A number of nuclei are present in this region. To them pass stimuli from olfactory and taste organs as well as sensations from various visceral structures of the body. Particularly important are connections with the more strictly olfactory areas of the cerebral hemispheres; the sense of smell plays a large role in visceral nervous activities. These nuclei have efferent connections, posteriorly, with autonomic centers. The hypothalamus controls to a considerable degree the activity of the pituitary; as will be seen, some hypothalamic nuclei actually secrete hormones which pass to the neurohypophysis. The range of hypothalamic regulatory functions is incompletely known. It is, however, of interest that (for example) temperature regulation in reptiles, birds, and mammals and, in the last class, heart beat, respiration rate, blood pressure, sleep and gut activities are controlled or influenced by the hypothalamus.

The thalamus proper is in lower vertebrate classes an area of modest importance. Its ventral, motor part may be considered an anterior outpost of the motor column of the brain stem; it is in every class a motor coordinating center, and is further a relay center on the motor path from the basal nuclei of the hemispheres back to the brain stem.

In lower vertebrates the dorsal, sensory, region of the thalamus appears to be merely an anterior extension of the sensory correlation areas connected with the tectal region of the midbrain. Its importance increases proportionately with the increased development of association centers in the cerebral hemispheres. Even in vertebrates with a lowly brain organization, a certain amount of sensory data may be passed forward from the brain stem, particularly the reticular system, by relay in the thalamus to the cerebral hemispheres for synthesis there with olfactory stimuli. With a high degree of development of association centers in the hemispheres of amniotes, there is a great development of nuclei in the dorsal thalamus for relay purposes. In the mammalian stage (with the practical abandonment of the tectal association center) the thalamus reaches the height of its development. In mammals all somatic sensations are assembled in the gray matter of the cerebral cortex; and all this sensory material (excepting, of course, olfaction) is relayed to it via the dorsal thalamus. Conspicuous elements in its structure are the *lateral geniculate body*, whence optic stimuli are projected upward to the hemispheres, the *medial geniculate body*, which relays auditory stimuli, and the *ventral nucleus*, which transmits somatic sensory stimuli.

Cerebral Hemispheres. The evolution of the cerebral hemispheres is the most spectacular story in comparative anatomy. These paired outgrowths of the forebrain began their history, it would seem, simply as loci of olfactory reception. Early in tetrapod history they became large and important centers of sensory correlation; by the time the mammalian stage is reached, the greatly expanded surfaces of the hemispheres have become the dominant association center, seat of the highest mental faculties. The development of centers of such importance in this anterior, originally olfactory, segment of the brain emphasizes the importance of the sense of smell in vertebrates. The acustico-lateralis system and vision, are, as we have seen, senses upon which important correlation mechanisms were erected early in vertebrate history, but in the long run smell has proved dominant. Smell is of little account in higher primates, such as ourselves. But in following down the ancestral line from mammals to their early vertebrate ancestors, it appears that this sense has been throughout a main channel through which information concerning the outside world has been received. It is thus but natural that its brain centers should form a base upon which higher correlative and associative mechanisms have been built.

Presumably the brain tube of the earliest vertebrates was, like that of Amphioxus, a single, unpaired structure all the way forward to its anterior end; the cavity of the telencephalon was a median, unpaired terminal ventricle, as it is today in the early embryo of every type. In all vertebrates the most anterior part of the wall of the third ventricle is considered as belonging to the telencephalon, but in land vertebrates most of that brain segment consists of distinct paired structures, the lateral ventricles and the tissues surrounding them. Most fishes—cyclostomes, Chondrichthyes, actinopterygians—show a transitional condition, for there is, for much of the length of the end brain, a single ventricular cavity which bifurcates only distally.

In even the lowest of living vertebrates, the cyclostomes, each half of the end brain is subdivided into two parts, the *olfactory bulb* and the hemisphere. The bulb is a terminal swelling in which the fibers of the olfactory nerve end; its size varies with the acuteness of the sense of smell; it is, for example, small to minute in birds. Here is located the primary olfactory nucleus. From its cells, fibers pass back (sometimes with a relay en route) to be distributed to the various regions of the hemisphere. Depending on the configuration of the head and braincase, bulb and hemisphere may be in close contact or may be well separated, with a distinct *olfactory tract* between them.

Primitively, as seen in cyclostomes, the hemisphere is merely an *olfactory lobe*—an area in which olfactory sensations are assembled and learned olfactory reactions relayed to more posterior centers for correlation with other sensory impulses (Figs. 394, *A*, 395, *A*). At this level of development few if any fibers ascend from the stem to the hemispheres for correlation there. In general, fiber paths from olfactory areas follow two routes: ventrally to end in visceral centers in the hypothalamus, or dorsally to the habenulae in the epithalamus and thence to the tectum or motor areas of the brain stem.

A higher stage, although still primitive, is that seen in the amphibians (Figs. 394, *B*, 395, *B*); sharks are at approximately the same stage of cerebral development. Here most of the tissues of the hemispheres can be divided regionally into three areas, of interest because of their history in more progressive types. All three areas receive olfactory stimuli and exchange fibers with one another; all three discharge to the brain stem. Ventrally lies the region of the *basal nuclei*, essentially equivalent to the corpus striatum of mammals, and destined

Fig. 396. Abberrant types of forebrains. Section of left hemispheres of *A*, a teleost (codfish); *B*, a bird (parrot). In teleosts the roof of the ventricles is only a membrane; the gray matter has been pushed downward and inward to join the basal nuclei (or striatum) as an epistriatum. In birds the cortex is little developed but there is (analagous to the teleosts) a great development of the basal nuclei (or corpus striatum); a dorsal region termed the hyperstriatum is believed to be a correlation center of high order. *v*, Ventricle. Basal nuclei hatched.

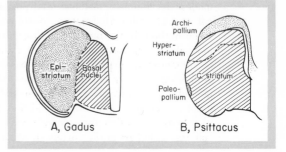

A, Gadus   B, Psittacus

in higher stages to move into the central parts of the hemisphere. The basal nuclei form a correlation center at an early evolutionary stage and become increasingly more important in this regard in more advanced groups. Sensory impulses are "projected" upward into the basal nuclei from the thalamus for correlation with olfactory sensations; descending fibers carry impulses from the basal nuclei to centers in the thalamus and midbrain tegmental region.

The gray matter of all parts of the hemisphere except the basal nuclei tends progressively to move outward toward the surface, and thus becomes the *cerebral cortex*, or *pallium* ("cloak"). In the amphibian stage the gray matter is still largely internal, but these terms may nevertheless be used in the light of later history. A band of tissue along the lateral surface of the hemisphere is termed the *paleopallium*. This area remains largely olfactory in character, and the paleopallial region is that of the olfactory lobes in higher stages. Dorsally and medially lies the *archipallium*, which is antecedent to the hippocampus of mammals. This area is to a minor extent a correlation center in all land vertebrates, with ascending fibers from the diencephalon as well as fibers from olfactory bulb and lobe and appears to be related to "emotional" behavior. The tract from this region to the hypothalamus is the main component of the fiber bundle termed the *fornix* in mammals.

An aberrant type of forebrain is seen in the dominant fishes of today, the teleosts and their relatives (Fig. 396, *A*). Here the gray matter of the hemispheres has been crowded downward and inward to form massive structures bulging up into the ventricles from below. These masses include both the basal nuclei or striatum and tissues above it representing the pallial areas; the roof of the hemispheres is but a thin, non-nervous membrane. This peculiar development is probably to be correlated with the fact that olfaction is relatively unimportant in teleosts.

The reptile hemispheres are advanced over the amphibian type in both complexity of organization and relative size compared with other brain parts. Roof and side walls of the hemispheres show in the main an essentially primitive arrangement of the pallial areas, but some of the gray matter has spread outward toward the surface. The basal nuclei are large and have moved inward to occupy a considerable area in the floor. Strong projection fiber bundles run to the basal nuclei from the thalamus and back from them to the brain stem; the basal nuclei are obviously correlation centers of importance.

In birds (Fig. 396, *B*) the hemispheres are further enlarged. Their evolutionary development, however, has taken place in a fashion radically different from that seen in mammals. Presumably correlated, as in teleosts, with the great reduction of the sense of smell in birds generally, there is very little development of the cerebral cortex; there is a very small area of paleopallium, and a modest development, at the medial posterior areas of the hemispheres, of a cortical area of archipallial nature; despite some current uncertainty there appears to be nothing in the bird brain to correspond to the neopallium, described below, which is the seat of the highest brain activities of a mammal. Instead, there is an enormous expansion of the basal ganglia, or corpus striatum. In lower vertebrates such structures are divided by workers in neurology into several components, with which we will not concern ourselves here. In birds there is, in addition, a massive new dorsal addition to the basal ganglia series termed the *hyperstriatum*, which appears over much of the upper surface of the bird hemispheres. This part of the corpus striatum is most prominently developed in those avian forms which appear to be more "intelligent" and capable of learning. Apart from this variable development, however, the corpus striatum appears to function in a fashion very different from the mammalian neopallium. In birds we see a complex series of action patterns which may be called forth to meet a great variety of situations. Most are, however, stereotyped; the actions are innate, instinctive. The bird, its brain dominated by its basal nuclei, is essentially a highly complex mechanism with relatively little of the learning capacity which in mammals is associated with the development of the expanded neopallium.

The first faint traces of mammalian cortical development are to be seen in certain reptiles (Figs. 394, *D*, 395, *D*). In the hemispheres of these forms we find, between paleopallium and archipallium, a small area of superficial gray matter of a new type, that of the *neopallium*. Even at its inception it is an association center, receiving, like the basal nuclei, fibers which relay to it sensory stimuli from the brain stem and, in turn, sending "commands" directly to the motor columns.

The evolutionary history of the mammal brain is essentially a story of neopallial expansion and elaboration. The cerebral hemispheres have attained a bulk exceeding that of all other parts of the brain, particularly through the growth of the neopallium, and dominate functionally as well. This dominance is apparent in mammals of all types, but is particularly marked in a variety of progressive forms, most especially in man. In even the more primitive mammals (Figs. 394, *E*, 395, *E*) the neopallium has expanded over the roof and side walls of the hemispheres. It has crowded the archipallium on to the median surface above; the paleopallium is restricted to the ventrolateral part of the hemispheres, below the *rhinal fissure*—a furrow which marks the boundary between olfactory and nonolfactory areas of the cortex. With still further neopallial growth (Figs. 394, *F*, 395, *F*) the archipallium is folded into a restricted area on the median part of the hemispheres, where it remains as the *hippocampus*,* and the olfactory lobes, which include the paleopallium, come to constitute but a small ventral hemisphere region—the *pyriform lobe*. The corpus striatum persists as a relay center for the more automatic reactions.

As it develops in mammalian evolution, the neopallium assumes newer and higher types of neural activity in correlation and association and also takes over many of the functions previously exercised by brain stem centers and many of those of the basal nuclei. The midbrain tectum loses its former importance and is reduced to a reflex center. Auditory and other somatic sensations are relayed on forward to the thalamus, most of the optic fibers are intercepted there, and all are projected from thalamus to hemispheres by great fiber tracts. We have seen thalamic connections of this sort for the basal nuclei had evolved in lower vertebrate groups, and in birds powerful projection tracts evolved in connection with that dominant brain region. In mammals, however, the greater part of these fibers plunge on through the basal nuclei—here termed the *corpus striatum*†—to radiate out to the neopallial surface. With all the sensory data thus made available, the appropriate motor "decision" is made by the cortex. As mentioned earlier (p. 540), one set of stimuli is sent from cortex to cerebellum by way of the pons for appropriate regulatory effects; there are cortical connections to the cor-

---

* So called because of its fancied resemblance (in section) to a sea horse, with its coiled tail.

† The name is due to the striated appearance caused by the passage of the fiber bundles through the gray matter of the basal nuclei.

pus striatum and even some discharge to the hypothalamus and thence to the autonomic system. The main motor discharge, however, is by way of the *pyramidal tract,* a fiber bundle which extends directly, without intervening relay, from the neopallial cortex to "voluntary" motor regions of brain stem and cord —a feature emphasizing the dominating position of the cerebral cortex in mammals.

With expansion, the cerebral hemispheres tend to cover and envelop the other brain structures. In a primitive mammalian brain (Fig. 385, *A,* p. 528) the cerebrum leaves much of the midbrain exposed; but in a majority of living mammals (as in Fig. 383, *B,* p. 527) the midbrain and part of the cerebellum are overlapped. The paired ventricles and the "old-fashioned" areas associated more purely with olfaction—olfactory bulb, pyriform lobe, hippocampus, and related tracts and nuclei—have been shifted and distorted, with the growth of the mammalian hemispheres, into patterns which are difficult to compare with those of lower and more simply built brains (Fig. 397).

Since the neopallium is essentially a thin sheet of laminated cellular material, underlain by the white fibrous mass of the cerebrum, simple increase in hemisphere bulk fails to keep cortical expansion in step with increase in fiber volume; surface folding is necessary. In small or primitive mammals the neopallial surface is often smooth; in large or more progressive types the surface is generally highly convoluted—thrown into folds which greatly increase the surface area. The folds are termed *gyri,* the furrows between, *sulci.* These are prominent landmarks on the brain surface, and it was once believed that in some cases they are structural boundary markers for specific cortical areas. Further study, however, shows that (apart from the rhinal fissure and, to some degree, a central sulcus in primates) there is no fixed relationship between the convolution pattern and the structural subdivisions of the cortex.

In man, most particularly, the hemisphere is often described as composed of a series of lobes—a *frontal lobe* anteriorly, a *parietal lobe* at the summit, an *occipital lobe* at the posterior end, and a lateral *temporal lobe.* These terms are, however, purely topographic, and have no precise meaning as regards the architecture or functioning of cortical areas.

The gray matter of the neopallium has a complex histologic structure with, in placentals, as many as six superposed cellular layers and masses of interven-

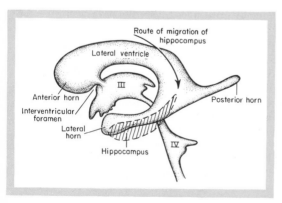

Fig. 397. The brain ventricles of an advanced mammalian type (Homo) in lateral view from the left. The ventricles are represented as solid objects, the brain tissue being removed. With expansion of the cerebral hemisphere, the lateral ventricle has expanded backward to a posterior horn in the occipital lobe, and downward and forward laterally to a lateral horn in the temporal lobe. With this backward and downward expansion, various shifts in position of brain parts occurred. The hippocampus, which developed dorsally on the median surface of the hemisphere (cf. Fig. 395, *F*) has been rotated, in advanced mammals, backward and downward into a ventral position near the midline.

Fig. 398.   Lateral view of *A*, the brain of a shrew; *B*, the cerebrum of man; to show cortical areas.

ing fibrils—this in contrast to paleopallial and archipallial regions, in which but two to four cell layers are present. It is estimated that in some of the larger mammalian brains the number of neopallial cells may run into the billions. The white matter internal to the gray includes, besides a fan of cortical connections to and from lower brain regions, a great interweaving meshwork of fibers which connect every part of the cortex with every other. An *anterior commissure* (Fig. 393, p. 532), connecting olfactory portions of the two hemispheres is present in all vertebrates, and other commissural fibers are present in the fornix; to connect the neopallial structures a massive new commissure, the *corpus callosum* (Fig. 385, *B*, p. 528), develops in placental mammals.

The complex "wiring" system connecting all parts of the cortex with one another would suggest that the gray matter is essentially a unit, equipotent in all its parts for any cerebral activity. This is to some extent true; experiments show that in laboratory animals a good part of the neopallium may be destroyed without permanently interfering with normal activity, and the results of injury and disease conditions show that the same holds for certain areas of the human brain. On the other hand, it is clear that certain cortical areas are normally associated with specific functions (Fig. 398). We have previously discussed the "old-fashioned" cortical regions devoted mainly to olfactory sensations—the paleopallium and archipallium, represented in mammals in the pyriform lobe and hippocampus, respectively. Regional differentiation is present in the neopallium as well. The front part of the hemispheres includes a motor area. The posterior part is associated with sensory perception. Special regions are associated with eye and ear, in occipital and temporal lobes, while the areas for sensations received from the skin and proprioceptive organs are situated farther forward, close to the motor area. In primates a *central sulcus* which crosses the top of the hemisphere from medial to lateral surfaces divides (although not exactly) motor and sensory areas. Along its front margin are specific motor areas for each subdivision of the body and limbs, arranged in linear order; along the back margin is an exactly parallel arrangement of loci for sensory reception from the various members. In many mammals nearly the entire surface of the neopallium is occupied by areas associated more or less closely with specific sensory or motor functions. In man, particularly, however, we find that these specific functional areas occupy only a relatively small part of the neopallium. Between them have developed large areas of gray matter, most conspicuously one occupying much of the frontal lobe, which are not associated with specific sensory or motor functions. They are, in consequence, sometimes termed "blank areas." This is the reverse of the case; as shown by injury to these areas, they are the seat of our highest mental properties, including learning ability, initiative, foresight, and judgment.

Size of cerebral hemispheres might be thought of as giving a clue to the mental abilities of a mammal. This is true in a sense, but subject to strong qualification. If the amount of cortical surface present is related in any way to intelligence, it is obvious that of two brains of the same size, one with convoluted hemispheres is better than one with a smooth surface. The bulk of the animal concerned affects brain size, presumably because of the need of greater terminal areas for the increased sensory and motor connections, but the increase in brain size as a whole is not absolutely proportionate to body bulk, and large animals tend to have relatively small brains without, it seems, any loss of mental powers. That absolute brain size is not a criterion of intellect is indicated by the fact that the brain of a whale may have five times the volume of that of a man. Nor is the proportion of brain size to body size a perfect criterion, for small South American monkeys may have a brain one fifteenth or one twentieth of body weight, while the brain weight of an average man is but one fortieth that of the body. A final and most important factor that must be taken into account is the relative complexity of the cortical sheet.

Brain Patterns—Summary. In earlier paragraphs of this chapter we described the principal structural and functional elements of the brain and certain of their interconnections. The more important features may be summarized here.

In the posterior part of the brain stem—the medulla oblongata—there is present a series of sensory and motor columns closely comparable to those of the spinal cord and connected with them by the reticular system. As in the cord, direct reflexes may take place between sensory and motor columns. The history of brain evolution, however, has been mainly one of the development, above and

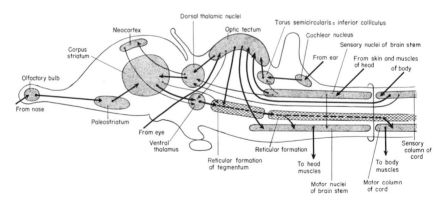

Fig. 399. Diagram of the main centers and "wiring" arrangement of a reptile, in which the tectal region of the midbrain plays a dominant role; the corpus striatum (basal ganglia) is of some importance as a correlation center, but the neocortex (neopallium) is unimportant. The reticular formation of the brain stem (cross hatched) is important in carrying motor impulses to nuclei of the stem and cord. In this oversimplified diagram only a limited number of paths between somatic receptors and effectors are included; visceral centers and paths are omitted, as are cerebellar connections (shown in Fig. 390, p. 531).

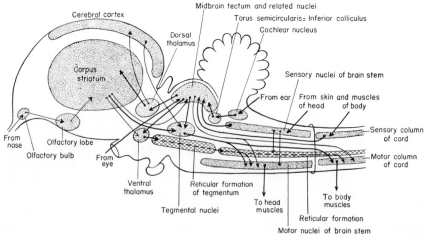

Fig. 400. A "wiring diagram" of a bird brain, comparable to that of Figure 399. The midbrain tectum is still of importance, but the corpus striatum is the dominant center in many regards.

in front of the medulla, of higher centers of coordination and association, interposed between sensory and motor areas. In such centers sensory data are assembled and synthesized and resultant motor stimuli sent out to the motor columns of brain stem and cord. These centers have been in the main built up, as dorsal outgrowths of laminated gray matter, about areas primarily concerned with the special senses of the head region—acustico-lateralis, visual, and olfactory.

1. The primary area of reception for equilibrium and lateral line stimuli lies in the sensory columns of the medulla oblongata; above this developed the cerebellum, important in all vertebrates. This organ initiates no bodily movement, apart from adjustments in posture, but insures that motor directives initiated in other centers be carried out in proper fashion. It may receive fibers from all the somatic senses, but is principally informed by the adjacent acustico-lateralis centers and by fibers from the proprioceptive system of the muscles and tendons. Its outgoing, regulatory stimuli are for the most part sent to the midbrain and thence distributed to the motor areas. In mammals, where the cortex assumes direct control over most motor responses, powerful circuits are established connecting cerebellum and cortex in both directions (Fig. 390, p. 531).

2. In lower vertebrates the main centers dominating nervous activity are situated in the anterior regions of the brain stem. (*a*) A great center of coordination in which motor activity is initiated is established in the tectum of the midbrain, in which the primary visual center is situated (Fig. 399). To this region are relayed also stimuli from the nose, ear, and other somatic senses; from it are sent out stimuli to the motor columns. As we ascend the vertebrate scale the tectal area becomes rivalled and then exceeded by the association centers of the cerebral hemispheres; in birds, despite the great development of the corpus striatum, the tectum is still prominent, but in mammals most of the sensory data formerly assembled in the tectum are, instead, relayed to the neopallium via the thalamus, and the tectum is reduced to a reflex center. (*b*) The tectal centers are somatic in nature; corresponding centers for visceral sensations and visceral

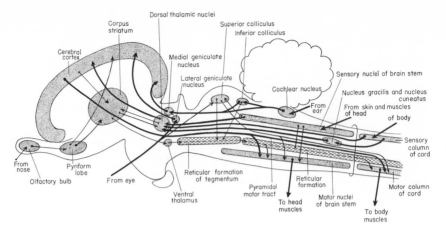

Fig. 401. A "wiring diagram" of a mammalian brain comparable to Figures 399 and 400. The midbrain tectum is reduced to a minor reflex center, and the corpus striatum is relatively unimportant; most sensory impulses are projected "upward" to the cerebral cortex, whence a direct motor path (pyramidal tract) extends to the motor centers of brain stem and cord.

motor responses were early established farther anteriorly and ventrally, in the hypothalamus. This situation remains little changed throughout the vertebrate series.

3. As the vertebrate scale is ascended, the cerebral hemispheres, originally only a center for olfactory sensation, have become more and more important as association centers. (*a*) First of cerebral areas to gain importance is that of the basal nuclei, the corpus striatum. Fiber tracts from the thalamus relay somatic sensations to this body, and return fibers carry motor stimuli back to the midbrain and thence to the motor columns. In reptiles the corpus striatum is a prominent structure which rivals the older tectal center in importance, and in birds the corpus striatum, with the new addition of the hyperstriatum, becomes a large, complex, and dominant center (Fig. 400). (*b*) In mammals, descended along a different evolutionary line from that leading to birds, a different development has occurred. The new master organ is the neopallium, a greatly expanded gray cortical area for correlation, association, and learning. This assumes the greater part of the higher functions once concentrated in the tectum or corpus striatum, gains a complete array of somatic sensory data through projection fibers from the thalamus, and develops direct motor paths to the motor columns of the brain stem and spinal cord (Fig. 401).

17

ENDOCRINE
ORGANS

In the last chapter we described, in the nervous system, an exceedingly complicated but highly efficient method of coordinating bodily activities by "messages" received from and sent to specific areas of the body with speed and precision. We shall here consider a second integrative system, under which information and directives are carried through the blood stream by chemical "messengers," the *hormones* produced by *endocrine glands*. This method of transmission is, of course, slower than transmission by nerve impulse, and hormonal effects are often broadly distributed over the body to a variety of organs and tissues, in contrast to the "pin-pointing" possible in the case of the nervous system. But despite the seeming irrationality and vagueness of hormonal transmission, many of the hormones are not only important but absolutely essential for the maintenance of the life of the organism.

For convenience, I have gathered in this chapter data on all the known hormone producing structures of the body, although they do not form an organ system, but are scattered here and there throughout the body—in some cases literally from stem to stern—and may derive from a variety of organ systems or organs or may develop as discrete units. The situation is somewhat similar to that of hemopoietic organs—just as it makes no difference in which part of the body blood corpuscles are produced, so the area of production of hormones is inconsequential, as long as they can be passed into some element of the circulatory system and thence be distributed throughout the body.

Neural and hormonal systems of communication, while distinct, are far from independent of one another. Directly or indirectly, the nervous system may be powerfully affected by hormones. On the other hand, the "master gland" of the endocrine system, the hypophysis, is strongly influenced by the adjacent hypothalamus, and some of its hormones are actually produced by ganglia in that brain region; again, the adrenal medulla, although an endocrine organ, is actually composed of modified nerve cells.

Which is the older regulatory system, nervous or endocrine? There is no clear answer to this; probably both evolved in parallel fashion. Elementary nervous systems are present in the most primitive of metazoan animals; numerous hormonal systems are known in invertebrates, and undoubtedly many more await discovery. Any chemical material given off by a cell as a result of its metabolic processes is liable to have some effect, favorable or deleterious, on other organs. There quite surely went on, in the course of the rise of chordates, processes of evolutionary selection of chemical products favoring the survival and well-being of the organism—processes quite comparable in nature to those under which morphologic structures were evolved.

THE HYPOPHYSIS

Below the diencephalic region of the brain, lies a small but most essential structure, the major endocrine organ of the body, the *pituitary gland* or *hypophysis cerebri* (Figs. 209, p. 301, 381–385, pp. 526–528; 402–404, pp. 555–557). In most vertebrates the pituitary tissues form a single compact mass, contained in a pocket (the *sella turcica*) in the floor of the braincase. Actually, however, the gland is a dual structure, its two portions having very different embryologic origins and functioning in different fashions.

Downward from the embryonic diencephalon extends a hollow, finger-like process, the infundibulum. Upward from the embryonic mouth there grows an ectodermal pocket, the hypophyseal pouch (Rathke's pouch). This latter usually closes over in adult life, but remains open in a few fishes (notably the cyclostomes). From both these embryonic structures there proliferate masses of tissue which unite to form the adult pituitary.

The terminology applied to the subdivisions of the pituitary has been variable and confusing. It is best considered as consisting of two parts or lobes in accordance with embryologic origins. The greater part of its substance and that most important in hormone formation, is included (1) in the *adenohypophysis*, derived from the hypophyseal pouch. This consists of masses of secretory cells, of which the major portion is (a) the *pars distalis*; there is often, particularly in mammals (b) a distinct *pars tuberalis*, an upgrowth around the stalk of the infundibulum, and (c) a *pars intermedia*, which tends to fuse with the neural part of the gland.* The other "half" of the gland is (2) the *neurohypophysis*. The glandular part of the neurohypophysis is the *lobus nervosus*, or neural lobe, lying close beside the adenohypophysis in the sella turcica; but the *infundibulum*, from the bottom of which the neural lobe develops, is also to be included in the neurohypophysis, and, as we shall see, a fraction of the hypothalamus forms an integral part of the neurohypophyseal mechanism and might properly be included as well.

The adenohypophysis, histologically, consists of masses and cords of secretory epithelial cells separated by sinusoids and supported by a loose framework of connective tissue. The greater part of its mass is included in the pars distalis. At least two types of gland cells are present, but there is little evidence to suggest association of specific cell types with the production of specific hormones. The intermediate lobe consists of polygonal secretory cells. The pars tuberalis, when present, consists of cells which appear to have little if any secretory function.

* The term "anterior lobe" is frequently used to designate the pars distalis, with or without the pars tuberalis; "posterior lobe" may designate the neurohypophysis, or neural lobe only, but may include the pars intermedia as well.

SUBARACHNOID SPACE
PIA MATER
OPTIC CHIASMA
DURA MATER
SUPRAOPTICO-HYPOPHYSEAL
TRACT
PARS TUBERALIS
PERIOSTEUM
DURA MATER
PARS DISTALIS
RESIDUAL LUMEN

THIRD VENTRICLE
MAMMILLARY BODY
CEREBRAL PEDUNCLE
TUBERO-HYPOPHYSEAL TRACT
SUBARACHNOID SPACE
ARACHNOID MEMBRANE
DIAPHRAGMA SELLAE
PARS NERVOSA
PARS INTERMEDIA
PONS
SUBDURAL SPACE
SPHENOID BONE

Fig. 402.   Section through a human pituitary and the adjacent structures at the base of the brain. (From Turner.)

Very different in nature is the neural lobe. This contains, as a storage depot, amounts of hormonal material which can be passed on into the small blood vessels which ramify here. Present, too, are branched cells which were once thought to produce the secretions of the neurohypophysis. Now they are believed to be no more than supporting materials, comparable to the neuroglia in other parts of the central nervous system. In recent years there has been made the interesting discovery that the secretions found in this "gland" are not produced there, but are neurosecretions produced by cells in the true brain substance of the hypothalamus.

Among the various small nuclei of the hypothalamus, two are of concern here. Anterior to the infundibulum, just above the optic chiasma, are the appropriately named paired *supraoptic nuclei.* In an analogous position behind the infundibulum are the *paraventricular nuclei.* From both these pairs of nuclei there pass down bundles of stout axons into the neural lobe, and similar fibers appear also to originate to some extent from other hypothalamic centers. The cell bodies in these nuclei can be seen histologically to have secretory powers. It is possible that their axons have some degree of ability to transmit ordinary nerve impulses, but it is clear that their main function is to enable hormonal materials produced in the cell bodies to flow down their lengths into the neural lobe, where they are stored pending release into the blood stream.

The hypophysis as described above is of the type found in typical mammals; very different anatomic features are found in some lower vertebrates. In the lamprey there is no distinct infundibulum or formed neural lobe, and the neural lobe homologue is simply a plate of tissue lying in the floor of the diencephalon. Again, the hypophyseal pouch is not closed but, as discussed in an early chapter (p. 299, Fig. 231), is a tube lying below the diencephalon and opening outward and upward to the surface in conjunction with the nasal pouch. The lamprey adenohypophysis consists of clusters of epithelial tissue detached dorsally from this tube and underlying the neural lobe plate. The two parts of the pituitary are separated by tissues corresponding to the arachnoid and pia mater of other parts of the brain wall and containing blood vessels as well as some connective tissue.

In cartilaginous fishes and actinopterygians there has developed a distinct infundibulum (from which a vascular sac projects at the posterior margin) and there is a well formed mass of neural lobe tissue; below, the hypophyseal pouch

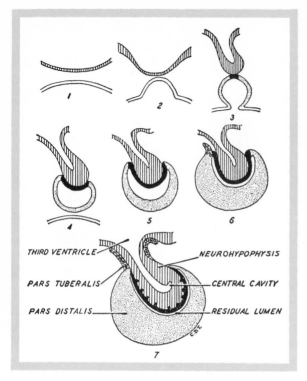

THIRD VENTRICLE

PARS TUBERALIS

PARS DISTALIS

NEUROHYPOPHYSIS

CENTRAL CAVITY

RESIDUAL LUMEN

Fig. 403. Diagrams showing stages in the development of the mammalian pituitary from brain tissue (hatched) and from the hypophyseal (Rathke's) pouch. As will be seen, only the neurohypophysis is formed from neural material; the three other parts, constituting the adenohypophysis, are derived from the pouch epithelium. (After Turner.)

has closed in almost every case and its epithelium forms a massive adenohypophysis in which, however, there are no well marked subdivisions. Peculiar to these two groups is the fact that the lower surface of the neural lobe is irregular, and finger-like processes may extend down from it into the area of the adenohypophysis; the two parts, however, are still distinctly separated throughout by a vascular cleft.

We would expect that in a lungfish we would find conditions approximating those expected in the ancestors of land vertebrates. This is the case. Conditions are simpler than in cartilaginous and ray-finned fishes; there is no vascular sac to complicate the picture, and the neural lobe is a rather flat sheet of tissue, little thickened except posteriorly. The marked cleavage between the two primary parts of the hypophysis has in great measure disappeared; instead, a part of the adenohypophysis tissue is closely applied posteriorly to the neural lobe in a fashion comparable to the mammalian pars intermedia, and is separated by a cleft from the major portion of the adenohypophysis, which presumably represents the pars distalis. Amphibian hypophyses are similar in nature, but the neural lobe is somewhat better defined. In reptiles there is some growth of the neural lobe, but it is only in mammals that it tends to assume a compact and more or less spherical structure. The development of a distinct pars intermedia is somewhat variable in amphibians, reptiles, and birds; even in mammals this area is not defined in such groups as insectivores, edentates and carnivores.

The pituitary, particularly the adenohypophysis, is subject to strong influence by other endocrine organs; this is readily accomplishable, since both major parts of the gland are well supplied with blood vessels from the internal carotid system, and the hypothalamic ganglia forming the neural lobe secretions are reached by intracranial vessels. But in addition the adenohypophysis is, we are certain, greatly influenced by the brain, and the manner in which this influence is effected is a matter of interest. In many fishes nerve fibers pass from the neural lobe into the body of the adenohypophysis, thus affording a reasonable path by which brain activity can affect glandular activity here. But in lungfish and tetrapods this not the case. Nerve fibers may enter the pars intermedia, but (except for some which appear to be autonomic fibers for blood vessels) none penetrate to the pars distalis, where almost all of the hormones are formed. In this condition, how does the brain influence the gland?

Apparently indirectly, through a curious local portal system of tiny blood vessels. The vessels supplying arterial blood to the adenohypophysis pass close to or through the floor of the diencephalon anterior to the infundibulum. The tract carrying neural secretions to the neural lobe passes through this same area, which, particularly in mammals, tends to form a bit of a swelling on the lower surface of the brain, termed the *median eminence*. In lungfishes and tetrapods the blood vessels to the adenohypophysis do not run directly to that gland, but enter the region of the median eminence, break up into a capillary system, then re-collect as a set of small portal veins to pass on to the pars distalis. It is thought that in passage through the median eminence the blood picks up neurohumoral materials which are the agents transmitting "information" from the brain to the

Fig. 404. Median sagittal sections of *A*, the teleost Anguilla; *B*, the shark Scylliorhinus; *C*, the lungfish Protopterus; *D*, an amniote. Adenohypophysis, fine hatching; neurohypophysis, stipple. *Ch*, Optic chiasma; *Me*, median eminence; *Nh*, neurohypophysis; *Nl*, formed neural lobe; *Np*, preoptic neurosecretory nuclei; *Pv*, portal vessels; *Sv*, saccus vasculosus. To show especially the neurosecretory supply to the neurohypophysis and the portal system of lungfish and tetrapods. (From Wingstrand in Gorbman, Comparative Endocrinology, John Wiley and Sons.)

gland. This seems like a curiously roundabout way of accomplishing an important function; but no other effective method is known or suggested.

Attempts have been made to identify predecessors of the hypophysis, or of its components, in lower chordates. In *Amphioxus* there is a pit in the anterior part of the neural tube (where a brain should be, if *Amphioxus* had a brain) which has been compared to an infundibulum, but the nature of this small structure is uncertain. Below, in the roof of the mouth, is another small pit suggesting the pouch of embryonic vertebrates from which the adenohypophysis is formed. But this pit appears to be merely a mucus-secreting, rather than a hormone-secreting, structure. In adult tunicates (Fig. 6, p. 18) there is present a *neural gland* which is in certain regards suggestive of a pituitary. This gland opens into what is morphologically the dorsal side of the entrance to the pharynx, and lies close below the ganglion which is the closest approach to a brain structure present in the simple nervous system of the adult tunicate. Morphologically, the neural gland could be reasonably considered as antecedent to the hypophysis. But there is at present no positive evidence that it is an endocrine-producing structure.

Some nine or ten hormones are known to be produced by the pituitary and still others have been, or are, suspected to be present. The greater part of the work concerned with them has been done on the mammalian pituitary, but most of the whole series are present throughout the vertebrate classes (although, for example, the hormones of the neurohypophysis are weakly developed in elasmobranchs, and the cyclostome situation is incompletely known). Most of the pituitary hormones are produced by the adenohypophysis, principally by the pars distalis. All are proteins or polypeptides. They may be listed and briefly described:

GROWTH HORMONE or SOMATOTROPHIN (STH). This has a very broad influence on growth and metabolism, in general, with marked influence on growth of skeleton and muscle, metabolism of fats and carbohydrates, and retention of protein nitrogen in the tissues; it further acts to enhance the effect of other hormones on the activity of thyroid, adrenal cortex, and reproductive organs.

CORTICOTROPHIN (ACTH). Vital for adrenal cortex activity in secretion of hormones and exerts some metabolic influence in other regards.

THYROTROPHIN (TSH). Essential for the stimulation of the thyroid to form and release thyroid hormones.

PROLACTIN. This and the following two hormones are mainly associated with sexual structures and activities, and hence are termed *gonadotrophïc hormones.* They are best known (and named) from their observed effects in mammals. Prolactin stimulates milk secretion and prolongs the functional life of the corpus luteum (and consequent continued secretion of progesterone, cf. p. 567). We know little of its function in other vertebrate classes except for such observations as its stimulus of the crop gland for feeding the young in pigeons and stimulating newts to enter the water for reproductive purposes.

LUTEINIZING or INTERSTITIAL CELL-STIMULATING HORMONE (LH or ICSH). Influences maturation of the gonads and production of sex hormones (cf. pp. 565–567); acts in formation of corpora lutea and secretion of progesterone in the ovary; stimulates the interstitial cells of the testis, thus promoting the production of androgens and the maturation of sperm.

FOLLICLE-STIMULATING HORMONE (FSH). Stimulates the growth of ovarian follicles and, in conjunction with the last, promotes estrogen secretion and ovula- 'ion; may possibly promote spermatogenesis.

INTERMEDIN, or MELANOCYTE-STIMULATING HORMONE (MSH).   Acts to disperse pigment granules in melanophores and in darkening of the skin. In contrast to the hormones above, this (as the name indicates) is produced by the intermediate portion of the gland when this is distinctly developed.

MELANOPHORE-CONCENTRATING HORMONE (MCH).   In fishes and amphibians but not, apparently, in amniotes, there is present a hormone which, in opposition to intermedin, causes contraction of melanophore pigment granules.

In contrast to the wealth of hormones produced by the adenohypophysis, the secretions given off by the neurohypophysis are only two in number—*vasopressin* or antidiuretic hormone (ADH) and *oxytocin*. The two are very similar in chemical composition, both being peptides containing a series of eight amino acids, six being common to the two hormones. The effects of the two overlap to some degree, as might be expected. Vasopressin is principally associated with increasing blood pressure through contraction of arterioles and controlling water output or intake in a variety of fashions in different forms. Oxytocin is best known from its effects on the female mammal in promoting contraction of uterine muscle and mammary gland development and milk ejection after the birth of young; it appears, however, that it has sexual effects on at least certain other vertebrates—spawning in minnows, for example. It seems clear that, in contrast to the importance of the numerous hormones of the adenohypophysis, those of the neural lobe play a relatively modest part in the body economy and are not indispensable.

PARATHYROID GLANDS

We have noted earlier the trend for the development of outgrowths of tissue from the gill pouches of the embryo in every class of vertebrates (Figs. 245, 246, 249, pp. 339, 340, 345). Notable in tetrapods is the presence in the adult of small glandular structures, termed the *parathyroid glands*. They are variable in position and number, but there are usually two pairs, which are derived from the third and fourth pairs of gill pouches. Under the microscope the mature parathyroid exhibits densely packed masses of cells usually arranged in cords (Fig. 405). The greater part of them are *principal cells* (with a pale, clear cytoplasm) which appear to be the essential elements of the gland; in addition there is, in mammals, at least, a small percentage of *oxyphil cells*, filled with granules which stain with acid dyes. The name "parathyroid" is a misleading one, for functionally these little glands differ widely from the thyroid, although found in the adult in the neighborhood of that gland and sometimes (as in man) embedded in it. Attention was called to them when it was discovered that extirpation of parts of the human thyroid in which these little bodies were enclosed resulted in death of the patient from disturbance of calcium metabolism. Although no pure material has as yet been extracted from parathyroid tissues, it is thought that there is present, most probably, only a single hormone of a protein nature. The hormone is principally involved in the metabolism of calcium and phosphorus. Although the amount of calcium in the body fluids is small, the presence of a proper amount is essential for neuromuscular functioning; if the level is too low, tetanus and death may occur. Highly important is the relation of this hormone to maintenance of the bony skeleton. The greater part of the substance of bone is calcium phosphate; bone materials are being constantly renewed, and unless

BLOOD VESSEL   THYROID FOLLICLES   MUSCLE

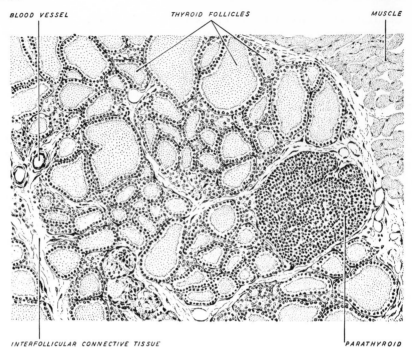

INTERFOLLICULAR CONNECTIVE TISSUE   PARATHYROID

Fig. 405.   Thyroid and parathyroid tissues of the rat. (From Turner.)

adequate supplies of "new" calcium and phosphorus are available, skeletal degeneration occurs.

No structures exactly comparable to parathyroids are known in fishes. The need for calcium regulation would seem to be as great in fishes with bony tissues as in tetrapods, and the seeming absence of glands secreting an appropriate hormone has been a puzzling situation. Recent work suggests the possibility that a fish equivalent is the *ultimobranchial gland.* In many vertebrates tissues may be budded off the last gill pouch of the embryo in much the same fashion that parathyroid and thymus tissues are derived from more anterior members of the gill pouch series. These tissues come to form a pair of small glandular bodies, found beneath the esophagus of most fish groups (cyclostomes excepted), and in one instance abnormalities in this gland are paralleled by skeletal abnormalities, suggesting a function similar to that of the tetrapod parathyroids.

THYROID GLAND

Of glandular derivatives from the pharynx, such structures as the thymus and parathyroids are paired structures, formed by outgrowths from the gill pouches. In contrast is the *thyroid gland,* likewise of pharyngeal origin, but originating as a median ventral pouchlike outgrowth from a point well forward in the pharyngeal floor (Figs. 246, 248, 249, pp. 340, 345). Found in every group of vertebrates, the thyroid is situated in fishes below the gill chamber; in tetrapods it is generally ventral to the windpipe at some point along the length of the neck. The gland remains a single structure in many fish groups, in reptiles, and in mammals, although distinctly bilobed in many cases; its name comes from its shield-shaped appearance in man. In amphibians and likewise in birds the thyroid becomes paired. In teleosts it has separated into right and left halves, and these in turn may be broken up into smaller units; in some teleosts bits of thyroid tissue come to lie in such unlikely places as the spleen, kidneys, heart, and even the eyes. Small accessory masses of thyroid tissue are also found in a variety of amniotes. (These are sometimes termed parathyroids, making for regrettable confusion with the radically different glands described above.)

Rich in blood vessels, the gland is composed of numerous small, spherical *thyroid follicles,* bound together by connective tissue (Fig. 405). Each follicle consists of a cuboidal epithelium of secretory cells, surrounding and discharging into a central cavity filled with a gluelike *colloid substance.* In this colloid are found, in storage, quantities of an iodine-containing protein, *thyroglobulin,* from which, through hydrolysis, are formed the iodine-bearing hormones *thyroxine* and *triiodothyronine*—the former far the more common, the latter when present the more potent. Hormone output from the thyroid is in great measure controlled by the pituitary; but a variety of environmenal stimuli may also be influential. It is obvious that for proper functioning of the gland a steady, if small, amount of iodine must be present in the food supply of the animal.

The thyroid products are without question highly important in maintaining general tissue metabolism. In birds and mammals the degree of metabolic activity necessary to maintain body temperatures is in great measure maintained through the influence of the thyroid hormones. In a hibernating mammal, thyroid activity decreases; in a hibernating amphibian (as would be expected), the reverse is true. Thyroid hormones are influential in the development of the nervous system and in behavior; they are concerned with reproductive functions and with growth phenomena; most spectacular of thyroid functions is its control of metamorphosis in amphibians.

The thyroid has a pedigree which stretches far back in chordate history. In both Amphioxus and tunicates, we have noted, there are present ciliated and partly glandular channels along which food particles strained out of the water current are carried back to the intestinal region. Such a channel in the floor of the pharynx of Amphioxus is that frequently termed the *endostyle,* and a like structure is found in tunicates (Figs. 4–6, pp. 15, 16, 18). In both Amphioxus and tunicate endostyles there are produced iodine compounds, although compounds differing from those of the thyroid hormone; they are obviously carried on into the digestive tract with the food materials.

In the Ammocoetes larva of lampreys, alone among living vertebrates, we find a similar feeding habit and a series of ciliated grooves much like those of Amphioxus and tunicates. The ventral groove terminates posteriorly, however, in a deep pouch in the pharyngeal floor (Fig. 231, *A,* p. 324). This pouch is subdivided in complicated fashion, and contains a number of epithelial cell types, some of which are glandular, and there is produced an iodine-bearing material which is carried on down the digestive tract. The term endostyle has been applied to this pouch (although, of course, the homology of this gland with the groove from which it arises is not an exact one).

The endostyle, including the Ammocoetes gland, is a median ventral pharyngeal structure, comparable in position to the thyroid gland. Is it truly homologous? The lamprey gives us a positive, conclusive answer. At metamorphosis the larval endostyle pouch closes off from the gut and breaks up into a series of follicles indisputably thyroid in structure.

It would appear that the history of the thyroid gland, in phylogeny as in lamprey ontogeny, has been one in the course of which a feeding structure has been transformed into a gland of internal secretion. It is significant that clinically the thyroid hormone can be taken by mouth, whereas other hormones, when introduced into the digestive tract in an unaltered state, are destroyed by gastric and intestinal juices. Early in chordate evolution, secretion of iodine compounds began in the endostyle while this was still a part of the feeding mechanism, the "hormone" being taken on into the gut with food materials. With the abandonment of filter feeding the endostyle lost its original function as a constituent of the pharynx; the thyroid gland has, as an endocrine structure, continued its glandular activity.

PANCREATIC ISLANDS

Although the greater part of the glandular tissue of the pancreas is devoted to the production of enzymes which pass through ducts to the intestine, areas of tissue of another type can be seen, in nearly all forms studied, distributed through the gland as isolated islands (Fig. 263, p. 363). These "islets of Langerhans" consist of cells glandular in nature, but not furnished with ducts; they thus obviously form an endocrine organ, sending secretions out into the blood stream. The insular material is usually diffused among the ordinary tissues of the formed pancreas. In teleosts, however, small clusters of islet cells are spread here and there in the general gut region, and in a few fishes these tissues form a small special organ of their own.

It has long been known that disease or injury to the pancreas interferes with carbohydrate metabolism and produces the disease known as diabetes mellitus. We are now familiar with the fact that the islands produce a specific protein hormone, *insulin*. This material has an important regulatory action on metabolism, particularly of carbohydrates, by increasing their utilization by the tissues, moderating glucose formation in the liver, regulating the formation or storage of glycogen in the cells, and maintaining the blood sugar level. There is little nervous influence on insulin secretion, which appears to be mainly controlled by the level of sugar in the blood passing through the islands. A second substance, the polypeptide *glucagon*, is also produced in the pancreatic islands; this tends to increase blood sugar by the breaking down of glycogen in liver storage.

INTERRENAL TISSUES AND THE ADRENAL CORTEX

In most tetrapods there is found, adjacent to the kidneys and capping them, a pair of endocrine structures termed the *adrenal glands* (or epinephric glands, Figs. 273, 275, pp. 379, 382). Microscopic examination shows the presence in them of two different types of tissues, intermingled or juxtaposed in lower tetrapods, but in mammals forming distinct cortical and medullary layers of a single compact organ (Fig. 406). Both parts are endocrine glands, but of very different sorts. The medullary tissue is a modified part of the nervous system, as discussed later (p. 564). The cortical substance is of quite another nature. In fishes there are almost never formed adrenals. In sharks the two components are

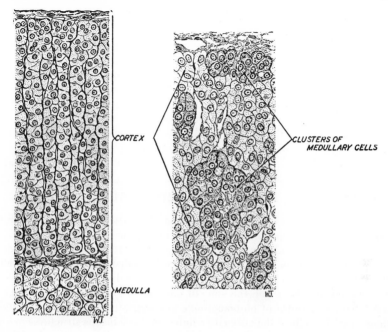

Fig. 406. A section through part of the adrenal gland (outer surface above) in a mammal (rat), with division into cortical and medullary layers, and a reptile (Heloderma), in which the two tissues are intermingled. (From Turner.)

quite distinct; in other fishes diffuse cell masses representing both components can be found between and around the kidneys and along the course of the major blood vessels dorsal to the celom. The cortical materials are termed *interrenal tissues.*

That the cortical material is vital for the maintenance of life was recognized more than a century ago, for human deaths from an ailment known as Addison's disease were invariably associated with deterioration of the adrenal cortex. The cortex cells have since been discovered to secrete a series of steroid hormones which have widespread influence over bodily functions in fashions which as yet are not fully understood. Some 40 or so steroids have been found to be present in this organ. Certain of them appear to be inactive; others, present in small amounts, are identical with sex hormones mainly produced elsewhere; still others are active hormones peculiar to the adrenal cortex, of which half a dozen or so appear to be most important. In general, the total effect of cortical hormones is in aiding the body to meet long-continued environmental stresses, rather in contrast to the function of the adrenal medulla (as discussed below) in coping with brief emergencies. More specific effects, among others, are to influence salt and water balance in the cells and body fluids, and to influence metabolism (particularly of carbohydrates). As examples, aldosterone is extremely potent in salt retention; cortisol, cortisone, and corticosterone mainly affect metabolic processes. It is probable that a variety of substances of these sorts are present in all vertebrates. Unfortunately our knowledge at present is mainly confined to mammals, and even here there appears to be considerable variation in cortical products. Aldosterone is as yet known only in mammals and birds, but cortisol, cortisone, and corticosterone have been reported in all vertebrate classes. The secretion of these hormones (except, apparently, aldosterone) is in great measure influenced by the pituitary hormone ACTH.

The importance of cortex hormones in water and salt regulation suggests a relationship of some sort between the cortical materials and the kidneys. That this physiologic association and the topographic propinquity of kidney and adrenal are not accidental, but have historic significance, is indicated by the embryologic origin of the cortical tissues. They appear as strands of cells which bud off from the epithelium of the roof of the celom medial to the developing kidney tubules (and lateral to the gonads). Kidney and adrenal cortex are thus derived from adjacent regions of the embryonic mesoderm.

CHROMAFFIN TISSUES AND THE ADRENAL MEDULLA

Very different in origin and function from the cortical portion of the adrenal gland is its medullary portion and structures antecedent to it in lower vertebrates. Here we are dealing with a portion of the nervous system which has been modified to perform an endocrine function. We have seen that the visceral motor nerve supply to the internal organs of the body is of a peculiar type in which the impulses do not directly reach the smooth muscles or glands concerned, but are relayed through a series of postganglionic neurons, which give off neurohumors at their tips. The cells of the adrenal medulla and homologous structures in lower vertebrates are much modified postganglionic neurons.

In various instances there are described clusters of cells here and there in the vertebrate body, particularly along the region near the dorsal aorta or adjacent to sympathetic ganglia, which are termed *chromaffin cells* because of the readiness with which they stain with certain potassium salts. Embryologically, they arise from cells migrating downward along the path of the visceral nerve rami, and are thus identical in origin with the postganglionic neurons of the sympathetic system. In fishes, small masses of such cells, often associated with interrenal tissues, are present between the kidneys and along the dorsal wall of the body cavity. They are often and appropriately termed *paraganglia*, since they are embryologically identical with the sympathetic ganglia, which they may adjoin, particularly in sharks (Fig. 372, p. 513). In tetrapods occasional small cell clusters of this type persist,* but most of the chromaffin material is concentrated into a compact mass of tissue which forms part of the adrenal gland capping the kidney. In mammals the chromaffin cells are concentrated in the center of the adrenal body forming its medulla; in lower tetrapods they are more diffuse, and interspersed with the cortical component (Fig. 406).

These cell masses are innervated by preganglionic autonomic nerve fibers; on stimulation they give off into the blood stream two related chemicals which are identical with those given off by the postganglionic fibers of the sympathetic system—*adrenalin* and *noradrenalin,* with the difference, however, that here the former is the more abundant product. The cells of the adrenal medulla do not look like nerve cells, for they lack any fiber processes. But since they are homologous with postganglionic sympathetic neurons, it is not surprising that they produce comparable neurohumors. The difference is that, whereas the true postgan-

---

* Bodies along the mammalian carotids and other arterial "arches" above the heart are sometimes referred to as paraganglia but are actually sensory structures.

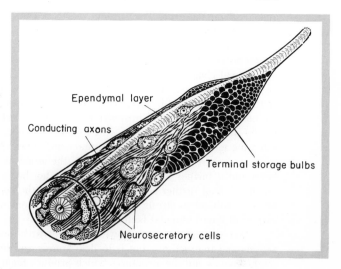

Fig. 407. Urohypophysis of an eel. The end of the spinal cord is seen as if transparent (except for the inner, ependymal layer of cells). Visible are a number of secretory neurons, the axons along which the secretion flows, and the swollen bulbs at the ends of the axons. (After Enami, in Gorbman, Comparative Endocrinology, John Wiley and Sons.)

glionic sympathetic cell produces only a tiny amount of adrenalin-like material which affects only structures immediately adjacent, the mass of adrenal cells are capable of rapidly releasing large quantities of these materials, which may have a strong, immediate "shotgun" effect on all parts of the body when carried about by the circulatory system, and "brace" the organism to meet emergencies.*

UROHYPOPHYSIS

Just as in all vertebrates a special anterior secretory area of the central nervous system may develop as the neurohypophysis, so in most, if not all, fishes a posterior secretory system may arise, to which (not unreasonably) the term *urohypophysis* has been given. This is highly developed in many teleosts (Fig. 407). In the nerve cord, toward the end of the tail region, can be found large cells, obviously secretory in nature. Fibers—axons—extend backward from these cells and terminate in bulbous tips, which are filled with secreted material. These bulbs are most commonly clustered together on the underside of the cord, causing here a slight swelling or a wartlike structure, readily visible to the naked eye on dissection. In elasmobranchs similar secretory cells are found in the tail region; the end bulbs are absent, however, although masses of secreted material are present in the area into which the axons of the secreting cells run. The nature of the secretion is as yet imperfectly known, but it appears to influence regulation of salt content of the blood and in teleosts appears to affect the secretion of gas into the swim bladder.

SEX HORMONES

Far more than in the case of any other activity, reproduction in vertebrates is powerfully influenced by hormones, with regard to both anatomic structures

---

* But while it is massive emergency outflows, mainly of adrenalin, from the adrenal medulla that have been of major interest in the study of this organ, it appears that there is a normal, constant but much smaller, output of medullary hormones.

and behavior patterns. The subject merits a volume in itself; here we will but briefly note the aspects of this complex picture which are of morphologic significance. A "chain of command" is involved in sex hormone action. Gonad hormones stimulate to development and sexual differentiation secondary and accessory sexual characters, including not only sperm and egg ducts, and copulatory organs, but such sexually distinctive features as the plumage of birds, hair types and mammary glands in mammals, and in many instances even major sexual differences in body size and proportions. But the gonadal hormones do not operate purely on their own initiative, for, as noted earlier, their production is in considerable measure regulated by pituitary hormones. A step further, the pituitary, we have seen, is strongly influenced by the adjacent hypothalamic region of the brain and is further influenced, reflexly, by hormones from the gonads and other organs. A final further step is that, as regards the conduct of sexual matters, the brain is subject to strong "pressures," both from within the body and from a variety of environmental factors.

Our present concern, however, is not with these interesting but far flung actions and interactions, but is to deal simply and briefly with the nature of the sex hormones and the structures which produce them.

With one exception,* the sex hormones produced by the gonads are steroids, termed *androgens* in the case of those primarily produced by the testis, and *estrogens* in the case of the ovary. These steroids are very similar in chemical composition to the hormones of the adrenal cortex. So close, in fact, are the relationships that, so to speak, the gonads and cortex are unable to completely sort out their respective roles as hormone producers. A limited amount of sex hormones may be detected amongst the cortical secretions, and a small fraction of the gonadal hormone products are substances proper to the adrenal cortex. Still further, male and female gonads are not completely differentiated as regards their products, for the male gonads, where tested, are found to secrete a certain amount of female hormone and vice versa.

This similarity of hormone products between adrenal cortex and gonads correlates with the similarity in origin of the cells which produce them. Apart from the actual sex cells (which are not implicated in hormone production), all the materials making up the gonads are derived, we have seen (p. 388), from the mesoderm lining the dorsal rim of the celomic cavity on either side of the midline, and the cortical adrenal cells, as noted earlier in this chapter, are derived from the adjacent region of the mesoderm, between gonad and kidney.

In the case of the male gonad, the major androgen, where analysis has been made, is the steroid *testosterone;* other compounds are recovered from testes, but these may be metabolic products derived from this potent and probably primary substance which, when experimentally injected, is generally highly effective in producing male structural growth and behavior patterns. In the case of the female gonadal products, the estrogens, *estradiol* and *estrone*, are the major steroids concerned, the former much the more potent. What cellular elements in the gonads produce these sex hormones? In the testis, the major source appears to be distinctive *interstitial cells* (Fig. 286, p. 394). Cells of this type, derived from the mesodermal epithelium surrounding the gonad, are unknown in lower chordates but are present in every major vertebrate group, although varying in abundance

* A female hormone, the protein *relaxin*, which in mammals relaxes the pelvic symphysis and facilitates birth of offspring, and also has functions aiding in reproduction in lower vertebrates.

from group to group and also, in some cases at least, varying in abundance at different phases of the breeding season. These cells, as their name indicates, are quite separate from the formed seminiferous tubules or ampullae, and lie (together with connective tissue) in the interstices between them. In certain cases, however, a second source of androgens appears to be present. In the lining of the tubules or ampullae there are found, beside the sperm-producing elements, supporting cells (Sertoli cells, Fig. 286, p. 394) which have the same embryonic origin as the interstitial cells and may have similar hormone-producing potentialities.

In the ovary there may be a certain amount of interstitial tissue (cf. Fig. 285, p. 393), but most of ovarian cellular materials—of common embryonic origin with the interstitial cells—are engaged, as follicle cells, in furnishing sustenance to the developing eggs. In addition to this function the follicle cells are the major producers of estrogens, although the minor amount of interstitial tissue present may also be concerned in this process.

Apart from the production of the primary sex hormones, we find that in the case of the ovary a second type of steroid hormone formation may occur. When an egg bursts from the ovary, one would expect the follicle in which it had been enclosed to degenerate. This appears to be the case in many groups. But in mammals, most notably, there is no immediate degeneration. Instead, the follicle cells long persist to form a yellow-colored material, the *corpus luteum,* filling the empty follicle. The corpus luteum cells in mammals secrete an important steroid hormone, *progesterone;* this prepares the uterine epithelium for implantation of the ovum and, if fertilization and implantation are accomplished, stimulates the development of a placenta. But although major interest in the corpus luteum and its hormonal function has been centered on mammals, with their placental type of development, it is found that a corpus luteum, likewise apparently productive of progesterone, develops after the bursting of the egg follicle in elasmobranchs; still further, although no typical corpus luteum is formed in other vertebrate groups, progesterone has nevertheless been discovered in the ovary of certain other vertebrate types (including birds). A small percentage of elasmobranchs and a few lower tetrapods bear their young alive, but in general no major specific function is known for progesterone in lower vertebrates. This suggests that we have in progesterone an example of the process of hormonal evolution proposed at the beginning of this chapter—that of a chemical product given off by a tissue which originally had little positive function, but later found a useful role in the economy of the body and in mammals has become an important hormone.

The nature and functions of the mammalian placenta are part of the story of vertebrate embryology rather than vertebrate anatomy. We may, however, note here that during the course of pregnancy, the mammalian placenta itself becomes an endocrine-producing organ, secreting a number of steroids including not only estrogen and progesterone but also a special gonadotrophic hormone of its own which is important in maintaining pregnancy.

GASTROINTESTINAL HORMONES

It is known that the stomach and intestine may produce hormonal substances which play a part in the regulation of digestion. However, we are here dealing with matters rather different from those discussed earlier in this chapter. Whereas most hormones form an interlocking system, often with checks and balances on one another, the *gastrointestinal hormones* do not appear to be affected by other hormones or even by other members of their own group. Further, they do not arise from specific endocrine glands, but from tissues which serve other functions as well. Again, our knowledge of these hormones is almost entirely confined to mammals, and we have little knowledge as to whether or not they are present in other vertebrate classes.

It is claimed, but far from completely proved, that the mucosa of the pyloric region of the stomach produces a hormone termed *gastrin* in response to the local presence of food, and that this material is carried through the blood stream to the fundus region, causing secretion of hydrochloric acid. In the intestine the formation of hormones is more definitely established. The passage of food into the upper end of the mammalian small intestine causes the mucosa of the region to release into the blood stream a polypeptide termed *secretin;* this causes the flow of pancreatic juice into the intestine, and also appears to have some effect on the flow of bile and production of intestinal juices. There is evidence of the presence of a second intestinal hormone, *pancreozymin,* which tends to stimulate the pancreas to increased enzyme formation and the consequent enrichment of the pancreatic juice. A third hormone product of the intestinal mucosa is *cholecystokinin,* whose production is stimulated by the entrance of fats and other food materials, and whose effect is to evacuate the gallbladder. It is known that when neutral fat enters the duodenum and comes in contact with its mucosa, the movements of the stomach and its production of hydrochloric acid are slowed down, with the beneficent result of delaying the further passage of food into the intestine until it has had time to cope with its difficult task of fat digestion. This result is believed to be due to one or more agents produced by the duodenal mucosa, to which the term *enterogastrone* has been applied.

FRINGES OF THE HORMONE SYSTEM

Some borderline matters may be noted briefly. For example, the peptide angiotonin, which may be found in the blood stream, is highly effective in causing high blood pressure, and its presence is primarily the result of kidney activity. The "hormone" is not produced in the kidney, however; a kidney enzyme, renin, is responsible for initiating chemical changes in proteins in the blood stream which cause eventual production of the "hormone." Again, evidence indicates that red blood cell formation is influenced by a hormonal agent, and there are observations suggesting that here, again, the kidney is involved in some fashion. The mast cells, mentioned in our discussion of connective tissues, secrete such important chemicals as heparin, histamine, and serotonin, and by stretching a definition a bit we might regard the mast cells as unicellular endocrine "organs."

There are a number of body structures whose tissues have a glandular appearance and hence have been suspected, despite the absence of convincing evidence, of having endocrine properties. Most often cited in this category are the pineal and parapineal structures which, as in the case of the mammalian pineal organ, tend to persist even when their original visual function has been lost. Now and again observations have been made as to bodily changes consequent on removal or disease of the mammalian pineal, or effects on the pineal following such operations as castration. But the situation is far from clear, and recent hypotheses as to pineal function have little to support them. We have noted earlier that the functions of the thymus are not too well known; endocrine activity has been suggested—but not demonstrated. Again, ultimobranchial bodies, budded off from the last gill pouch, have been thought to have some possible hormonal nature, and we have noted some suggestion that a fish ultimobranchial gland may function after the fashion of a parathyroid. However, small ultimobranchial structures are present in tetrapods, which have true parathyroids as well; their function here is quite unknown.

1

A SYNOPTIC CLASSIFICATION OF CHORDATES

The classification given here is presented primarily for the purpose of allowing the student to place in their proper position the forms discussed in the text. In consequence, no attempt is made to list the genera of vertebrates, and in many cases families, suborders, and even orders are neglected when such subdivisions of groups lack interest for present purposes. To fill out the picture, the more important fossil forms are mentioned, although our anatomic knowledge of them is practically confined to the skeletal system.

In addition to the major terms in the classification given below, (1) the first three subphyla are often termed *Protochordata*, lower chordates, in contrast to the *Vertebrata*; (2) among the vertebrates, the term *Gnathostomata*, jawed vertebrates, may be used to contrast all other higher vertebrate groups with the class *Agnatha*; (3) *Tetrapoda* is frequently used for amphibian and higher four-footed types in contrast with *Pisces*, fishes in a broad sense; (4) *Amniota*, referring to features of embryonic development found in reptiles, birds, and mammals, may be used for these three classes, all fishes and the amphibians as well being grouped as *Anamniota*.

PHYLUM CHORDATA

SUBPHYLUM HEMICHORDATA

(Little or no development of notochord or dorsal nerve cord. Often considered as constituting a separate phylum, distinct from the Chordata, although closely related)

Class Pterobranchia

(*Simple, Sessile, Plantlike Animals, Gathering Food by Ciliated Lophophores*)
(*Fig. 8, A, B, p. 20*)

571

Class Enteropneusta

(*Worm-shaped Burrowers, with Well Developed Gill Apparatus. The Acorn Worms*)
(*Figs. 8, F; 9*)

SUBPHYLUM UROCHORDATA

(The tunicates, with notochord and nerve cord well developed in larvae in many cases, but adults sessile or floating organisms, mainly consisting of an elaborate gill apparatus) (Figs. 6, 7, 8, *C–E*)

SUBPHYLUM CEPHALOCHORDATA

(Amphioxus, with notochord, nerve cord, and gill apparatus all well developed in the adult stage) (Fig. 4, p. 15)

SUBPHYLUM VERTEBRATA

(Generally with developed backbone and with other advanced structures in skeleton, brain, kidneys, etc., characteristic of true vertebrates)

Class Agnatha

(*Jawless Vertebrates*)

Orders Osteostraci, Anaspida, Heterostraci. These constitute the ostracoderms of the Silurian and Devonian periods. Representatives of these three groups are shown in Figure 18 (p. 38); Cephalaspis-like forms of the Osteostraci are also shown in Figures 19 and 232 (pp. 38, 326).

Order Cyclostomata. The living cyclostomes (Figs. 16, 17, pp. 36, 37).

SUBORDER MYXINOIDEA. Hagfishes.
SUBORDER PETROMYZONTIA. Lampreys.

Class Placodermi

(*Primitive Jawed Vertebrates; Extinct and Confined to the Paleozoic*)

Order Acanthodii. Spiny "sharks" (Fig. 20, *A*, p. 40).
Order Arthrodira. The arthrodires; jointed-necked fishes (Fig. 20, *B*).
Order Antiarchi. Related to arthrodires, but with peculiar bony "arms" (Fig. 20, *C*).
Order Macropetalichthyida.
Order Stegoselachii. The last two orders are modified arthrodire relatives which are suspected of being transitional, with reduction of bony armor, to the sharklike fishes.

Class Chondrichthyes
(Cartilaginous Fishes)

SUBCLASS ELASMOBRANCHII *(Sharks and Related Forms)*

Order Cladoselachii. Primitive Paleozoic sharks (Fig. 22, *A*, p. 42).

Order Selachii. Typical sharks, Paleozoic to Recent, with claspers, narrow-based fins, and so forth (Fig. 22, *B*).

Order Batoidea. The skates and rays (Fig. 23, p. 43).

SUBCLASS HOLOCEPHALI *(Differing from Sharks in Having an Operculum, Upper Jaws Fused to Skull, and so on)*

Order Bradyodonti. Paleozoic forms, poorly known, mainly represented by tooth plates.

Order Chimaerae. The chimaeras (Fig. 22, *C*).

Class Osteichthyes
(The Higher Bony Fishes) *(see Fig. 25)*

SUBCLASS ACTINOPTERYGII *(Ray-Finned Fishes)*

Superorder Chondrostei. Primitive ray-finned fishes, with heterocercal tails, and so forth, represented by fossil palaeoniscoids (Fig. 29, *A*, p. 49), mainly Paleozoic, and three modern types: Polypterus (Fig. 29, *B*), the sturgeons (Fig. 30, *B*, p. 50), and the paddlefish (Fig. 30, *A*).

Superorder Holostei. Dominant ray-finned forms of the Mesozoic, with abbreviate heterocercal tails, and so on; living forms include the gar pike and Amia (Fig. 31, p. 51).

Superorder Teleostei. The dominant fishes of Cenozoic and Recent times, with a homocercal tail. Include many thousands of forms, classed in a number of orders (Fig. 33, 34, pp. 53, 54).

SUBCLASS SARCOPTERYGII (CHOANICHTHYES) *(With Fleshy Fins)*

Order Crossopterygii. Forms broadly ancestral to land vertebrates. Mainly Paleozoic fossils; one aberrant living form (Fig. 27, p. 47).

Order Dipnoi. The lungfishes, including three living genera. Many similarities to ancestral types, but aberrant in teeth, skulls, and so forth (Fig. 28, p. 48).

Class Amphibia
(Tetrapods, but without Development of Amniote Type of Egg)

SUBCLASS APSIDOSPONDYLI *(Amphibians in Which Vertebral Centra Were Primitively Formed by Pleurocentra and Intercentra [cf. Figs. 104, 105, pp. 166, 168])*

Superorder Labyrinthodontia. The stem Amphibia, extinct, but dominant in late Paleozoic and Triassic times. Includes many dozens of fossil genera arranged in several orders.

Superorder Salientia, Order Anura. (Subclass position uncertain) The frogs and toads; living forms have highly specialized limbs and shortened trunks, and so on. Pleurocentra and intercentra reduced or absent.

SUBCLASS LEPOSPONDYLI *(Vertebral Centra Formed as Single Structures, often Spool-shaped)*

Orders Aistopoda, Nectridia, Microsauria. These are late Paleozoic fossils; the last consists of small forms from which the two living orders may have descended.

Order Urodela. The salamanders and newts, with a normal body form, but many degenerate characters.

Order Apoda (or Gymnophiona). Wormlike, burrowing types.

Class Reptilia

(Amniotes, but without Advanced Avian or Mammalian Characters [cf. Fig. 37, p. 59])

SUBCLASS ANAPSIDA *(Without a Temporal Opening)*

Order Cotylosauria. Archaic "stem reptiles" of the late Paleozoic and Triassic.

Order Chelonia (Testudinata). The turtles.

SUBCLASS SYNAPTOSAURIA *(Extinct Groups, Characterized by a Single Temporal Opening High Up on the Side of the Cheek)*

Order Protorosauria. Includes various obscure Permian and Mesozoic reptiles.

Order Sauropterygia. The plesiosaurs and their relatives; marine Mesozoic reptiles swimming by means of limbs transformed into powerful paddles.

SUBCLASS ICHTHYOPTERYGIA

Order Ichthyosauria. The ichthyosaurs, with a body highly specialized for marine life.

SUBCLASS LEPIDOSAURIA *(Diapsid Type of Temporal Region; without Archosaur Specializations)*

Order Eosuchia. Permian and Triassic ancestral diapsids.

Order Rhynchocephalia. The living Sphenodon of New Zealand and fossil relatives.

Order Squamata. Lizards and snakes. Related to the last, but temporal arches reduced.

SUBCLASS ARCHOSAURIA *(Ruling Reptiles. Diapsid Temporal Region, with Specializations Tending toward Bipedal Life [cf. Fig. 38, p. 62])*

Order Thecodontia. Triassic ancestors of dinosaurs, birds, and others.

Order Crocodilia. Crocodiles and alligators; degenerate amphibious survivors of archosaur group.

Order Pterosauria. Extinct flying reptiles with membrane wing.

Order Saurischia. "Reptile-like" dinosaurs with triradiate pelvis. Carnivores and large amphibious forms.

Order Ornithischia. "Birdlike" dinosaurs with tetraradiate pelvis; herbivorous. Bipeds (including duckbills), armored and horned quadrupeds.

SUBCLASS SYNAPSIDA *(Lateral Temporal Opening; Forms Leading to Mammals. Extinct)*

Order Pelycosauria. Primitive Permian mammal-like reptiles, close to stem reptiles.

Order Therapsida. Advanced mammal-like forms of late Permian and Triassic (Fig. 42, p. 68).

Class Aves
(Winged Archosaur Descendants, with Feathers, Temperature Control, and so forth)

SUBCLASS ARCHAEORNITHES *(Primitive Jurassic Fossil Birds with Many Reptilian Characters [Fig. 39, p. 64])*

SUBCLASS NEORNITHES *(All Other, "Modernized," Birds)*

Superorder Odontognathae. Toothed birds of the Cretaceous.

Superorder Palaeognathae. Including mainly the ostrich-like birds, or ratites, with relatively primitive structures (Fig. 40, p. 65).

Superorder Neognathae. All remaining birds, arranged in a considerable number of orders, but all essentially similar in most anatomic features (Fig. 41, p. 66).

Class Mammalia
(Animals with Hair, Nursing Habit, Brain of Advanced Type, and so on)

SUBCLASS PROTOTHERIA *(Egg-Laying Mammals)*

Order Monotremata. The duckbill and spiny anteater of the Australian region.

SUBCLASS THERIA *(Mammals Bearing the Young Alive)*

Infraclass and Order Pantotheria. Small Jurassic fossil mammals, probably ancestral to remaining groups. (There are several further Jurassic orders of obscure relationships.)

Infraclass Allotheria, Order Multituberculata. An extinct group of primitive but aberrant mammals, perhaps comparable in habits to later rodents. Jurassic to Eocene.

Infraclass Metatheria, Order Marsupialia. The pouched mammals, as opossum and many Australian types. Young born alive, but at immature stage.

Infraclass Eutheria. The higher mammals, with an efficient placenta (Fig. 44, p. 71).

Order Insectivora. Ancestral placentals and modern descendants, such as shrews, moles, hedgehog.

Order Chiroptera. Bats.

Order Primates. Essentially an arboreal offshoot of the primitive placental stock (Fig. 45, p. 72).

SUBORDER LEMUROIDEA (PROSIMII). Tree shrews and lemurs.

SUBORDER TARSIOIDEA. Tarsius and extinct relatives, transitional between lemurs and monkeys.

SUBORDER ANTHROPOIDEA. Monkeys, apes, and man.

Infraorder Platyrrhini. South American monkeys, with nostrils opening sideways.

Family Hapalidae. Marmosets.

Family Cebidae. Typical South American monkeys.

Infraorder Catarrhini. Old World monkeys, apes, and man; nostrils open downward.

Family Cercopithecidae. Old World monkeys.

Family Simiidae. Manlike apes.

Family Hominidae. Men.

Order Carnivora. The carnivores (Fig. 46, p. 74).

SUBORDER CREODONTA. Extinct archaic carnivores.

SUBORDER FISSIPEDIA.   Modern land carnivores.
   Infraorder Eucreodi.   Extinct ancestors of modern types.
   Infraorder Arctoidea.   The dogs and relatives.
      Family Mustelidae.   Primitive. Weasels, skunks, badgers, otters,
        and so on.
      Family Canidae.   Dogs, wolves, foxes.
      Family Procyonidae.   Raccoons, pandas, kinkajous.
      Family Ursidae.   Bears.
   Infraorder Aeluroidea.   The "cats" and relatives.
      Family Viverridae.   Civets, mongoose, and the like; primitive Old
        World aeluroids.
      Family Hyaenidae.   Hyenas.
      Family Felidae.   Cats, lions, tigers, and others.
SUBORDER PINNIPEDIA.   Marine carnivores: seals, sea lion, walrus.
Order Condylarthra.   Primitive extinct ungulates.
**Orders Amblypoda, Dinocerata, Embrithopoda, Astrapotheria,
Litopterna, Notoungulata.**   Extinct orders of ungulates, mainly of
archaic character, the last three characteristic of South America.
Order Perissodactyla.   Odd-toed ungulates (Fig. 47, p. 75).
SUBORDER HIPPOMORPHA.
      Family Equidae.   Horses, asses, zebras.
      Family Titanotheriidae.   Titanotheres—large, ungainly, horned,
        fossil forms.
      Family Chalicotheriidae.   Extinct forms related to the last two—
        but with claws, not hoofs.
SUBORDER TAPIROMORPHA.
      Family Tapiridae.   Tapirs.
      Family Rhinocerotidae.   Rhinoceroses.
Order Artiodactyla.   Even-toed ungulates (Fig. 48, p. 76).
SUBORDER SUINA.   Relatively primitive types with simple stomachs, in-
   cluding the following living families as well as several extinct ones:
      Family Suidae.   Pigs of the Old World.
      Family Dicotylidae.   Peccaries of the New World.
      Family Hippopotamidae.   The hippopotamus.
SUBORDER RUMINANTIA.   Cud chewers, with complex stomach, and seleno-
   dont teeth.
   Infraorder Tylopoda.   Primitive cud chewers, including, in addition to
     early extinct families:
      Family Camelidae.   Camels, llamas.
      Family Oreodontidae.   The oreodons, short-legged ruminants abun-
        dant in North American fossil deposits.
   Infraorder Pecora.   Advanced ruminants, mostly with horns or antlers,
     including, besides extinct forms:
      Family Tragulidae.   Chevrotains, tiny, hornless, deerlike animals
        of the tropical Old World.
      Family Cervidae.   The deer tribe.
      Family Giraffidae.   The giraffe and okapi of Africa.
      Family Antilocapridae.   The American pronghorn.
      Family Bovidae.   The cattle family, mainly Old World forms, in-
        cluding bison, sheep, goats, and numerous types of antelopes.

Order Hyracoidea. The conies of Africa and Syria; rabbit-like in habits, but actually ungulates. This order and the next two are the subungulate orders—related, and probably of African origin.

Order Proboscidea. The elephants and fossil relatives, mammoths and mastodons.

Order Sirenia. The sea cows—manatee and dugong; an aquatic offshoot of an ungulate stock.

Order Cetacea. Whales.

SUBORDER ARCHAEOCETI. Extinct ancestral whales.

SUBORDER ODONTOCETI. The toothed whales, porpoises, dolphins.

SUBORDER MYSTICETI. Whalebone whales.

Order Edentata. So-called "toothless" mammals, developed in South America.

SUBORDER PILOSA. Hairy edentates.

Infraorder Gravigrada. Extinct ground sloths.

Infraorder Tardigrada. Family Bradypodidae. Tree sloths.

Infraorder Vermilingua. Family Myrmecophagidae. South American anteaters.

SUBORDER LORICATA. Armored edentates.

Family Dasypodidae. Armadillos.

Family Glyptodontidae. The extinct giant glyptodonts.

Order Tubulidentata. The aardvark of Africa; an anteater, but not related to the preceding order.

Order Pholidota. The Old World pangolin, an anteater, but not closely related to the last two orders.

Order Rodentia. Gnawing animals (except rabbit group). A number of subgroups, of which the most important are:

SUBORDER SCIUROMORPHA. Squirrels, gophers, woodchuck, and others.

SUBORDER CAVIAMORPHA. Guinea pig and many other South American rodents, New World porcupines.

SUBORDER MYOMORPHA. Rats and mice.

Order Lagomorpha. Hares and rabbits; gnawing forms, but not closely related to last order.

APPENDIX

2

SCIENTIFIC
TERMINOLOGY

In anatomic terminology common Latin (or Greek) words are used as such for any part of the body for which the ancients had a name. For numerous other structures, scientific names have been invented (1) by using, in a new sense, some classical word which seemed to be descriptive of the part concerned, or (2) commonly, by combining Greek or Latin roots to form a new compound term. The student frequently attempts to memorize such terms without understanding their meaning and with consequent mental indigestion. We give here the roots from which many of these descriptive terms and compounds are derived, as an aid to comprehension. As will be seen, some names formed by the anatomists are rather fanciful or far-fetched; some are none too appropriate. This list is not intended, of course, as a glossary or dictionary of scientific words. We have not, for instance, included common names of bones and muscles. Most of the terms used in this book are defined or discussed in the text. For a wider vocabulary, use of a standard biologic or medical dictionary* is recommended, but the larger editions of Webster and the like are satisfactory in most regards. Abbreviations: *F.*, French; *G.*, Greek; *L.*, Latin; *NL.*, "New" Latin; *Sp.*, Spanish.

A-, ab. L. prefix implying separation.
Abdomen. L., from *abdere* (?), to hide.
Abducens. L., *ab*, away, + *ducens*, leading.
Abductor. L., *ab*, away, + *ducere*, to lead.
Accessory. L., *accessorius*, supplementary.
Acelous. G., *a*, not, + *koilos*, hollow.
Acetabulum. L., *acetabulum*, vinegar cup.
Acoustic. G., *akoustikos*, pertaining to hearing.
Acrania. G., *a*, without, + *krania*, heads.
Acrodont. G., *akron*, height or extremity, + *odous*, tooth.
Acromion. G., *akron*, height or extremity, + *omos*, shoulder.

* Such as Dorland's American Illustrated Medical Dictionary. 23rd ed. Philadelphia, W. B. Saunders Company, 1957.

578

Ad. L. prefix, to, toward, at, or near.

Adductor. L., *ad,* to, + *ducere,* to lead.

Adrenal. L., *ad,* near, + *renes,* kidneys.

Alisphenoid. L., *ala,* wing, + G., *sphen,* wedge, + G., *eidos,* form.

Allantois. G., *allas,* sausage, + *eidos,* form, appearance.

Alveolus. L., *alveolus,* little cavity.

Ambiguus. L., *ambiguus,* uncertain, changeable.

Amnion. G., *amnion,* fetal membrane.

Amphi-. G. prefix, on both sides; hence, around or double.

Amphibia. G,, *amphi,* double, + *bios,* life.

Amphicelous. G., *amphi,* both, + *koilos,* hollow.

Amphioxus. G., *amphi,* both, + *oxys,* sharp.

Amphiplatyan. G., *amphi,* both, + *platys,* flat.

Amphistylic. G., *amphi,* both, + *stylos,* pillar.

Ampulla. L., *ampulla,* a flask or vessel swelling in the middle.

A-, an-. G. prefix (alpha privative), without or not.

Ana-. G. prefix, on, upward, throughout, frequently, or reinforcing a meaning.

Analogy. G., *ana,* according to, + *logos,* due ratio; hence, proportionate.

Anamniota. G., *an,* without, + *amnion,* fetal membrane.

Anapsid. G.,. *an,* not, + *apsis,* arch.

Anastomosis. G., *anastomoein,* to bring to a mouth, cause to communicate.

Ankylosis. G., *ankylosis,* stiffening of the joint.

Annulus. L., *anulus (annulus),* a ring.

Anura. G., *an,* without, + *oura,* tail.

Anus. L., *anus,* fundament.

Apo. G. prefix, from.

Apoda. G., *a,* without, + *poda,* feet.

Aponeurosis. G., *apo,* from, + *neuron,* tendon.

Apophysis. G., *apo,* from, + *physis,* growth.

Appendicular. L., *appendere,* to hang upon.

Arachnoid. G., *arachnes,* spider, + *eidos,* shape or likeness.

Arch-, archi-. G. prefix, first or chief; hence, primitive or ancestral.

Archenteron. G., *arch,* first, + *enteron,* intestine, gut.

Archipallium. G., *archi,* first, + *pallium,* cloak.

Archipterygium. G., *archesthai,* to begin, + *pterygion,* a little wing.

Arcualia (pl.). L., *arcualis,* bow-shaped.

Arrector. L., *arrigere,* to raise.

Arytenoid. G., *arytaina,* jug, + *eidos,* shape or likeness.

Astragalus. G., *astragalos,* ankle bone, used as a die (commonly pl.).

Atrium. L., *atrium,* court, entrance hall.

Auditory. L., *audire,* to hear.

Auricle. L. dim., *auricula,* external ear.

Auto-. G. prefix, *autos,* self.

Autonomic. G., *autos,* self, + *nomos,* law.

Autostylic. G., *autos,* self, + *stylos,* pillar.

Axial. L., *axis,* axle of a wheel, the line about which any body turns.

Azygos. G., *a,* not, + *zygon,* yoke; hence, unpaired.

Basal. L., *basis,* footing or base.

Basi-. L. prefix, pertaining to the base.

Basibranchial. L., *basis,* base, + *branchiae,* gills.

Basihyoid. L., *basis*, base, + G., *hyoeides*, Y-shaped.
Bi-. L. prefix, two, twice, or double.
Biceps. L., *bis*, twice, + *caput*, head.
Bilateral. L., *bi*, two, + *latus*, side.
Blasto-. G. prefix, bud, germ, or sprout.
Blastocele. G., *blastos*, germ, + *koilos*, hollow.
Blastoderm. G., *blastos*, germ, + *derma*, skin.
Blastodisc. G., *blastos*, germ, + *diskos*, a round plate, quoit.
Blastomere. G., *blastos*, germ, + *meros*, part.
Blastopore. G., *blastos*, germ, + *poros*, passage, opening.
Blastula. L. dim. of G. *blastos*, germ.
Brachial. L., *brachialis*, belonging to the arm.
Brachium (pl. **-ia**). L., *brachium*, arm, especially the forearm.
Branchial. L., *branchiae*, or G., *branchia*, gills.
Branchiostegal. G., *branchia*, gills, + *stegein*, to cover.
Bronchus. G., *bronchia*, end of windpipe.
Buccal. L., *bucca*, cheek.
Bulbus. L., *bulbus*, bulb, swollen root.
Bunodont. G., *bounos*, mound, + *odous*, tooth.
Calcaneum. L., *calcaneum*, heel.
Callosum. L., *callosus, -a, -um*, thick-skinned.
Calyx (pl. **calices**). L., *calyx*, husk, cup-shaped protective covering.
Caninus. L., *caninus*, pertaining to a dog.
Capillary. L., *capillaris*, pertaining to the hair.
Capitulum. L. dim. (*caput*), small head.
Caput (pl. **capita**). L., *caput*, head.
Carapace. NL., *carapax*, bony or chitinous covering.
Cardiac. G., *kardiakos* (*kardia*), pertaining to the heart.
Cardinal. L., *cardinalis*, pertaining to a door hinge.
Carnassial. F., *carnassier*, carnivorous (L., *caro, carnis*, flesh).
Carnivorus. L., *caro*, flesh, + *vorare*, to devour.
Carnosus. L., *carnosus*, fleshy.
Carpus. G., *karpos*, wrist.
Cartilago (pl. **-agines**). L., *cartilago*, gristle, cartilage.
Caudal. L., *cauda*, tail.
Cava. L., *cavus, -a, -um*, hollow.
Cavernosus. L., *caverna*, a hollow or cave.
Cecum. L., *caecus, -a, -um*, blind.
Celiac. G., *koilia*, belly.
Celom (e). G., *koiloma*, a hollow.
Cephalic. G., *kephale*, head.
Cephalo-. G. combining form, *kephale*, head.
Ceratobranchial. G., *keras*, horn, + *branchia*, gills.
Ceratotrichia. G., *keras*, horn, + *thrix*, hair.
Cerebellum. L. dim., *cerebrum*, brain.
Cerebrum. L., *cerebrum*, brain.
Cervical. L., *cervix*, neck.
Chiasma. G., *chiasma*, figure of X.
Choana (pl. **-ae**). G., *choane*, funnel.
Choledochus. G., *chole*, bile, + *dochos* (*dechomai*), container.

Chondrichthyes. G., *chondros*, cartilage, + *ichthys*, fish.
Chondro-. G., combining form, cartilaginous.
Chondroblast. G., *chondros*, cartilage, gristle, + *blastos*, shoot or germ.
Chondroclast. G., *chondros*, cartilage, + *klaein*, to break.
Chorda. G., *chorde*, string of gut, cord.
Choroid. G., *chorion*, skin, + *eidos*, likeness.
Chorion. G., *chorion*, skin.
Chromaffin. G., *chroma*, color, + L., *affinis*, showing affinity for.
Chromatophore. G., *chroma*, color, + *pherein*, to bear.
Chromosome. G., *chroma*, color, + *soma*, body.
Chyme. G. *chymos*, juice.
Ciliary. L., *cilium* (pl. *cilia*), eyelash.
Circum-. L. prefix, around.
Cloaca. L., *cloaca*, sewer, drain.
Cnemial. G., *kneme*, lower leg.
Cochlea. L., *cochlea* (G., *kochlias*), spiral, snail shell.
Colon. L., *colon*, great gut.
Columella. L. dim. (*columna*), little pillar.
Commissure. L., *commissura* (*cum* + *mittere*), connection.
Concha. L., *concha*, bivalve, oyster shell.
Condyle. G., *kondylos*, knuckle.
Conjunctiva. L., *conjunctivus*, connecting.
Constrictor. L., *constringere*, to draw together.
Coprodeum. G., *kopros*, dung, + *hodaios*, pertaining to a way.
Corium. G., *chorion*, skin, leather.
Cornea. L., *corneus*, horny.
Coronary. L., *coronarius*, pertaining to a wreath or crown; hence, encircling.
Cortex. L., *cortex*, bark, rind.
Cortical. L., *cortex, -icis*, bark, rind.
Cosmin. G., *kosmos*, orderly arrangement, + *eidos*, form.
Costa. L., *costa*, rib.
Costal. L., *costa*, rib.
Cranial. G., *kranion*, skull.
Cribriform. L., *cribrum*, sieve, + *forma*, form.
Cricoid. G., *krikos*, ring, + *eidos*, form.
Crista. L., *crista*, crest.
Crus (pl. **crura**). L., *crus*, leg.
Ctenoid. G., *kteis* (gen. *ktenos*), a comb, + *eidos*, form.
Cuneiform. L., *cuneus*, wedge, + *forma*, shape.
Cutis. L., *cutis*, skin.
Cycloid. G., *kyklos*, circle, + *eidos*, form.
Cystic. G., *kystis*, the bladder, a bag or pouch.
Cytoplasm. G., *kytos*, cell, + *plasma*, plasma, anything molded.
De-. L. prefix signifying down, away from, deprived of.
Deciduous. L., *deciduus* (*de* + *cado*), falling off.
Decussatio. L., *decussatio*, crosswise intersection.
Decussation. L., *decussatio*, intersection of two lines, as in Roman X.
Deferens. L., *de*, away, + *ferens*, carrying.
Dens. L., *dens, dentis*, tooth.
Depressor. L., *de*, down, + *premere*, to press.

Dermal. G., *derma*, skin.

Dermatome. G., *derma*, skin, + *temnein*, to cut.

Di-. G., *dis*, twice; hence, twofold or double.

Di-, dia-. G. prefix, through, between, apart, across.

Diaphragm. G., *diaphragma*, partition, midriff.

Diaphysis. G., *dia*, between, + *physis*, growth.

Diapophysis. G., *dia*, apart, + *apophysis*, outgrowth.

Diapsid. G., *di*, double, + *apsis*, arch.

Diarthrosis. G., *dia*, through, + *arthroun*, to fasten by a joint.

Diastema (pl. **-ata**). G., *diastema*, interval.

Digit. L., *digitus*, finger.

Diphycercal. G., *diphyes*, twofold, + *kerkos*, tail.

Diplospondylous. G., *diploos*, double, + *spondyle*, vertebra.

Dipnoi. G., *di*, double, + *pnein*, to breathe.

Distal. L., *distare*, to stand apart.

Dorsal. L., *dorsum*, back.

Duct. L., *ducere*, to lead or draw.

Duodenum. L., *duodeni*, twelve (meaning twelve fingerbreadths).

E-, ex-. L. prefix, out, out of, from.

Ectepicondyle. G., *ek*, out, + *epi*, upon, + *kondylos*, knuckle, knob.

Ectoderm. G., *ektos*, outside, + *derma*, skin.

Effector. L., *efficere*, to bring to pass.

Efferent. L., *ex*, out, + *ferre*, to bear.

Ejaculatory. L., *e*, out, + *jacere*, to throw.

Ek-, ekto-. G. prefix, out of, from, outside.

Embolomerous. G., *en*, in + *ballein*, to throw, + *meros*, portion or part.

En-, endo-. G. prefix, in, within.

Endocardium. G., *endon*, within, + *kardia*, heart.

Endochondral. G., *endon*, within, + *chondros*, cartilage.

Endocrine. G., *endon*, within, + *krinein*, to separate.

Endoderm. G., *endon*, within, + *derma*, skin.

Endolymph. G., *endon*, within, + L., *lympha*, water.

Endometrium. G., *endon*, within, + *metra*, womb.

Endoneurium. G., *endon*, within, + *neuron*, nerve.

Endoskeleton. G., *endon*, within, + *skeletos*, dried up.

Endostyle. G., *endon*, within, + *stylos*, pillar.

Endothelium. G., *endon*, within, + *thele*, nipple.

Entepicondyle. G., *entos*, in, + *epi*, upon, + *kondylos*, knuckle.

Enzyme. G., *en*, in, + *zyme*, leaven.

Ependyma. G., *ependyma*, upper garment.

Epiaxial. G., *epi*, on, + *axis*, center line.

Epibranchial. G., *epi*, on, + *branchia*, gills.

Epicardium. G., *epi*, on, + *kardia*, heart.

Epicondyle. G., *epi*, on, + *kondylos*, knuckle.

Epidermis. G., *epi*, on, + *derma*, skin.

Epididymis. G., *epi*, on, + *didymoi*, testicles.

Epiglottis. G., *epi*, on, + *glotta*, tongue.

Epimere. G., *epi*, on, + *meros*, part.

Epineurium. G., *epi*, on, + *neuron*, nerve.

Epiphysis. G., *epi*, on, + *physis*, growth.

Epiploic. G., *epiploon*, caul, omentum.
Epithalamus. G., *epi*, on, + *thalamos*, chamber.
Epithelium. G., *epi*, on, + *thele*, nipple.
Erythrocyte. G., *erythros*, red, + *kytos*, cell.
Esophagus. G., *oisein* (*phero*), to carry, + *phagein*, to eat.
Ethmoid. G., *ethmos*, sieve, + *eidos*, form.
Excretion. L., (*excretus*) *ex*, out, + *cernere*, to sift.
Exocrine. G., *ex*, out, + *krinein*, to separate.
Extensor. L., *ex*, out, + *tendere*, to stretch.
Extrinsic. L., *extrinsecus*, on the outside.
Facialis. L., *facies*, face.
Falciform. L., *falx*, sickle, + *forma*, shape.
Falx. L., *falx, falcis*, sickle.
Fascia (pl. **-iae**). L., *fascia*, band.
Fiber. L., *fibra*, string, thread.
Fibril. NL., *fibrilla*, a little thread.
Filoplume. L., *filum*, thread, + *pluma*, soft leather, down.
Filum. L., *filum*, thread.
Fimbria. L., *fimbriae*, threads, fringe.
Firmisternal. L., *firmus*, steadfast, strong, + G., *sternon*, chest.
Fissure. L., *fissura* (*findo*), a cleft.
Flagellum (pl. **-a**). L., *flagellum*, a little whip.
Flexor. L., *flexus*, bent.
Flocculus. NL. dim. (*floccus*), a tuft of wool.
Follicle. L., *folliculus*, a small bag.
Fornix. L., *fornix*, arch or vault.
Fovea. L., *fovea*, small pit.
Frontal. L., *frons, frontis*, forehead, brow.
Fundus. L., *fundus*, bottom.
Funiculus. L., *funiculus*, a slender rope.
Gametes. G., *gametes*, spouse.
Ganglion. G., *ganglion*, a swelling under the skin.
Gastralia (pl.). G., *gaster*, belly
Gastrula. NL. dim. (from G., *gaster*, stomach).
Geniculate. L., *geniculatus*, with bent knee.
Genital. L., *genitalis* (*gigno*), pertaining to birth.
Germinal. L., *germen*, bud, germ.
Germinative. L., *germen*, bud, germ.
Glans. L., *glans*, acorn.
Glenoid. G., *glene*, socket, + *eidos*, form.
Glomerulus. L. dim. of *glomus*, a ball.
Glomus (pl. **glomera**). L., *glomus*, ball.
Glossopharyngeus. G., *glossa*, tongue, + *pharynx*, throat.
Glottis. G., *glottis*, mouth of the windpipe.
Gluteus. G., *gloutos*, rump.
Gnathos. G., *gnathos*, jaw.
Gnathostomata (pl.). G., *gnathos*, jaw, + *stoma*, mouth.
Gonad. G., *gone*, seed.
Granulocytes. L., *granulum*, small grain, + G., *kytos*, cell.
Granulosus. L., *granulosus*, full of grains.

Granulum. L., *granulum,* small grain.

Guanin (e). Sp., *guano,* dung of sea fowl.

Guanophore. Sp. from Peruvian, *huanu,* dung, + G., *pherein,* to bear.

Gubernaculum. L., *gubernaculum,* helm.

Gular. L., *gula,* throat.

Gyrus (pl. **gyri**). G., *gyros,* a turn.

Habenula. L., *habena,* strap.

Haemal, hemal. G., *haima,* blood.

Hamatum. L., *hamatus,* hook-shaped.

Hemi-. G. prefix, signifying half.

Hemibranch. G., *hemi,* half, + *branchia,* gills.

Hemichordata. G., *hemi,* half, + *chorde,* string.

Hemipenis. G., *hemi,* half, + L., *penis,* penis.

Hemisphere. G., *hemi,* half, + *sphaira,* ball.

Hemocytoblast. G., *haima,* blood, + *kytos,* cell, + *blastos,* germ.

Hemoglobin. G., *haima,* blood, + L., *globus,* sphere.

Hemopoietic. G., *haima,* blood, + *poietikos,* creative.

Hepatic. L., *hepar,* liver.

Hetero-. G. combining form signifying other, different.

Heterocelous. G., *heteros,* other, + *koilos,* hollow.

Heterocercal. G., *heteros,* other, + *kerkos,* tail.

Heterodont. G., *heteros,* other, + *odous,* tooth.

Heterotopic. G., *heteros,* other, + *topos,* place.

Hippocampus. G., *hippos,* horse, + *kampos,* sea monster.

Histology. G., *histos,* web, + *logos,* discourse, account.

Holo-. G. combining form signifying whole.

Holoblastic. G., *holos,* whole, + *blastos,* germ.

Holobranch. G., *holos,* whole, + *branchia,* gills.

Holocephali. G., *holos,* whole, + *kephale,* head.

Holonephros. G., *holos,* whole, + *nephros,* kidney.

Holostei. G., *holos,* whole, + *osteon,* bone.

Homo-. G. combining form signifying one and the same.

Homocercal. G., *homos,* same, + *kerkos,* tail.

Homoiothermous. G., *homos,* same, + *themos,* hot.

Homolecithal. G., *homos,* same, + *lekithos,* yolk.

Homology. G., *homos,* same, + *logos,* ratio.

Hormone. G., *hormaein,* to excite.

Humor. L., *humor,* moisture, fluid.

Hyaline. G., *hyalos,* glass.

Hyoid. G., *hyoeides,* U-shaped.

Hyomandibular. G., *upsilon* (Y-shaped letter) + L., *mandibula,* jaw.

Hyostylic. G., *upsilon* (Y-shaped letter) + *stylos,* pillar.

Hypaxial. G., *hypo,* under, + L., *axis,* center line, axis.

Hypo-. G. prefix signifying under, below.

Hypobranchial. G., *hypo,* below, + *branchia,* gills.

Hypoglossal. G., *hypo,* under, + *glossa,* tongue.

Hypomere. G., *hypo,* under, + *meros,* part.

Hypophysis. G., *hypo,* under, + *physis,* growth.

Hypothalamus. G., *hypo,* under, + *thalamos,* chamber, couch.

Hypsodont. G., *hypsos,* height, + *odous,* tooth.

Hypural. G., *hypo*, under, + *oura*, tail.

Ileum. G., *eilein*, to wind or turn.

In-. L. prefix signifying not; also signifying in, into, within, toward, on.

Incisor. L., *incisus* (*incidere*), cut.

Incus. L., *incus*, anvil.

Inductor. L., *inducere*, to lead on, excite.

Infra-. L. prefix signifying below, lower than.

Inframeningeal. L., *infra*, below, + G., *meninx*, membrane.

Infraparietal. L., *infra*, below, + *paries*, wall.

Infraspinous. L., *infra*, below, + *spina*, spine.

Infundibulum. L., *infundibulum*, a funnel.

Inguinal. L., *inguina*, groin.

Integument. L., *in*, over, + *tegere*, to cover.

Inter-. L. prefix signifying between, among.

Intercalated. L., *inter*, between, + *calare*, to call.

Intercostal. L., *inter*, between, + *costa*, rib.

Intermaxillary. L., *inter*, between, + *maxilla*, jaw.

Interrenal. L., *inter*, between, + *renes*, kidneys.

Interstitial. L., *inter*, between, + *sistere*, to set.

Intervertebral. L., *inter*, between, + *vertebra*, joint.

Intestine. L., *intus*, within.

Intrinsic. L., *intrinsecus*, inward.

Invagination. L., *in*, in, + *vagina*, sheath.

Invertebrate. L., *in*, not, + *vertebratus*, jointed.

Iridocyte. G., *iris*, *-idos*, rainbow, + *kytos*, cell.

Iris. G., *iris*, rainbow.

Ischiofemoral. G., *ischion*, hip, + L., *femur*, thigh.

Ischium (pl. **-ia**). G., *ischion*, hip.

Iso-. G. prefix signifying equal.

Isolecithal. G., *isos*, equal, + *lekithos*, yolk.

Isomer. G., *isos*, equal, + *meros*, part.

Jejunum. L., *jejunus*, empty (of food).

Jugal. L., *jugum*, yoke.

Jugular. L., *jugularis* (*jugulum*), pertaining to the neck.

Labial. L., *labialis* (*labia*), pertaining to the lips.

Lacerate. L., *lacerare*, to tear.

Lacrimal. L., *lacrima*, tear.

Lagena. L., *lagena*, flask.

Lamina (pl. **-ae**). L., *lamina*, thin plate.

Larva (pl. **-ae**). L., *larva*, ghost, mask.

Larynx. G., *larynx*, upper part of windpipe.

Lateral. L., *lateralis* (*latus*), pertaining to a side.

Lepidotrichia. G., *lepis*, scale, + *thrix*, hair.

Leukocyte. G., *leukos*, white, + *kytos*, cell.

Levator. L., *levare*, to raise.

Ligamentum. L., *ligamentum*, a bandage.

Lipid. G., *lipos*, fat, + *eidos*, resemblance.

Lipo-. G. combining form signifying fat.

Lipophore. G., *lipos*, fat, + *phoros* (*phero*), bearing.

Lobus. G., *lobos*, lobe.

Lophodont. G., *lophos*, ridge, + *odous*, tooth.
Lucidum. L., *lucidus* (*lux*), full of light, clear.
Lumbar. L., *lumbare*, apron for the loins.
Luteum. L., *luteus*, yellow.
Lymphocyte. L., *lympha*, water, + G., *kytos*, cell.
Macrophage. G., *makros*, large, + *phagein*, to eat.
Macula. L., *macula*, spot, stain.
Malleus. L., *malleus*, hammer.
Mammillary. L., *mamillaris* (*mamma, -ae*), of or in the breast.
Marginal. L., *marginalis* (*margo*), bordering.
Marsupium. L., *marsupium*, pouch.
Mastoid. G., *mastos*, breast, + *eidos*, resemblance.
Matrix. L., *matrix* (*mater*), womb, groundwork, or mold.
Meatus (pl. **-us**). L., *meatus*, passage.
Medial. L., *medialis* (*medius*), pertaining to the middle.
Mediastinum. L., *mediastinus*, servant, drudge.
Medulla. L., *medulla*, marrow, pith.
Melanin. G., *melas, melanos*, black.
Membrane. L., *membrana*, skin.
Meninx (pl. **meninges**). G., *meninx*, membrane.
Mes-, meso-. G. prefix signifying middle.
Mesencephalon. G., *mesos*, middle, + *en*, in, + *kephale*, head.
Mesenchyme. G., *mesos*, middle, + *en*, in, + *chymos*, juice.
Mesentery. G., *mesos*, midway between, + *enteron*, gut.
Mesocardium. G., *mesos*, middle, + *kardia*, heart.
Mesoderm. G., *mesos*, middle, + *derma*, skin.
Mesolecithal. G., *mesos*, middle, + *lekithos*, yolk.
Mesonephros. G., *mesos*, middle, + *nephros*, kidney.
Mesopterygium. G., *mesos*, middle, + *pterygion*, little wing.
Mesorchium. G., *mesos*, middle, + *orchis*, testis.
Mesovarium. G., *mesos*, middle, + L., *ovarium*, ovary.
Meta-. G., prefix meaning after, next; denoting change of time or situation.
Metabolic. G., *metabole*, change.
Metacarpus. G., *meta*, after, + L., *carpus*, wrist.
Metamere. G., *meta*, after, + *meros*, part.
Metamorphosis. G., *meta*, signifying change, + *morphe*, form.
Metanephros. G., *meta*, after, + *nephros*, kidney.
Metapleura. G., *meta*, after, + *pleura*, side.
Metapodial. G., *meta*, after, + *pous, podos*, foot.
Metatarsus. G., *meta*, after, + L., *tarsus*, ankle.
Metencephalon. G., *meta*, after, + *enkephalos*, brain.
Molar. L., *molaris* (*mola*), pertaining to a millstone.
Monocyte. G., *monos*, single, + *kytos*, cell.
Mucus. L., *mucus*, snivel, slippery secretion.
Multangulum. L., *multus*, many, + *angulus*, angle.
Myelencephalon. G., *myelos*, marrow, + *enkephalos*, brain.
Myelin. G., *myelos*, marrow.
Myo-. G. combining form signifying muscle.
Myocardium. G., *mys, myos*, muscle, + *kardia*, heart.
Myocomma. G., *mys, myos*, muscle, + *komma*, implying separation.

Myodome. G., *mys, myos*, muscle, + L., *domus*, house.

Myomere. G., *mys, myos*, muscle, + *meros*, part.

Myotome. G., *mys, myos*, muscle, + *tome*, a cutting.

Naris (pl. -es). L., *naris*, nostril.

Neopallium. G., *neos*, youthful, new, + L., *pallium*, cloak.

Nephridia. G., *nephridios*, belonging to the kidneys.

Nephrotome. G., *nephros*, kidney, + *tome*, a cutting.

Neural. G., *neuron*, nerve.

Neurenteric. G., *neuron*, nerve, + *enteron*, gut.

Neurilemma. G., *neuron*, nerve, + *lemma*, husk, sheath.

Neuro-. G. combining form signifying nerve.

Neuroglia. G., *neuron*, nerve, + *gloia*, glue.

Neurohumor. G., *neuron*, nerve, + L., *humor*, fluid.

Neuromast. G., *neuron*, nerve, + *mastos*, round hill.

Neuron. G., *neuron*, sinew, tendon; equivalent of L. *nervus;* whence, nerve.

Neuropil. G., *neuron*, nerve, + *pilos*, felt.

Nictitating. L., *nictare*, to wink.

Nidamental. L., *nidamentum*, materials for a nest.

Node. L., *nodus*, knot.

Notochord. G., *noton*, back, + *chorde*, cord.

Nuchal. L., *nucha*, nape of the neck.

Obliquus. L., *obliquus*, slanting.

Oculomotor. L., *oculus*, eye, + *motor*, mover.

Odontoblast. G., *odous*, tooth, + *blastos*, shoot, germ.

Olecranon. G., *olekranon*, point of the elbow.

Olfactory. L., *olere*, to smell, + *facere*, to make.

Omasum. L., *omasum*, paunch.

Omentum. L., *omentum*, adipose membrane enclosing the bowels.

Omphalo-. G. combining form (*omphalos*) signifying the navel.

Ontogeny. G., *onta*, things that exist, + *gennan*, to beget.

Operculum. L., *operculum*, lid.

Ophthalmic. G., *ophthalmos*, eye.

Opistho-. G. prefix signifying backward, behind.

Opisthocelous. G., *opisthe*, behind, + *koilos*, hollow.

Opisthonephros. G., *opisthe*, behind, + *nephros*, kidney.

Optic. G., *opsis*, sight.

Osseous. L., *os* (pl. *ossa*), bone.

Ossicle. L., *ossiculum*, small bone.

Osteoblast. G., *osteon*, bone, + *blastos*, germ.

Osteocyte. G., *osteon*, bone, + *kytos*, cell.

Otic. G., *otikos*, belonging to the ear.

Otolith. G., *ous, otos*, ear, + *lithos*, stone.

Ovum (pl. **ova**). L., *ovum*, egg.

Oxyphil. G., *oxys*, acid, + *philos*, friend.

Paleontology. G., *palaios*, ancient, + *onta*, existing things, + *logos*, science.

Paleopallium. G., *palaios*, ancient, + L., *pallium*, covering.

Pallium. L., *pallium*, cloak.

Palma. L., *palma*, the (open) hand.

Palpebra. L., *palpebra*, eyelid.

Pancreas. G., *pan*, all, + *kreas*, flesh.

Papilla.　L., *papilla*, pimple.

Para-.　G. prefix signifying alongside of, near.

Parabronchii.　G., *para*, beside, + *bronchos*, windpipe.

Paracentrum.　G., *para*, near, + *kentron* (L. *centrum*), center.

Parachordal.　G., *para*, beside, + *chorde*, cord.

Paraganglion.　G., *para*, along, beside, + *ganglion*, knot.

Paraphysis.　G., *para*, beside, + *physis*, growth.

Parapsid.　G., *para*, beside, + *apsis*, arch.

Parathyroid.　G., *para*, near, + *thyreos*, oblong shield, + *eidos*, form.

Parencephalon.　G., *para*, beside, + *enkephalon*, brain.

Parietal.　L., *paries*, wall.

Parotid.　G., *para*, near + *ous*, *otos*, ear.

Pecten.　L., *pecten*, comb.

Pectoral.　L., *pectoralis* (*pectus*), belonging to the breast.

Pedunculus.　L., *pediculus*, a little foot.

Pelvic.　L., *pelvis*, basin.

Peri-.　G. prefix meaning around.

Pericardial.　G., *peri*, around, + *kardia*, heart.

Perichondrium.　G., *peri*, around, + *chondros*, cartilage.

Perichordal.　G., *peri*, around, + *chorde*, cord.

Perilymph.　G., *peri*, around, + L., *lympha*, fluid.

Perimysium.　G., *peri*, around, + *mys*, muscle.

Periosteum.　G., *peri*, around, + *osteon*, bone.

Peristalsis.　G., *peristaltikos*, clasping and compressing.

Peritoneum.　G., *peritonaion*, membrane containing the lower viscera.

Phallic.　G., *phallikos*, pertaining to the penis.

Pharynx.　G., *pharynx*, throat.

Photophore.　G., *phos*, *photos*, light, + *pherein*, to bear.

Phylogeny.　G., *phylon*, race, + *gennan*, to beget.

Pineal.　L., *pinea*, pine cone.

Pinna (pl. **-ae**).　L., *penna*, *pinna*, feather; hence, wing.

Pisiform.　L., *pisum*, pea, + *forma*, shape.

Pituitary.　L., *pituita*, slime, phlegm.

Placenta.　L., *placenta*, a flat cake.

Placode.　G., *plax*, plate, + *eidos*, likeness.

Planta.　L., *planta*, sole of the foot.

Plastron.　F., *plastron*, breastplate.

Platybasic.　G., *platys*, broad, flat, + L., *basis*, base.

Plectrum.　G., *plektron*, hammer.

Pleuro-.　G. combining form signifying the side.

Pleurocentrum.　G., *pleura*, side, + *kentron* (L., *centrum*), center.

Pleurodont.　G., *pleura*, ribs, side, + *odous*, tooth.

Plexus (pl. **-us**).　L., *plexus*, plaiting, braid.

Pneumatic.　G., *pneumatikos*, pertaining to breath.

Poikilothermous.　G., *poikilos*, changeful, + *thermos*, heat.

Pons.　L., *pons*, *pontis*, bridge.

Portal.　L., *porta* (pl. *-ae*), gate.

Porus.　G., *poros*, passage.

Prae-, pre-.　L. prefix signifying before, in front.

Premolar.　L., *pre*, in front, + *molaris*, molar.

Prepuce. L., *praeputium*, foreskin.

Primordial. L., *primordium*, beginning.

Pro-. G. or L. prefix signifying before, in front of, or prior.

Procelous. G., *pro*, in front, + *koilos*, hollow.

Proctodeum. G., *proktos*, anus, + *hodaios*, pertaining to a way.

Profundus. L., *profundus*, deep.

Pronator. L., *pronare*, to bend forward.

Pronephros. G., *pro*, before, + *nephros*, kidney.

Proprioceptor. L., *proprius*, special, + *capere*, to take.

Prosencephalon. G., *pros*, before, + *enkephalos*, brain.

Prostate. L., *pro*, in front, + *stare*, to stand.

Protonephros. G., *protos*, first, + *nephros*, kidney.

Protoplasm. G., *protos*, first, + *plasma*, form.

Proximal. L., *proximus*, next.

Pseudobranch. G., *pseudes*, false, + *branchia*, gills.

Pterygoid. G., *pteryx*, wing, + *eidos*, likeness.

Pterylae. G., *pteron*, feather, + *hyle*, a wood.

Pubis (pl. **-es**). L., *pubis*, mature.

Pulmonary. L., *pulmo*, lung.

Pygal. G., *pyge*, rump.

Pygostyle. G., *pyge*, rump, + *stylos*, pillar.

Pylorus. G., *pylouros*, gate-keeper.

Pyriform. L., *pirum*, pear, + *forma*, shape.

Quadriceps. L., *quattuor*, four, + *caput*, head.

Quadrigeminus. L., *quadrigeminus*, fourfold, four.

Radial. L., *radius*, rod, spoke.

Receptor. L., *recipere*, to take back, receive.

Rectus. L., *rectus*, straight.

Remiges (pl.). L., *remex*, rower.

Renal. L., *renes*, kidneys.

Rete. L., *rete*, network.

Reticulum. L., *reticulum*, a little net.

Retina. L., *rete*, net.

Retractor. L., *retrahere*, to draw back.

Retrices. L., *retro*, back, + *cedere*, to go.

Rhachitomous. G., *rhachis*, spine + *temnein*, to cut.

Rhinal. G., *rhis*, nose.

Rhombencephalon. G., *rhombas*, kind of parallelogram, + *enkephalos*, brain.

Rostrum (pl. **-a**). L., *rostrum*, beak.

Rotator. L., *rotare*, to whirl about.

Ruminare. L., *ruminari*, to chew the cud.

Sacculus. L., *sacculus*, a little bag.

Sacrum. L., *sacer*, sacred.

Sagittal. L., *sagitta*, arrow.

Salpinx. G., *salpinx*, trumpet.

Sarcolemma. G., *sarx*, flesh, + *lemma*, husk, skin.

Scala. L., *scala*, staircase.

Sclera. G., *skleros*, hard.

Sclerotic. G., *skleros*, hard.

Sclerotome. G., *skleros*, hard, + *temnein*, to cut.

Scrotum. L., *scrotum* (*scrotum*), skin.

Sebaceous. L., *sebum*, tallow, grease.

Selenodont. G., *selene*, moon (hence, crescent), + *odous*, tooth.

Seminiferous. L., *semen*, seed, + *ferre*, to bear.

Septum. L., *saeptum*, fence.

Sinus (pl. **-us**). L., *sinus*, curve, cavity, bosom.

Somatic. G., *soma* (pl. *somata*), body.

Somatopleure. G., *soma*, body, + *pleura*, side.

Somite. G., *soma*, body, + suffix *-ite*, indicating origin.

Spermatozoon (pl. **-a**). G., *sperma*, seed, + *zoon*, animal.

Sphenoid. G., *sphen*, wedge, + *eidos*, likeness.

Sphincter. G., *sphingein*, to bind tight.

Spina. L., *spina*, thorn.

Spiracle. L., *spiraculum*, air hole.

Splanchnic. G., *splanchna*, viscera.

Splanchnopleure. G., *splanchna*, viscera, + *pleura*, side.

Stapes. L., *stapes*, stirrup.

Stereospondylous. G., *stereos*, solid, + *sphondylos*, vertebra.

Stomodeum. G., *stoma*, mouth, + *hodaios*, pertaining to a way.

Stratus (pl. **strata**). L., *stratus*, layer.

Striatum. L., *striatus*, grooved, streaked.

Styloid. G., *stylos*, pillar, + *eidos*, likeness.

Sub-. L. prefix signifying under, beneath, near.

Subcostal. L., *sub*, under, + *costa*, rib.

Sublingual. L., *sub*, under, + *lingus*, tongue.

Subunguis. L., *sub*, under, + *unguis*, nail.

Subvertebral. L., *sub*, under, + *vertebra*, joint.

Sulcus. L., *sulcus*, furrow.

Supinator. L., *supinare*, to bend backward.

Supracostal. L., *supra*, above, + *costa*, rib.

Supraspinatus. L., *supra*, above, + *spina*, thorn.

Sym-, syn-. G. prefix signifying with or together.

Sympathetic. G., *syn*, together, + *pathein*, to suffer.

Symphysis. G., *syn*, together, + *physis*, growth.

Synapse. G., *syn*, together, + *haptein*, to fasten.

Synarthrosis. G., *syn*. together, + *arthron*, joint.

Synsacrum. G., *syn*, together, + L., *sacer* (*os sacrum*), sacrum.

Syrinx. G., *syrinx*, pipe.

Tabular. L., *tabula*, board, table.

Talonid. L., *talus*, heel, + G., *eidos*, form.

Tapetum. L., *tapete*, carpet.

Tarsus. G., *tarsos*, sole of the foot.

Tectum. L., *tectum* (*tego*), roof.

Tegmentum. L., *tegumentum*, a covering.

Tela. L., *tela*, web.

Telencephalon. G., *telos*, end, + *enkephalos*, brain.

Telolecithal. G., *telos*, end, + *lekithos*, yolk.

Temporal. L., *temporalis*, belonging to time.

Temporal. L., *tempora*, the temples.

Tendon. L., *tendere*, to stretch.

Tentorium. L., *tentorium*, tent.

Terminalis. L., *terminare*, to limit.

Testis. L., *testis,* testicle.
Tetrapod. G., *tetra,* four, + *pous,* foot.
Thalamus. G., *thalamos,* chamber or couch.
Thecodont. G., *theke,* case, sheath, + *odous,* tooth.
Thorax (thoracis). G., *thorax,* breastplate, breast.
Thrombocytes. G., *thrombos,* clot, + *kytos,* cells.
Thymus. G., *thymos,* sweetbread.
Thyroid. G., *thyreos,* shield, + *eidos,* form.
Trabecula (pl. -ae). L., *trabecula,* a little beam.
Trachea. G., *tracheia,* windpipe.
Triceps. L., *tres,* three, + *caput,* head.
Trigeminus. L., *trigeminus,* born three together.
Triquetrum. L., *triquetrus,* three-cornered, triangular.
Trochanter. G., *trochos,* wheel, pulley.
Trochlea. G., *trochilia,* pulley.
Trophoblast. G., *trophe,* nourishment, + *blastos,* shoot, germ.
Tropibasic. G., *trope,* a turning, + L., *basis,* base.
Tuberculum. L., *tuberculum,* a small hump.
Tunica. L., *tunica,* undergarment.
Turbinal. L., *turbo,* a top, anything that spins or shows turning.
Tympanic. L., *tympanum,* drum.
Umbilical. L., *umbilicus,* navel.
Unciform. L., *uncus,* hook, + *forma,* shape.
Uncinate. L., *uncinatus,* furnished with a hook.
Urea. G., *ouron,* urine.
Urodela. G., *oura,* tail, + *delos,* evident.
Urodeum. G., *ouron,* urine, + *hodaios,* pertaining to a way.
Urogenital. G., *ouron,* urine, + L., *genitalis,* genital.
Uropygial. G., *orros,* end of os sacrum, + *pyge,* rump.
Urostyle. G., *oura,* tail, + *stylos,* pillar.
Uterus. L., *uterus,* womb.
Utriculus. L., *utriculus,* small skin or leather bottle.
Vagus. L., *vagus,* wandering.
Valvula. L., *valvula,* a little fold or valve.
Vas. L., *vas,* vessel.
Vascular. L., *vasculum,* small vessel.
Ventral. L., *venter,* belly.
Ventricle. L., *ventriculus,* little cavity, loculus.
Vermiform. L., *vermis,* worm, + *forma,* shape.
Vesicle. L., *vesicula,* a small bladder.
Vestibulum. L., *vestibulum,* entrance court.
Vibrissa (pl. -ae). L., *vibrissa,* hair in the nostril.
Villus (pl. villi). L., *villus,* shaggy hair.
Visceral. L., *viscera,* entrails, bowels.
Vitelline. L., *vitellus,* yolk of egg.
Vitreus. L., *vitreus,* of glass; hence, transparent.
Viviparous. L., *vivus,* living, + *parere,* to beget.
Vomer. L., *vomer,* ploughshare.
Xiphiplastron. G., *xiphos,* sword, + F., *plastron,* breastplate.
Zygapophysis. G., *zygon,* yoke, + *apophysis,* process of a bone.
Zygomatic. G., *zygoma,* cheekbone.

Latin Word Endings

Although scientific terms are often used in English form, some knowledge of the use of these words in Latin form is desirable. Latin is a highly inflected language, with a variable series of terminations for nouns and adjectives expressing not only singular and plural numbers, but also genders (of an artificial nature) and a variety of cases; still further, there are several different systems of forming such terminations ("declensions"). Fortunately, however, nearly all use of scientific terms involves only two cases—nominative and genitive. Less than a score of endings affixed to the word root will cover most instances.

Adjectives (which must agree in gender, number, and case with their nouns) are "declined" according to one of the two following schemes, for each of which a common adjective is used as an example (the ending, attached to the root, is in boldface).

First and Second Declension (Combined)

	Masculine	*Neuter*	*Feminine*
Nominative singular	magn**us**	magn**um**	magn**a**
Nominative plural	magn**i**	magn**a**	magn**ae**
Genitive singular	magn**i**		magn**ae**
Genitive plural	magn**orum**		magn**arum**

Third Declension

	Masculine and Feminine	*Neuter*
Nominative singular	grand**is**	grand**e**
Nominative plural	grand**es**	grand**ia**
Genitive singular	grand**is**	
Genitive plural	grand**ium**	

Most nouns follow one of these same schemes. Thus, *fibula* is a feminine noun of the first declension and is declined *fibula, fibulae, fibulae, fibularum; humerus* is a masculine noun of the second declension, declined *humerus, humeri, humeri, humerorum; sternum, sterna, sterni, sternorum,* a neuter noun of the second declension; *cutis, cutes, cutis, cutium* (skin), a feminine noun of the third declension.

There are, however, two complications: (1) in the third declension most nouns have a short form for the nominative singular, a longer root for the other case endings. Thus *femur* (third declension neuter) becomes *femora,* and so on, in other cases; other typical examples are *meninx, meninges; foramen, foramina; caput, capita.* (2) A few nouns used anatomically belong to a further declension—a fourth declension. Of masculine words of this gender—*plexus* and *meatus* are examples—the plural spelling is the same as the singular; hence the English form is preferable for common use. A common neuter noun of this declension is *cornu* (horn), declined *cornu, cornua, cornus, cornuum.*

APPENDIX

3

REFERENCES

Below are listed a few of the more useful general works, or works on special topics or animal types, review articles, and a limited number of original research papers and monographs. To look further into the literature of any special topic, these two publications are most useful:

Zoological Record, 1864–date. London.

Each annual volume lists all papers published during the year concerning each class of vertebrates, and follows this with classified lists of those papers which deal with various topics in anatomy, embryology, and so forth.

Biological Abstracts, 1926–date. Philadelphia.

A voluminous journal which attempts to abstract and index all papers published in any field of biology.

In the sections which follow, the more generally useful works are listed first, followed by works of a more specialized nature or more restricted anatomical interest.

GENERAL

Bolk, L., Göppert, E., Kallius, E., and Lubosch, W.: Handbuch der vegleichenden Anatomie der Wirbeltiere. 6 vols. Berlin and Vienna, Urban and Schwartzenberg, 1931–1939. A comprehensive work on vertebrate anatomy by many specialists; includes extensive bibliographies.

Bronn, H. G., *et al.*: Klassen und Ordnungen des Thier-Reichs. Leipzig and Heidelberg, Winter 1874–date. A voluminous work by various authors, published in parts, some old, some new, some as yet incomplete, which gives great attention to the anatomy of the various vertebrate groups as well as to classification and distribution.

Kükenthal, W., and Krumbach, T., editors: Handbuch der Zoologie. Berlin and Leipzig, W. de Gruyter & Company, 1923–date. A work similar to the last in scope; incomplete, as yet.

Grassé, P. P.: Traité de Zoologie, Anatomie, Systematique, Biologie. Vols. 1–17. Paris, Masson et Cie, 1948–1958. Not yet complete. Vol. IX treats of lower chordates; vols. X–XVII of vertebrates.

Goodrich, E. S.: Studies on the Structure and Development of Vertebrates. London, The Macmillan Company, 1930. A stimulating discussion of many anatomic problems by a first rate authority. Reprinted by Dover Publications, New York, 1958.

593

Owen, R.: On the Anatomy of Vertebrates. 3 vols. London, Longmans, Green, 1866–1868. A classic, full of original observations.

Cuvier, G.: Leçons d'Anatomie Comparée. 5 vols. Paris, 1805. The first great comparative anatomy.

Young, J. Z.: The Life of Vertebrates. 2nd ed. London and New York, Oxford University Press, 1962. An excellent, group by group account, not only of structure but of life habits and functions of the vertebrates.

Marinelli, W., and Strenger, A.: Vergleichende Anatomie und Morphologie der Wirbeltiere. Wien, Franz Deuticke, 1954, 1959. Parts so far issued treat of cyclostomes and Squalus.

Ihle, J. E. W., *et al.:* Vergleichende Anatomie der Wirbeltiere. Berlin, J. Springer, 1927. A substantial volume on comparative anatomy by Dutch authors, translated into German.

Böker, H.: Einführung in die vergleichende biologische Anatomie der Wirbeltiere. 2 vols. Jena, Gustav Fischer, 1935, 1937.

Romer, A. S.: The Vertebrate Story. Chicago, University of Chicago Press, 1959. An elementary account of vertebrate evolution.

Colbert, E. H.: Evolution of the Vertebrates. New York, Wiley, 1955.

Romer, A. S.: Vertebrate Paleontology. 2nd ed. Chicago, University of Chicago Press, 1945.

Piveteau, J.: Traité de Paléontologie. 8 vols. Paris, Masson et Cie, 1952–1958. A comprehensive work, five volumes of which treat of vertebrates. The volume on fishes not yet published.

Thompson, D. W.: On Growth and Form. 2nd ed. Cambridge, England, Cambridge University Press, 1942.

Nomina Anatomica. Revised by the International Anatomical Nomenclature Committee, Baltimore, Williams & Wilkins Company, 1956.

Prosser, C. L., and Brown, F. A., Jr.: Comparative Animal Physiology. 2nd ed. Philadelphia, W. B. Saunders Company, 1961. Contains much data on physiology of vertebrates as a whole. (The data of standard texts on human physiology such as the work next cited apply well to mammals but in a much lesser degree to other vertebrate groups.)

Ruch, T. C., and Fulton, J. F.: Medical Physiology and Biophysics. (18th edition of Howell's Textbook of Physiology) Philadelphia, W. B. Saunders Company, 1960.

Buddenbrock, W. von: Vergleichende Physiologie. 4 vols. Basel, Birkhäusen, 1950–1956.

CELLS AND TISSUES

Scott, G. G., and Kendall, J. I.: The Microscopic Anatomy of Vertebrates. 3rd ed. Philadelphia, Lea and Febiger, 1947.

Cole, C. A.: Comparative Histology, New York, Blakiston Company, 1955.

Krause, R.: Mikroskopische Anatomie der Wirbeltiere. Berlin, W. de Gruyter & Company, 1923.

Maximow, A., and Bloom, W.: A Textbook of Histology. 5th ed. Philadelphia, W. B. Saunders Company, 1948. This and the two following are representative histologies based on human material.

LeGros Clark, W. E.: The Tissues of the Body. 2nd ed. London and New York, Oxford University Press, 1945.

Windle, W. F.: Textbook of Histology. 3rd ed. New York, McGraw-Hill, 1960.

De Robertis, E. D. P., Nowinski, W. W., and Saez, F. A.: General Cytology. 3rd ed. Philadelphia, W. B. Saunders Company, 1960.

Baldwin, E.: An Introduction to Comparative Biochemistry. 3rd ed. Cambridge, England, Cambridge University Press, 1952.

EMBRYOLOGY

DeBeer, G. R.: Embryos and Ancestors. London and New York, Oxford University Press, 1951.

Brachet, A., Dalcq, A., and Gérard, P.: Traité d'Embryologie des Vertébrés. 2nd ed. Paris, Masson et Cie, 1935.

Nelsen, O. E.: Comparative Embryology of Vertebrates. New York, Blakiston Company, 1953.

Hertwig, O., and others: Handbuch der vergleichenden und experimentellen Entwickelungslehre der Wirbeltiere. 3 vols. Jena, Fischer, 1901–1906. A comprehensive, well illustrated work; out of date in certain aspects.

Kerr, J. G.: Text-Book of Embryology, Vol. II. Vertebrata with the Exception of Mammals. London, Macmillan Company, 1919.

Witschi, E.: Development of Vertebrates. Philadelphia, W. B. Saunders Company, 1956.

Willier, B. H., Weiss, P. A., and Hamburger, V., editors: Analysis of Development. Philadelphia, W. B. Saunders Company, 1955.
Waddington, C. H.: Principles of Embryology. London, George Allen & Unwin, 1956.
Arey, L. B.: Developmental Anatomy. 6th ed. Philadelphia, W. B. Saunders Company, 1954. Primarily mammalian and human.
Hamilton, W. J., Boyd, J. D., and Mossman, H. W.: Human Embryology. 2nd ed. Cambridge, England, Helfer, 1952.
Starck, D.: Embryologie. Stuttgart, Thieme, 1955.
Patten, B. M.: Foundations of Embryology. New York, McGraw-Hill, 1958.
Patten, B. M.: Early Embryology of the Pig, 3rd ed. New York, McGraw-Hill, 1948.
Lillie, F. R.: Development of the Chick; revised and edited by H. L. Hamilton. New York, Holt, 1952.
Patten, B. M.: Early Embryology of the Duck. 4th ed. New York, McGraw-Hill, 1951.
Waddington, C. H.: The Epigenetics of Birds. London, Cambridge University Press, 1952.
Romanoff, A. L.: The Avian Embryo. New York, The Macmillan Company, 1960.
Hörstadius, S.: The Neural Crest. London, Oxford University Press, 1950.

SKIN

Schaffer, J.: Die Hautdrüsenorgane der Säugetiere. Berlin and Wien, Urban und Schwarzenberg, 1940.
Fox, L. D.: Animal Biochromes and Structural Colours. London, Cambridge University Press, 1953.
DuShane, G.: The embryology of vertebrate pigment cells. Part I. Amphibia. Quart. Rev. Biol. *18*:109–127, 1943; Part II. Birds. *19*:98–117, 1944.
Parker, G. H.: Animal Color Changes and their Neurohumors. London, Cambridge University Press, 1948.
Lillie, F. R.: On the development of feathers. Biol. Rev. *17*:247–266, 1942.
Paris, P.: Recherches sur la gland uropygienne des oiseaux. Arch. Zoologie Expérimental et Générale *53*:132–276, 1914.
Harvey, E. N.: Bioluminescence. New York, Academic Press, 1952.

SKELETON

Reynolds, S. H.: The Vertebrate Skeleton. 2nd ed. Cambridge, 1913.
Gregory, W. K.: Evolution Emerging. 2 vols. New York, The Macmillan Company, 1951. Extremely valuable illustrations.
Kummer, B.: Bauprinzipien des Skelets. Stuttgart, Thieme, 1959.
Murray, P. D. F.: Bones. A study of the Development and Structure of the Vertebrate Skeleton. London, Cambridge University Press, 1936.
Haines, R. W.: The evolution of epiphyses and of endochondral bone. Biol. Rev. *17*:267–292, 1942.
Gray, J.: How Animals Move. London, Cambridge University Press, 1953.
Goodrich, E. S.: On the scales of fish, living and extinct, and their importance in classification. Proc. Zool. Soc. London, 751–774, 1908.
Kerr, T.: The scales of primitive living actinopterygians. Proc. Zool. Soc. London *122*:55–78, 1952.
Schmalhausen, J. J.: Zur Morphologie der unpaaren Flossen. Ztschr. wissenschaftliche Zoologie *100*:509–587; *104*:1–80, 1912–1913.
Goodrich, E. S.: On the dermal fin-rays of fishes—living and extinct. Quart. J. Microscopical Sc. *47*:465–522, 1904.
Williams, E. E.: Gadow's arcualia and the development of tetrapod vertebrae. Quart. Rev. Biol., *34*:1–32, 1959.
Piiper, J.: On the evolution of the vertebral column in birds. Philos. Trans. Roy. Soc. London (*B*) *216*:285–351, 1928.
Westoll, T. S.: The Lateral Fin-fold Theory and the Pectoral Fins of Ostracoderms and Early Fishes. In Westoll, T. S., ed.: Studies on Fossil Vertebrates. London, University of London, 180–211, 1958.
Gregory, W. K., and Raven, H. C.: Studies on the origin and early evolution of paired fins and limbs. Ann. New York Acad. Sc. *42*:273–360, 1944.
Parker, W. K.: A Monograph on the Structure and Development of the Shoulder Girdle and Sternum. London, Ray Society, 1868.
Watson, D. M. S.: The evolution of the tetrapod shoulder girdle and fore-limb. J. Anat. *52*:1–63, 1917.

Schaeffer, B.: The morphological and functional evolution of the tarsus in amphibians and reptiles. Bull. Am. Museum Natural Hist. *78*:395–472, 1941.

Gregory, W. K., Miner, R. W., and Noble, G. K.: The carpus of Eryops and the primitive cheiropterygium. Bull. Am. Museum Natural Hist. *48*:279–288, 1923.

Fisher, H. I.: Adaptations and comparative anatomy of the locomotor apparatus of New World vultures. Am. Midland Naturalist *35*:545–727, 1946.

Berger, A. J.: The comparative functional morphology of the pectoral appendage in three genera of Cuculidae. Am. Midland Naturalist *47*:513–605, 1952.

Romer, A. S.: The Osteology of Reptiles. Chicago, University of Chicago Press, 1956.

Shufeldt, R. W.: Osteology of birds. Bull. New York State Museum *130*:5–381, 1909.

Flower, W. H.: An Introduction to the Osteology of the Mammalia. 3rd ed. London, The Macmillan Company, 1885. An old but useful little book. (Reissued by Dover Press, New York, 1962.)

Jayne, H.: Mammalian Anatomy. Part I. The Skeleton of the Cat. Philadelphia, Lippincott Company, 1898.

SKULL

DeBeer, G. R.: The Development of the Vertebrate Skull. London and New York, Oxford University Press, 1937. Publication preceded by a series of detailed papers on various forms by DeBeer and colleagues. Good bibliography.

Parker, W. K.: Structure and development of the skull. A long series of papers on the following forms: Ostrich, Fowl, Rana, Batrachia, Salmon, Pig, Urodela, Tropidonotus, Lacertilia, Acipenser, Lepidosteus, Edentata and Insectivora, Birds, Sharks and Skates, Crocodilia, Opisthocomus, in the following journals: Philos. Trans. Roy. Soc. London (*B*) *156, 159, 161, 163, 164, 167, 169, 170, 173, 176*, 1866–1885; Tr. Zool. Soc. London *9, 10, 11, 13*, 1875–1891; Tr. Linnean Soc. London, Zoology, *1, 2*, 1875–1888. Old but well illustrated and valuable.

Gregory, W. K.: Fish skulls: A study of the evolution of natural mechanisms. Tr. Am. Philosophical Soc. *23*:75–481, 1933.

Schauinsland, H.: Beiträge zur Entwickelungsgeschichte und Anatomie der Wirbeltiere: Sphenodon, Callorhynchus, Chamaeleo, Zoologica (Stuttgart) *16*:1–98, 1903.

Gaupp, E.: Das Chondrocranium von Lacerta agilis. Anatomische Hefte (Arb.) *15*:433–595, 1900.

Peyer, B.: Die Entwicklung des Schädelskelettes von Vipera aspis. Morphologisches Jahrbuch *44*:563–621, 1912.

Radovanovic, M.: Osteologie des Schlangenkopfes. Jenaische Ztschr. Naturwissenschaft *71*:179–312, 1937.

Brock, G. T.: On the development of the skull of Leptodeira hotamboia. Quart. J. Microscopical Sc. *73*:289–334, 1929.

Bellairs, A. d'A.: The anterior brain-case and interorbital septum of Sauropsida with a consideration of the origin of snakes. J. Linnean Soc. London, Zoology, *41*:482–512, 1949.

Versluys, J.: Das Streptostylie-Problem und die Bewegungen im Schädel bei Sauropsiden. Zoologische Jahrbücher (Anat.), Supplement *15*(2): 545–714, 1912.

Jollie, M. T.: The head skeleton of the lizard. Acta Zoologica, *41*:1–64, 1960.

Lakjer, T.: Studien über die Gaumenregion bei Sauriern im Vergleich mit Anamniern und primitiven Sauropsiden. Zoologische Jahrbücher *49*:57–356, 1927.

Hofer, H.: Neuere Untersuchungen zur Kopfmorphologie der Vögel. Basel, Acta 11th Congrès International d'Ornithologie 104–137, 1955.

Crompton, A. W.: The development of the chondrocranium of Spheniscus demersus with special reference to the columella auris of birds. Acta Zoologica *34*:71–146, 1953.

Lang, C.: Das Cranium der Ratiten mit besonderer Berücksichtigung von Struthio camelus. Ztschr. wissenschaftliche Zoologie *159*:165–224, 1956.

Jollie, M. T.: The head skeleton of the chicken and remarks on the anatomy of this region in other birds. J. Morphol. *100*:389–436, 1957.

Starck, D.: Zur Morphologie des Primordialcraniums von Manis javanica Desm. Morphologisches Jahrbuch *86*:1–122, 1941. One of a series of mammal skull studies by Starck and his students.

Kampen, P. N. van: Die Tympanalgegend des Säugetierschädels. Morphologisches Jahrbuch, *34*:321–722, 1905.

MUSCLES

Fisher, H. I., and Goodman, D. C.: The Myology of the Whooping Crane, Grus americana. Illinois Biological Monographs, *24*, no. 2, 1955.

Shufeldt, R. W.: The Myology of the Raven. New York, Macmillan Company, 1890.

Maurer, F.: Die Entwicklung der ventralen Rumpfmuskulatur bei Reptilien. Morphologisches Jahrbuch *26*:1–60, 1898.

Straus, W. L., and Rawles, M. E.: An experimental study of the origin of the trunk musculature and ribs in the chick. Am. J. Anat. *92*:471–510, 1953.

Gilbert, P. W.: The origin and development of the human extrinsic ocular muscles. Contrib. Embryol. *36*:59–78, 1957.

Braus, H.: Die Muskeln und Nerven der Ceratodusflosse. Semon's Zoologische Forschungsreisen in Australien *1*:137–300, 1901.

Sewertzoff, A. N.: Studien über die Entwickelung der Muskeln, Nerven und des Skeletts der Extremitäten der niederen Tetrapoda. Bull. Soc. Impériale Naturalistes Moscou (n.s.) *21*:1–430, 1907.

Romer, A. S.: The development of tetrapod limb musculature—the shoulder region of Lacerta. J. Morphol. *74*:1–41, 1944.

Romer, A. S.: The development of the thigh musculature of the chick. J. Morphol. *43*:347–385, 1927.

Fürbringer, M.: Zur vergleichenden Anatomie des Brustschulterapparates und der Schultermuskeln. Jenaische Ztschr. Naturwissenschaft *36*:289–736, 1902; Morphologisches Jahrbuch *1*, 1875; *7*, 1873; *8*, 1874; *34*, 1902.

Sy, M.: Funktionell-anatomische Untersuchungen am Vogelflügel. J. Ornithologie *84*:199–296, 1936.

Hudson, G. E.: Studies on the muscles of the pelvic appendage in birds. Am. Midland Naturalist *18*:1–108, 1937.

Howell, A. B.: Morphogenesis of the shoulder architecture: Aves. Auk *54*:363–375, 1937.

Edgeworth, F. H.: The Cranial Muscles of Vertebrates. London, The Macmillan Company, 1935.

Drüner, L.: Zungenbein-, Kiemenbogen- und Kehlkopf-Muskeln der Urodelen. Zoologische Jahrbücher, Abteilung für Anatomie und Ontogenie der Tiere *15*:435–622; *19*:361–690, 1902–1904.

Lakjer, T.: Studien über die Trigeminus-versorgte Kaumuskulatur der Sauropsiden. Copenhagen, C. A. Reitzel, 1926.

Haas, G.: Die Kiefermuskulatur und die Schädelmechanik der Schlangen in vergleichender Darstellung. Zoologische Jahrbücher, Abteilung für Anatomie und Ontogenie der Tiere *53*:127–198, 1931. See also *ibid. 52*:1–218, 1930.

Starck, D., and Barnikol, A.: Beiträge zur Morphologie der Trigeminusmuskulatur der Vögel (besonders der Accipitres, Cathartidae, Striges und Anseres). Morphologisches Jahrbuch *94*:1–64, 1954.

Hofer, H.: Zur Morphologie der Kiefermuskulatur der Vögel. Zoologische Jahrbücher *70*:427–556, 1950.

Cheng, C. C.: The development of the shoulder region of the opossum, Didelphys virginiana, with special reference to the musculature. J. Morphol. *97*:415–471, 1955.

Grandfert, H.: Electric fishes. Scientific American *203*:115–120, 1960.

CELOM

Butler, G. W.: On the subdivision of the body-cavity in lizards, crocodiles, and birds. Proc. Zool. Soc. London 452–474, 1889; snakes, 477–498, 1892.

Mall, F. P.: Development of the human coelom. J. Morphol. *12*:395–453, 1897.

Keith, A.: The nature of the mammalian diaphragm and pleural cavities. J. Anat. Physiol. *39*:243–284, 1905.

Wells, L. J.: Development of the human diaphragm and pleural sacs. Carnegie Inst. Washington, Contrib. Embryol. *35*:107–134, 1954.

MOUTH AND PHARYNX

Sonntag, C. F.: The comparative anatomy of the tongues of the Mammalia. Proc. Zool. Soc. London, 1920, 115–129; 1921, 1–29, 277–322, 497–521, 741–755, 757–767; 1922, 639–657; 1923, 129–153, 515–529; 1924, 725–741, 743–755.

Tims, H. W., and Henry, C. B.: Tomes' Dental Anatomy. New York, The Macmillan Company, 1923.

Owen, R.: Odontography—A Treatise on the Comparative Anatomy of the Teeth. London, Hippolyte Bailliere, 1840. Despite its antiquity, a valuable comprehensive account.

Scott, J. H., and Symons, N. B. B.: Introduction to Dental Anatomy. Edinburgh and London, E. and S. Livingstone, 1952.

Appelbaum, E.: Enamel of sharks teeth. J. Dent. Res. *21:*251–257, 1942.

Edmund, A. G.: Tooth Replacement Phenomena in the Lower Vertebrates. Contribution 52, Life Sciences Division, Royal Ontario Museum, Toronto, 1960.

Gregory, W. K.: A half century of trituberculy. The Cope-Osborn theory of dental evolution, with a revised summary of molar evolution from fish to man. Proc. Am. Philosophical Soc. *73:*169–317, 1934.

Woskoboinikoff, M.: Der Apparat der Kiemenatmung bei den Fischen. Zoologische Jahrbücher, Abteilung für Anatomie und Ontogenie der Tiere *55:*315–488, 1932.

Copeland, D. E.: The cytological basis of chloride transfer in the gill of Fundulus heteroclitus. J. Morphol. *82:*201–227, 1948; *87:*369–380, 1950.

Adams, W. E.: The cervical region of the Lacertilia. J. Anat. *74:*57–71, 1939.

Klapper, C. E.: The development of the pharynx of the guinea pig with special emphasis on the fate of the ultimobranchial body. Am. J. Anat. *79:*361–397, 1946.

Jones, F. R. H., and Marshall, N. B.: The structure and functions of the teleostean swimbladder. Biol. Rev. *28:*16–83, 1953.

Rauther, M.: Zur vergleichenden Anatomie der Schwimmblase der Fische. Ergeb. Zoologie *5:*1–66, 1922.

Ballantyne, F. M.: Air bladder and lungs; a contribution to the morphology of the air bladder of fish. Tr. Roy. Soc. Edinburgh *55:*371–394, 1927.

Müller, B.: The air sacs of the pigeon. Smithsonian Miscellaneous Collections *1:*365–414, 1908.

Locy, W. A., and Larsell, O.: The embryology of the birds' lung. Am. J. Anat. *19:*447–501, 1916.

Huntington, G. S.: A critique of theories of pulmonary evolution in the Mammalia. Am. J. Anat. *27:* 99–201, 1920.

DIGESTIVE SYSTEM

Slijper, E. J.: Die physiologische Anatomie der Verdauungsorgane bei den Vertebraten. Tabulae Biologicae *21:*1–81, 1946.

Peterson, H.: Beiträge zur Kenntniss des Baues und der Entwickelung des Selachierdarmes. Jenaische Ztschr. Naturwissenschaft *43:*619–652; *44:*123–148, 1908.

Jacobshagen, E.: Untersuchungen über das Darmsystem der Fische und Dipnoer. II. Jenaische Ztschr. Naturwissenschaft *49:*373–810, 1913.

Hopkins, G. S.: On the enteron of American ganoids. J. Morphol. *11:*411–442, 1895.

Greene, C. W.: Anatomy and histology of the alimentary tract of the king salmon. Bull. U. S. Bureau Fisheries, *32:*73–100, 1912.

Blake, I. H.: Studies on the comparative histology of the digestive tube of certain teleost fishes. J. Morphol. *50:*39–70, 1930; *60:*77–102, 1936.

Mitchell, P. C.: On the intestinal tract of birds; with remarks on the valuation and nomenclature of zoological characters. Tr. Linnean Soc. London, Zoology *8:*173–275, 1901.

Calhoun, M. L.: Microscopic Anatomy of the Digestive System of the Chicken. Ames, Iowa, Iowa State College Press, 1954.

Pernkopf, E.: Beiträge zur vergleichende Anatomie des vertebraten Magens. Ztschr. Anat. *91:*329–390, 1930.

Hirsch, G. C.: Magenlose Fische. Zoologischer Anzeiger, Ergänzungsband *145:*302–326, 1950.

Cornselius, C.: Morphologie, Histologie und Embryologie des Muskelmagens der Vögel. Morphologisches Jahrbuch *54:*507–559, 1925.

Kaden, L.: Über Epithel und Drüsen des Vogelschlunds. Zoologische Jahrbücher. Abteilung für Anatomie und Ontogenie der Tiere. *61:*421–466, 1936.

Elias, H.: Liver morphology. Biol. Rev. *30:*263–310, 1955.

Gorham, F. W., and Ivy, A. C.: General function of the gall bladder from the evolutionary standpoint. Field Museum of Natural History, Zoology Series, *22:*159–213, 1938.

Hill, W. C. O.: A comparative study of the pancreas. Proc. Zool. Soc. London 581–631, 1926.

URINARY AND REPRODUCTIVE SYSTEMS

Fraser, E. A.: The development of the vertebrate excretory system. Biol. Rev. *25:*159–187, 1950.

Conel, J. L.: The urogenital system of myxinoids. J. Morphol. *29:*75–164, 1917.

Borcea, J.: Recherches sur le système uro-genital des elasmobranchs. Arch. Zoologie expérimentale et générale (4) *4:*199–484, 1906.

Kempton, R. T.: Studies on the elasmobranch kidney. J. Morphol. *73*:247–263, 1943; Biol. Bull. *104:* 45–56, 1953.

Kimdahl, M.: Zur Entwicklung der Exkretionsorgane von Dipnoërn und Amphibien. Acta Zoologica, *19:* 1–190, 1938.

Gray, P.: The development of the amphibian kidney. Quart. J. Microscopical Sc. *73:*507–546, 1930; *75:*425–466, 1932; *78:*445–473, 1936.

Semon, R.: Studien über den Bauplan des Urogenitalsystems der Wirbeltiere. Dargelegt an der Entwickelung dieses organsystems bei Ichthyophis glutinosus. Jenaische Ztschr. Naturwissenschaft, *26:* 89–203, 1892.

Buchanan, G., and Fraser, E. A.: The development of the urinogenital system in the Marsupialia with special reference to Trichosurus vulpecula. Part 1. J. Anat. *53:*35–95, 1918.

Smith, H. W.: The Kidney. London and New York, Oxford University Press, 1951.

Huber, G. C.: On the morphology of the renal tubules of vertebrates. Anat. Rec. *13:*305–339, 1917.

Edwards, J. G.: Studies on aglomerular and glomerular kidneys. Am. J. Anat. *42:*75–108, 1928; Anat. Rec. *44:*15–28, 1929.

Smith, H. W.: Water regulation and its evolution in fishes. Quart. Rev. Biol. *7:*1–26, 1932.

Smith, H. W.: From Fish to Philosopher. Boston, Little, Brown and Company, 1953. Vertebrate evolution with kidney evolution as the leitmotif.

Swift, C. H.: Origin and early history of primordial germ cells in the chick. Am. J. Anat. *15:*483–516, 1914.

Everett, H. B.: The present status of the germ-cell problem in vertebrates. Biol. Rev. *20:*45–55, 1945.

Witschi, E.: Migration of the germ cells of human embryos from the yolk sac to the primitive gonadal folds. Carnegie Inst. Washington, Contrib. Embryol. *32:*67–80, 1948.

Maschkowzeff, A.: Zur Phylogenie der Geschlechtsdrüsen und der Geschlechtsausfuhrgänge bei den Vertebrata auf Grund von Forschungen betreffend die Entwicklung des Mesonephros und der Geschlechtsorgane bei den Acipenseriden, Salmoniden und Amphibien. Zoologische Jahrbücher, Abteilung für Anatomie und Ontogenie der Tiere *59:*1–68, 201–276, 1934–35.

Moore, C. R.: The biology of the mammalian testis and scrotum. Quart. Rev. Biol. *1:*4–50, 1926.

Boyden, E. A.: The development of the cloaca in birds. Am. J. Anat. *30:*163–201, 1922.

Leigh-Sharpe, W. H.: The comparative morphology of the secondary sexual characters of elasmobranch fishes. J. Morphol. *34:*245–265; *35:*359–380; *36:*221–243; *42:*307–308, 1920–1926.

CIRCULATORY SYSTEM

Jordan, H. E.: The evolution of blood-forming tissues. Quart. Rev. Biol. *8:*58–76, 1933.

Chèvremont, M.: Le système histiocytaire ou réticulo-endothélial. Biol. Rev. *23:*267–295, 1948.

Krogh, A.: The Anatomy and Physiology of Capillaries. New Haven, Yale University Press, 1929.

Drinker, C. K., and Jaffey, J. M.: Lymphatics, Lymph and Lymphoid Tissue. Cambridge, Harvard University Press, 1941.

Foxon, G. E. H.: Problems of the double circulation in vertebrates. Biol. Rev. *30:*196–228, 1955.

O'Donoghue, C. H., and Abbott, E.: The blood-vascular system of the spiny dogfish, Squalus acanthias Linn., and Squalus sucklii Gill. Tr. Roy. Soc. Edinburgh, *55:*283–890, 1928.

Robertson, J. I.: The development of the heart and vascular system of Lepidosiren paradoxa. Quart. J. Microscopical Sc. *59:*53–132, 1913.

O'Donoghue, C. H.: The blood-vascular system of the tuatara, Sphenodon punctatus. Philos. Tr. Roy. Soc. London (*B*) *210:*175–252, 1920.

O'Donoghue, C. H.: The circulatory system of the common grass snake (Tropidonotus natrix). Proc. Zool. Soc. London 612–647, 1912.

Hochstetter, T.: Beiträge zur Anatomie und Entwickelungsgeschichte des Blutgefässsystemes der Krokodile. Voeltzkow, A., Reise in Ostafrika, *4:*1–139, 1906.

Hill, W. C. O.: The blood-vascular system of Tarsius. Proc. Zool. Soc. London, *123:*655–692, 1953.

Heuser, C. H.: The branchial vessels and their derivatives in the pig. Carnegie Inst. Washington, Contrib. Embryol. *15:*121–139, 1923.

Davis, D. D., and Storey, H. E.: The carotid circulation in the domestic cat. Publications, Field Museum of Natural History, Zoology, *28:*5–47, 1943.

Reagan, F. P.: A century of study upon the development of the eutherian vena cava inferior. Quart. Rev. Biol. *4:*179–212, 1929.

Butler, E. G.: The relative role played by the embryonic veins in the development of the mammalian vena cava posterior. Am. J. Anat. *39:*267–353, 1927.

Barnett, C. H., Harrison, R. J., and Tomlinson, J. D. W.: Variations in the venous systems of mammals. Biol. Rev. *33:*442–487, 1958.

Padget, D. H.: The development of the cranial venous system in man, from the viewpoint of comparative anatomy. Carnegie Inst. Washington, Contrib. Embryol. *36:*79–140, 1957.

Greil, A.: Beiträge zur vergleichenden Anatomie und Entwicklungsgeschichte des Herzens und des Truncus arteriosus der Wirbeltiere. Morphologisches Jahrbuch *31:*123–310, 1903.

Davies, F., and Francis, E. T. B.: The conducting system of the vertebrate heart. Biol. Rev. *21:*173–188, 1946.

Benninghoff, A.: Beiträge zur vergleichenden Anatomie und Entwicklungsgeschlichte des Amphibienherzens und zur Phylogenie des Reizleitungssystems. Morphologisches Jahrbuch *51:*354–412, 1921.

Kern, A.: Das Vogelherz. Morphologisches Jahrbuch *56:*264–315, 1926.

SENSE ORGANS

Parker, G. H.: Smell, Taste, and Allied Senses in the Vertebrates. Philadelphia, Lippincott Company, 1912.

Baradi, A. F., and Bourne, G. H.: Gustatory and olfactory epithelia. Internat. Rev. Cytol. *2:*289–330, 1953.

Noble, G. K., and Schmidt, A.: The structure and function of the facial and labial pits of snakes. Proc. Am. Philosophical Soc. *77:*263–288, 1937.

Pumphrey, R. J.: The sense organs of birds. Ibis, *90:*171–199, 1948; Annual report of the Smithsonian Institution 305–330, 1948.

Allison, A. C.: The morphology of the olfactory system in vertebrates. Biol. Rev. *28:*195–244, 1953.

Burne, R. H.: The anatomy of the olfactory organ of teleostean fishes. Proc. Zool. Soc. London 610–662, 1909.

Parsons, T. S.: Studies on the comparative embryology of the reptilian nose. Bulletin, Museum of Comparative Zoology, Harvard, *120:*104–277, 1959.

Fänge, R., Schmidt-Nielsen, K., and Osaki, H.: The salt gland of the herring gull. Biol. Bull. *115:*162–171, 1958.

Walls, G. L.: The vertebrate eye and its adaptive radiation. Cranbrook Institute of Science, Bulletin No. 19, 1942.

Rochon-Duvigneaud, A.: Les Yeux et la Vision des Vertébrés. Paris, Masson et Cie, 1943.

Polyak, S.: The Vertebrate Visual System. Chicago, University of Chicago Press, 1958.

Detweiler, S. R.: Vertebrate Photoreceptors. New York, The Macmillan Company, 1943.

Bellairs, A. d'A., and Boyd, J. D.: The lachrymal apparatus in lizards and snakes. Proc. Zool. Soc. London *117:*81–101, 1947; *120:*269–309, 1950.

Wright, M. E.: The lateral line system of sense organs. Quart. Rev. Biol. *26:*264–280, 1951.

Dijkgraaf, S.: Bau und Funktionen der Seitenorgane und des Ohrlabyrinths der Fische. Experientia *8:*205–216, 1952.

Lowenstein, O.: The equilibrium function of the vertebrate labyrinth. Biol. Rev. *11:*113–145, 1936.

Werner, S. C.: Das Gehörorgan der Wirbeltiere und des Menschen. Leipzig, George Thieme, 1960.

Retzius, G.: Das Gehörorgan der Wirbelthiere. Morphologisch-histologische Studien. 2 vols. Stockholm, 1881–1884.

Chranilov, N. S.: Beiträge zur Kenntniss der Weber'schen Apparates der Ostariophysi. Zoologische Jahrbücher, Abteilung für Anatomie und Ontogenie der Tiere, *49:*501–597, 1927; *51:*323–462, 1929.

Reed, H. D.: The morphology of the sound-transmitting apparatus in caudate Amphibia. J. Morphol. *33:*325–375, 1920.

Versluys, J.: Die mittlere und äussere Ohrsphäre der Lacertilia und Rhynchocephalia. Zoologische Jahrbücher, Abteilung für Anatomie und Ontogenie der Tiere, *12:*161–406, 1898. See also *Ibid. 18:*107–188, 1902.

Gaupp, E.: Die Reichertsche Theorie (Hammer- Amboss- und Kieferfrage). Arch. Anat. Physiol. Supplement *V:*1–417, 1913. On evolution of middle ear ossicles.

NERVOUS SYSTEM

Kappers, C. U. A., Huber, G. C., and Crosby, E. C.: The Comparative Anatomy of the Nervous System of Vertebrates, Including Man. 2 vols. New York, The Macmillan Company, 1936. A mine of information on comparative neurology, but difficult to work for one not a neurologist.

Kappers, C. U. A.: The Evolution of the Nervous System in Invertebrates. Vertebrates and Man. Haarlem, Erven F. Bohn, 1929.

Herrick, C. J.: An Introduction to Neurology. 5th ed. Philadelphia, W. B. Saunders Company, 1931.

Papez, J. W.: Comparative Neurology. New York, Thomas Y. Crowell Company, 1929. (Reprinted 1961.)

Johnston, J. B.: The Nervous System of Vertebrates. Philadelphia, P. Blakiston's Son and Company, 1906.

Detweiler, S. R.: Neuroembryology. New York, The Macmillan Company, 1936.

Bullock, T. H.: The anatomical organization of the nervous system of Enteropneusta. Quart. J. Microscopical Sc. *86:*55–111, 1945.

Silén, L.: On the nervous system of Glossobalanus marginatus Meek. Acta Zoologica *31:*149–175, 1950.

Weiss, P. A.: In vitro experiments on the factors determining the course of the outgrowing nerve fiber. J. Exper. Zool. *68:*393–448, 1934.

Herrick, C. J.: The doctrine of nerve components and some of its applications. J. Comp. Neurol. *13:* 301–312, 1903.

Franz, V.: Nervensystem der Akranier. Jenaische Ztschr. Naturwissenschaft *59:*401–526, 1923.

Tretjakoff, D.: Das periphere Nervensystem des Flussneunauges. Ztschr. wissenschaftliche Zoologie, *129:*359–952, 1927.

Goodrich, E. S.: On the spinal nerves of the Myxinoidea. Quart. J. Microscopical Sc. *80:*153–158, 1937.

Lindström, T.: On the cranial nerves of the cyclostomes with special reference to the N. trigeminus. Acta Zoologica *30:*315–458, 1949.

Herrick, C. J.: The cranial nerves of the bony fishes. J. Comp. Neurol. *9:*153–455, 1899; cf. also *10:* 265–322, 1900; *11:*177–249, 1901.

Norris, H. W.: Cranial nerves of Siren lacertina. J. Morphol. *24:*245–338, 1913.

Watkinson, G. B.: The cranial nerves of Varanus bivittatus. Morphologisches Jahrbuch *35:*450–472, 1906.

Willard, W. A.: The cranial nerves of Anolis carolinensis. Bulletin, Museum of Comparative Zoology, Harvard *59:*17–116, 1915.

Mitchell, G. A. G.: Anatomy of the Autonomic Nervous System. Edinburgh and London, E. and S. Livingstone, Ltd., 1953.

Nicol, J. A. C.: Autonomic nervous systems in lower chordates. Biol. Rev. *27:*1–49, 1952.

Campenhout, E. van: Historical survey of the development of the sympathetic nervous system. Quart. Rev. Biol. *5:*23–50, 217–234, 1930.

Yntema, C. L., and Hammond, W. S.: The development of the autonomic nervous system. Biol. Rev. *22:* 344–359, 1947.

Boeke, J.: The autonomic (enteric) nervous system of Amphioxus lanceolatus. Quart. J. Microscopical Sc. *77:*623–658, 1935.

Johnels, A. G.: On the peripheral autonomic system of the trunk region of Lampetra planeri. Acta Zoologica *37:*251–285, 1956.

Young, J. Z.: The autonomic system of selachians. Quart. J. Microscopical Sc. *75:*571–624, 1933.

Young, J. Z.: On the autonomic nervous system of the teleostean fish, Uranoscopus scaber. Quart. J. Microscopical Sc. *74:*492–525, 1931.

Weed, L. W.: The development of the cerebro-spinal spaces in pig and in man. Carnegie Inst. Washington, Contrib. Embryol. *5:*3–116, 1917.

Stefanelli, A.: The mauthnerian apparatus in the Ichthyopsida. Quart. Rev. Biol. *21:*17–34, 1951.

Herrick, C. J.: The Brain of the Tiger Salamander. Chicago, University of Chicago Press, 1948.

Norris, H. W., and Hughes, S. P.: The cranial, occipital and anterior spinal nerves of the dogfish. J. Comp. Neurol. *31:*293–395, 1920.

Portmann, A.: Études sur la cérébralisation chez les oiseaux. Alauda *14:*2–20, 1946; *15:*1–15, 1947.

Herrick, C. J.: Brains of Rats and Men. Chicago, University of Chicago Press, 1926.

Krieg, W. J. S.: Functional Neuroanatomy. Philadelphia, Blakiston Company, 1942.

Larsell, O.: The development of the cerebellum in man in relation to its comparative anatomy. J. Comp. Neurol. *87:*85–129, 1947.

ENDOCRINE ORGANS

Turner, C. D.: General Endocrinology. 2nd ed. Philadelphia, W. B. Saunders Company, 1960.

Gorbman, A., editor: Comparative Endocrinology. New York, John Wiley and Sons, 1959.

Pickford, G. E., Palay, S. L., Chambers, H. A,, and Atz, E. H.: Fish endocrinology. Bulletin of the Bingham Oceanographic Collection *14:*1–16, 1953.

Green, J. D.: The comparative anatomy of the hypophysis, with special reference to its blood supply and innervation. Am. J. Anat. *88:*225–311, 1951.

Fields, W. S., Guillemin, R., and Carton, C. A., editors: Hypothalamic-hypophysial Interrelationships. A Symposium. Houston, Baylor University College of Medicine, 1956.

Bargmann, W.: The neurosecretory system of the diencephalon. Endeavour *19:*125–133, 1960.

602

THE VERTEBRATE BODY

Lynn, G. W., and Wachowski, H. E.: The thyroid gland and its functions in cold-blooded vertebrates. Quart. Rev. Biol. 26:123–168, 1951.
Goldsmith, E. D.: Phylogeny of the thyroid: descriptive and experimental. Ann. New York Acad. Sc. 50: 282–316, 1949.
Boyd, J. D.: The development of the thyroid and parathyroid glands and the thymus. Ann. Roy. Coll. Surgeons England 7:455–471, 1950.
Watzka, M.: Vergleichende Untersuchungen über den ultimobranchialen Körper. Ztschr. mikroscopisch-anatomisches Forschung 34:485–533, 1933.
Marshall, F. H. A.: The Physiology of Reproduction. London, Longmans, Green, 1960.

LOWER CHORDATES

Grassé, P.-P., editor: Traité de Zoologie. Tome XI. Échinodermes-Stomocordés- Procordés. Paris, Masson et Cie, 1948. Contains a comprehensive account of lower chordates by Dawydoff, Brien, Drach, and others.
Garstang, W.: The morphology of Tunicata. Quart. J. Microscopical Sc. 72:51–187, 1928.
Franz, V.: Morphologie der Acranier. Ergebn. Anat. u. Entwicklungsgeschichte 27:464–692, 1927.
Willey, A.: Amphioxus and the Ancestry of Vertebrates. New York, Columbia University, 1894.

FISHES

Dean, B.: A Bibliography of Fishes. 3 vols. New York, American Museum of Natural History, 1916-1923.
Berg, L. S.: Classification of Fishes, Both Recent and Fossil. Ann Arbor, Edwards Bros., 1947. A translation of a Russian original. A new edition in Russian published in 1949.
Goodrich, E. S.: A Treatise on Zoology, edited by E. Ray Lankester. Part IX. Vertebrata Craniata, Fascicule I. "Cyclostomes and Fishes." London, The Macmillan Company, 1909. A mine of data on fish anatomy; badly indexed, however.
Norman, J. R.: A History of Fishes. 3rd ed. London, Ernest Benn, Ltd., 1947. Life history, habits, and so on, as well as structure.
Bigelow, H. B., and Schroeder, W. C., editors: Fishes of the Western North Atlantic. New Haven, Sears Foundation for Marine Research, 1948. Designed as a comprehensive account of marine fishes. The first two volumes mainly devoted to sharks and rays.
Moy-Thomas, J. A.: Palaeozoic Fishes. London, Methuen and Co., Ltd., 1939.
Romer, A. S.: The early evolution of fishes. Quart. Rev. Biol. 21:33–69, 1946.
Brown, M. E.: The Physiology of Fishes. 2 vols. New York, Academic Press, 1957. Despite the limitation of the title, gives in the main a comprehensive account of fish biology and anatomy.
Breder, C. M.: The locomotion of fishes. Zoologica (New York) 4:159–297, 1926.
Allis, E. P. Jr.: The cranial muscles and cranial and first spinal nerves in Amia calva. J. Morphol. 12:487–808, 1897. This and the following works by Allis are well-illustrated accounts of cranial anatomy.
Allis, E. P. Jr.: The skull and cranial and first spinal muscles and nerves in Scomber scomber. J. Morphol. 18:45–328, 1903.
Allis, E. P. Jr.: The cranial anatomy of the mail-cheeked fishes. Zoologica (Stuttgart) 22:1–219, 1909.
Allis, E. P. Jr.: Cranial anatomy of Polypterus. J. Anat. 56:189–294, 1922.
Allis, E. P. Jr.: The cranial anatomy of Chlamydoselachus anguineus. Acta Zoologica 4:123–221, 1923.
Cole, F. J.: A monograph on the general morphology of the myxinoid fishes, based on a study of Myxine. Tr. Roy. Soc. Edinburgh, 49:293–344, 1913.
Daniel, J. F.: The Elasmobranch Fishes. 3rd ed. Berkeley, University of California Press, 1934. Shark anatomy.
Dean, B.: Chimaeroid fishes. Carnegie Institution of Washington, Publication 32, 1906.
Millot, J.: Le troisième coelacanthe. Le Naturaliste Malagache, 1er Supplement, 1954. Superficial structures of Latimeria.
Millot, J., and Anthony, J.: Anatomie de Latimeria chalumnae. I. Squelette, Muscles et Formations de Soutien. Paris, Centre National de la Recherche Scientifique, 1958. The first of a series of anatomical monographs on this interesting animal.
Greil, A.: Entwickelungsgeschichte des Kopfes und des Blutgefässsystems von Ceratodus forsteri. Semon's Zoologische Forschungsreise in Australien 1:661–1492, 1908–1913.

AMPHIBIA

Noble, G. K.: The Biology of the Amphibia. New York, McGraw-Hill Book.Company, Inc., 1931; reprinted by Dover Publications, New York, 1954.

Francis, E. T. B.: The Anatomy of the Salamander. London and New York, Oxford University Press, 1934.

Ecker, A., Wiedersheim, R., and Gaupp, E.: Anatomie des Frosches. 3 vols., 2nd ed. Braunschweig, Friedrich Viewig und Sohn, 1888–1904. A thorough account of frog anatomy, which has passed through the hands of three successive authors.

Holmes, S. J.: The Biology of the Frog. 4th ed. New York, Macmillan Company, 1927.

Wiedersheim, R.: Die Anatomie der Gymnophionen. Jena, Gustav Fischer, 1879.

Romer, A. S.: Review of the Labyrinthodontia. Bulletin, Museum of Comparative Zoology, Harvard, *99:* 1–368, 1947.

REPTILES

Bellairs, A. d'A.: Reptiles. London, Hutchinson's University Library, 1957.

Pope, C. H.: The Reptile World. New York, Alfred A. Knopf, 1955.

Ditmars, R. L.: Reptiles of the World. New York, The Macmillan Company, 1933.

Oliver, J. A.: The Natural History of North American Amphibians and Reptiles. Princeton, Princeton University Press, 1955.

Carr, A.: Handbook of Turtles. Ithaca, Cornell University Press, 1952.

Bellairs, A. d'A., and Underwood, G.: The origin of snakes. Biol. Rev. *26:*193–237, 1951.

Reese, A. M.: The Alligator and its Allies. New York, G. P. Putnam Sons, 1915.

Colbert, E. H.: Dinosaurs, Their Discovery and Their World. New York, E. P. Dutton and Company, 1961.

Williston, S. W.: Water Reptiles of the Past and Present. Chicago, University of Chicago Press, 1914.

BIRDS

Pycraft, W. P.: A History of Birds. London, Methuen and Company, 1910. Includes anatomy.

Thompson, J. A.: The Biology of Birds. London, The Macmillan Company, 1923.

Newton, A., and Gadow, H.: A Dictionary of Birds. London, Adam and Charles Black, 1893–1896.

Strong, R. M.: A bibliography of birds. Publication, Field Museum of Natural History, Zoology, *25:* 1939–1959.

Marshall, A. J.: Biology and Comparative Physiology of Birds. 2 vols. New York, Academic Press, 1960–1961.

Wolfson, A., editor: Recent Studies in Avian Biology. Urbana, University of Illinois Press, 1955.

Bradley, O. C.: The Structure of the Fowl. 2nd ed. London, Oliver and Boyd, Ltd., 1938.

Chamberlain, I. W.: Atlas of Avian Anatomy. East Lansing, Michigan State College, Agricultural Experiment Station, 1943.

Heilmann, G.: The Origin of Birds. New York, D. Appleton-Century Company, 1926.

Holmgren, N.: Studies on the phylogeny of birds. Acta Zoologica *36:*243–328, 1955.

Fürbringer, M.: Untersuchungen zur Morphologie und Systematik der Vögel. Zugleich ein Beitrag zur Anatomie des Stütz- und Bewegungsorgane. 2 vols. Amsterdam and Jena, Gustav Fischer, 1888. Old but still basic work, including excellent comparative anatomical data.

Boas, J. E. V.: Biologisch-anatomische Studien über den Hals der Vögel. Kongelige Danske Videnskabernes Selskab, naturvidenskabelig og mathematisk Afdeling, Series 9, *1:*101–222, 1929.

Webb, M.: The ontogeny of the cranial bones, cranial peripheral and cranial parasympathetic nerves, together with a study of the visceral muscles of Struthio. Acta Zoologica *38:*81–203, 1957.

Groebbels, F.: Der Vogel. Volume 1. Atmungswelt und Nahrungswelt. Berlin, Gebrüder Borntraeger, 1932. Volume 2. Geschlecht und Fortpflanzung, 1937.

De Beer, G.: Archaeopteryx lithographica. London, British Museum (Natural History), 1954.

MAMMALS

Simpson, G. G.: The principles of classification and a classification of mammals. Bulletin, American Museum of Natural History *88:*1–350, 1945.

Weber, M., Burlet, H. M. de, and Abel, O.: Die Säugetiere. 2 vols., 2nd ed. Jena, Gustav Fischer, 1927–1928. A standard work on mammalian anatomy and classification.

Flower, W. H., and Lydekker, R.: An Introduction to the Study of Mammals, Living and Extinct. London, Adam and Charles Black, 1891. Old, but still useful.

Bourlière, F.: The Natural History of Mammals. New York, Alfred A. Knopf, 1954.

Young, J. Z.: The Life of Mammals. London, Oxford University Press, 1957.

Sisson, S., and Grossman, J. D.: The Anatomy of the Domestic Animals. 3rd ed. Philadelphia, W. B. Saunders Company, 1938. A comprehensive account of horse anatomy; ox, sheep, pig, and dog are covered more briefly.

Davison, A., and Stromsten, F. A.: Mammalian Anatomy, with Special Reference to the Cat. 7th ed. Philadelphia, P. Blakiston's Son and Company, 1937.

Reighard, J. E., and Jennings, H. S.: Anatomy of the Cat. 3rd ed. New York, Henry Holt and Company, Inc., 1935.

Bradley, O. C., and Grahame, T.: Topographical Anatomy of the Dog. 5th ed. New York, The Macmillan Company, 1943.

Baum, H., and Zietzschmann, O.: Handbuch der Anatomie des Hundes. Berlin, P. Parey, 1936.

Greene, E. C.: Anatomy of the rat. Tr. Am. Philosophical Soc. (n.s.) *27:*1–370, 1935.

Howell, A. B.: Anatomy of the Wood Rat. Baltimore, Williams and Wilkins Company, 1926.

Gerhardt, U.: Das Kaninchen. Leipzig, H. E. Ziegler and R. Woltereck, 1909.

Ellerman, J. R.: The Families and Genera of Living Rodents. 3 vols. London, British Museum (Natural History), 1940–1949.

Bensley, B. A., and Craigie, E. H.: Practical Anatomy of the Rabbit. 8th ed. Philadelphia, Blakiston Company, 1948.

Howell, A. B.: Aquatic Mammals. Springfield, Illinois, Charles C Thomas, 1930.

Slijper, E. J.: Die Cetaceen, Vergleichend-Anatomisch und Systematisch. Capita Zoologica *6, 7:*1–590, 1936.

Nickel, R., Schummer, A., and Seiferle, E.: Lehrbuch der Anatomie der Haustiere. Bd. 1: Bewegungsapparat. 2nd ed. Berlin and Hamburg, Parey, 1961. Bd. 2 Eingeweide, 1960.

Hill, W. C. O.: Primates. Comparative Anatomy and Taxonomy. 3 vols. Edinburgh, University Press, 1953, 1955, 1957. Planned to include all primates; volumes on higher forms have not yet appeared.

Hofer, H., Schultz, A. H., and Starck, D., editors: Primatologia. 4 vols. Basel, Karger, 1956–1958. Not yet complete.

LeGros Clark, W. E.: Early Forerunners of Man. Baltimore, Williams and Wilkins Company, 1934. A discussion of the anatomy of lower primates.

Hartman, C. G., and Straus, W. L., Jr., editors: The Anatomy of the Rhesus Monkey. Baltimore, Williams and Wilkins Company, 1933.

Howell, A. B.: Gross Anatomy: A Brief Systematic Presentation of the Macroscopic Structure of the Human Body. New York, D. Appleton-Century Company, Inc., 1939. More detailed accounts of human anatomy are available in the larger standard texts, such as Cunningham, Gray, and Morris.

Woollard, H. H.: The anatomy of Tarsius spectrum. Proc. Zool. Soc. London *70:*1071–1184, 1936.

LeGros Clark, W. E.: History of the Primates. 6th ed. London, British Museum (Natural History), 1958.

LeGros Clark, W. E.: The Antecedents of Man. Chicago, Quadrangle Books, 1960.

INDEX